BIOCHEMISTRY OF THE AMINO ACIDS

AMINO ACIDS

Volume II

BIOCHEMISTRY

OF

THE AMINO ACIDS

Second Edition

ALTON MEISTER

Department of Biochemistry
Tufts University School of Medicine
Boston, Massachusetts

Volume II

1965

ACADEMIC PRESS

NEW YORK   LONDON

ACADEMIC PRESS INC.
111 Fifth Avenue, New York, New York 10003

United Kingdom Edition published by
ACADEMIC PRESS INC. (LONDON) LTD.
Berkeley Square House, London W. 1

LIBRARY OF CONGRESS CATALOG CARD NUMBER: 65-12768

Third Printing, 1972

PRINTED IN THE UNITED STATES OF AMERICA.

Preface
to the Second Edition

The author has attempted, as in the first edition, to present a comprehensive picture of the current status of amino acid biochemistry. It is apparent to those who have followed the biochemical literature of the last eight years that we are now in the midst of an extraordinarily productive period, and that much of the important progress made has concerned the amino acids. Thus, about a hundred new amino acids have been discovered and more than this number of amino acid analogs have been synthesized and studied. The incorporation of certain amino acid analogs into proteins has been amply substantiated. Earlier work on the transaminases and other vitamin B_6 enzymes has been extensively elaborated with highly purified enzymes. The study of protein synthesis has exploded from a stage in which a handful of biochemists was interested in the problem to one in which hundreds are now working. Recent studies provide explanations for the translation of genetic information into the amino acid sequences of proteins as well as for the mechanisms of the individual steps involved in peptide bond formation. These investigations and others that have elucidated most of the enzymatic steps involved in the biosynthesis and transformations of the protein amino acids now make it possible to approach such problems as the control of enzyme synthesis, the mechanism of action of hormones, and the chemical defects associated with certain human diseases.

In the second edition it has been necessary to revise and expand virtually every section of the first edition; most of the original text has been completely rewritten. It was inevitable that there would be a considerable increase in the number of pages, and indeed the second edition is more than double the size of the first and contains more than twice as many references to the literature. It has therefore seemed desirable to publish the present edition in two volumes, each of which contains the complete subject index. Chapter I was enlarged to include recently discovered amino acids and peptides. Chapters II and III of the second edition cover the area presented in Chapter II of the first edition. The study of amino acid antagonists has proceeded far beyond the nutritional stage, and a separate chapter (Chapter III) has therefore been written. Chapter IV covers amino acid transport and many of the "general reactions" of amino acids including oxidative deamination, nonoxidative deamination, the action of amino acid oxygenases, and the multitude of reactions catalyzed by vitamin B_6 enzymes. Protein synthesis and the synthesis of smaller molecules containing peptide bonds are now covered in a separate chapter (Chapter V). (About nine pages of the original edition were devoted to protein synthesis in comparison to 83 pages in the present edition.) Volume II (Chapters VI and VII) is concerned with the intermediary metabolism of the amino acids. Although the outlines of the pathways of biosynthesis and metabolism of most of the protein amino acids were known at the time the first edition of this book was written, a considerable increase in knowledge of this area has been achieved, and about three times as much space is devoted to this field as in the first edition. The final chapter of Volume II deals with disorders of amino acid metabolism in man; several new diseases associated with defects of amino acid metabolism have been discovered in the last few years, and it seems probable that the number of such conditions is much larger than hitherto suspected.

The most dramatic developments of the last eight years have been in the area of protein synthesis; the data that have been obtained about the nucleic acid-amino acid code, the mechanism of protein synthesis, and the elaboration of these findings in terms of genetics and in the control of enzymatic activity (and therefore of metabolism) seem to represent only a starting point for more exciting future investigations. Although the individual steps in the intermediary metabolism of the protein amino acids are largely understood, there are still some hazy areas, and more information about the relative quantitative importance of various pathways is needed. In addition, the mechanisms of most of these enzymatic reactions are not yet known nor is the manner in which these enzymes are controlled fully understood. The presence in nature of more than a hundred nonprotein amino acids raises additional questions about biosynthesis, metabolism, and function; these phenomena have not yet been extensively investigated nor have the effects of these potential amino acid antagonists on animal organisms been fully evaluated. Another important problem that remains for future investigation is the mechanism of transport of amino acids. Thus, it is evident that although the present edition of this work represents an expansion and largely rewritten version of the original text, it must also be accepted as a statement and summary of presently available data upon which future developments will be built.

A number of attempts have been made in recent years to improve and standardize biochemical nomenclature. Although such efforts have been of some value, potentially confusing situations have sometimes developed because of the continued use in the literature of more than one term for a given compound. In this treatise nomenclature has been used that will be understandable in terms of current usage in the literature rather than any specific set of rules. It is probable that the final nomenclature of this field will be achieved only when progress has stopped. Well-known abbreviations such as ATP, DPN, DNA, and RNA, and others which are defined in the text have been used sparingly. The text was completed toward the end of 1963 and the beginning of 1964. An attempt was made to add in proof, insofar as possible, pertinent material that appeared later than this (to approximately the middle of 1964).

ALTON MEISTER

January, 1965

Acknowledgments

The author is pleased to acknowledge the help of individuals who called his attention to errors and omissions in the first edition, provided him with manuscripts and figures prior to publication, and offered advice. He is appreciative of the permission granted by several authors and publishers to reproduce various tables and figures, whose sources are cited in the text. He is particularly grateful to his students for their stimulation, assistance in reading proofs, and patience during the time that the second edition was being written. He is also indebted to Dean Joseph M. Hayman, Jr., for his skill in maintaining at Tufts University School of Medicine an environment so free of administrative problems that even a chairman of a department may work in the laboratory and write a book. The author wishes to thank John J. Corrigan, Ezra Khedouri, P. R. Krishnaswamy, James M. Manning, Kivie Moldave, Elizabeth Dodd Mooz, Jonathan S. Nishimura, Gerhard Schmidt, Saul Slapikoff, Daniel Wellner, and Edith Wilson of the Department of Biochemistry of Tufts University School of Medicine, and Alexander E. Braunstein, Morris E. Friedkin, Van L. Johnson, Roy L. Kisliuk, Owen J. Koeppe, Herbert Tabor, Sidney Udenfriend, and Hubert B. Vickery for various and valued assistance in offering advice and constructive criticisms, and in proofreading. It is a pleasure to thank Miss Selma Frank and her associates, especially Mrs. Patience Barry and Miss Susan Doughty, for their careful and skillful efforts in drawing structures, typing, and checking references. Finally, the author wishes to acknowledge the patience, encouragement, and valuable assistance of his wife, Leonora Garten Meister, who read the entire galley proof and assisted in preparing the subject index, and also his sons Jonathan and Kenneth Meister for help in organizing the references for publication.

Table of Contents

Chapter VII.   Some Disorders of Amino Acid Metabolism in Man 1021

Contents
of Volume I

Tables and Figures
Volumes I and II

Metabolism
Summary Schemes, Volume II

CHAPTER VI

Intermediary Metabolism of the Amino Acids

"...in the study of the intermediate processes of metabolism we have to deal, not with complex substances which elude ordinary chemical methods, but with simple substances undergoing comprehensible reactions."—HOPKINS (1913).

A. General Considerations

Current knowledge of the reactions involved in the biosynthesis and degradative metabolism of the amino acids in animals and microorganisms is sufficiently complete to permit construction of metabolic charts and maps in which a number of compounds are related to each other by a series of arrows. Although the emphasis of earlier studies was placed on the intermediates formed in metabolism, many recent investigations have been concerned with the "arrows." Thus, there is now much interest in the structure and mechanism of action of enzymes, in the synthesis of enzymes (especially control of synthesis), and in the regulation of enzymatic activities. The experimental data that form the basis of our "metabolic maps" have come from nutritional investigations, studies with isotopically labeled compounds, experiments with mutant organisms, and enzyme studies. Other approaches have involved the use of amino acid analogs and other antimetabolites, and clues to metabolic reactions have also begun to come from investigations of feedback control phenomena.

The purely nutritional approach provided important evidence that led ultimately to the elucidation of metabolic reactions. For example, the early observation that phenylalanine is essential in the diet of mammals while tyrosine is not, indicated that mammals possessed enzymatic equipment for the conversion of phenylalanine to tyrosine. Nutritional studies also paved the way for understanding of the mechanisms involved in the conversion of methionine sulfur to cystine sulfur, in the inter-relationships between arginine, proline, ornithine, and glutamate, and in other metabolic phenomena. In two cases (methionine and threonine), nutritional studies resulted in the discovery and characterization of new amino acids.

Mutant strains of microorganisms have proved to be exceedingly powerful tools in the study of amino acid biosynthesis. The discovery of alternative growth factors for amino acid-requiring mutants has frequently been of key importance, e.g., the finding that shikimic acid could replace several aromatic growth factors. Mutants blocked at various stages of biosynthesis characteristically accumulate intermediates, which can often be detected by their growth effects on other mutants. Study of human mutations has also afforded insight into normal metabolic path-ways. Considerable information has come from work with perfusion systems, tissue slices, homogenates, tissue extracts, and purified enzymes. The use of isotopically labeled compounds has had wide application in the study of intermediary metabolism, and this technique, combined with other approaches, has given both initial clues and unequivocal proof of the occurrence of many metabolic transformations. Studies with labeled compounds have provided information not easily derived from other studies concerning the specificity of enzymes toward symmetrical molecules.

Perusal of this chapter will reveal much evidence for the "unity of biochemistry." Just as nature uses the same amino acids for the synthesis of virtually all of the proteins, she often uses the same type of chemical reaction for several metabolic purposes. In a sense these are variations on a theme, but the question as to which is the theme and which are the variations cannot yet be answered. Several examples may be cited. Virtually all amino acids undergo transamination reactions leading to the corresponding α-keto acids. Many amino acids may be oxidatively deaminated to the corresponding α-keto acid, but several possessing β-hydroxyl or sulfhydryl groups undergo deamination and dehydration catalyzed by specific enzymes requiring vitamin B_6. Six amino acids (aspartate, β-methylaspartate, phenylalanine, tyrosine, histidine, di-hydroxyphenylalanine) are deaminated by reactions that yield the corresponding α,β-unsaturated compounds. Many free amino acids are decarboxylated by vitamin B_6-containing decarboxylases, but three amino acids (threonine, serine, cysteine) are decarboxylated by other mechanisms. Glutamine is a key compound in nitrogen transfer reactions;

its amide nitrogen atom is transferred to intermediates used in the synthesis of purines, histidine, tryptophan, diphosphopyridine nucleotide, pyrimidines, urea (in certain organisms), glucosamine, and other compounds. It is surprising that such nitrogen transfer reactions have not been observed with asparagine, but these may be revealed by future work. The α-amino group of aspartic acid is transferred in several reactions (purine and arginine synthesis) that involve formation of fumarate. Other key compounds in the intermediary metabolism of amino acids include S-adenosylmethionine, whose methyl group is transferred to a great variety of compounds, and β-hydroxy-β-methylglutaryl-coenzyme A, which represents a branching point compound between the metabolism of leucine, fatty acids, and (via mevalonic acid) a number of isoprenoid compounds. N-Acylation is used in several pathways, thus, N-succinyl-α,ϵ-diaminopimelic acid, α-N-acetylornithine, and N-acetylglutamate are intermediates in the formation of the diamino acids. The function of the acyl groups seems to be analogous to that of the N-carbobenzyloxy group as used by the organic chemist in providing an intermediate less capable of cyclization. On the other hand, the function of N-acetylglutamate in urea biosynthesis and of certain naturally occurring N-acyl amino acids is not yet clear. Other examples of the economy practiced by nature in the use of chemical intermediates and reactions include the use of biotin in the fixation of carbon dioxide, folic acid in the metabolism of one-carbon units, coenzyme A in the metabolism of the branched-chain amino acids, the formation and transfer of the carbamyl group, and the use of 5-phosphoribosyl-1-pyrophosphate for the synthesis of histidine, purines, pyrimidines, nicotinic acid, and tryptophan. Just as methionine and glutamine are special compounds that supply methyl groups and nitrogen atoms, respectively, glycine and serine are frequently used as carbon chain precursors of other compounds. The citric acid cycle provides not only energy for biosynthetic reactions, but also the α-keto acid precursors of several amino acids.

Although there are many similar reactions in metabolism, there is excellent evidence that the enzymes that catalyze even analogous reactions are different. Thus, the enzymes of the citric acid cycle do not catalyze the formation of α-ketoadipic and α-ketoisocaproic acids, and the synthesis and cleavage of cystathionine are catalyzed by two sets of different enzymes, depending on whether cysteine or homocysteine is the product. In general, enzymes that catalyze biosynthesis are different from those that catalyze degradation, but a clear-cut distinction is not possible because certain degradative reactions yield products that can be utilized for biosynthesis. There is also evidence that the formation of a compound that is a common intermediate in the biosynthesis of several products can be catalyzed by several enzymes. For example, several aspartokinases are present in *Escherichia coli*; all of these catalyze the same reaction, but each is inhibited by a different amino acid end product. There are now many examples of end-product inhibition in which the product of a sequence of biosynthetic reactions inhibits the enzyme that catalyzes the first step (1). Such feedback inhibition provides a rapid mechanism for stopping the production of a compound since it is the concentration of inhibitor which determines the degree of inhibition. Another cellular mechanism for regulation of enzyme activity is the control of enzyme synthesis. There are many examples of repression and induction of enzyme synthesis; the enzymes that catalyze the various steps in biosynthesis of an amino acid are often repressed by the product (1). It is for this reason that accumulation of intermediates is not usually observed until the amino acid product of the pathway is utilized. Where the biosynthesis of several amino acids (e.g., the branched-chain amino acids) shares enzymes, repression seems to require the presence of all of the products (2), but "multivalent repression" of this type is probably only part of the over-all repression mechanism (1, 3, 4). The mechanism by which low-molecular-weight compounds influence the rate of enzyme synthesis, i.e., by repression or induction, is not yet known. This problem has been the subject of a number of recent reviews and conferences (1, 5–8). According to current belief, compounds that induce the formation of enzyme act by reversing the action of a repressor, hence inducers are "derepressors." The mechanism of control of repressible and inducible enzymes must involve a system that can be affected by a low-molecular-weight compound. It is conceivable that the end product acts directly with nucleic acid to inhibit synthesis, or to produce a repressor substance, possibly a protein, that inhibits the formation of messenger ribonucleic acid. It is noteworthy that amino acid analogs as well as naturally occurring amino acids can serve both as repressors and inducers of enzyme synthesis. There is good evidence that the systems responsible for repression and induction of enzyme formation are under genetic control, as are those that lead to the synthesis of constitutive enzymes, which are not markedly responsive to changes in the intracellular environment. Although the mechanisms responsible for the control of enzyme synthesis cannot yet be described in chemical terms, it is apparent that such control mechanisms are extraordinarily important in the regulation of cellular metabolism and that they may be crucial in the evolutionary sense for survival of the cell.

The presence of several enzymes within a cell that can catalyze the same reaction but are susceptible to inhibition by different amino acids indicates a new type of enzyme specificity, which must ultimately be explained in terms of chemical structure. Although most of the studies on control mechanisms have been carried out with microorganisms, it seems probable that similar phenomena occur and are of equal importance in the metabolism of animals and higher plants; recent studies on enzymes of animal tissues support this view.

Several microorganisms have been isolated which apparently lack the usual mechanism for the control of amino acid biosynthesis. Some of these have been useful in the commercial production of amino acids. For example, Kinoshita *et al.* (9) found that certain microorganisms obtained by screening procedures accumulate significant quantities of L-glutamic acid (e.g., several milligrams of glutamic acid per milliliter of culture medium). The highest level of glutamate production was observed with a new species of micrococcus (*Micrococcus glutamicus*), which produced as much as 0.25 mole of glutamic acid from 1 mole of glucose. Other amino acids which can be produced in this manner include aspartic acid, alanine, glycine, serine, valine, leucine, lysine, ornithine, and α,ε-diaminopimelic acid (10). A procedure involving the use of amino acid antagonists has also provided mutants which excrete the corresponding amino acids, and which are resistant to the added analogs. Thus, *E. coli* mutants that are resistant to ethionine and thienylalanine excrete methionine and phenylalanine, respectively (11).

The fact that many biosynthetic and degradative pathways are virtually the same in widely different species is impressive, but also serves to emphasize certain exceptions, e.g., the existence of two separate pathways for the biosynthesis of lysine. The evolutionary significance of this situation is probably related to the utilization of diaminopimelic acid for the synthesis of cell walls. The extensive body of data on the amino acid requirements of animals indicates that the enzymatic equipment necessary for the synthesis of about half of the protein amino acids is not operative in animals. The striking observation that the same eight amino acids are required by a large number of animal species and also by several microorganisms suggests that a considerable amount of genetic information was deleted at an early stage in evolution. This conclusion is based on the assumption that all of the enzymes needed for the synthesis of such amino acids as tryptophan, phenylalanine, lysine, threonine, methionine, valine, isoleucine, leucine, and histidine are not present in animals. (It should be stated, however, that unsuccessful efforts to find all of these enzymatic activities in animal tissues do not seem to be recorded in the literature.) The availability of preformed amino acids and the consequent dispensability of a large number of enzymes may have provided animals with a selective evolutionary advantage. It may be noted that several of the dietary nonessential amino acids for animals (e.g., glutamate, aspartate, alanine) can be synthesized in a single step by enzymes that function also in the degradation of these amino acids. On the other hand, by ingesting such amino acids as isoleucine, valine, leucine, phenylalanine, and tryptophan, animals are spared the cellular work involved in synthesizing the large number of enzymes required for the production of these amino acids. Although tyrosine would seem to be equally as available as phenylalanine in the diets of animals, an enzymatic mechanism exists for the conversion of phenylalanine to tyrosine; this pathway is not present in most microorganisms. The existence of the human condition phenylpyruvic oligophrenia suggests that the development of this enzyme system may have special evolutionary significance in relation to cerebral function.

Most investigations of amino acid metabolism have been carried out with animals and a few microorganisms. There has been a tendency for biochemists to study "major quantitative" pathways. Although the most obvious reactions—in terms of quantitative significance—are often the first to be discovered, some pathways of minor quantitative significance can be of considerable physiological importance. The recent emphasis on control mechanisms, protein synthesis, and enzymatic reaction mechanisms may have obscured to some extent the fact that a number of significant metabolic pathways have not yet been fully elucidated. In addition, remarkably few investigations have been carried out on the higher plants. It seems probable that most of the protein amino acids are synthesized and degraded by reactions that are similar to those already observed in microorganisms and animals. However, plants contain many amino acids which are not present in microorganisms and in animals, and whose metabolism has not been elucidated. The utilization of amino acids for the synthesis of special plant products such as alkaloids is another area about which there is less than sophisticated knowledge. Recent studies have shown that certain amino acids (e.g., methionine, phenylalanine, tyrosine, tryptophan, ornithine, lysine) are utilized in highly interesting and novel ways for the biosynthesis of alkaloids and other plant products. Earlier hypotheses (12–14) about alkaloid biosynthesis are only now being put to experimental test.

It has been known for more than a century that atmospheric nitrogen is used as a source of nitrogen by certain microorganisms, and many investigations have dealt with this transformation. In 1960, Carnahan *et al.* (15) observed nitrogen fixation in cell-free enzyme preparations from *Clostridium pasteurianum* and subsequently similar investigations were carried out on other organisms by several groups of investigators. In these studies, atmospheric nitrogen was converted to ammonia and nitrogen-containing organic compounds, including glutamine and asparagine. Thus far, there seems to be no definite information about the nature of the intermediates involved in nitrogen fixation, and it appears that these are enzyme-bound. Several reviews have appeared recently on the fixation of nitrogen, nitrification, and related reactions (15–18).

In a highly interesting approach to the problem of organic compound formation under possible primitive earth conditions, Miller (19–21) demonstrated the formation of amino acids (glycine, sarcosine, DL-alanine, β-alanine, DL-α-aminobutyric acid, and α-aminoisobutyric acid) as well as other compounds (e.g., lactic acid, formic acid, acetic acid) in a system containing methane, ammonia, hydrogen, and water. This mixture, which may approximate that of the earth's atmosphere in the early stages of formation, was subjected to electric discharges for a week or more. The amino acids may have been formed by hydrolysis of nitriles formed in turn by reactions of aldehydes and hydrogen cyanide produced by electrical discharge. Later work showed that amino acids can also be produced under other conditions which are thought by some to approximate the primordial state (22–25). Thus, carbon dioxide can serve as the sole source of carbon, and amino acids were produced when an aqueous mixture of formaldehyde and potassium nitrate was irradiated with ultraviolet light. In an experiment in which a mixture of hydrocyanic acid and aqueous ammonia was heated at 90° for 18 hours, many compounds were formed, including adenine, aspartic acid, threonine, serine, glutamic acid, glycine, alanine, isoleucine, leucine, β-alanine, α,β-diaminopropionic acid, α-aminobutyric acid, and urea (25). Irradiation of mixtures of adenine, ribose, and ethyl metaphosphate gave adenosine and adenosine mono-, di-, tri-, and tetraphosphates (26). It seems then that a variety of organic compounds as well as amino acids can be formed under conditions that might have existed on the primitive earth. There is now a voluminous literature on experiments of this type and on hypotheses concerning chemical evolution (24, 27, 28). The discovery of amino acids in anthracite and in fossils estimated to be about 360 million years old (29–31) may inspire additional speculation. However, chemical evolution may have begun 2–4 billion years ago. In one study, aspartic acid, glutamic acid, and glycine were found after hydrochloric acid hydrolysis of fossil human bone (29); in another, these amino acids as well as valine, leucine, proline, and alanine were identified (31). At the very least these observations suggest that amino acids are reasonably stable.

B. Alanine

The reversible formation of L-alanine from pyruvate by transamination is catalyzed by preparations of a number of animal tissues, plants and

Table I

ENZYMATIC REACTIONS THAT LEAD TO THE FORMATION AND UTILIZATION
OF L-ALANINE

Formation	Utilization
Transamination (see p. 340)	Transamination
Reductive amination of pyruvate (see p. 313)	Oxidative deamination (see p. 304)
Decarboxylation of aspartate (see p. 335)	Peptide and protein synthesis
Cleavage of kynurenine, 3-hydroxykynurenine, and related compounds (see p. 854)	
Desulfination of cysteinesulfinic acid (see p. 802)	

microorganisms, and a relatively specific valine-alanine transaminase has been found in *Escherichia coli*. L-Alanine is formed by reductive amination of pyruvate, and as a product of the decarboxylation of L-aspartate, the cleavage of kynurenine and related compounds, and the desulfination of cysteinesulfinic acid (see Table I). Alanine formation in the tryptophanase (see p. 878), and cysteine desulfhydrase (see p. 793) reactions can probably be ascribed to the amination of pyruvate formed in these reactions.

Many organisms synthesize alanine by more than one pathway, and this probably explains why relatively few organisms exhibit an alanine requirement for growth. L-Alanine supports the growth of a mutant of *E. coli* that is blocked in the transamination of α-ketoisovalerate and α-keto-β-methylvalerate to valine and isoleucine, respectively, provided that isoleucine is present in the medium; the explanation for the growth-promoting effect of alanine lies in the fact that the organism possesses valine-alanine transaminase (see p. 730). Thus, it is the amino group of alanine which is utilized under these conditions, and indeed alanine can be replaced by α-aminobutyrate (which also transaminates with α-keto-isovalerate) as well as by valine. Microorganisms that exhibit a growth response to alanine have been used in microbiological procedures for the determination of alanine (32). Some organisms can use both optical isomers of alanine; utilization of the L-isomer may require vitamin B_6. As discussed elsewhere (see p. 371), such organisms convert L-alanine to D-alanine, which is utilized for the synthesis of cell-wall material; the racemase requires pyridoxal 5'-phosphate. The observation that certain microorganisms can grow on either L- or D-alanine, but not on pyruvate, suggests that they lack ability to catalyze the transamination or reductive amination of pyruvate. The reversible formation of D-alanine in certain bacteria is catalyzed by D-specific transaminases, but the major pathway of D-alanine formation is racemization of L-alanine. Both D- and L-alanine are oxidatively deaminated by the respective amino acid oxidases.

C. β-Alanine and β-Aminoisobutyric Acid

Biosynthesis

These amino acids arise in the metabolism of pyrimidines and as products of transamination of the corresponding ω-aldehydes. Additional possible pathways for the formation of β-alanine include α-decarboxylation of L-aspartate (see p. 335), and amination of acrylyl-coenzyme A. β-Aminoisobutyric acid might also be formed by α-decarboxylation of β-methylaspartic acid (see p. 609); the *erythro*-L-isomer corresponds to D-α-methyl-β-alanine.

Stadtman (33) described the synthesis of β-alanyl-coenzyme A from acrylyl-coenzyme A and ammonia catalyzed by preparations of *Clostridium propionicum*:

$$CH_2{=}CHC{-}S{-}CoA + NH_3 \rightleftharpoons CH_2CH_2C{-}S{-}CoA$$
$$\underset{O}{\Vert} \qquad\qquad\qquad \underset{NH_2}{|} \quad \underset{O}{\Vert}$$

β-Alanyl-coenzyme A is the first known example of an enzymatically formed amino acyl-coenzyme A derivative. Acrylyl-coenzyme A aminase was purified and shown to function optimally at relatively high concentrations of ammonium chloride and at high values of pH (34). These findings suggest that NH_3 rather than NH_4^+ is the enzymatically active form. The equilibrium of the reaction favors amination, but reversibility was demonstrated. At this time there seems to be no evidence for the formation of β-alanyl-coenzyme A from free β-alanine.

β-Alanine and β-aminoisobutyric acid are formed in the degradation of pyrimidines. Fink and associates (35, 36) found that administration of deoxyribonucleic acid, dihydrothymine, or thymine to rats resulted in urinary excretion of β-aminoisobutyric acid. The formation of β-aminoisobutyric acid from dihydrothymine, and of β-alanine from dihydrouracil was demonstrated in rat liver slices. After incubation of labeled thymine with rat liver slices, chromatographic evidence was obtained for the formation of dihydrothymine and β-ureidoisobutyric acid (carbamyl-β-aminoisobutyric acid) (36, 37). Administration of C^{14}-uracil to rats led to urinary excretion of radioactive dihydrouracil, β-ureidopropionic acid (carbamyl-β-alanine), and β-alanine (38). These observations led to work on cell-free systems. Thus, enzyme preparations from rat liver were obtained that catalyze formation of β-alanine from uracil, dihydrouracil, and β-ureidopropionic acid (36, 39). An enzyme that catalyzes interconversion of β-ureidopropionic acid and β-alanine (as well as β-ureidoisobutyric acid and β-aminoisobutyric acid) has been purified from beef (40) and rat (41) liver. The degradation of uracil to β-alanine, carbon dioxide, and ammonia by *Clostridium uracilicum* occurs by analogous reactions (42).

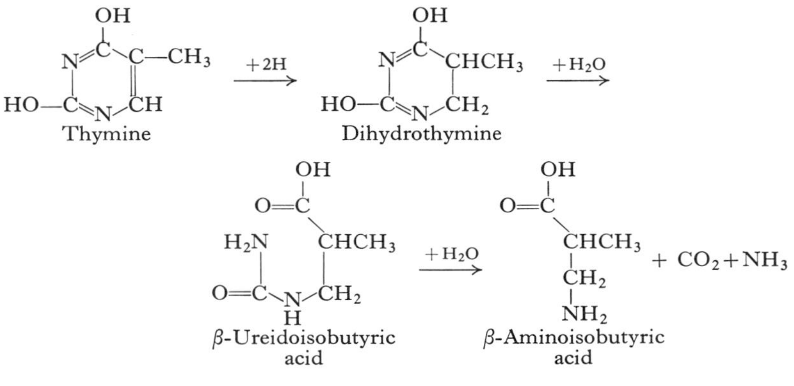

Thymine $\xrightarrow{+2H}$ Dihydrothymine $\xrightarrow{+H_2O}$ β-Ureidoisobutyric acid $\xrightarrow{+H_2O}$ β-Aminoisobutyric acid $+ CO_2 + NH_3$

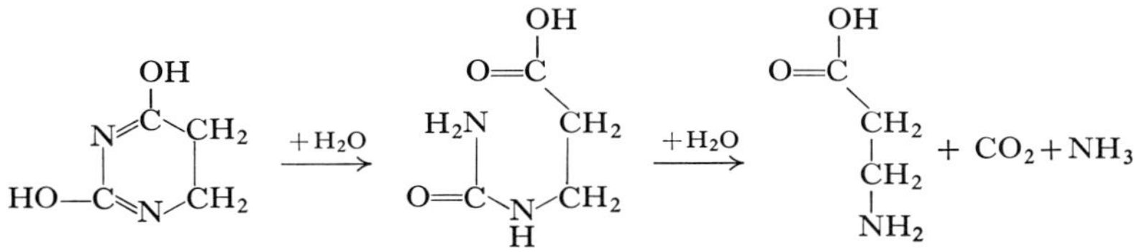

$$\text{Dihydrouracil} \xrightarrow{+H_2O} \beta\text{-Ureidopropionic acid} \xrightarrow{+H_2O} \beta\text{-Alanine} + CO_2 + NH_3$$

Another pathway that leads to the formation of β-alanine is catalyzed by certain microorganisms which convert the 3-carbon moieties of spermine and spermidine to β-alanine (43, 44). A number of organisms cleave spermidine to propane-1,3-diamine, and several of these catalyze further oxidation of the latter compound to β-alanine. The 4-carbon chain of spermidine is oxidized to γ-aminobutyric acid by some microorganisms (see p. 788).

β-Alanine and β-aminoisobutyric acid are reversibly formed in the following transamination reactions catalyzed by an enzyme obtained from hog kidney (45):

β-Aminoisobutyrate + α-ketoglutarate ⇌ methylmalonate semialdehyde + glutamate
β-Alanine + α-ketoglutarate ⇌ malonate semialdehyde + glutamate

Methylmalonate semialdehyde is a product of valine and propionate metabolism (see p. 748). A pathway from propionate to β-alanine has been formulated (46) (see p. 750).

The possibility that other pathways for the formation of β-alanine exist in certain plants and microorganisms is suggested by the natural occurrence of β-aminopropionitrile, which has been obtained from a toxic constituent of *Lathyrus odoratus* seeds (see p. 121). Another compound structurally related to β-alanine, β-nitropropionic acid, is produced by a strain of *Aspergillus flavus* (47). β-Aminopropionitrile and β-nitropropionic acid might be converted to β-alanine in certain organisms.

Degradation

β-Alanine is deaminated *in vivo* and by a variety of tissue preparations (48, 49). Pihl and Fritzson (50) found that C^{14}-β-alanine is rapidly metabolized by the rat; their data suggest deamination of β-alanine followed by decarboxylation to acetate:

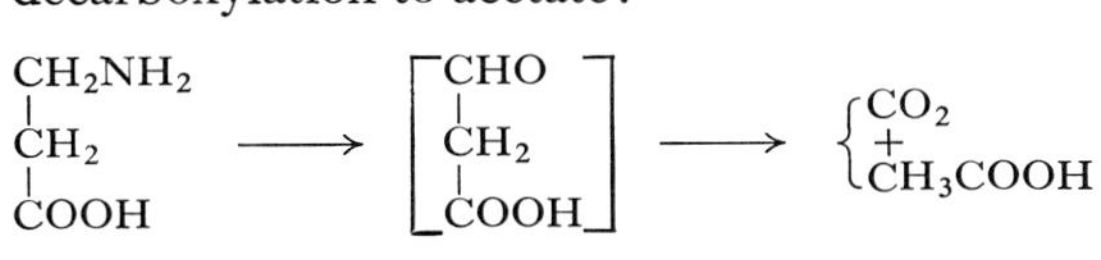

$$\begin{matrix} CH_2NH_2 \\ CH_2 \\ COOH \end{matrix} \longrightarrow \begin{bmatrix} CHO \\ CH_2 \\ COOH \end{bmatrix} \longrightarrow \begin{cases} CO_2 \\ + \\ CH_3COOH \end{cases}$$

The first step is probably catalyzed by transaminase, but the subsequent steps in animal tissues have not yet been clarified. More definitive work has been carried out with bacterial systems.

Hayaishi and colleagues (51) isolated a transaminase from *Pseudomonas fluorescens* that catalyzes the formation of malonate semialdehyde and L-alanine from β-alanine and pyruvate. The same organism possesses an enzyme that catalyzes conversion of malonate semialdehyde to acetyl-coenzyme A and carbon dioxide in the presence of coenzyme A and diphosphopyridine nucleotide. Apparently a single enzyme catalyzes the simultaneous dehydrogenation and decarboxylation of malonate semialdehyde; no evidence was found for the intermediate participation of malonyl-coenzyme A, acetaldehyde, or malonyl semialdehyde-coenzyme A.

Cell-free extracts of *Clostridium propionicum*, obtained by enrichment culture on β-alanine, catalyze formation of propionate and acetate according to the following over-all equation (52):

$$3NH_2CH_2CH_2COOH + 2H_2O \rightarrow 2CH_3CH_2COOH + CH_3COOH + CO_2 + 3NH_3$$

The deamination of β-alanine was more rapid than the production of propionate, and intermediate formation of β-hydroxypropionate was demonstrated. The observation that deamination of β-alanine required

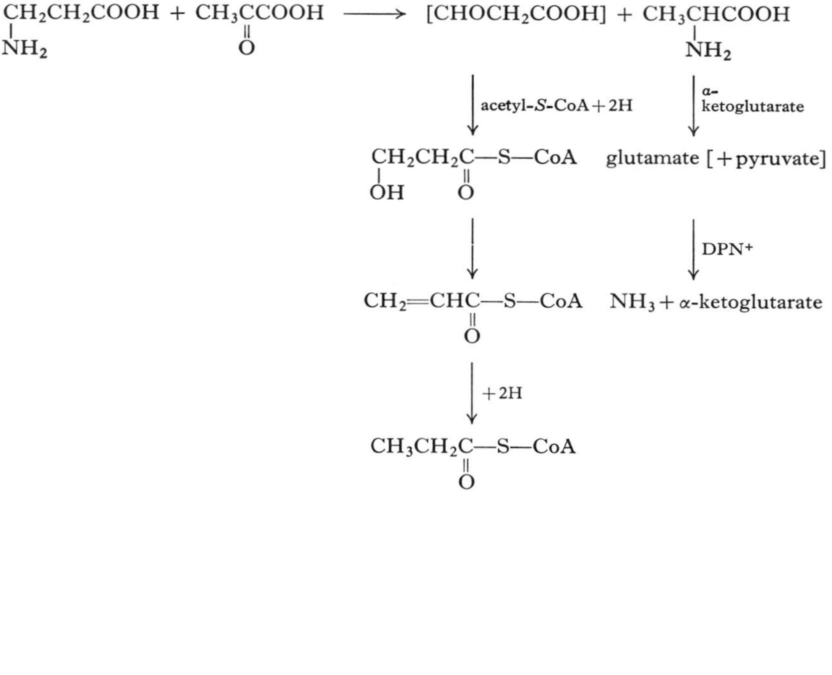

$$
\begin{array}{ccc}
\underset{\underset{NH_2}{|}}{CH_2CH_2COOH} + \underset{\underset{O}{\|}}{CH_3CCOOH} \longrightarrow [CHOCH_2COOH] + \underset{\underset{NH_2}{|}}{CH_3CHCOOH}
\end{array}
$$

acetyl-*S*-CoA + 2H $\downarrow$ $\qquad$ $\downarrow$ α-ketoglutarate

$$
\underset{\underset{OH}{|}}{CH_2CH_2C}\underset{\underset{O}{\|}}{-S-CoA} \qquad glutamate\ [+pyruvate]
$$

$\downarrow$ $\qquad$ $\downarrow$ DPN+

$$
CH_2{=}CHC\underset{\underset{O}{\|}}{-S-CoA} \qquad NH_3 + α\text{-ketoglutarate}
$$

$\downarrow$ +2H

$$
CH_3CH_2C\underset{\underset{O}{\|}}{-S-CoA}
$$

catalytic amounts of pyruvate and α-ketoglutarate indicates that the first step is transamination of β-alanine with pyruvate to yield alanine, which transaminates with α-ketoglutarate; the glutamate formed is deaminated by glutamate dehydrogenase. It is surprising that there was no evidence for formation of free malonate semialdehyde, or for the presence of β-hydroxypropionate dehydrogenase. It is possible that enzyme-bound malonate semialdehyde is formed and converted to β-hydroxypropionyl-coenzyme A, which is dehydrated to acrylyl-coenzyme A. Extracts of

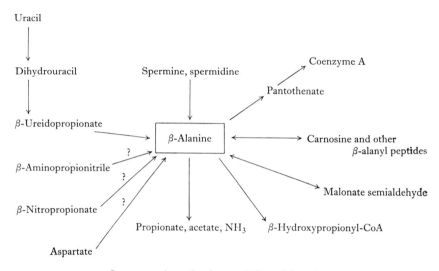

Summary scheme for the metabolism of β-alanine.

C. propionicum catalyze the reduction of β-hydroxypropionate to propionate, and of acrylyl-coenzyme A to propionyl-coenzyme A. According to the proposed pathway, pyruvate functions in several ways. In addition to its role in transamination with β-alanine, pyruvate is oxidized to acetyl-coenzyme A, which is utilized for formation of β-hydroxypropionyl-coenzyme A; pyruvate oxidation is coupled with reduction of acrylyl-coenzyme A. The product of the transamination reaction of β-alanine in this system differs from that found in other reactions in being enzyme-bound. Pyruvate, rather than α-ketoglutarate, is active in transamination in the *Clostridium* system and also with the enzyme from *Pseudomonas* (51) but mammalian β-alanine transaminase utilizes α-ketoglutarate (46).

β-Alanine is a constituent of carnosine, anserine, and related peptides (see p. 118) and is a precursor of pantothenic acid. The synthesis of pantothenic acid from pantoic acid and β-alanine is considered elsewhere (see p. 456). The utilization of β-alanine for quinolinic acid synthesis in mammals has been described (see p. 861).

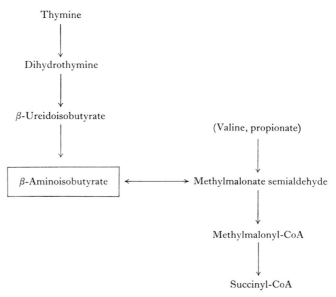

Summary scheme for the metabolism of β-aminoisobutyrate.

D. Aspartic Acid and Asparagine

General Considerations

Transamination provides a significant pathway for the interconversion of aspartate and oxaloacetate in many cells. The biotin requirement for aspartate synthesis reflects the function of this vitamin as a cofactor in the reactions leading to incorporation of carbon dioxide into oxaloacetate (53–59). Transamination of aspartate and asparagine (see p. 352) and decarboxylation of aspartate (see p. 335) have been considered above. Transamination precedes oxidative metabolism of aspartate carbon in rat tissue preparations (60). Aspartate nitrogen is utilized for urea formation (see p. 686), and serves both as a precursor of purines (see p. 630) and pyrimidines (see p. 612). Neither L- nor D-aspartate is attacked at an appreciable rate by the general amino acid oxidases. D-Asparagine is not oxidized by hog kidney D-amino acid oxidase, but L-asparagine is a substrate for snake venom L-amino acid oxidase. There is evidence for a D-aspartic acid oxidase in the kidney of several species (see p. 300).

Asparagine

Although it has been known for some time that asparagine is synthesized in plants, microorganisms, and animal tissues, until recently little information was available about the mechanism of asparagine biosynthesis. Ravel and her associates (61) have obtained a partially purified enzyme from *Lactobacillus arabinosus* that catalyzes the following reaction:

$$\text{L-Aspartate} + \text{ATP} + \text{NH}_3 \rightleftharpoons \text{L-asparagine} + \text{AMP} + \text{pyrophosphate}$$

The details of these and other studies on asparagine biosynthesis are considered elsewhere (see p. 457).

A number of animal (62–70, 77–80) and plant (71) tissues, and microorganisms (72–75) exhibit asparaginase activity. Evidence for the occurrence of a bacterial D-asparaginase has been obtained (76). The deamidation of asparagine that requires the presence of α-keto acids ("asparaginase II") results from transamination of asparagine to α-ketosuccinamic acid, which is hydrolyzed by a specific amidase that does not attack asparagine (see p. 352). Guinea pig serum contains considerable amounts of asparaginase (77), and the enzyme has been partially purified from this source (78–80). The enzyme is associated with the α_2-globulin fraction of guinea pig serum. It is highly specific for L-asparagine; although isoasparagine and other amides are not attacked at significant rates, the enzyme exhibits slight but definite activity toward D-asparagine. The unique presence of this enzyme in guinea pig serum has been noted by several investigators; no asparaginase activity has been found in the serum of the cat, rat, dog, monkey, chicken, pig, sheep, cow, horse, and man. Rabbit serum exhibits less than 1% of the activity of guinea pig serum. In the light of these findings, it is not surprising that the blood concentration of asparagine in guinea pigs is only 10% of that found in other mammalian species (81). The observation that guinea pig serum, but not the sera of other animals, exerted an inhibitory effect on several transplantable mouse and rat lymphomas (82, 83) raises the question as to whether the antineoplastic effect is due to asparaginase. Preliminary studies (84) are not inconsistent with this conclusion, but additional work is required since the asparaginase preparations used in these studies were far from pure. If asparaginase is the antitumor agent, the function of asparagine in the growth and maintenance of such tumors would clearly be worth investigation.

At this time asparagine does not appear to have a function in animal tissues other than that of a protein constituent. Asparagine accumulates in a number of plants and could have a special metabolic function. That asparagine amide nitrogen is utilized by wheat embryos for the synthesis of glycinamide ribonucleotide (see p. 632) is suggested by the observation that asparagine was more active than glutamine in forming glycinamide ribonucleotide from phosphoribosylpyrophosphate. Both asparagine and NH_4^+ were more active than glutamine when this reaction was studied with ribose-5-phosphate (see p. 633) (85). It is possible that asparagine functions in amide nitrogen transfer reactions analogous to those in which glutamine participates (see p. 624), but this does not seem to have been extensively examined. The unusual accumulation of asparagine in virus-infected plants (86) suggests an alteration of pyrimidine or purine metabolism. Study of this phenomenon at the enzymatic level might throw light on both the biosynthesis of asparagine and its utilization.

Conversion of Aspartate to Fumarate

There are several enzymatic reactions known in which aspartate is converted to fumarate; these include deamination catalyzed by aspartase, formation of adenylosuccinic acid, formation of arginine (see p. 686), and synthesis of 5-amino-4-imidazolecarboxamide ribonucleotide (see p. 632).

In certain microorganisms and higher plants (87–95), aspartate is reversibly deaminated to fumarate by the enzyme aspartase:

$$\begin{array}{ccc}
\text{COOH} & & \text{COOH} \\
| & & | \\
\text{CH}_2 & \rightleftharpoons & \text{CH} \\
| & & \parallel \\
\text{CHNH}_2 & & \text{HC} \quad + \text{NH}_3 \\
| & & | \\
\text{COOH} & & \text{COOH}
\end{array}$$

Bacterial aspartase has been partially purified (92, 93); the equilibrium favors deamination, and in the presence of fumarase deamination goes to completion. Ellfolk has concluded that the enzyme contains a sulfhydryl group and that it is activated by certain metal ions (93). Aspartase has not yet been found in mammalian tissues, and it apparently functions in a degradative rather than synthetic role in microorganisms (96). In early studies of aspartase, Gale (91) found evidence for an aspartase that required adenylic acid as a coenzyme.

Studies of the reaction catalyzed by aspartase in the presence of D_2O have shown that the aspartic acid formed contained one atom of deuterium per molecule, indicating that addition of hydrogen to the β-carbon atom is stereospecific. The mono-deutero-L-aspartic acid formed was converted to deutero-L-malic acid, which was examined by nuclear magnetic resonance. These observations indicate a *cis*-addition of ammonia to fumaric acid (97). In another investigation (98), the amination and hydration of fumarate by the aspartase and fumarase, respectively, of *Bacillus cadaveris* when carried out in D_2O gave only mono-deuterated products, and little deuterium was incorporated in the residual fumarate. Crystalline pig heart fumarase (99), bacterial fumarase, and bacterial aspartase catalyze deuterium addition specifically to the same position on the methylene group of L-malate or L-aspartate.

Aspartase preparations also catalyze the formation of *N*-hydroxy-L-aspartic acid from fumarate and hydroxylamine (100). Hydroxylamine apparently serves as an analog of ammonia, but it is conceivable that similar reactions are involved in formation of the naturally occurring *N*-hydroxy amino acids (see pp. 98 and 754).

The conversion of asparagine to fumaramic acid (see p. 8) is analogous to the reaction catalyzed by aspartase. It would be of interest to look for an enzyme that could catalyze this reaction.

β-Methylaspartic Acid

Studies on the fermentation of glutamate by *Clostridium tetanomorphum* showed that extracts of this organism catalyze the reversible conversion of glutamate to ammonia and mesaconate in the presence of α,α'-dipyridyl (101, 102). Treatment of such extracts with charcoal removed a factor needed for the decomposition of glutamate (see p. 618), but the treated extracts were found to catalyze the formation of a new amino acid from mesaconate and ammonia. The new amino acid was shown to be β-methylaspartate, probably the L-*threo*-isomer (103). A purified preparation of the enzyme, β-methylaspartase (104), which catalyzes the following reaction, was obtained:

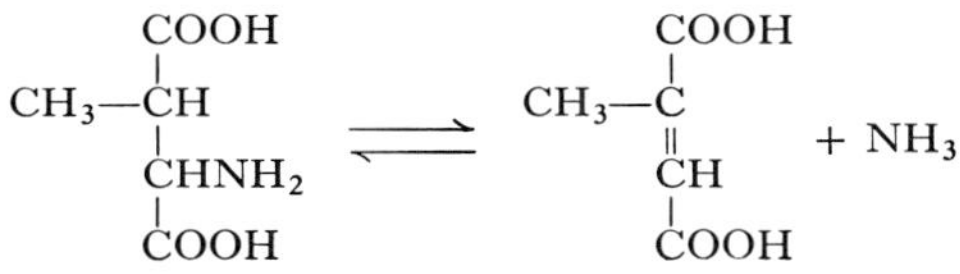

$$\begin{array}{ccc}
\text{COOH} & & \text{COOH} \\
| & & | \\
\text{CH}_3\!-\!\text{CH} & \rightleftharpoons & \text{CH}_3\!-\!\text{C} \\
| & & \parallel \quad +\ \text{NH}_3 \\
\text{CHNH}_2 & & \text{CH} \\
| & & | \\
\text{COOH} & & \text{COOH}
\end{array}$$

threo-β-Methyl-L-aspartate is a much better substrate than the L-*erythro*-isomer; however, the enzyme also exhibits some activity toward L-aspartate. Since mesaconate is apparently not a substrate of aspartase, β-methylaspartase and aspartase are probably different enzymes. The equilibrium of the conversion of *threo-β*-methyl-L-aspartate to mesaconate and ammonia was studied under conditions in which the formation of the L-*erythro*-isomer was negligible; the apparent equilibrium constant was $0.31M$ at pH 9.7. The enzyme can be employed for the synthesis or decomposition of *threo-β*-methyl-L-aspartate by suitable adjustment of the concentrations of reactants. When *C. tetanomorphum* is grown on glutamate, energy is derived from the conversion of glutamate to ammonia, acetate, butyrate, and carbon dioxide; *threo-β*-methyl-L-aspartate and mesaconate are intermediates in this fermentation. β-Methylaspartase may function in the synthesis of glutamate in organisms that have sources of mesaconate and ammonia.

β-Methylaspartase requires both monovalent and divalent cations for activity; the most active cation pair is Mg^{++} and K^+ (101). There is evidence that free β-methylaspartate is the actual substrate, which combines with an Mg^{++}-enzyme complex (101a). The L-*threo-β*-methyl-aspartate formed from mesaconate in the presence of D_2O contains deuterium only at carbon atom 3, and the enzyme catalyzes exchange between the deuterium atom of such labeled β-methylaspartate and the medium (101b). In the conversion of β-methylaspartate to glutamate (see p. 618) there is no incorporation of hydrogen from the medium (101c).

Adenylosuccinic Acid

Carter and Cohen (105, 106) isolated adenylosuccinic acid from yeast and demonstrated that yeast preparations catalyze the reversible formation of this compound from fumaric acid and adenylic acid:

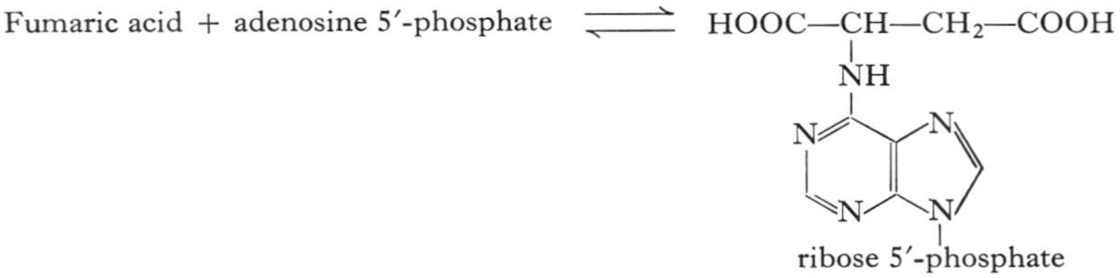

Fumaric acid + adenosine 5′-phosphate $\rightleftharpoons$ HOOC—CH—CH$_2$—COOH

ribose 5′-phosphate

The enzyme that catalyzes this reaction (adenylosuccinase) was isolated and partially purified; synthesis of adenylosuccinic acid on a preparative scale is feasible (108). Other studies showed that adenylosuccinate is an intermediate in the formation of adenylic acid from inosinic acid, and Lieberman (109) obtained an enzyme from *Escherichia coli* that catalyzes the formation of adenylosuccinate from inosinic acid and L-aspartate in the presence of guanosine triphosphate (GTP):

Inosinic acid + L-aspartate + GTP → adenylosuccinate + GDP + inorganic phosphate

Adenylosuccinic acid was isolated from liver (110) and from *Penicillium chrysogenum* (111), and the dephosphorylated derivative, adenosylsuccinic acid (107), occurs in *Neurospora* (112) and in human cerebrospinal fluid (113). 6-Succinylaminopurine has been found in *Neurospora* (112, 114) and in human urine (115).

The D-succinyl isomer of adenylosuccinic acid and the corresponding D- and L-isomers of the 6-thio analog of adenylosuccinic acid have been synthesized (116). The L-succinyl isomer of the 6-thio analog inhibits cleavage of adenylosuccinic acid by adenylosuccinase; the 6-thio analog itself is slowly cleaved to 6-thio inosinic acid and either fumarate or malate (the primary product may be fumarate which is converted to malate by fumarase). The D-succinyl isomers of adenylosuccinic acid and its 6-thio analog are not attacked by adenylosuccinase nor do they serve as inhibitors. Other aspects of the specificity of this enzyme are considered below (see p. 636).

Hydroxyaspartic Acid

Sallach and Peterson (117) showed the formation of β-hydroxy-aspartic acid by transamination between dihydroxyfumaric acid (in equilibrium with oxaloglycolic acid) and glutamate; the reaction is catalyzed by an enzyme present in a variety of animal tissues.

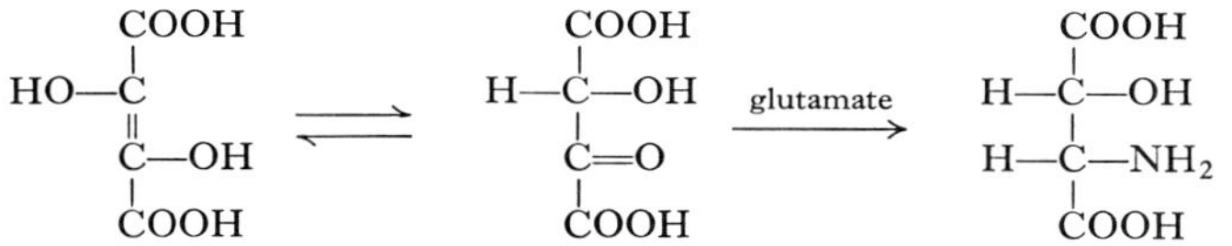

COOH	COOH	COOH
HO—C	H—C—OH glutamate	H—C—OH
C—OH	C=O	H—C—NH$_2$
COOH	COOH	COOH
Dihydroxyfumaric acid	Oxaloglycolic acid	β-Hydroxy-L-aspartic acid

The product of this reaction is *erythro*-β-hydroxy-L-aspartic acid (118). The further metabolism of β-hydroxyaspartic acid in animal tissues has not yet been fully investigated. There is evidence that this amino acid competitively inhibits glutamate-aspartate transaminase (119). The nonenzymatic decarboxylation of oxaloglycolic acid yields glycolic aldehyde and hydroxypyruvic acid (see p. 661), suggesting that an intermediate enol compound is formed which is converted to hydroxy-pyruvate, or to malonate semialdehyde, which undergoes decarboxylation (120).

Conversion of β-hydroxyaspartic acid to N-carbamyl-β-hydroxyaspartate in the presence of carbamyl phosphate and animal tissue preparations has been demonstrated (121). Further metabolism of carbamyl hydroxyaspartate would be expected to lead to 5-hydroxyuridine compounds; 5-hydroxyuridine is reported to inhibit nucleic acid synthesis.

In *Micrococcus denitrificans*, glyoxylate is converted to oxaloacetate via the intermediate formation of β-hydroxyaspartate, probably the *erythro*-form. Studies on the growth of this organism and enzymatic investigations indicate that glyoxylate and glycine condense by an aldolase-type reaction to yield β-hydroxyaspartate, which is converted to oxaloacetate by an enzyme tentatively named "β-hydroxyaspartate dehydratase" (122). This pathway provides an alternative route from glyoxylate to the citric acid cycle.

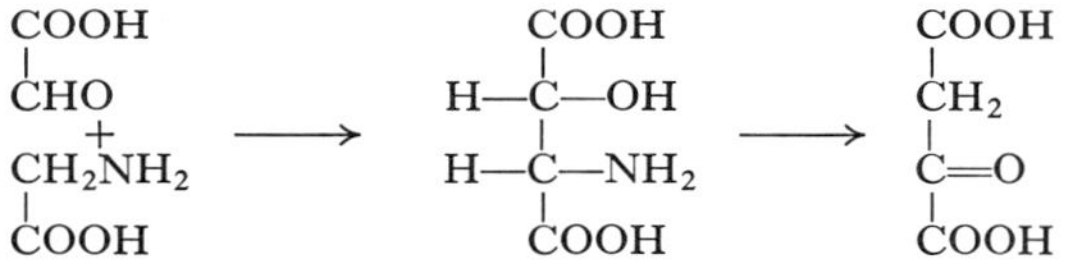

$$
\begin{array}{ccccc}
\text{COOH} & & \text{COOH} & & \text{COOH} \\
| & & | & & | \\
\text{CHO} & & \text{H—C—OH} & & \text{CH}_2 \\
+ & \longrightarrow & | & \longrightarrow & | \\
\text{CH}_2\text{NH}_2 & & \text{H—C—NH}_2 & & \text{C=O} \\
| & & | & & | \\
\text{COOH} & & \text{COOH} & & \text{COOH}
\end{array}
$$

Synthesis of the Pyrimidine Ring

Aspartic acid is the major precursor of pyrimidine carbon and nitrogen via the intermediate orotic acid. Thus, three of the carbon atoms and one nitrogen atom of the pyrimidine ring are provided by aspartate:

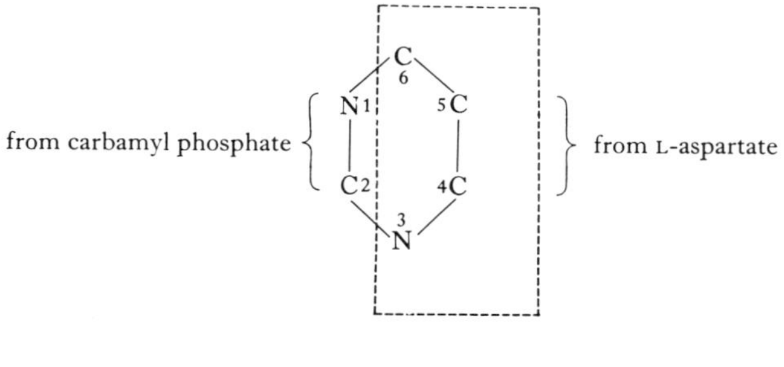

from carbamyl phosphate { N1, C2, C6 }   from L-aspartate { 5C, 4C, 3N }

Reichard (123) has provided an authoritative review of the enzymatic reactions that lead to pyrimidine biosynthesis. Early nutritional studies on microorganisms demonstrated a relationship between aspartate and pyrimidine metabolism; for example, pyrimidines exert a sparing effect on aspartate (124). Aspartic acid carbon was found to be incorporated into pyrimidine carbon in rat liver (125). Other studies showed that the pyrimidine requirement of microorganisms can be supplied by orotic acid, and there is considerable evidence that carbamyl aspartic acid (ureidosuccinic acid) is a precursor of orotic acid (126–130). The participation of carbamyl phosphate (see p. 688) and aspartic acid in the biosynthesis of orotic acid and the pyrimidines is indicated in Scheme 1.

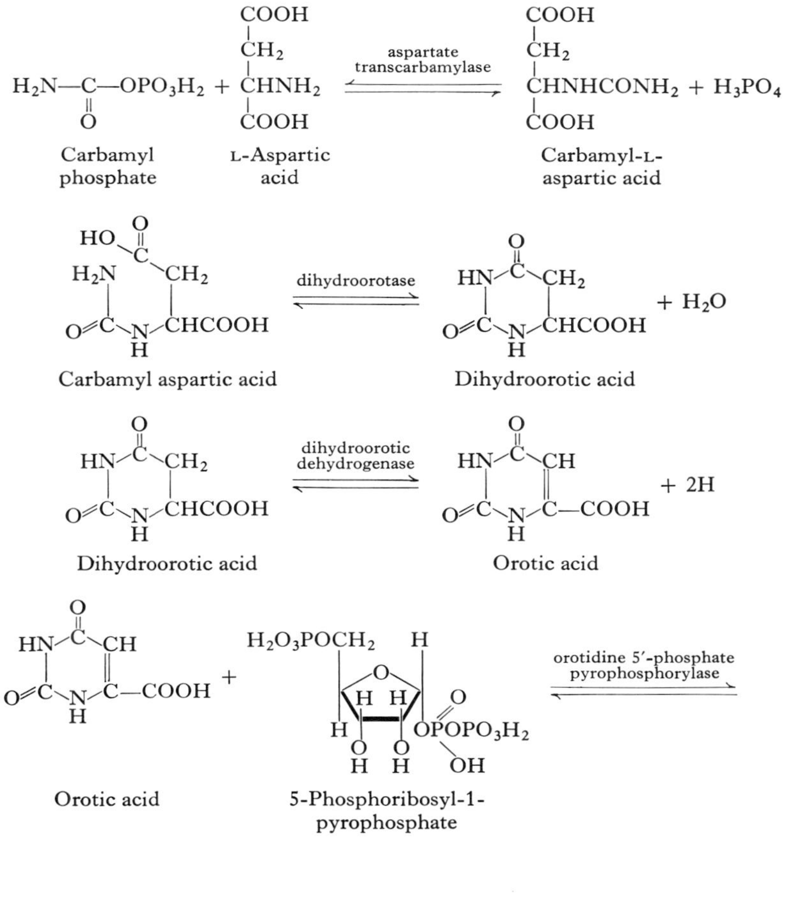

$$
\begin{array}{ccc}
& \text{COOH} & \text{COOH} \\
& | & | \\
& \text{CH}_2 & \text{CH}_2 \\
\text{H}_2\text{N—C—OPO}_3\text{H}_2 + & \text{CHNH}_2 & \text{CHNHCONH}_2 + \text{H}_3\text{PO}_4 \\
\quad\quad\quad \| & | & | \\
\quad\quad\quad \text{O} & \text{COOH} & \text{COOH}
\end{array}
$$

aspartate transcarbamylase

Carbamyl phosphate   L-Aspartic acid   Carbamyl-L-aspartic acid

Carbamyl aspartic acid   dihydroorotase   Dihydroorotic acid   + H₂O

Dihydroorotic acid   dihydroorotic dehydrogenase   Orotic acid   + 2H

Orotic acid   5-Phosphoribosyl-1-pyrophosphate   orotidine 5′-phosphate pyrophosphorylase

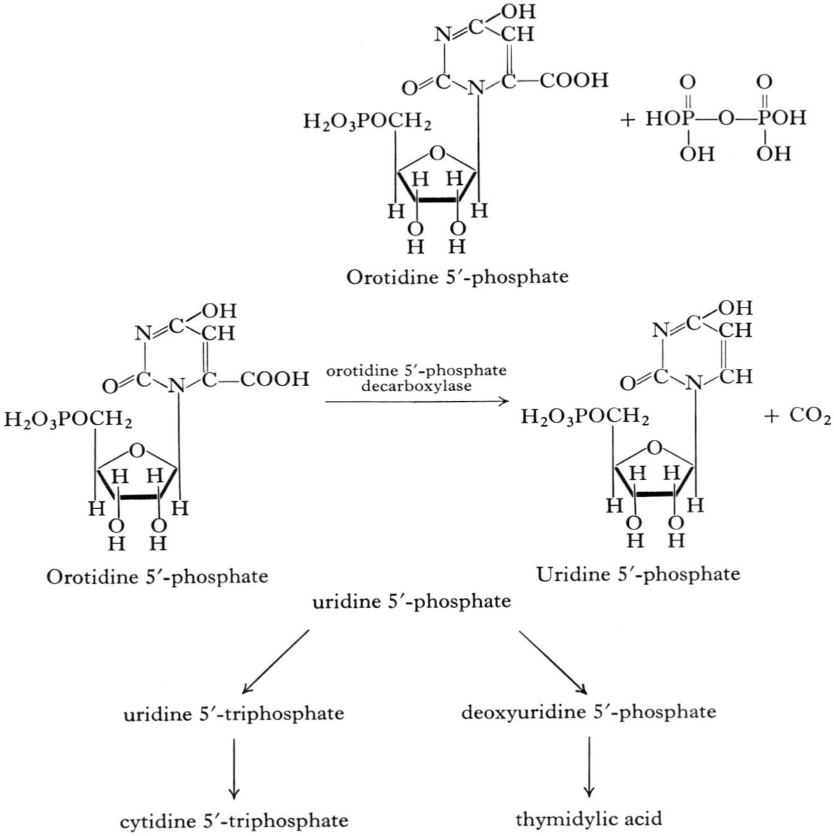

Orotidine 5′-phosphate

$$\text{Orotidine 5′-phosphate} \xrightarrow[\text{decarboxylase}]{\text{orotidine 5′-phosphate}} \text{Uridine 5′-phosphate} + CO_2$$

Orotidine 5′-phosphate   Uridine 5′-phosphate

uridine 5′-phosphate

uridine 5′-triphosphate   deoxyuridine 5′-phosphate

cytidine 5′-triphosphate   thymidylic acid

SCHEME 1. Biosynthesis of orotic acid and the pyrimidines.

Aspartate transcarbamylase (ureidosuccinic synthetase) is widely distributed in animal and plant tissues and in microorganisms (123, 131). The enzyme from *Escherichia coli*, which has been crystallized, has a molecular weight of about 220,000 (132). Its activity in *E. coli* (133) and lettuce seedlings (134) is regulated by feedback end-product inhibition and repression of enzyme synthesis. The probable feedback inhibitor in *E. coli* is cytidine 5′-triphosphate; studies by Gerhart and Pardee (135) indicate that the active site of the enzyme and the "feedback inhibitor" site are separate, but the latter can influence the active site. After treatment with heat, urea, or heavy metal ions, the enzyme can no longer be inhibited by cytidine 5′-triphosphate; such treatment increases activity and alters the K_m for aspartate and the pH optimum.

An enzyme that catalyzes the degradation of carbamyl aspartate to carbon dioxide, ammonia, and L-aspartate (ureidosuccinase) has been obtained from *Zymobacterium oroticum* (136). This reaction is analogous to that catalyzed by urease, and is essentially irreversible. *Z. oroticum*, other microorganisms (137, 127) and animal tissues (138) catalyze the reversible conversion of carbamyl aspartate to dihydroorotate. Homogenates of rat liver, which also possess dihydroorotase, convert carbamyl aspartate and dihydroorotate to orotate (138). Dihydroorotic dehydrogenase, the enzyme that catalyzes the reversible conversion of dihydroorotate to orotate, has been studied in bacterial systems (127, 137) and has been crystallized from *Z. oroticum* (139, 140). The crystalline enzyme is of special interest in that it contains both flavin adenine dinucleotide and flavin mononucleotide. The enzyme also contains one mole of iron per mole of flavin. The enzyme-bound flavin is bleached rapidly by reduced diphosphopyridine nucleotide and by substrate, and the hydrogen transfer is stereospecific, i.e., the enzyme removes a hydrogen atom from the α-side of reduced diphosphopyridine nucleotide (141).

The conversion of orotic acid to uridine nucleotides (142) does not take place at the level of free pyrimidine. Kornberg and associates made the important discovery that 5-phosphoribosyl-1-pyrophosphate is the key intermediate in the conversion of orotate to orotidine 5′-phosphate (143–145), and they isolated orotidine 5′-phosphate pyrophosphorylase from yeast. These studies have been amply confirmed, and the same reaction was found to occur in animal tissues (146).

The decarboxylation of orotidine 5′-phosphate, catalyzed by orotidine 5′-phosphate decarboxylase, also takes place in bacterial (144) and animal tissues (147, 148). The conversion of uridine 5′-phosphate to the triphosphate requires a series of kinase reactions (144, 149–151). Cytidine nucleotides are formed by amination of uridine nucleotides. Lieberman (152, 153) observed the following reaction in the presence of an enzyme isolated from *E. coli*:

Uridine 5′-triphosphate + ammonia + adenosine 5′-triphosphate →

cytidine 5′-triphosphate + adenosine 5′-diphosphate + inorganic phosphate

No cytidine 5′-triphosphate was formed when ammonia was replaced by glutamine; however, subsequent work has shown that glutamine is the major amino donor in the synthesis of cytidine nucleotides in *E. coli* (153a) and in animal tissues (see p. 626).

It is conceivable that there are pathways of pyrimidine biosynthesis that do not involve orotic acid; several *Neurospora* mutants which require pyrimidines were found to grow in media containing α-amino-butyric acid or threonine, but not aspartic acid or other amino acids (155, 156); incorporation of aminofumaric acid diamide into rat liver pyrimidine nucleotides has also been reported (138). However, these observations per se do not constitute satisfactory evidence for the existence of additional

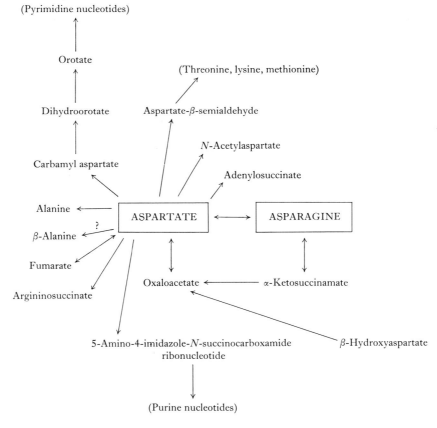

Summary scheme for the metabolism of aspartate and asparagine.

pathways of pyrimidine synthesis; further studies are required. The formation of uracil from β-alanine by reversal of reactions described above (see p. 603) could represent a physiological mechanism for uracil synthesis, and conversion of uracil to uridine nucleotides has been observed; the possible function of such reactions in the biosynthesis of uridine nucleotides has been discussed by Reichard (123).

Other Reactions of Aspartic Acid

N-Acetyl-L-aspartic acid has been found in brain (157) (see p. 9), and its biosynthesis is considered elsewhere (see p. 445). The participation of aspartic acid in the biosynthesis of arginine, threonine, lysine, methionine, and purines is discussed in later sections of this chapter.

E. Glutamic Acid and Glutamine

General Considerations

Many reactions of glutamic acid and glutamine are considered elsewhere in this volume. These include the glutamate dehydrogenase reaction (see p. 310), oxidation of D-glutamic acid (see p. 300) and of L-glutamine (see p. 306), synthesis of glutamine (see p. 446), decarboxylation of L-glutamic acid (see p. 329), transamination of D- and L-glutamic acids (see p. 338) and of L-glutamine (see p. 349), γ-glutamyl transfer reactions (see p. 478), relationships between glutamic acid, ornithine, proline, and arginine (see p. 715), formation of phenylacetylglutamine (see p. 442), the function of glutamine in ammonia transport, storage, urinary ammonia formation (see p. 285), and as an essential amino acid for the growth of animal cells grown in tissue culture (see p. 216). Glutamic acid and glutamine are widely distributed as constituents of protein (see p. 20), and glutamine is a prominent amino acid constituent of mammalian blood (see p. 110). Glutamine amide nitrogen is utilized in a number of transfer reactions (see p. 622). Glutamic acid is a constituent of glutathione (see p. 119), the folic acid compounds (see p. 122), and a variety of γ-glutamyl compounds (see pp. 120).

α-Ketoglutarate is probably the major precursor of glutamate in most cells (158–162); amination is catalyzed by glutamate dehydrogenase and transaminase. Glutamate is also formed from histidine (see p. 825), proline (see p. 715), hydroxyproline (see p. 727), by the hydrolysis of glutamate-containing compounds (e.g., glutathione, glutamine), and in certain organisms from β-methylaspartate. Additional pathways of glutamate biosynthesis have been postulated [see, for example (163)]; thus, in *Acetobacter suboxydans*, which does not have a citric acid cycle, glutamate might be derived from γ-hydroxyglutamate. The latter compound could be formed by a series of reactions involving condensation of oxaloacetate with glyoxylate or of acetate and pyruvate (164).

The Mesaconate Pathway

Extracts of *Clostridium tetanomorphum* catalyze the reversible conversion of glutamate to β-methylaspartate (see p. 609). The reaction requires a coenzyme which was identified as a derivative of pseudovitamin B_{12} (165, 166). The coenzyme contains two moles of adenine, one of which is attached to ribose as in pseudovitamin B_{12}. The other was at first believed to be attached to the corrin ring, but later work indicates that this is an adenosine moiety whose 5'-carbon atom is attached to the cobalt atom replacing cyanide (167). The adenyl cobamide coenzyme (see p. 774) was purified from *C. tetanomorphum* and found to contain one mole each of cobalt, phosphate, ribose, two moles of adenine, and no cyanide (168). Two additional cobamide coenzymes have been isolated: 5,6-dimethyl-benzimidazolyl cobamide and benzimidazolyl cobamide coenzymes; these are also active in the β-methylaspartate-glutamate isomerase reaction (169).

The coenzyme can be removed from crude extracts by treatment with charcoal; after this treatment, such extracts catalyze the interconversion of β-methylaspartate and mesaconate (see p. 609). Experiments with C^{14}-glutamate showed that the methyl carbon atom of mesaconate is derived from carbon atom 3 of glutamate and that the formation of the branched-chain structure of mesaconate involves cleavage between carbon atoms 2 and 3 of glutamate (or a related straight-chain compound), and formation of a new bond between carbon atoms 2 and 4 (170). These findings may be represented as follows:

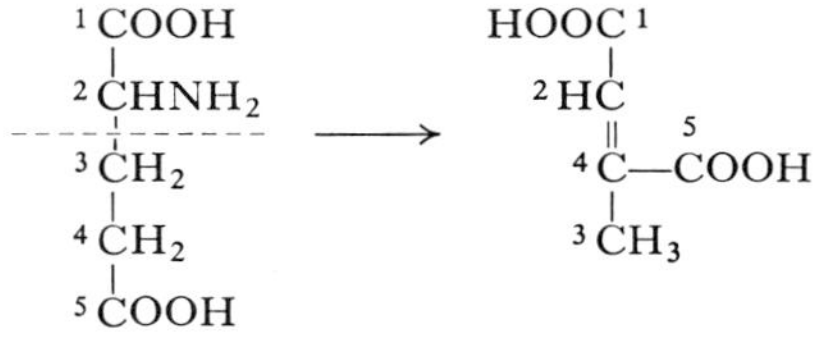

$$
\begin{array}{ll}
^1\text{COOH} & \text{HOOC}\,^1 \\
| & | \\
^2\text{CHNH}_2 & ^2\text{HC} \\
\text{-----} \longrightarrow & \parallel \quad ^5 \\
^3\text{CH}_2 & ^4\text{C—COOH} \\
| & | \\
^4\text{CH}_2 & ^3\text{CH}_3 \\
| & \\
^5\text{COOH} & \\
\end{array}
$$

Glutamic acid   Mesaconic acid

The degradation of mesaconate in extracts of *C. tetanomorphum* yields acetate, butyrate, and CO_2; studies with labeled glutamate indicate the following pathway:

$$
\begin{array}{ccc}
\overset{1}{\text{HOOC}} & \overset{1}{\text{COOH}} & \overset{1}{\text{COOH}} \\
| & | & | \\
\overset{2}{\text{HC}} & \overset{2}{\text{CH}_2} & \overset{2}{\text{CH}_3} \\
\| \; ^5 & | & + \\
\overset{4}{\text{C}}\text{—COOH} & \text{HO—}\overset{4}{\text{C}}\text{—COOH}^5 & \text{O=}\overset{4}{\text{C}}\text{—COOH}^5 \\
| & | & | \\
\overset{3}{\text{CH}_3} & \overset{3}{\text{CH}_3} & \overset{3}{\text{CH}_3}
\end{array}
$$

Mesaconic acid   Citramalic acid

$$
\begin{array}{ccc}
\text{O=}\overset{4}{\text{C}}\text{—COOH}^5 & \overset{5}{\text{CO}_2} & \\
| & + & \\
\overset{3}{\text{CH}_3} & [\overset{3}{\text{CH}_3}\overset{4}{\text{C}}\text{=O}] & \longrightarrow \quad \overset{3}{\text{CH}_3}\overset{4}{\text{CH}_2}\overset{3}{\text{CH}_2}\overset{4}{\text{COOH}}
\end{array}
$$

Metabolism of L- and D-Glutamic Acids in Animals

The degradative metabolism of glutamic acid in animals involves oxidative deamination or transamination followed by oxidation of the resulting α-ketoglutarate in the citric acid cycle. Studies in which the labeling patterns of tissue glutamate, aspartate, and alanine were determined after administration of DL-glutamic acid-2-C^{14} to rats indicated conversion to succinate via α-ketoglutarate as the primary route when glutamate was administered intraperitoneally (171, 172). When glutamate was injected into the cecum, carbon atom 2 was converted to the methyl carbon atom of acetate. When the glutamate was administered by stomach tube, both pathways were utilized. A study of the individual optical isomers of glutamate showed that L-glutamate was metabolized via α-ketoglutarate after intraperitoneal injection and that carbon atom 2 of both isomers of glutamate was converted to the methyl carbon atom of acetate when labeled glutamate was introduced into the cecum. These findings suggest that when glutamate is injected into the cecum degradation by the intestinal bacteria takes place via the glutamate-mesaconate pathway.

The metabolism of D-glutamic acid follows a special pathway in certain animals. This was first indicated by the studies of Ratner (173), who found that when DL-glutamate was administered to rats, most of the D-isomer was excreted in the urine as D-pyrrolidone carboxylate. These observations were confirmed by others (172, 174), and it was found that incubation of D-glutamate with rat liver and kidney slices led to cyclization (172). An enzyme activity that catalyzes the optically specific cyclization of D-glutamate to D-pyrrolidone carboxylate is present in the kidney, liver, and certain other tissues of several mammals, including the rat, mouse, and man (175, 176). It was partially purified from mouse kidney and found to require manganese or magnesium ions for activity. The enzyme, which catalyzes the reversible conversion of D-glutamate to D-pyrrolidone carboxylate, does not act on L-glutamic acid, D- or L-glutamine, nor does it catalyze synthesis of glutamine. The distribution of the enzyme is similar to that of mammalian D-amino acid oxidase; both are more active in kidney than in liver. Kidney D-amino acid oxidase does not exhibit appreciable activity toward D-glutamic acid and it is curious that another D-specific enzyme is present in mammalian kidney, apparently for the special purpose of catalyzing the intramolecular acylation of D-glutamate. The observation that freshly voided normal human urine contains D-pyrrolidone carboxylate (and very little of the L-isomer) provides a logical basis for the suggestion that this enzyme has a physiological function. The function of mammalian D-amino acid oxidase and of the D-glutamate cyclizing enzyme may be to act upon D-amino acids present in the diet or formed by bacteria of the intestinal flora. There is now no evidence that D-amino acids function in mammalian metabolism, but a quantitatively small pathway may have thus far been overlooked.

There is substantial evidence that the conversion of glutamate to aspartate by various animal tissue preparations proceeds by reactions involving transamination and the citric acid cycle; studies by Krebs and associates (154, 177) do not support the suggestion that glutamate is converted to aspartate in the brain by a mechanism involving γ-decarboxylation (178), but a complete report of the data indicating the latter pathway has not yet appeared.

Experiments with N^{15}-labeled ammonia in intact cats suggest that there is a compartmentalization of glutamate metabolism in the brain. After administration of N^{15}-ammonia the α-amino group of cerebral glutamine contained more isotope than did glutamate, suggesting that the newly formed glutamine arose from a small and metabolically active compartment of glutamate which was not in rapid equilibrium with the total tissue glutamate. In contrast, the α-amino group of hepatic glutamate contained more label than did the liver glutamine, indicating that the glutamate used for glutamine synthesis mixes with total tissue glutamate (179).

Glutathione

The synthesis of glutathione from glutamate, glycine, and cysteine takes place in two steps:

Glutamate + cysteine + ATP $\rightleftharpoons$ γ-glutamylcysteine + ADP + inorganic phosphate

γ-Glutamylcysteine + glycine + ATP $\rightleftharpoons$ glutathione + ADP + inorganic phosphate

These reactions have been considered in detail above (see p. 452). The enzymes that catalyze these reactions also catalyze the synthesis of several analogous tripeptides. Glutathione functions as a coenzyme for glyoxylase (180), formaldehyde dehydrogenase (181), keto-enol tautomerase (see p. 907), DDT [1,1,1-trichloro-2,2-bis(*p*-chlorophenyl)ethane] dehydrochlorinase (183), and for the isomerization of maleylacetoacetate (see p. 905). Its suggested function as a constituent of glyceraldehyde 3-phosphate dehydrogenase (182) is not supported by recent work (184). Although one is tempted to attribute almost any effect of glutathione to its sulfhydryl group, the dramatic feeding response to glutathione exhibited by hydra (185) is also elicited by ophthalmic acid (186). Glutathione reductase, an enzyme that catalyzes the reversible pyridine nucleotide-dependent oxidation of glutathione, has been found in a variety of plant and animal tissues (see p. 799). Glutathione, other γ-glutamyl peptides, and related γ-glutamyl compounds participate in a variety of γ-glutamyl transfer reactions of the following type (see p. 478):

Glutathione + amino acid $\rightleftharpoons$ γ-glutamylamino acid + cysteinylglycine

Such reactions can also lead to the formation of glutathione (187), but these are probably not of quantitative significance. Knox (188) has written a comprehensive review on glutathione.

Glutamine

McIlwain and associates (189, 190) observed in 1939 that glutamine was necessary for the optimal growth of certain microorganisms; they found that the growth of *Streptococcus hemolyticus* was greatly increased when a heart muscle extract was added to the growth medium. The growth factor was subsequently isolated and shown to be glutamine (189); this was the first isolation of glutamine from an animal source. Later studies indicated that many other organisms exhibit a similar requirement for glutamine [see, for example (191–202)]. In addition to its effect on growth, there is much evidence that glutamine is required for a number of specific cellular processes; for example, it was reported in early work that glutamine could replace glutamine-containing peptides in increasing the formation of toxin by *Clostridium tetani* (197). It now appears that the major, if not the only, biosynthetic pathway leading to the synthesis of glutamine is the reaction catalyzed by the widely distributed enzyme, glutamine synthetase (203):

$$\text{Glutamate} + NH_3 + ATP \rightleftharpoons \text{glutamine} + ADP + \text{inorganic phosphate}$$

Detailed consideration of the mechanism of glutamine synthesis is presented elsewhere (see p. 446).

Glutamine participates in a wide variety of metabolic reactions, many of which are associated with the transfer of its amide nitrogen atom and consequently lead to the formation of glutamate. Enzyme activity capable of catalyzing the hydrolysis of glutamine to glutamate and ammonia has long been known, but the function of such glutaminases has not always been clear. It is possible that certain enzymes described initially as glutaminases also catalyze other reactions. Lang in 1904 observed that preparations of a number of animal tissues catalyzed the deamidation of glutamine (204). Later, Krebs reported that extracts of mammalian brain, retina, liver, and kidney deamidated glutamine (205). Greenstein and associates (67, 206–210) discovered two types of deamidation phenomena in animal tissues. One of these (catalyzed by "glutaminase I") is a deamidation catalyzed by phosphate and to a lesser extent by arsenate and sulfate, and the other (catalyzed by "glutaminase II") requires α-keto acids. The latter was shown to be associated with transamination of glutamine leading to α-ketoglutaramic acid, which is deamidated by a separate enzyme (see p. 349).

"Glutaminase I" is associated with the mitochondrial fraction of liver, kidney, brain, and HeLa cells (207, 208, 211–215), but can be obtained in a soluble form (212, 213, 216, 217). The mechanism of activation by certain anions is not yet understood, although it has been suggested (213) that divalent ions protect the enzyme against inactivation. It is of interest that phosphate, bicarbonate, and arsenate catalyze a somewhat analogous nonenzymatic reaction leading to the formation of pyrrolidone carboxylate (218). Homoglutamine (α-aminoadipamic acid), α-methylglutamine, and γ-methylglutamine are also nonenzymatically deamidated at the same or more rapid rates than glutamine (219); yet, these compounds are hydrolyzed slowly or not at all by purified glutaminases (220). Many data on the inhibition and specificity of glutaminases have appeared in the literature and several interesting suggestions concerning the mechanism of the reaction have been made (216, 217).

Administration of dilute hydrochloric acid or ammonium chloride to rats increases the renal glutaminase activity (221–223). Similar findings have been made in studies on guinea pigs (224). The increase in renal glutaminase is associated with greater excretion of ammonia, and is prevented by administration of DL-ethionine. Renal glutaminase also hydrolyzes α-methylglutamine, but exhibits no activity toward D-glutamine; the reported hydrolysis of isoglutamine by this enzyme is probably due to the presence of glutamine in the isoglutamine preparation used.

Plant tissues (71, 225) and certain microorganisms (226–232) also exhibit glutaminase activity, and partially purified preparations of glutaminase have been obtained from bacterial sources. Certain glutaminase preparations catalyze the transfer of the γ-glutamyl group to hydroxylamine (220). These reactions proceed in the absence of added cations or nucleotides, and in this respect differ from the γ-glutamyl transfer reaction catalyzed by glutamine synthetase (see p. 446). A purified enzyme from *Azotobacter* catalyzes hydrolysis of both isomers of glutamine and asparagine as well as the hydrolysis of L-γ-glutamyl-hydroxamate to hydroxylamine and glutamate (233). In contrast to the hydrolysis of the amides, the latter reaction does not proceed to completion, and it was shown that this enzyme catalyzes the synthesis of γ-glutamylhydroxamate from glutamate and hydroxylamine. Although the hydrolysis of glutamine is associated with a relatively large change in free energy, the standard free energy of hydrolysis of γ-glutamylhydroxamate is approximately 700 calories per mole (see also p. 447).

Waelsch and associates (234, 235) found that extracts of *Proteus vulgaris* catalyze exchange of N^{15}-ammonia with the amide groups of glutamine and asparagine, and also the formation of γ-glutamylhydroxamate and β-aspartylhydroxamate from hydroxylamine and the respective α-amino acid-ω-amides. The formation of hydroxamates under these conditions may be ascribed to the ability of hydroxylamine to serve in place of a natural substrate, or perhaps to the reaction of hydroxylamine with enzyme-bound γ-glutamyl or β-aspartyl moieties. It is of interest that purified guinea pig serum asparaginase catalyzes the formation of β-aspartylhydroxamate when the enzyme is incubated with hydroxylamine and asparagine or aspartate (220). It seems probable that the group of enzymatic activities that have been designated γ-glutamyl transferases and β-aspartyl transferases on the basis of their ability to catalyze hydroxamate formation are enzymes that catalyze specific reactions involving activation of the ω-carboxyl groups of these dicarboxylic amino acid amides.

Glutamine participates in a large number of amide nitrogen transfer reactions (236). Thus, glutamine amide nitrogen is utilized in the synthesis of the imidazole ring of histidine (see p. 819), two of the reactions involved in purine ring biosynthesis (see p. 630), the synthesis of the amide group of diphosphopyridine nucleotide, the synthesis of D-glucosamine-6-phosphate, and in other reactions. Preiss and Handler (237–241) have shown that the final steps in the biosynthesis of diphosphopyridine nucleotide are:

Nicotinic acid + 5-phosphoribosyl-1-pyrophosphate →
  deamido-nicotinic acid mononucleotide + pyrophosphate

Deamido-nicotinic acid mononucleotide + ATP ⇌
  deamido-diphosphopyridine nucleotide + pyrophosphate

Deamido-diphosphopyridine nucleotide + glutamine + ATP →
  diphosphopyridine nucleotide + glutamate + adenosine 5′-phosphate + pyrophosphate

The enzyme that catalyzes the amidation of deamido-diphosphopyridine nucleotide was purified from baker's yeast; the purified preparation did not exhibit glutaminase activity nor was asparagine active in place of glutamine. However, synthesis was observed when ammonia was added in place of glutamine. The K_m values at pH 7.4 for glutamine and un-ionized ammonia are of about the same order. The pH-activity curve with glutamine exhibits a broad optimum from pH 6.2 to 7.6, while that with ammonium chloride increases with increase of pH to an optimum between pH 8.2 and 9.0. These findings suggest that un-ionized ammonia is the enzymatically active form. Substitution of hydroxylamine for ammonia led to the formation of a hydroxamate; this observation and the fact that inorganic pyrophosphate is formed suggest an enzyme-bound acyl adenylate intermediate.

The conversion of xanthylic acid to guanylic acid has also been shown to involve amide nitrogen transfer from glutamine, but in certain systems ammonia is active.

Xanthylic acid + glutamine + ATP + H_2O →
  guanylic acid + glutamate + adenosine 5′-phosphate + pyrophosphate

A purified enzyme preparation obtained from pigeon liver was active with glutamine and ammonia, and when xanthylic acid labeled with O^{18} in the 2-hydroxyl group was used, isotope appeared mainly in the phosphate group of adenosine 5'-phosphate (242–244). Similar enzymes have been found in rabbit bone marrow and calf thymus (245–247). In experiments with N^{15}-amide-labeled glutamine, the amide nitrogen entered guanylic acid without significant dilution. Ammonium chloride was active in place of glutamine; in these experiments and in those with pigeon liver preparations, relatively high concentrations of ammonium chloride were required, but the concentrations of un-ionized ammonia in both cases were approximately the same as those required for activity with glutamine. An enzyme preparation from *Aerobacter aerogenes* catalyzes the amination of xanthylic acid utilizing ammonia rather than glutamine (248). Hydroxylamine inhibited the reaction irreversibly; no evidence for the formation of a hydroxamate was obtained, but hydroxylamine inactivated the enzyme when both adenosine triphosphate and xanthylic acid were present. These observations suggest that adenosine triphosphate and xanthylic acid combine with the enzyme to form an activated complex capable of reacting with hydroxylamine.

Studies on the synthesis of D-glucosamine-6-phosphate in animals (249, 250) and in bacteria (251) have shown that the glucosamine carbon chain is derived from glucose. Early studies indicated that glutamine functioned in hyaluronate synthesis in streptococci (252) and that extracts of *Neurospora crassa* catalyzed the formation of glutamate and a product with the properties of glucosamine-6-phosphate from glutamine and hexose phosphate (253); later work (254) showed that glucosamine was formed when extracts of streptococci were incubated with glucose, adenosine triphosphate, and glutamine. The synthesis of glucosamine-6-phosphate from glucose-6-phosphate and glutamine has been observed with an enzyme preparation from rat liver (255). Hexosamine synthesis was somewhat more rapid with glucose-6-phosphate than with fructose-6-phosphate. On the other hand, enzyme preparations that were free of phosphohexoisomerase obtained from *E. coli*, *N. crassa*, and rat liver utilized only fructose-6-phosphate as the acceptor (256). The reaction may therefore be represented as follows:

Fructose-6-phosphate + glutamine → glucosamine-6-phosphate + glutamate

The mechanism of this reaction requires additional study. Although experiments with N^{15}-labeled glutamine have not yet been carried out, it appears probable that the reaction involves a transfer of the glutamine amide nitrogen to the fructose carbon chain. Although there do not appear to be many examples of the reactivity of amide groups in the chemical literature, reaction of amide groups with carbonyl groups have been observed under favorable steric conditions (see, for example, refs. 257, 258). The reactivity of the glutamine amide group could be enhanced by favorable orientation on the surface of the enzyme.

Studies on HeLa cells have shown that glutamine amide nitrogen is the direct precursor of 2 nitrogen atoms of the purine ring and of the amino group of guanine (259, 260). These results are to be expected on the basis of other investigations on purine biosynthesis (see p. 630) and guanine formation (see above). However, HeLa cells also use the amide nitrogen atom of glutamine for synthesis of 1 nitrogen atom of the pyrimidine ring and exogenous ammonia does not function as a direct precursor of pyrimidine nitrogen. In the HeLa cell the amide nitrogen atom of glutamine is not incorporated into α-amino acid nitrogen nor is ammonia utilized significantly for amino acid formation. The data suggest that carbamyl phosphate is synthesized in this cell by a mechanism involving glutamine (see p. 698).

In HeLa cells, the cytidine amino group is derived from glutamine (260), and work on other mammalian systems has led to similar findings. Thus, the conversion of uridine 5′-phosphate to cytidine nucleotides catalyzed by enzyme preparations from rat liver and Novikoff tumor requires adenosine triphosphate, magnesium ions, and glutamine. Glutamate, asparagine, ammonium ion, and aspartate are not active in place of glutamine. This reaction is stimulated by low concentrations of guanosine 5′-phosphate or guanosine 5′-triphosphate (261, 262).

The amino groups of anthranilic and p-aminobenzoic acids also arise from the amide nitrogen atom of glutamine. Thus, cell-free extracts of a mutant of *E. coli*, blocked in the conversion of anthranilic acid to indole-3-glycerol phosphate, catalyzed the formation of anthranilic acid from shikimic acid 5-phosphate in the presence of L-glutamine and magnesium ions. Anthranilic acid formation was markedly reduced when glutamine was replaced by asparagine, ammonium chloride, glutamate, or aspartate (263) (see also, p. 842). Evidence for the formation of p-aminobenzoic acid from shikimic acid 5-phosphate and L-glutamine has been obtained in experiments with cell-free extracts of baker's yeast. Other amino donors including asparagine and ammonium chloride were much less active (264), and in experiments with N^{15}-amide-labeled glutamine, there was no significant dilution of the isotopic nitrogen found in the amino group of *p*-aminobenzoic acid (265).

Amide nitrogen transfer reactions might be involved in the synthesis of the glycinamide moieties of oxytocin and vasopressin, and in the formation of the amide groups of vitamin B_{12}. Although the biosynthesis of asparagine catalyzed by a bacterial enzyme utilizes free ammonia, there is evidence that the glutamine amide nitrogen atom is the precursor of asparagine amide nitrogen in growing cultures of HeLa cells (266). Thus, when the cells were grown in the presence of N^{15}-amide-labeled glutamine, significant quantities of isotope were incorporated into the protein asparagine, and the content of isotope of the amide groups of glutamine and asparagine, respectively, in these studies was similar. Experiments carried out with N^{15}-labeled ammonia showed that little isotope was incorporated into asparagine. A report that asparagine is formed by reversible amide nitrogen transfer from glutamine to aspartic acid (267) requires further study [see p. 457; (268)].

It is of interest that a number of the enzymes that catalyze amide nitrogen transfer from glutamine also utilize ammonia; the K_m values for un-ionized ammonia and glutamine are of the same order of magnitude. These observations and studies on the effect of pH indicate that the un-ionized form of ammonia is probably the reactive species rather than ammonium ion. Glutamine, which may be considered as an acyl derivative of ammonia, possesses an unprotonated nitrogen atom, which would be available for transfer reactions in which the un-ionized form of ammonia may also participate. Ammonia is not active in the synthesis of D-glucosamine-6-phosphate, a reaction which, in contrast to the other amide nitrogen reactions, does not require adenosine triphosphate. Virtually all of the reactions involving amide nitrogen transfer are inhibited by aza-L-serine or 6-diazo-5-oxo-L-norleucine. These antibiotics (see p. 95) act as competitive inhibitors of glutamine and glutamate. The degree of inhibition by either antibiotic varies with different enzymes. Several observations suggest that the inhibitor is bound to the enzyme as part of an activated complex. Studies on inhibition by azaserine of reactions involved in purine biosynthesis are considered below (see p. 634). Attention has been given to the possibility that glutamine has a direct function (other than that of providing ammonia by hydrolysis) in urea formation (see p. 698). Glutamine seems to function directly in arginine synthesis in *Lactobacillus arabinosus* and there is good evidence that extracts of *Agaricus bisporus* utilize glutamine rather than ammonia for citrulline synthesis (see p. 697). Other phenomena in which glutamine has been reported to participate include its stimulation of glycolysis (269–271). The mechanism by which glutamine reduces the voluntary consumption of alcohol by rats (272) is apparently not yet understood.

The very high concentrations of glutamine (as well as asparagine) in certain higher plants (273–280) suggests that these amides are of special metabolic significance in these organisms; amide formation could be a mechanism for ammonia detoxification or nitrogen storage, or both. Certain γ-substituted glutamate derivatives are also found in plants including γ-methylglutamine (see p. 63).

Waelsch and collaborators (281–285) have obtained evidence for the exchange of the amide nitrogen atoms of several proteins with N^{15}-ammonia and various amines. An enzyme ("transglutaminase") that catalyzes the replacement of some amide groups of protein-bound glutamine residues was obtained from guinea pig liver. The enzyme also catalyzes hydrolysis of protein amide groups and the same protein amide groups are involved in both replacement and hydrolysis reactions. These interesting studies indicate that proteins may bind pharmacologically active amines at glutamine amide positions. Deamidation of protein could provide ammonia for various metabolic reactions. Certain of these experiments suggest that liberation of protein amide nitrogen is accompanied by formation of linkages between the ε-lysyl amino groups and the γ-carboxyl groups of proteins.

Decarboxylation of Glutamic Acid

Decarboxylation of L-glutamate to γ-aminobutyric acid (see p. 329) is a significant pathway of glutamate in the mammalian brain and also in certain higher plants and microorganisms. Fowden and associates (286, 287) observed transamination of γ-aminobutyric acid in extracts of mitochondria from cotyledons of peanut seedlings; pyruvate was more active than α-ketoglutarate (see p. 64). Evidence was obtained for the conversion of γ-aminobutyrate to succinate. The metabolism of γ-aminobutyrate by *Saccharomyces cerevisiae* and *Torulopsis utilis* was also investigated; transamination to succinic semialdehyde, and enzymatic reduction of the latter compound to γ-hydroxybutyric acid by a dehydrogenase that required reduced triphosphopyridine nucleotide was reported. Recent work has led to the identification of γ-hydroxybutyric acid in extracts of human, rat, and pigeon brain (287a).

The labeling patterns observed in isolated tissue glutamate, aspartate, alanine, and glycogen in male rats after administration of γ-aminobutyric acid-γ-C^{14} suggest that virtually all of the catabolism of γ-aminobutyric acid *in vivo* proceeds via succinate (288). Considerable quantities of γ-aminobutyric acid are present in the central nervous system, and various ideas have been expressed concerning the possible role of this amino acid in the transmission of nerve impulses (289–293). In one study, application of various amino acids to the external surfaces of spinal neurons led to excitation of the nerve cells. The most active of the excitatory amino acids examined were glutamic acid, β-aminoglutaric acid, aspartic acid, cysteic acid, and cysteinesulfinic acid (292). A report has appeared describing the oxidation of γ-aminobutyric acid to β-hydroxy-γ-aminobutyric acid by homogenates of rabbit and guinea pig brain. Oxygen utilization was observed and paper chromatographic studies suggested formation of β-hydroxy-γ-aminobutyric acid (294).

Studies on *Clostridium aminobutyricum*, which can utilize γ-aminobutyric acid as its major sources of carbon, nitrogen, and energy, indicate that the degradation of γ-aminobutyrate involves a coupling of the following reactions (295):

2 γ-Aminobutyrate $+ 2$ acetyl-coenzyme A $\rightarrow$
$$2\,NH_3 + 2 \text{ crotonyl-coenzyme A} + 2 \text{ acetate}$$

Crotonyl-coenzyme A $+$ DPNH $+$ H$^+$ $\rightarrow$ butyryl-coenzyme A $+$ DPN$^+$

Crotonyl-coenzyme A $+$ DPN$^+$ $+$ coenzyme A $+$ H$_2$O $\rightarrow$
$$2 \text{ acetyl-coenzyme A} + \text{DPNH} + \text{H}^+$$

---

2 γ-Aminobutyrate $+$ H$_2$O $+$ coenzyme A $\rightarrow$
$$2NH_3 + \text{butyryl-coenzyme A} + 2 \text{ acetate}$$

The last equation, which is the sum of the others, indicates that the degradation of 2 moles of γ-aminobutyric acid leads to formation of one mole of a high-energy compound. The pathway of γ-aminobutyrate metabolism in this organism includes transamination with α-ketoglutarate and reduction of succinic acid semialdehyde to γ-hydroxybutyrate (295a).

Synthesis of the Purine Ring

The amide nitrogen atom of glutamine is the precursor of two of the nitrogen atoms of the purine ring, and for this reason purine biosynthesis is considered in this section. This arrangement is quite arbitrary, however, because both aspartate and glycine as well as formate and carbon dioxide are also utilized for purine biosynthesis, as discussed below.

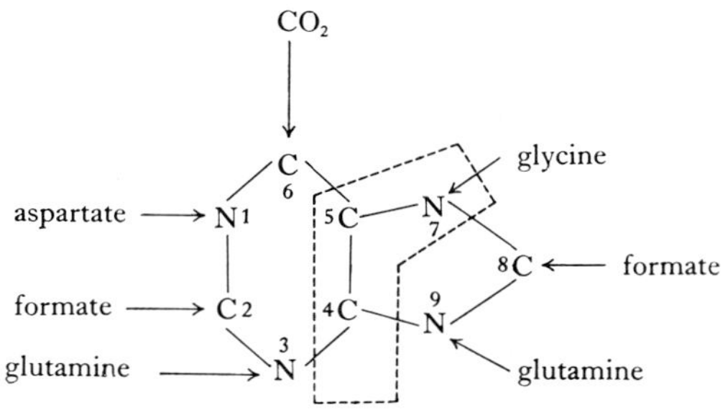

The possibility that amino acids might serve as precursors of the purine ring was considered in relatively early investigations. That arginine and histidine were not direct nitrogen donors in purine synthesis, despite their similarity in structure, was proved by studies with isotopic compounds (296, 297). On the other hand, it was found that slices of pigeon liver could synthesize hypoxanthine, and that addition of glutamine and oxaloacetate to such tissue preparations resulted in an increased rate of hypoxanthine synthesis (298–300).

Considerable impetus was given to the investigation of purine biosynthesis by isotopic studies in which important information concerning the origin of the nitrogen and carbon atoms of the purine ring was obtained. In these studies isotopically labeled compounds were administered to pigeons, and the distribution of isotope in the excreted uric acid was investigated. In this way it was determined that (a) glycine is the precursor of carbon atoms 4 and 5, and nitrogen atom 7 (301, 302), (b) carbon dioxide is the precursor of carbon atom 6 (301, 303), (c) formate is the precursor of carbon atoms 2 and 8 (303), (d) glutamine is the precursor of nitrogen atoms 3 and 9 (304), and (e) aspartic acid supplies nitrogen atom 1 (304, 307). In experiments with extracts of pigeon liver it was found that 2 moles of formate, 1 mole of carbon dioxide, and 1 mole of glycine are used in the formation of 1 mole of hypoxanthine (305), and it was subsequently found that, for each mole of glycine incorporated into hypoxanthine, the amide group of glutamine supplies 2 atoms of nitrogen. About half of the incorporated amide nitrogen was found in the 9-position of the purine ring, and half in the 1 plus 3 nitrogens. With N^{15}-aspartic acid or N^{15}-glutamic acid, incorporation was found only in the 1 plus 3 nitrogen fraction (304). These findings were consistent with the possibility that the amide group of glutamine was the precursor of position 1 (or 3) nitrogen, and that the other nitrogen atom arose from α-amino nitrogen. Subsequent work showed that nitrogen atom 1 is supplied by aspartic acid (307).

In studies on the synthesis of inosinic acid by a pigeon liver preparation (in the presence of glycine, formate, bicarbonate, ribose 5-phosphate, 3-phosphoglyceric acid, and citrovorum factor), it was observed that addition of either L-glutamine or L-asparagine stimulated inosinic acid synthesis (305). Less stimulation was observed with aspartate plus glutamate, and no effect was noted with a variety of other amino acids. When glutamine plus glutamate or asparagine plus aspartate were added, there was no appreciable increase in inosinic acid formation above that obtained with the amides separately. On the other hand, addition of glutamine plus aspartate and, to a slightly lesser extent, asparagine plus glutamate, produced considerable increases in inosinic acid formation. The evidence therefore suggested that there is a requirement for a 4-carbon and a 5-carbon atom dicarboxylic acid derivative, one of which must possess an ω-amide group. These results are explicable in terms of synthesis of glutamine from glutamate and ammonia derived from asparagine, possibly by enzymatic hydrolysis of the latter.

The observation that inosinic acid is a precursor of hypoxanthine in pigeon liver suggested that ribonucleotide derivatives might be formed early in the biosynthetic pathway leading to purines (306). A finding of considerable significance was the isolation of 4-amino-5-imidazole-carboxamide from sulfonamide-inhibited cultures of *Escherichia coli* (308, 309). Subsequent studies indicated that sulfonamide-inhibited *E. coli* accumulated 4-amino-5-imidazolecarboxamide ribonucleoside (310, 311). Following these discoveries, investigations mainly in the laboratories of Greenberg and Buchanan led to elucidation of the enzymatic reactions involved in the biosynthesis of inosinic acid.

When a pigeon liver preparation was incubated with glutamine, adenosine 5'-triphosphate, ribose 5-phosphate, and formate, two compounds, glycinamide ribonucleotide and formylglycinamide ribonucleotide, accumulated (312–315). The formation of the latter required formate and tetrahydrofolic acid. These and the subsequent enzymatic reactions leading to the formation of inosinic acid are illustrated in Scheme 2; reviews of this area have appeared (316, 317).

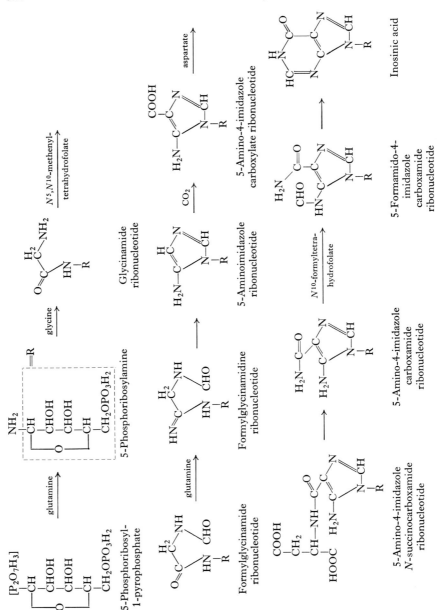

Scheme 2. Enzymatic reactions leading to the formation of inosinic acid.

The mechanism of glycinamide ribonucleotide synthesis became clear as a result of the discovery of 5-phosphoribosyl-1-pyrophosphate (see p. 615). The enzyme 5-phosphoribose pyrophosphokinase catalyzes the transfer of the pyrophosphate moiety of adenosine triphosphate to ribose 5-phosphate. 5-Phosphoribosyl-1-pyrophosphate reacts with glutamine to yield 5-phosphoribosylamine. This reaction, which is catalyzed by the enzyme 5-phosphoribosyl pyrophosphate amidotransferase, may be represented as follows (318, 319):

5-Phosphoribosyl-1-pyrophosphate + glutamine + H_2O →
   5-phosphoribosylamine + pyrophosphate + glutamate

The instability of 5-phosphoribosylamine has thus far prevented its isolation, but synthetic preparations of this compound obtained by reaction of ribose 5-phosphate with liquid ammonia were active when incubated with glycine and adenosine triphosphate in the enzymatic synthesis of glycinamide ribonucleotide. 5-Phosphoribosylamine-1-pyrophosphate amidotransferase has been purified from pigeon liver and separated from the enzyme that catalyzes the synthesis of glycinamide ribonucleotide (320). It catalyzes neither exchange between pyrophosphate and the pyrophosphate moiety of 5-phosphoribosyl-1-pyrophosphate, nor between glutamate and glutamine. No evidence has been obtained for reversibility of the reaction, which appears to involve inversion at carbon atom 1 of the ribose moiety; 5-phosphoribosyl-1-pyrophosphate has the α-configuration, while the naturally occurring purine nucleotides possess the β-configuration. 5-Phosphoribosylamine is also formed nonenzymatically from ribose 5-phosphate and ammonia; although this reaction proceeds only to a slight extent in aqueous solution under conditions used for enzymatic studies (321), it probably accounts for the finding that certain enzyme preparations that cannot catalyze the synthesis of 5-phosphoribosyl-1-pyrophosphate are able to catalyze glycinamide ribonucleotide formation from glycine, ribose 5-phosphate, ammonia, and adenosine triphosphate (322).

The formation of glycinamide ribonucleotide from 5-phosphoribosylamine and glycine takes place in accordance with the following equation (315):

5-Phosphoribosylamine + glycine + ATP $\rightleftharpoons$
   glycinamide ribonucleotide + ADP + phosphate

This reaction, which is similar to those involved in the synthesis of glutamine (see p. 446) and glutathione (see p. 452), is reversible (319, 320).

The enzyme involved also catalyzes formation of glycine hydroxamate from glycine, adenosine triphosphate, and hydroxylamine. Glycine hydroxamate is also formed when the enzyme, glycinamide ribonucleotide, adenosine diphosphate, and inorganic phosphate are incubated with hydroxylamine. When O^{18}-phosphate was incubated with glycinamide ribonucleotide, adenosine diphosphate, and enzyme, isotopic oxygen was found in the glycine formed (320).

The formation of formylglycinamide ribonucleotide takes place as follows (312):

$(N^5,N^{10}$-Methenyltetrahydrofolate$)^+$ + glycinamide ribonucleotide →
formylglycinamide ribonucleotide + tetrahydrofolate + H^+

The enzyme has been purified from chicken liver (323), but crude preparations of it can utilize N^{10}-formyltetrahydrofolic acid due to the presence of cyclohydrolase, which catalyzes the reversible hydration of N^5, N^{10}-methenyltetrahydrofolic acid to N^{10}-formyltetrahydrofolic acid (324).

The enzyme that catalyzes the synthesis of formylglycinamidine ribonucleotide from formylglycinamide ribonucleotide according to the following equation,

Formylglycinamide ribonucleotide + ATP + glutamine + H_2O →
formylglycinamidine ribonucleotide + ADP + phosphate + glutamate

has been purified from pigeon liver (325, 326). Magnesium and potassium ions are needed and the reaction is markedly inhibited by azaserine and 6-diazo-5-oxo-L-norleucine (327). The enzyme does not catalyze exchange between inorganic phosphate and adenosine triphosphate, or between glutamate and glutamine. When radioactive azaserine is incubated with the enzyme, approximately stoichiometric quantities are bound to an enzyme sulfhydryl group (328).

The cyclization of formylglycinamidine ribonucleotide is catalyzed by an enzyme that has been isolated from chicken liver (325). The reaction is associated with cleavage of adenosine triphosphate to adenosine diphosphate and inorganic phosphate. 5-Aminoimidazole ribonucleotide reacts with carbon dioxide to yield 5-amino-4-imidazolecarboxylate ribonucleotide (329); the reaction requires high concentrations of bicarbonate or conditions in which the concentration of the product is reduced by subsequent enzymatic reaction. The product is converted to 5-amino-4-imidazole-N-succinocarboxamide ribonucleotide (329–331):

5-Amino-4-imidazolecarboxylate ribonucleotide + aspartate + ATP ⇌
5-amino-4-imidazole-N-succinocarboxamide ribonucleotide + ADP + phosphate

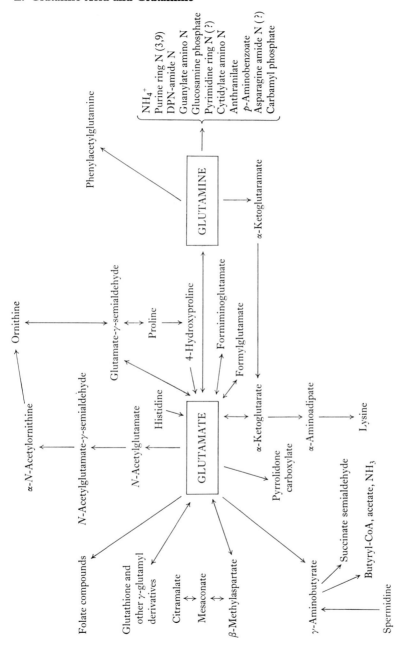

Summary scheme for the metabolism of glutamate and glutamine.

This is one of several reactions now known in which the α-amino group of aspartate is utilized in a condensation reaction. The N-succino compound is cleaved to fumaric acid and 5-amino-4-imidazolecarboxamide ribonucleotide (332) by an enzyme that is probably identical with adenylosuccinase (see p. 610); this conclusion is in accord with data on the ratio of the enzymatic activities during purification, and with studies of the enzymatic activities of several microorganisms (332, 333). It will be recalled (see p. 631) that 5-amino-4-imidazolecarboxamide and the corresponding ribonucleoside were previously isolated from sulfonamide-inhibited cultures of *E. coli*.

Formylation of the ribonucleotide compound takes place according to the following reaction:

N^{10}-Formyltetrahydrofolate + 5-amino-4-imidazolecarboxamide ribonucleotide →
5-formamido-4-imidazolecarboxamide ribonucleotide + tetrahydrofolate

Enzyme preparations that have been used for the study of this reaction (334–336) also contain inosinicase, which catalyzes cyclization of the 5-formamido compound to inosinic acid. Accumulation of the formamido compound has apparently not been observed, but the chemically synthesized compound is rapidly cyclized when incubated with the enzyme. Conversion of inosinic acid to adenylic acid occurs via the intermediate adenylosuccinic acid (see p. 610). Inosinic acid is oxidized to xanthylic acid by inosine 5′-phosphate dehydrogenase; subsequent amination of xanthylic acid to guanylic acid has been discussed above (see p. 624).

F. Glycine, Serine, and Sarcosine

These amino acids are considered together because of their close chemical and metabolic relationships. The metabolism of glycine involves conversion to serine and other amino acids, and incorporation into the purine ring, porphyrins, lipids, and carbohydrates; thus, although one of the simplest amino acids from the structural viewpoint, its intermediary metabolism represents an extremely complex picture only part of which is considered in this section.

Formation and Degradation of Glycine

The synthesis of glycine occurs in animals, plants, and microorganisms. Glycine synthesis occurs relatively rapidly in mammals; the dietary requirement for glycine by chicks suggests that glycine synthesis is growth-limiting under certain conditions (see p. 204). Glycine is formed by several reactions including conversion from serine (see p. 647),

cleavage of threonine to glycine and acetaldehyde (see p. 681), demethylation of sarcosine (see p. 665), and amination of glyoxylic acid (see p. 354).
Interconversion of glycine and serine occurs in many microorganisms
(337–341); thus, a number respond to either glycine or serine, and
isotopic competition experiments (339) in *Escherichia coli* are consistent
with conversion of serine to glycine. Mutants that respond only to serine
have been found, but these seem to be deficient in the transport of
glycine (342). The finding that glyoxylate does not support the growth of
glycine-requiring mutants, and negative results with glyoxylate in isotopic
competition studies in *E. coli* (339) suggest that appreciable conversion of
glyoxylate to glycine does not occur in these organisms, or possibly that
glyoxylate is not transported into the cell. However, under certain conditions, glyoxylate supports the growth of a *Neurospora* mutant that can
use either serine or glycine for growth (343). Conversion of glyoxylate
to glycine by transamination has been demonstrated in several systems
(344) (see p. 354); glyoxylate can arise from citrate or isocitrate (345–349),
or from carbohydrate via ribose 5-phosphate, glycolaldehyde, and
glycolate (350–352). The rapid incorporation of labeled CO_2 into
glycolic acid and glycine during photosynthesis suggests conversion of
glyoxylate to glycine (353–356). Another possible pathway of glyoxylate
formation is deamination of aminoethanol to glycolaldehyde, and
oxidation of the latter to glyoxylate (357, 358).

Glycine is a product of the anaerobic degradation of purines by
Clostridium cylindrosporum and *C. acidiurici* (359, 360). Rabinowitz and
collaborators obtained evidence for the following pathway of xanthine
degradation in these organisms:

Xanthine $\longrightarrow$ 4-Ureido-5-imidazolecarboxylic acid $\xrightarrow{Mn^{++}}$

4-Amino-5-imidazole-carboxylic acid $\longrightarrow$ 4-Aminoimidazole $\xrightarrow{-NH_3}$

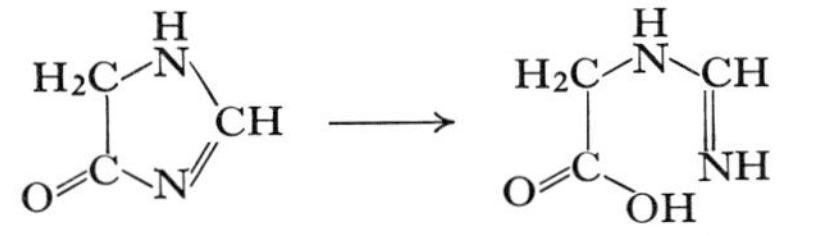

4-Imidazolone   Formiminoglycine

Except for the decarboxylation of 4-amino-5-imidazolecarboxylic acid, the reactions involved in the formation of formiminoglycine are hydrolytic. The conversion of formiminoglycine to glycine, formate, and ammonia requires adenosine diphosphate and orthophosphate and leads to the formation of adenosine triphosphate:

$$\text{Formiminoglycine} + \text{ADP} + \text{phosphate} + H_2O \rightleftharpoons \text{ATP} + \text{formate} + \text{glycine} + NH_3$$

This reaction requires tetrahydrofolate, and the first step involves reaction of the latter with formiminoglycine to yield glycine and N^5-formiminotetrahydrofolate. N^5-Formiminotetrahydrofolate is converted to N^5,N^{10}-methenyltetrahydrofolate by cyclodeaminase (see p. 658), and hydrolysis of the N^5,N^{10}-methenyl derivative yields N^{10}-formyl-tetrahydrofolate.

That glycine and glyoxylate are interconvertible in the rat was demonstrated by Weinhouse and collaborators (357, 361–363). Glycine, glyoxylate, and glycolate were rapidly oxidized by rat liver slices; the products included carbon dioxide, hippuric acid (formed in the presence of benzoate), and oxalic acid. Using an isotope-trapping procedure, evidence was obtained for the conversion of glycine to glyoxylate in rat liver homogenates. The formation of oxalate was found to occur from glyoxylate but not from glycine directly, and oxalate was formed only with relatively high glyoxylate concentrations. Further study revealed that oxalate is probably not formed under ordinary circumstances and that the α-carbon atoms of glycine, glycolate, and glyoxylate yield formate. The findings may be summarized as follows:

$$\underset{\overset{|}{NH_2}}{CH_2COOH} \longrightarrow \underset{\overset{\|}{O}}{CHCOOH} \quad \text{[transamination]} \tag{1}$$

$$\underset{\overset{\|}{O}}{CHCOOH} + \tfrac{1}{2}O_2 \longrightarrow HCOOH + CO_2 \tag{2}$$

$$\underset{\overset{\|}{O}}{CHCOOH} + \tfrac{1}{2}O_2 \longrightarrow HOOCCOOH \tag{3}$$

Reaction (3) can be catalyzed by xanthine dehydrogenase (364) and also by an enzyme present in pigeon liver (357). White shoots of *Oxalis pes-caprae* bulbs contain considerable quantities of oxalic acid, which is formed by oxidation of glyoxylate (365). The most probable pathway for the conversion of glycine to glyoxylate is by transamination (see p. 354). The oxidative deamination of glycine to glyoxylate catalyzed by preparations of glycine oxidase, which is probably identical with D-amino acid oxidase (see p. 299), requires very high concentrations of glycine and cannot be of much physiological significance.

Reaction (2) occurs nonenzymatically with hydrogen peroxide, but is also enzymatically catalyzed. Nakada and Sund found that the conversion of glyoxylate to formate and carbon dioxide by washed homogenates of rat liver was stimulated about 15-fold by addition of L-glutamate (366). A partially purified preparation of an enzyme that catalyzes the oxidative decarboxylation of glyoxylate was obtained from rat liver mitochondria extracts; maximal decarboxylation was obtained when diphospho-pyridine nucleotide, thiamine pyrophosphate, L-glutamate, and Mn^{++} ions were added. Addition of L-glutamate gave the greatest effect when the concentrations of glutamate and glyoxylate were the same. These observations led to the suggestion that glyoxylate and glutamate condense to form an intermediate, which is converted to N-formylglutamate and carbon dioxide by a pyridine nucleotide- and thiamine-dependent enzyme (tentatively designated glyoxylic acid dehydrogenase). The formyl moiety of formylglutamate could possibly be utilized via a folic acid derivative for the formation of serine, or released by hydrolysis as free formate (see p. 831).

$$
\begin{array}{c}
\text{COOH} \\
| \\
\text{CH}_2 \\
| \\
\text{CH}_2 \\
| \\
\text{CHNH}_2 \\
| \\
\text{COOH}
\end{array}
\;+\;
\begin{array}{c}
\text{CHO} \\
| \\
\text{COOH}
\end{array}
\;\longrightarrow\;
\begin{array}{c}
\text{COOH} \\
| \\
\text{CH}_2 \\
| \\
\text{CH}_2 \\
| \\
\text{CHN}{=}\text{CHCOOH} \\
| \\
\text{COOH}
\end{array}
\;+\; \text{H}_2\text{O}
$$

$$
\begin{array}{c}
\text{COOH} \\
| \\
\text{CH}_2 \\
| \\
\text{CH}_2 \\
| \\
\text{CHN}{=}\text{CHCOOH} \\
| \\
\text{COOH}
\end{array}
\;\xrightarrow[\substack{\text{thiamine} \\ \text{pyrophosphate}}]{\text{DPN}^+,\ \text{Mn}^{++}}\;
\begin{array}{c}
\text{COOH} \\
| \\
\text{CH}_2 \\
| \\
\text{CH}_2 \\
| \\
\text{CHNHCHO} \\
| \\
\text{COOH}
\end{array}
\;+\; \text{CO}_2
$$

However, alternative pathways are possible. Thus, glyoxylate might react with thiamine pyrophosphate to yield an intermediate such as (HOOC)(OH)CH-thiamine pyrophosphate (see p. 734), which, after decarboxylation, might react with glutamate to regenerate thiamine pyrophosphate and yield N-hydroxymethylglutamate. The latter compound could be a substrate for pyridine nucleotide-dependent oxidation to N-formylglutamate.

There is evidence that formate is oxidized rapidly to carbon dioxide:

$$HCOOH + H_2O_2 \rightarrow CO_2 + 2H_2O$$

The reaction, which has been observed in plant and animal tissues (367), could involve the peroxidase activity of catalase, and peroxide formed in the course of other reactions (357).

Studies on avian liver indicate that free glyoxylate is not formed in the degradation of glycine (368). Homogenates of avian liver catalyze formation of carbon dioxide from the carboxyl group of glycine without significant contribution from the α-carbon atom, and most of the α-carbon of glycine reacts with another molecule of glycine to form serine. Pyridoxal 5'-phosphate, diphosphopyridine nucleotide, and tetrahydrofolic acid stimulated these reactions when added to homogenates obtained from birds deficient in the respective vitamins. Earlier studies on the degradation of glycine by *Diplococcus glycinophilus* (369) indicated a similar pathway. This organism catalyzes the anaerobic conversion of glycine to acetic acid, associated with formation of carbon dioxide from the carboxyl carbon atom of glycine (370). This decarboxylation reaction requires pyridoxal phosphate and diphosphopyridine nucleotide, and the

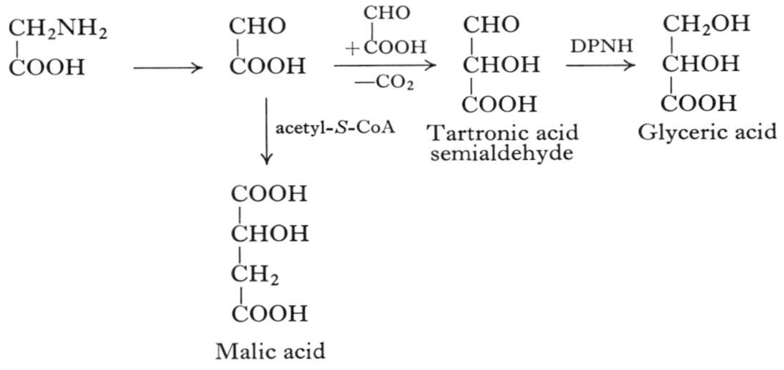

α-carbon atom of glycine is transferred to tetrahydrofolate. The decarboxylation of glycine may be represented as follows:

$$\text{Glycine} + \text{tetrahydrofolate} \;\rightarrow\; N^5, N^{10}\text{-methylenetetrahydrofolate} + CO_2 + NH_3 + 2H$$

A number of microorganisms, including *Pseudomonas*, catalyze the aerobic oxidation of glycine via glyoxylate (371–375a). Glyoxylate can be converted to malate by malate synthetase or via tartronic acid semialdehyde to glyceric acid.

Synthesis of Creatine and Creatinine

Creatine is formed by transamidination between arginine and glycine followed by methylation of the resulting guanidinoacetic acid (glycocyamine) (376–378):

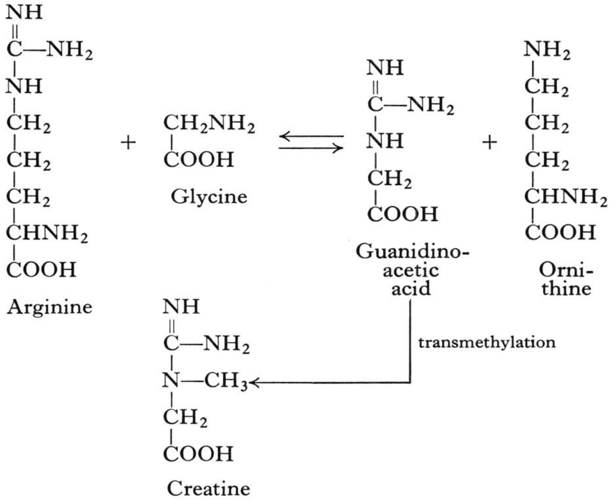

Transamidination is reversible and proceeds without addition of cofactors or adenosine triphosphate (379, 380). Transamidinase activity has been found in mammalian kidney and pancreas (378, 381, 382), human liver (383), and avian kidney and liver (376, 384). In contrast to the liver of the rat, rabbit, and dog, human liver has appreciable activity, but human pancreas has five times the activity of liver and kidney (383). Extrarenal transamidination is considerable, even in the rat, since nephrectomized rats convert C^{14}-glycine to creatine effectively (385). The arginine-glycine transamidinase activity of chick and duck liver is repressed by dietary creatine or guanidinoacetate; such repression may be of physiological significance in that it leads to conservation of arginine, glycine, and methionine for other metabolic functions including protein synthesis (386). Vitamin E-deficient rabbits exhibit very low kidney transamidinase activity, and it appears that the reduction in enzyme activity is due to the feedback repression of transamidinase activity produced by excess creatine presented to the kidneys (387). Feedback repression of transamidinase has also been observed in the livers of developing chick embryos (388, 389) and in the decidual tissues of pregnant rats (390).

Purified hog kidney transamidinase catalyzes transamidination between canavanine and glycine, and between arginine and canaline; other amidine donors include guanidinoacetic acid and homoarginine. Amidine acceptors (in addition to glycine, ornithine, and canaline) include γ-aminobutyric acid, β-alanine, lysine, and δ-aminovaleric acid. The presence of γ-guanidinobutyric acid in brain (391) indicates that transamidination of γ-aminobutyric acid (392) is of physiological significance. Incubation of arginine and hydroxylamine with kidney transamidinase and a similar enzyme obtained from *Streptomyces griseus* yields ornithine and hydroxyguanidine (393). Transamidinase is sensitive to inhibition by sulfhydryl reagents, and it has been suggested (393, 394) that the amidine group of the substrate is transferred to a sulfhydryl group of the enzyme to yield a thioamidine-enzyme intermediate.

Although it was originally believed that the conversion of guanidinoacetic acid to creatine occurs only in the liver, perfusion studies in the rat indicate that the kidney also catalyzes this reaction (395). The transmethylation reaction is not reversible. It is of interest that the dietary glycine requirement of the chick (see p. 204) is spared by creatine (399).

In progressive muscular dystrophy in man, the characteristically large excretion of creatine is associated with inability of the muscle to take up creatine; urinary creatine therefore does not arise from muscle, but from the liver (396). Phosphocreatine, formed in the muscle, is probably the major source of urinary creatinine:

$$
\begin{array}{c}
\overset{\overset{\displaystyle NH}{\|}}{\underset{\underset{\underset{\underset{COOH}{|}}{CH_2}}{|}}{\underset{|}{C}-NHPO_3H_2}} \\
N-CH_3
\end{array}
\longrightarrow
\begin{array}{c}
NH=C-\overset{H}{N} \\
| \qquad \backslash \\
CH_3-N-C \diagup C=O \\
\qquad H_2
\end{array}
+ H_3PO_4
$$

Phosphocreatine   Creatinine

The formation of creatinine from phosphocreatine may occur non-enzymatically (397), or it may be enzyme-catalyzed, or both. In view of recent studies which showed that incubation of rabbit muscle extracts with creatine phosphate gave creatine but not creatinine (398), it seems that the earlier conclusion that the reaction was catalyzed is in error. The problem deserves further investigation. Urinary creatinine in man is unaffected by dietary intake of methionine and glycine.

Porphyrin Synthesis

It was found a number of years ago that the nitrogen of hemin arose from glycine (400); subsequent study showed that the α-carbon atom (but not the carboxyl carbon atom) of glycine also contributed to hemin synthesis (401, 402). Studies in which the protoporphyrin molecule was degraded led to considerable understanding of the origin of this molecule (403–405). Thus, it was concluded that the four methene bridge carbon atoms arise from the α-carbon atom of glycine as do four carbons of the pyrrole rings. The pattern of labeling of protoporphyrin after formation from labeled intermediates of the citric acid cycle was also studied (405, 406).

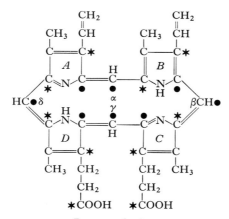

Protoporphyrin

(Asterisks indicate carboxyl carbon atoms of succinate; solid circles indicate α-carbon atoms of glycine.)

Shemin and associates (407–410) observed that the α-carbon atom of glycine is utilized equally for the pyrrole rings and for the methene bridges and postulated that the same glycine derivative is involved in the formation of these protoporphyrin carbon atoms. According to Shemin's scheme, "active" succinate (succinyl-coenzyme A) condenses with the α-carbon atom of glycine to yield α-amino-β-ketoadipic acid, which decarboxylates to give δ-aminolevulinic acid. The latter compound serves as a precursor of porphyrin or undergoes deamination to γ-ketoglutaraldehyde, which is converted to succinate and a one-carbon compound capable of being utilized for the synthesis of purines, serine, and the methyl group of methionine. When 5-C^{14}-δ-aminolevulinic acid was injected into ducks, isotope was found in the ureido groups of the purines, the β-carbon atom of serine, and the methyl moiety of methionine. It was also found that the succinyl moiety of δ-aminolevulinic acid gave rise to succinate (411). Administration of γ-ketoglutaraldehyde-5-C^{14} to pigeons led to labeling of uric acid, and when the C^{14}-aldehyde was administered to rats, radioactivity was found in the urinary formate. The enzymatic deamination by transamination (Chapter IV, Section H) of δ-aminolevulinic acid has been observed (412, 413).

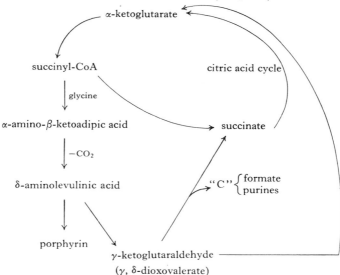

δ-Aminolevulinic acid (410, 414–416) was found to replace "active succinate" and glycine in porphyrin synthesis in duck red blood cells (407). Furthermore, the radioactivity of hemin formed in a system containing radioactive glycine or succinate was reduced by adding unlabeled δ-aminolevulinic acid. In studies with δ-aminolevulinic acid, labeled with N^{15} or with C^{14} in the δ-carbon atom, there was appreciable incorporation of isotope into heme. Other studies showed that protoporphyrin synthesized from δ-aminolevulinic acid-1,4-C^{14} exhibited the same labeling pattern as that observed in prophyrin synthesized from succinate-1,4-C^{14} (417). Shemin and collaborators proposed that two molecules of δ-aminolevulinic acid condense to yield a pyrrole precursor:

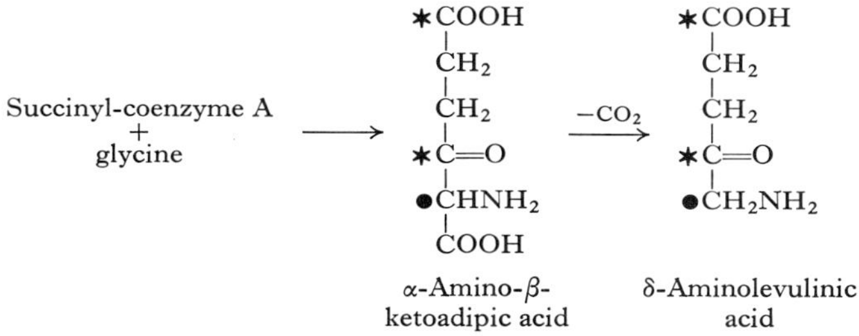

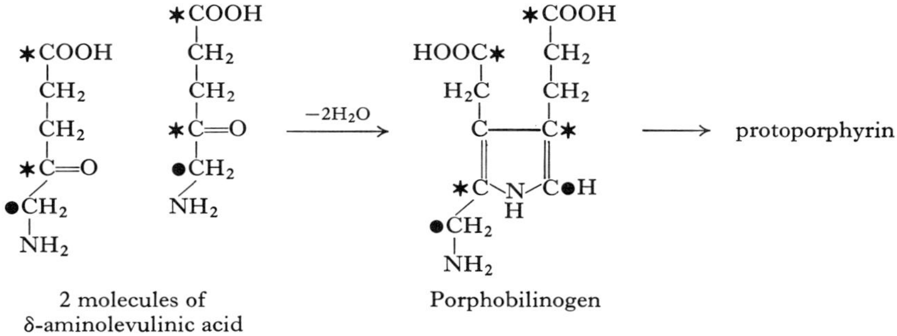

Subsequent studies showed that cell-free extracts of duck red blood cells catalyze formation of protoporphyrin from δ-aminolevulinic acid (408). The product of the condensation of two molecules of δ-aminolevulinic acid is identical with porphobilinogen (416, 418–421), which is excreted in the urine of patients with acute porphyria. There is now excellent evidence that δ-aminolevulinic acid is the precursor of heme, the porphyrin of chlorophyll and of bacteriochlorophyll (422) and the corrin ring of vitamin B_{12} (423–425). Six of the "extra" methyl groups of vitamin B_{12} arise from the methyl group of methionine (see p. 774).

The enzyme that catalyzes the synthesis of δ-aminolevulinic acid has been found in several sources including chicken reticulocytes, and

Rhodopseudomonas spheroides (426–430). δ-Aminolevulinic acid synthetase catalyzes the condensation of succinyl-coenzyme A and glycine to form δ-aminolevulinic acid and carbon dioxide. As indicated below, an enzyme-bound glycine-pyridoxal phosphate Schiff base is probably formed, which reacts with succinyl-coenzyme A. Condensation and loss of carbon dioxide may occur simultaneously; free α-amino-β-ketoadipic acid could be the product of condensation, but the latter compound is extremely unstable and would be expected to decarboxylate rapidly and spontaneously.

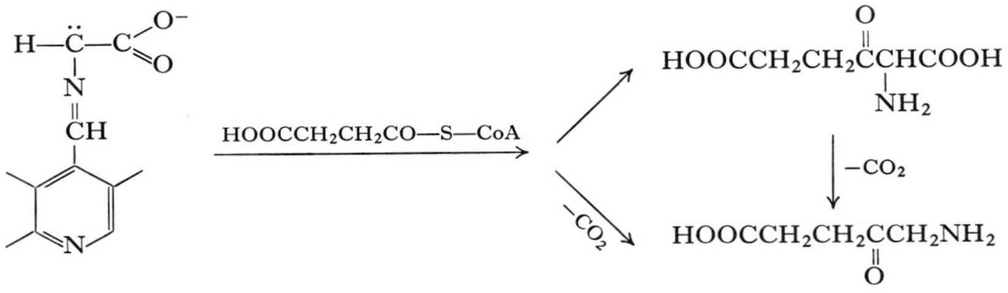

The function of the cofactors in this reaction was also shown in work with the red blood cells of vitamin B_6- and pantothenic acid-deficient ducklings; the rate of synthesis of heme from glycine-2-C^{14} or succinate-2-C^{14} was much lower than in cells from nondeficient animals, while δ-aminolevulinic acid incorporation was essentially unaffected by the vitamin deficiencies. Addition of pyridoxal 5′-phosphate *in vitro* stimulated the deficient cells to synthesize heme from glycine and succinate, but not from δ-aminolevulinic acid (431). Several enzymatic reactions lead to formation of succinyl-coenzyme A; in red blood cells the major mechanism is that provided by the citric acid cycle, i.e., oxidation of α-ketoglutarate. Succinyl-coenzyme A can also be formed by the succinyl thiokinase reaction, by enzymatic transfer of coenzyme A from acetoacetyl-coenzyme A to succinate, and through conversion of methylmalonyl-coenzyme A to succinyl-coenzyme A.

δ-Aminolevulinic acid synthetase is markedly inhibited by protohemin IX, indicating a feedback mechanism (432, 433).

Enzyme preparations that catalyze the synthesis of δ-aminolevulinic acid from glycine and succinyl-coenzyme A also catalyze the formation of aminoacetone from glycine and acetyl-coenzyme A (427, 429, 434, 435); certain other acyl-coenzyme A derivatives are also active. Reticulocyte

particle preparations (427) catalyze aminoacetone formation at about 25%
of the rate of δ-aminolevulinic acid synthesis. Other investigations have
demonstrated formation of aminoacetone from threonine (see p. 683).
It is of interest that normal human urine contains δ-aminolevulinic acid
as well as a compound with the properties of aminoacetone (436). Urata
and Granick (437) found that normal guinea pig liver mitochondria form
aminoacetone from glycine and pyruvate; frozen-thawed mitochondria
form aminoacetone from glycine and acetyl-coenzyme A or malonyl-
coenzyme A. An amino ketone product was also obtained from glycine
and propionyl-coenzyme A. There is evidence that aminoacetone is
oxidized by monoamine oxidase to yield methylglyoxal and ammonia
(see p. 683). Data have been reported suggesting that different enzymes
are involved in the utilization of the several acyl-coenzyme A derivatives
(438).

Several studies have been carried out on the enzymatic conversion of
δ-aminolevulinic acid to porphobilinogen and porphyrins (422, 439).
Three soluble enzyme fractions which are involved in the synthesis of
porphyrins have been obtained from red cells of chicken, rabbit, and man
by zone electrophoresis (440). One fraction catalyzes the conversion of
δ-aminolevulinic acid to porphobilinogen, another converts porphobilinogen to uroporphyrinogen III, and a third fraction decarboxylates
uroporphyrinogen to coproporphyrinogen. Similar enzymes have been
obtained from spinach, wheat germ, and chlorella. An enzyme was
obtained from spinach that catalyzed the formation of uroporphyrinogen I
from porphobilinogen (442). When this enzyme was incubated with one
obtained from wheat germ, uroporphyrinogen III was formed. A
dipyrrylmethane may be an intermediate in these reactions (443), but
other possibilities are not excluded. The decarboxylation of uroporphyrinogen III to coproporphyrinogen III is catalyzed by an enzyme
that has been obtained from rabbit reticulocytes (440). The formation of
protoporphyrin IX from coproporphyrinogen III is catalyzed by an
oxidase, which has been obtained from several sources including beef
liver mitochondria (444). Scheme 3 illustrates the synthesis of protoporphyrin IX and heme as proposed by Mauzerall and Granick (441).

Glycine-Serine Interconversion; Folic Acid Derivatives

Roepke *et al.* (337) in 1944 reported that either glycine or serine could
support the growth of an *E. coli* mutant, and they therefore suggested the
biological interconversion of these amino acids. Subsequent work has

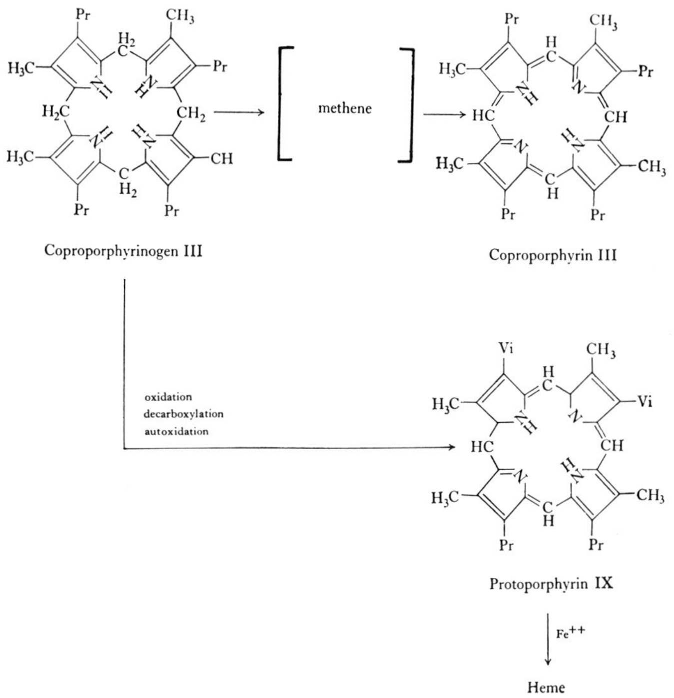

SCHEME 3. Protoporphyrin biosynthesis in the red cell from δ-aminolevulinate to iron protoporphyrin. Ac: CH₂COOH; Pr: CH₂CH₂COOH; Vi: CH=CH₂; δAl-ase: enzyme that condenses δ-aminolevulinic acid to porphobilinogen; UD-ase: enzyme that decarboxylates uroporphyrinogen to coproporphyrinogen; PBG: porphobilinogen [Taken from Mauzerall and Granick (441)].

shown that this reaction is of considerable significance in other micro-organisms and in animals.

Shemin first demonstrated the conversion of serine to glycine by administration of N^{15}-serine labeled with C^{13} in the carboxyl group together with benzoate to rats and guinea pigs; the C^{13} content of the hippuric acid glycine carboxyl carbon atom was about the same as that of the administered serine (445). The conversion of glycine to serine has also been demonstrated. There is now considerable evidence (446–449) for the reversible interconversion of glycine and serine, which involves a one-carbon unit represented as formic acid in the following scheme:

$$\underset{\underset{NH_2}{|}}{CH_2C^{13}OOH} + HC^{14}OOH \rightleftharpoons \underset{\underset{OH\ \ NH_2}{|\ \ \ \ |}}{C^{14}H_2CHC^{13}OOH}$$

This reaction has been observed in rat liver slices and in the intact rat. The β-carbon atom of serine is a precursor of the ureido carbons of uric acid in the pigeon (450); these carbon atoms of uric acid are known to arise from formate. The β-carbon atom of serine is also the precursor of the β-carbon atom of the aminoethanol of the liver lipid fraction (451). Serine synthesis from glycine and formate by lactic acid bacteria was shown to require pyridoxal (452). A requirement for vitamin B_6 was also demonstrated in chicks. Thus, liver preparations obtained from vitamin B_6-deficient chicks, or chicks treated with deoxypyridoxine, were less active in forming serine than similar preparations obtained from control animals (453, 454). Furthermore, partial reactivation of such preparations by addition of pyridoxal phosphate was observed.

Investigations of the nature of the biologically active one-carbon fragment began a number of years ago (see, for example 453, 455–458). Evidence was obtained that, under certain conditions, formaldehyde was utilized more rapidly than formate for serine synthesis. Formaldehyde is known to be a product of oxidation of sarcosine and other N-methylamino acids (459), and it was found that sarcosine can serve as a source of one-carbon units for serine synthesis (458). However, addition of unlabeled formaldehyde to a rat liver system that synthesized serine from labeled formate did not reduce the radioactivity of the serine formed (456). These and other (460–462) findings suggested that neither formaldehyde nor formate was the active one-carbon unit, and that the active compound might be an intermediate common to both (463). Several lines of evidence

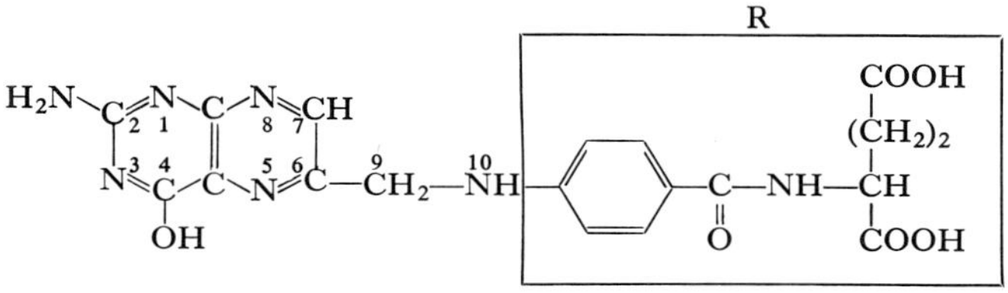

Pteroylglutamic acid (folic acid)

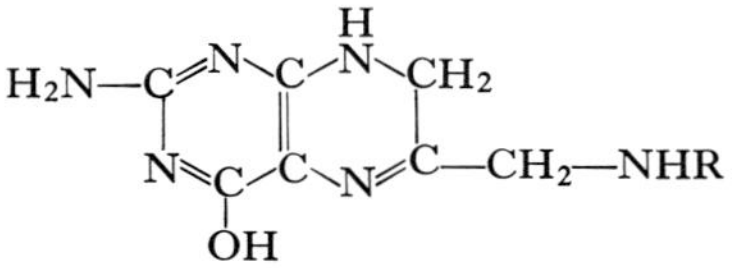

7,8-Dihydrofolic acid

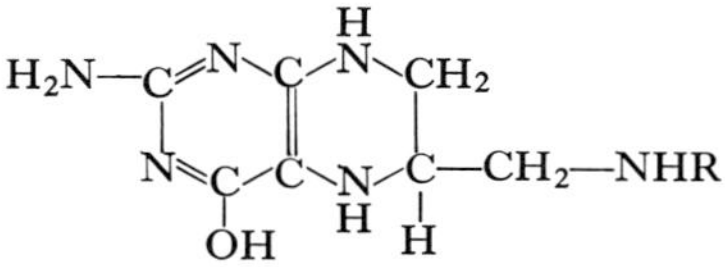

5,6,7,8-Tetrahydrofolic acid

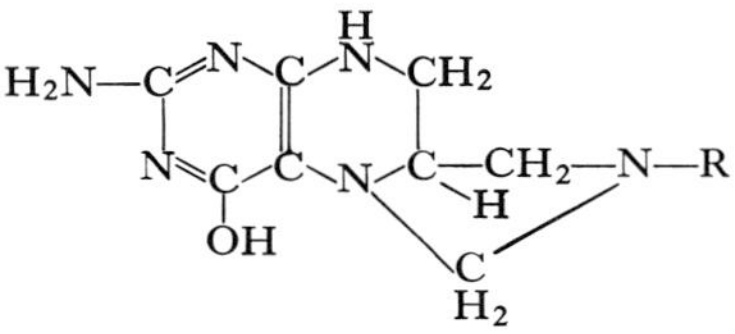

N^5,N^{10}-Methylenetetrahydrofolic acid
("active formaldehyde")

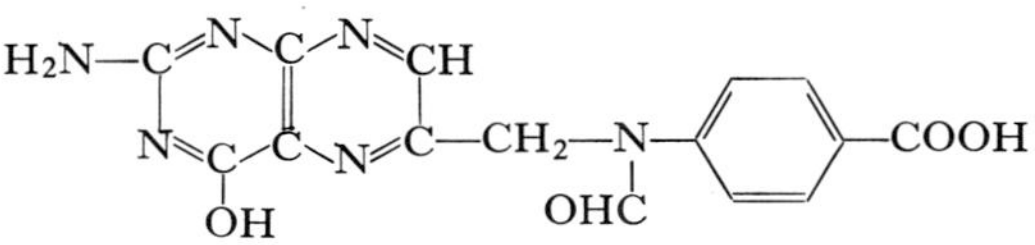

N^{10}-Formylpteroic acid (*Streptococcus lactis* R factor; SLR factor; rhizopterin)

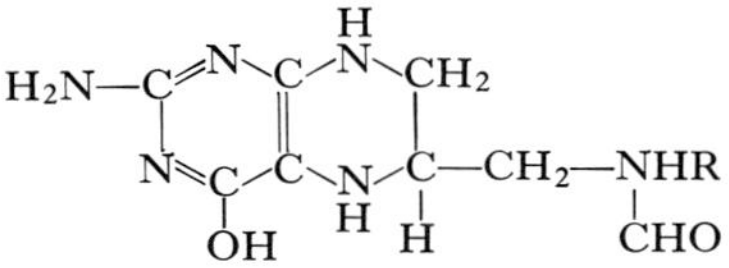

N^{10}-Formyltetrahydrofolic acid

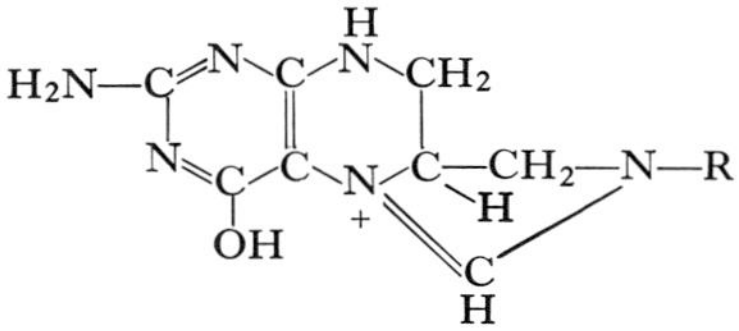

N^5,N^{10}-Methenyltetrahydrofolic acid
(anhydroleucovorin; isoleucovorin)

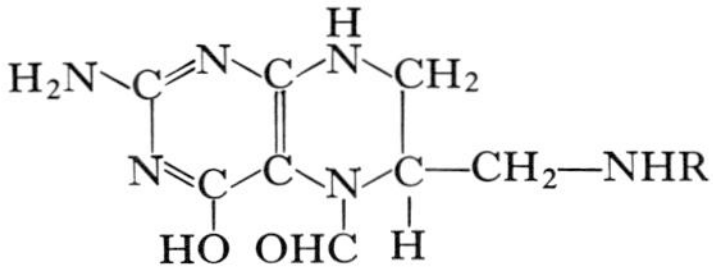

N^5-Formyltetrahydrofolic acid
(citrovorum factor; leucovorin;
folinic acid)

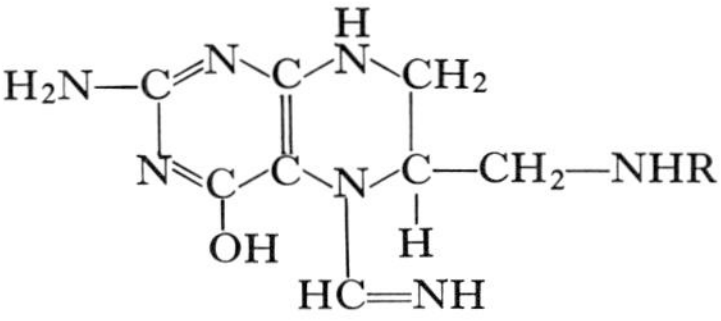

N^5-Formiminotetrahydrofolic acid

indicated that folic acid was involved in serine synthesis. For example, folic acid-deficient rats exhibited a reduced rate of incorporation of formate into serine (464). The interconversion of glycine and serine in several animals proceeded less rapidly in the presence of folic acid deficiency (450, 465–468), and studies on microorganisms (452, 469, 470) also supported the view that folic acid was involved in the glycine-serine interrelationship. This possibility was further strengthened by the knowledge that certain folic acid derivatives contained formyl groups, and could therefore conceivably function in formyl group transfer (463, 471–481).

Direct evidence for the participation of a folic acid compound was obtained in experiments with pigeon liver preparations that were capable of catalyzing the serine-glycine interconversion. Treatment of a pigeon liver preparation with Dowex-1 chloride followed by dialysis resulted in loss of activity (i.e., incorporation of C^{14}- glycine into serine), which could be restored by addition of tetrahydrofolic acid (482); similar results were obtained with rat liver preparations (453, 483). Tetrahydrofolic acid also stimulated serine formation from glycine and formaldehyde. Tetrahydrofolic acid alone did not restore the activity of inactivated pigeon liver preparations to catalyze serine formation from glycine and formate; however, addition of tetrahydrofolic acid, adenosine triphosphate, diphosphopyridine nucleotide, glucose 6-phosphate, and manganous ions restored activity (482, 483). These and similar (484, 485) results suggested that formate was converted in the presence of adenosine triphosphate to formyltetrahydrofolate, which was enzymatically reduced in the presence of diphosphopyridine nucleotide to a derivative at the oxidation level of formaldehyde. Folic acid exhibited some activity with the formate-utilizing system, but this was lower than that observed with tetrahydrofolic acid. Dihydrofolic acid activated the formaldehyde-glycine system less than tetrahydrofolic acid; when adenosine triphosphate, diphosphopyridine nucleotide, glucose 6-phosphate, and manganous ions were added together with dihydrofolic acid, activation was equivalent to that observed with tetrahydrofolic acid. Although folic acid can be enzymatically reduced to tetrahydrofolate (486), it is now known that dihydrofolic acid (rather than folic acid) is the first biosynthetic product formed (487, 488). Dihydrofolate is also formed from tetrahydrofolate during thymidylate synthesis (489). Reduction of dihydrofolate to the enzymatically active folic acid derivative tetrahydrofolate is catalyzed by dihydrofolic reductase:

$$\text{Dihydrofolate} + \text{TPNH} + \text{H}^+ \rightleftharpoons \text{tetrahydrofolate} + \text{TPN}^+$$

The enzyme has been prepared from a variety of sources and its substrate specificity has been studied (490). Dihydrofolate can theoretically exist in three possible tautomeric forms as shown below:

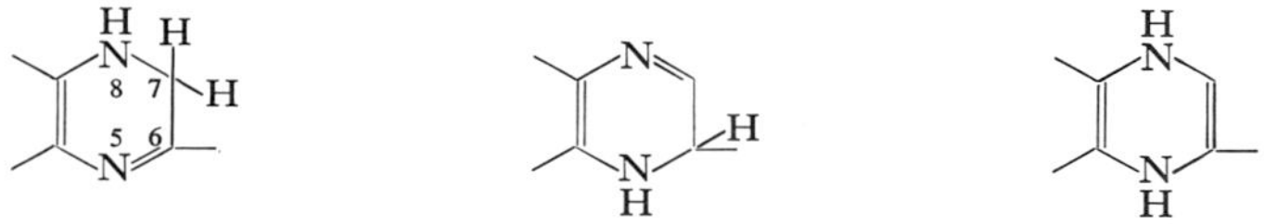

(7,8-)   (5,6-)   (5,8-)

Possible structures of dihydrofolate

Reduction of folate with hydrosulfite was thought to yield 7,8-dihydrofolate (491–494); however, studies were reported suggesting that the correct structure is the 5,8-isomer and that 7,8-dihydrofolate is formed by reduction of folate with potassium borohydride (495). On the other hand, more recent work confirms the earlier belief that dihydrofolate obtained by hydrosulfite reduction of folate is the 7,8-isomer (496). Thus, it was shown that enzymatic reduction of dihydrofolate in tritiated water gave unlabeled tetrahydrofolate, indicating hydrogen transfer to either the 5 or 8 positions (which bear exchangeable hydrogen atoms); this excludes the 5,8-isomer as the structure of dihydrofolate. In addition, reduction of folate to the dihydro form by hydrosulfite in tritiated or deuterated water gave a product containing isotope; one atom of deuterium was incorporated. Strong evidence that deuterium was added to a carbon atom that was also attached to a hydrogen atom was obtained from nuclear magnetic resonance studies; these data were obtained by comparison of folate and dihydrofolate and conclusively exclude both 5,6- and 5,8-dihydrofolate structures. Enzymatic reduction of dihydrofolate to tetrahydrofolate leads to the introduction of a new asymmetric center at carbon atom 6, and it has been established that dihydrofolic reductase catalyzes the formation of the l,L-diastereoisomer of tetrahydrofolate (497). There is evidence that only 50% of tetrahydrofolate prepared by chemical reduction is enzymatically active.

Enzyme preparations capable of catalyzing reversible formation of serine from formaldehyde and glycine have been obtained from microorganisms (498, 499) and avian (483) and mammalian liver (500–505). This enzyme has been designated serine aldolase, serine hydroxymethylase, serine transhydroxymethylase, and serine hydroxymethyl transferase. The nature of the active folic acid derivative that functions in this reaction has been the subject of considerable study and speculation; structures that have been considered include N^5-hydroxymethyltetrahydrofolate, N^{10}-hydroxymethyltetrahydrofolate, and N^5,N^{10}-methylenetetrahydrofolate. The reader is referred to the reviews of Rabinowitz (360), Huennekens and Osborn (506), and Friedkin (490) for many of the details of this extensive area of research. The available data indicate N^5,N^{10}-methylenetetrahydrofolate as the most probable structure for the derivative involved in the glycine-serine interconversion; however, the possibility that different preparations of the enzyme utilize different activated folic acid intermediates cannot be definitely excluded and it is conceivable (504) that all three of the suggested forms are in equilibrium. Formaldehyde reacts rapidly and nonenzymatically with tetrahydrofolate to yield products that include N^5,N^{10}-methylenetetrahydrofolate (507, 508). It has been reported that the reaction of formaldehyde with tetrahydrofolate is also catalyzed by an enzyme (formaldehyde-activating enzyme) present in pigeon liver (509). The product of this reaction, presumably N^5,N^{10}-methylenetetrahydrofolate, gave serine and tetrahydrofolate on incubation with serine hydroxymethylase, and was converted to N^{10}-formyltetrahydrofolate on incubation with hydroxymethyltetrahydrofolate dehydrogenase and triphosphopyridine nucleotide. "Active formaldehyde" prepared by nonenzymatic reaction between formaldehyde and tetrahydrofolate was stable to oxidizing agents, and was active in a number of enzymatic reactions. Reduction of N^5,N^{10}-methenyltetrahydrofolate by sodium borohydride gave a product with the properties of "active formaldehyde" (508).

Serine hydroxymethylase purified from rabbit liver exhibits an absorbancy maximum at 415 mμ (505). The enzyme reacts readily with cysteine as indicated by a decrease in the absorbancy at 415 mμ and the appearance, with concomitant loss of activity, of a new peak absorbancy at 330 mμ. The band at 330 mμ is probably due to the thiazolidine derivative of pyridoxal 5'-phosphate. After dialysis, the apoenzyme can be re-activated by addition of pyridoxal 5'-phosphate. The reaction catalyzed by the enzyme may be represented as follows:

$$\text{Serine} + \text{tetrahydrofolate} \;\rightleftharpoons\; N^5,N^{10}\text{-methylenetetrahydrofolate} + \text{glycine}$$

Enzyme activity can be conveniently determined in a system containing N^5,N^{10}-methylenetetrahydrofolate dehydrogenase and triphosphopyridine nucleotide by following the increase in absorbancy at 340 mμ due to reduced pyridine nucleotide formation.

N^5,N^{10}-Methylenetetrahydrofolate$+$TPN$^+$ $\rightleftharpoons$
$$\text{TPNH}+N^5,N^{10}\text{-methenyltetrahydrofolate}^+$$

A highly purified preparation of serine hydroxymethylase (mol. wt. 331,000) gave an absorbancy maximum at 340 mμ after treatment with sodium borohydride; after acid hydrolysis of the reduced enzyme, a fluorescent product was obtained which exhibited paper chromatographic and electrophoretic properties of ϵ-pyridoxyl-lysine. The enzyme contains 4 moles of pyridoxal 5′-phosphate per mole of protein. Incubation of the enzyme with α-methylserine gave N^5,N^{10}-methylenetetrahydrofolate and D-alanine, indicating that an α-hydrogen atom is not required for enzymatic activity. The function of pyridoxal 5′-phosphate in this reaction is considered elsewhere in this volume (see p. 404).

In addition to tetrahydrofolate, tetrahydropteroyltriglutamate was reported to be fully active for rabbit liver serine hydroxymethylase (504). A preparation of serine hydroxymethylase obtained from a clostridium was found to require polyglutamyl-pteridine derivatives in addition to diphosphopyridine nucleotide, pyridoxal 5′-phosphate, inorganic orthophosphate, and manganous ions; monoglutamyl pteridines were less active or inactive. The polyglutamyl-pteridine compounds required for such conversion of serine to glycine have been designated coenzyme C, and several active compounds (containing 2 to 6 glutamate residues as well as other amino acids) have thus far been isolated from *Clostridium cylindrosporum* (510, 511).

Wilson and Snell (512) isolated α-methylserine hydroxymethyl transferase, an inducible enzyme separable from serine hydroxymethyl transferase that is present in a pseudomonad which utilizes α-methylserine (see p. 95) or α-hydroxymethylserine as its sole carbon and nitrogen sources. The purified enzyme lost activity during dialysis at pH 8, and was fully reactivated by incubation with pyridoxal 5′-phosphate. It catalyzes the following reactions:

$(+)$-α-Methylserine$+$tetrahydrofolate $\rightleftharpoons$
$$N^5,N^{10}\text{-methylenetetrahydrofolate}+\text{D-alanine}$$

$(-)$-α-Ethylserine$+$tetrahydrofolate $\rightleftharpoons$
$$N^5,N^{10}\text{-methylenetetrahydrofolate}+\text{D-}\alpha\text{-aminobutyrate}$$

α-Hydroxymethylserine$+$tetrahydrofolate $\rightleftharpoons$
$$N^5,N^{10}\text{-methylenetetrahydrofolate}+\text{D-serine}$$

These reactions and the demonstration that α-methylserine is converted to D-alanine by serine hydroxymethylase (see above) clearly indicate that a substrate need not have an α-hydrogen atom. [Earlier work by Longenecker *et al.* (513) showed nonenzymatic cleavage of α-methylserine and α-hydroxymethylserine to formaldehyde and alanine (or serine) in the presence of pyridoxal and metal ions.] After growth of the adapted organism on racemic α-methylserine, (−)-α-methylserine was isolated from the culture filtrate (512). (+)-α-Methylserine was synthesized by allowing the enzyme to act on formaldehyde and D-alanine; in similar manner (−)-α-ethylserine was obtained from formaldehyde and D-α-aminobutyric acid. The enzyme did not act upon (−)-α-methylserine. The enzymatic data indicate that (+)-α-methylserine and (−)-α-ethylserine have analogous configurations; if inversion does not occur during the enzymatic reaction then the susceptible isomer of α-methylserine [(+)-α-methylserine] has the D-configuration if considered a derivative of alanine, i.e., α-hydroxymethyl-D-alanine, or the L-configuration if considered a derivative of serine, i.e., α-methyl-L-serine. Previous studies (514) showed that hydrolysis of N-chloroacetyl-α-methyl-DL-serine by hog kidney acylase gave (−)-α-methylserine and chloroacetyl-(+)-α-methylserine. If it is assumed that renal acylase cleaves only N-chloroacetyl L-amino acids, then the unsusceptible N-chloroacetyl amino acid can be considered as a derivative of either α-methyl-D-serine or its optical isomer, α-hydroxymethyl-D-alanine. One cannot ignore the possibility of inversion and the observation that both isomers of N-acetyl-α-methyl-DL-serine are hydrolyzed by acylase (514); an unequivocal assignment of configuration is not possible (see p. 152). Another interesting facet of this problem is that α-methylserine hydroxymethyl transferase distinguishes between the hydroxymethyl groups of α-hydroxymethylserine; α-hydroxymethylserine enzymatically synthesized from D-serine and C^{14}-formaldehyde liberated all of the labeled formaldehyde when the reaction was run in the direction of D-serine formation. A similar distinction between the hydrogen atoms of glycine is made by transaminase and D-amino acid oxidase (see p. 300).

N^5,N^{10}-Methylenetetrahydrofolate is also utilized by deoxycytidylate hydroxymethylase, an enzyme produced by phage-infected *Escherichia coli* (490, 515):

Deoxycytidylate + N^5,N^{10}-methylenetetrahydrofolate $\rightleftharpoons$
5-hydroxymethyldeoxycytidylate + tetrahydrofolate

This folic acid derivative is also required for thymidylate synthesis (516):

N^5,N^{10}-Methylenetetrahydrofolate + deoxyuridylate $\rightleftharpoons$ dihydrofolate + thymidylate

It can also be reduced to N^5-methyltetrahydrofolate, which is utilized in methionine biosynthesis (see p. 780):

N^5,N^{10}-Methylenetetrahydrofolate + DPNH + H$^+$ $\rightarrow$
N^5-methyltetrahydrofolate + DPN$^+$

Early observations showed that formate was a precursor of carbon atoms 2 and 8 of uric acid, carbon 2 of the imidazole ring of histidine, and carbon atom 3 of serine, and that these carbon atoms as well as formate and formaldehyde were converted to the methyl groups of methionine and thymine. It was also shown that carbon atom 3 of serine is transferred with its hydrogen atoms intact to the methyl groups of thymine and choline (517–519). These relationships may now be largely explained in terms of a series of enzymatic transformations involving various derivatives of tetrahydrofolate. Scheme 4 summarizes much of this information.

The enzyme N^5,N^{10}-methylenetetrahydrofolate (hydroxymethyl-tetrahydrofolate) dehydrogenase catalyzes the interconversion of tetrahydrofolate derivatives at the formate and formaldehyde levels of oxidation and thus provides a mechanism for the observed equilibrium between these two types of one-carbon units. The enzyme has been studied in preparations from beef and chicken liver (520, 521). At alkaline values of pH, disappearance of "active formaldehyde" is favored because of the marked tendency of the methenyl compound to hydrolyze to give N^{10}-formyltetrahydrofolate. N^5,N^{10}-Methenyltetra-hydrofolate is also hydrolyzed by an enzyme (N^5,N^{10}-methenyltetra-hydrofolate cyclohydrolase) at pH values about 7; the enzyme has been found in bacterial (360) and mammalian (522) sources. There is evidence that N^{10}-formyltetrahydrofolate may also be formed from N^5-formylte-trahydrofolate via N^5,N^{10}-methenyltetrahydrofolate or by isomerization of N^5-formyltetrahydrofolate (520). It can be synthesized from tetra-hydrofolate, formate, and adenosine triphosphate (523–526) in accord-ance with the following reaction:

Formate + ATP + tetrahydrofolate $\rightleftharpoons$
N^{10}-formyltetrahydrofolate + ADP + inorganic phosphate

The enzyme that catalyzes this reaction (tetrahydrofolic acid formylase; formyltetrahydrofolate synthetase) has been found in pigeon liver (527),

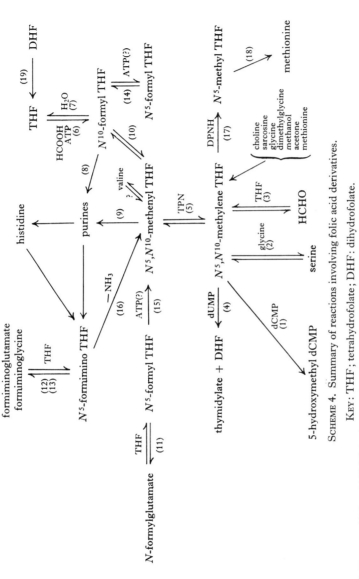

SCHEME 4. Summary of reactions involving folic acid derivatives.

KEY: THF; tetrahydrofolate; DHF: dihydrofolate.

(1) Deoxycytidylate (dCMP) hydroxymethylase
(2) L-Serine hydroxymethyltransferase
(3) Formaldehyde-activating enzyme
(4) Thymidylate synthetase
(5) N^5,N^{10}-Methylenetetrahydrofolate dehydrogenase
(6) Formyltetrahydrofolate synthetase
(7) N^{10}-Formyltetrahydrofolate deacylase
(8) 5-Amino-4-imidazolecarboxamide ribonucleotide trans-
    formylase
(9) Glycinamide ribonucleotide transformylase

(10) N^5,N^{10}-Methenyltetrahydrofolate cyclohydrolase
(11) Formylglutamate formyl transferase
(12) Formiminoglutamate formimino transferase
(13) Formiminoglycine formimino transferase
(14) N^5-Formyltetrahydrofolate isomerase
(15) N^5-Formiminotetrahydrofolate isomerase (cyclodehydrase)
(16) N^5-Formiminotetrahydrofolate cyclodeaminase
(17) N^5,N^{10}-Methylenetetrahydrofolate reductase
(18) N^5-Methyltetrahydrofolate methyl transferase
(19) Dihydrofolate reductase

Micrococcus aerogenes (523, 528), human erythrocytes (526), *Clostridium cylindrosporum*, and *C. acidiurici* (524, 525). The enzyme was obtained from the clostridia in crystalline form, and was found to have a molecular weight of approximately 230,000. The reaction involves transfer of O^{18} from formate to inorganic phosphate, and the enzyme also catalyzes the arsenolysis of formyltetrahydrofolate in the presence of catalytic quantities of adenosine diphosphate. An exchange of orthophosphate-P^{32} into adenosine triphosphate was observed which required the presence of all three substrates; on the other hand, adenosine diphosphate-triphosphate exchange occurred in the absence of tetrahydrofolate and formate. Although the experimental data were considered consistent with a mechanism involving a concerted reaction between the three substrates and the enzyme, stepwise formation of enzyme-bound intermediates cannot be excluded. Thus, an activated enzyme-formate intermediate might be formed on the enzyme in a manner analogous to that proposed for glutamine synthetase (see p. 446). Studies on the enzyme from *M. aerogenes* provided data suggesting a different mechanism involving enzyme-bound intermediates. Thus, spectrophotometric evidence was obtained for a reaction between enzyme, tetrahydrofolate, and adenosine triphosphate in the absence of formate; the findings, which are not conclusive, were interpreted in terms of a phosphorylated form of tetrahydrofolate. Intermediate formation of enzyme-bound formyl-phosphate seems to be the most attractive possibility but data are needed. It is of interest, however, that a formate-activating enzyme (formokinase) obtained from *Escherichia coli* catalyzes the formation of formylhydroxamate in the presence of formate, adenosine triphosphate, and hydroxyl-amine; stoichiometric quantities of formylhydroxamate, adenosine diphosphate, and inorganic phosphate are produced. The enzyme also catalyzes formation of adenosine triphosphate from adenosine diphosphate and chemically synthesized formylphosphate, and it was concluded that formylphosphate is the product in the forward direction (529). There is no evidence at present that this reaction involves a folic acid derivative. Extracts of *Clostridium cylindrosporum* have also been found to contain two formate kinases, neither of which is identical with formyltetrahydrofolate synthetase (529a).

It was stated above (see p. 640), that the α-carbon atom of glycine can serve as a source of one-carbon units and thus be converted to "active formate". As discussed in relation to the succinate-glycine cycle, deamination of δ-aminolevulinic acid leads to γ-ketoglutaraldehyde; the latter compound is cleaved to yield succinate and a one-carbon unit at the oxidation level of formaldehyde. Another possible pathway for conversion of the α-carbon atom of glycine to "active formate" is via oxidation of glyoxylate to formate (see p. 638). Although there is no evidence that folic acid participates in the reaction studied by Nakada and Sund (366) between glyoxylate and glutamate to yield N-formylglutamate (see p. 639), transformylation between N^5-formyltetrahydrofolate and glutamate has been observed (530):

N^5-Formyltetrahydrofolate + L-glutamate ⇌
                                    N-formyl-L-glutamate + tetrahydrofolate

Enzyme preparations that catalyze this reaction have been obtained from hog liver and plants (531) (see p. 831). There is also evidence for the participation of folic acid or pteridine derivatives in the hydroxylation of phenylalanine (see p. 897), the biosynthesis of pantoic acid (see p. 753), possibly in valine metabolism (see p. 741), and in the metabolism of choline and related compounds (see p. 665).

In early investigations on the serine-glycine interconversion, the possible intermediate formation of α-aminomalonic acid was considered but discarded on the basis that a symmetrical intermediate could not be consistent with the labeling data; thus, N^{15}-serine-1-C^{13} was converted to N^{15}-glycine-1-C^{13} without significant isotope dilution. The inadequacy of such reasoning was subsequently pointed out by Ogston (see p. 154). Now that there is considerable information about the glycine-serine interconversion and the participation of tetrahydrofolate in this reaction, there seems to be little reason to reconsider α-aminomalonic acid as an intermediate. However, subsequent investigations revealed an enzyme capable of decarboxylating α-aminomalonic acid to glycine (see p. 329). As yet, there is no evidence for the oxidation of serine to α-aminomalonic acid, but it is conceivable that such a reaction occurs, and therefore that an alternative pathway exists for conversion of serine to glycine.

A recent report (531a) describes the nonenzymatic hydroxylation of alanine to serine in a reaction mixture containing ferrous ions, ascorbate, and ethylenediaminetetraacetate. These findings suggest the possibility of an analogous enzymatic hydroxylation reaction.

Biosynthesis of Serine from Carbohydrate

Evidence for the biosynthesis of serine from a carbohydrate precursor has come from experiments on intact animals and from enzymatic investigations. Administration of labeled glycerol and glyceric acid to rats led to the formation of labeled serine (532–536); with carboxyl-labeled glyceric acid the serine was labeled mainly in the carboxyl group (532, 534). Studies in which labeled acetate and pyruvate were administered showed that the carbon chain of pyruvate was not directly converted to serine and suggested a pathway involving a symmetrical intermediate. Sallach (532, 535) demonstrated the existence of serine-alanine trans-aminase in mammalian liver and kidney and partially purified the enzyme from dog liver; alanine was specifically required as the amino donor. Ichihara and Greenberg (537) reported the formation of serine from glyceric acid, 3-phosphoglyceric acid, and 3-phosphohydroxy-pyruvic acid by rat liver homogenates. They also found evidence for formation of 3-phosphohydroxypyruvic acid from D-glyceric acid and 3-phosphoglyceric acid, formation of phosphoserine from D-glyceric acid, 3-phosphoglyceric acid, and 3-phosphohydroxypyruvic acid, and for the hydrolysis of phosphoserine to serine. Other studies (538–542) have established the existence of phosphoserine phosphatase. Although there is evidence for the presence in liver of a D-glyceric acid kinase which converts glyceric acid to 3-phosphoglyceric acid (537), recent work indicates that the phosphorylation of glycerate by adenosine triphosphate by mammalian liver mitochondria yields D-2-phosphoglycerate rather than the 3-isomer (543). Independent studies on an enzyme from peas demonstrated formation of phosphoserine from D-3-phosphoglycerate (544). These observations suggest two possible pathways for the bio-synthesis of serine in mammalian tissues as indicated below.

$$
\begin{array}{ccccc}
\text{COOH} & & \text{COOH} & & \text{COOH} \\
| & & | & & | \\
\text{CHOH} & \rightleftharpoons & \text{C}=\text{O} & \rightleftharpoons & \text{CHNH}_2 \\
| & & | & & | \\
\text{CH}_2\text{OH} & & \text{CH}_2\text{OH} & & \text{CH}_2\text{OH} \\
\text{D-Glyceric} & & \text{Hydroxypyruvic} & & \text{L-Serine} \\
\text{acid} & & \text{acid} & &
\end{array}
$$

$$
\begin{array}{ccccc}
\text{COOH} & & \text{COOH} & & \text{COOH} \\
| & & | & & | \\
\text{CHOH} & \rightleftharpoons & \text{C}=\text{O} & \rightleftharpoons & \text{CHNH}_2 \\
| & & | & & | \\
\text{CH}_2\text{OPO}_3\text{H}_2 & & \text{CH}_2\text{OPO}_3\text{H}_2 & & \text{CH}_2\text{OPO}_3\text{H}_2 \\
\text{D-3-Phosphoglyceric} & & \text{3-Phosphohydroxy-} & & \text{L-Phosphoserine} \\
\text{acid} & & \text{pyruvic acid} & &
\end{array}
$$

Willis and Sallach (545) purified a D-glycerate dehydrogenase from plants and beef liver that catalyzes the following reaction:

$$\text{D-Glycerate} + \text{DPN}^+ \text{ (TPN}^+\text{)} \rightleftharpoons \text{hydroxypyruvate} + \text{H}^+ + \text{DPNH (TPNH)}$$

This observation raises the question as to whether serine is formed in liver by a pathway not involving phosphohydroxypyruvic acid or phosphoserine. D-Glycerate might arise from either 2-phosphoglycerate or 3-phosphoglycerate or by oxidation of D-glyceraldehyde. At this time, evidence for the phosphoserine pathway is less complete, but it is conceivable that both pathways are operative in mammalian liver. On the other hand, Umbarger and Umbarger (546) have examined the activities of 3-phosphoglycerate dehydrogenase, phosphoserine-glutamate transaminase, and phosphoserine phosphatase in wild-type and two serine-requiring mutants of *Salmonella typhimurium,* and found that one mutant lacked 3-phosphoglycerate dehydrogenase and that the other was markedly deficient in phosphoserine phosphatase. Similar observations were made later on mutants of *E. coli* (547). The data therefore indicate that these enzymatic steps are involved in the microbial biosynthesis of serine. L-Serine inhibits 3-phosphoglycerate dehydrogenase activity suggesting that such inhibition could serve as a feedback mechanism to prevent excessive serine synthesis. In isotopic competition studies with extracts of *E. coli,* 3-phosphohydroxypyruvate and phosphoserine competed with glucose carbon for incorporation into serine (547).

O-Phosphoserine phosphatase has been investigated in several laboratories with generally similar findings (538–542). The enzyme, which has been found in chicken liver, rat liver, and baker's yeast, hydrolyzes both L- and D-isomers of O-phosphoserine and catalyzes exchange between L-serine and L-phosphoserine. The enzyme is inhibited by L- and D-serine, L-alanine, and glycine. It is of interest that the enzyme catalyzes the transfer of a phosphate group from D-phosphoserine to L-serine. This observation, the catalysis of a transfer reaction between L-serine and L-phosphoserine, and inhibition by serine suggest a double displacement mechanism. Thus, it is postulated that phosphoserine reacts with the enzyme to give an enzyme-phosphoserine complex; cleavage of the phosphorus-oxygen bond yields a phosphoryl-enzyme-(serine) complex, from which serine dissociates to give phosphoryl-enzyme. Hydrolysis yields enzyme and inorganic phosphate. The exchange is explained by reaction of serine with the phosphoryl-enzyme to give the phosphoryl-enzyme-(serine) complex followed by subsequent reformation of the enzyme-phosphoserine complex. Since the intermediates are the same for both the D- and L-substrates, the transfer of phosphate from D-phosphoserine to L-serine is plausible.

Relationships between Serine, 2-Aminoethanol, Choline, and Sarcosine

The discovery that sarcosine is a metabolite in the rat opened up a new facet of "one-carbon unit" metabolism. Horner and MacKenzie (548) found that when C^{14}-methyl-labeled methionine or betaine was administered together with sarcosine, there was appreciable labeling of the urinary sarcosine. Methyl-labeled sarcosine was converted to labeled formaldehyde and formate by liver preparations (549), and these products were also detected in the urine of animals injected with C^{14}-sarcosine; appreciable amounts of label were excreted as carbon dioxide. In the *in vitro* studies significant quantities of isotope appeared in glycine and serine. It became apparent that dimethylglycine was a precursor of sarcosine and evidence was found for the oxidation of dimethylglycine to sarcosine and formaldehyde by a specific oxidase not identical with sarcosine oxidase. Sarcosine oxidase, also present in liver, converts sarcosine to formaldehyde and glycine. Thus, both methyl groups of dimethylglycine (which is known to be formed by demethylation of betaine; see p. 665) are converted to formaldehyde by separate oxidases. The glycine formed can condense with an active one-carbon unit (formed also by these oxidations) to give serine. These observations and considerations led MacKenzie (458) in 1954 to propose a cyclic scheme in which betaine is converted via dimethylglycine to sarcosine; sarcosine is oxidized to glycine, which is converted to serine. Decarboxylation of serine gives 2-aminoethanol, which is methylated in several steps to yield choline, which undergoes oxidation to betaine. Similar but less elaborate schemes had been proposed earlier by Jukes (550) and duVigneaud (551). Evidence consistent with a similar pathway in plants has been obtained (552). Subsequent studies have confirmed and extended this cycle; a significant development was the recognition that the conversion of serine to 2-aminoethanol and the methylation of the latter compound occur when these compounds are components of the corresponding phosphatides. Phosphatides containing *N*-methylamino-ethanol and *N*-dimethylaminoethanol and the phosphoryl derivatives of these compounds have been found to occur naturally (553, 554).

It has long been known that serine is the precursor of 2-aminoethanol; thus, Stetten (555) observed that N^{15}-serine was converted to N^{15}-

aminoethanol. Elwyn *et al.* (556) found that in the rat the β-C^{14},β-D,N^{15} of serine were extensively utilized as a unit for aminoethanol synthesis. Although other findings also indicated the decarboxylation of serine to aminoethanol, detailed information about the nature of this reaction has only recently become available. In various experiments, labeled serine was found not to yield free aminoethanol (557–559). Thus, Wilson *et al.* (559) in experiments with slices and homogenates of rat liver and brain found that carbon from L-serine-C^{14} appeared earliest as the amino-ethanol of phospholipid; free aminoethanol and O-phosphoamino-ethanol were not intermediates in this conversion. Bremer *et al.* (558) found that when C^{14}-serine was injected into rats, radioactive amino-ethanol could be isolated from the liver phospholipid fraction, and concluded that decarboxylation of serine took place after this amino acid had been incorporated into phospholipids. Borkenhagen *et al.* (560) reported the finding of a phosphatidylserine decarboxylase in the liver and other tissues of the rat. Their evidence supports the following reaction sequence:

$$\text{Phosphatidylaminoethanol} + \text{L-serine} \rightleftharpoons \text{phosphatidyl-L-serine} + \text{aminoethanol}$$
$$\text{Phosphatidyl-L-serine} \rightarrow \text{phosphatidylaminoethanol} + CO_2$$

These findings therefore provide an explanation for decarboxylation of serine, which was first observed in bacteria many years ago by Nord (561). The studies of Bremer and colleagues (562, 563) and Gibson *et al.* (564, 565) indicate that the conversion of aminoethanol to choline also occurs after these compounds have been incorporated into phospholipids. When the biosynthesis of choline was studied in the rat after injection of radio-active methionine, C^{14}-monomethylaminoethanol and C^{14}-dimethyl-aminoethanol were isolated from the liver phospholipids, and these components exhibited a higher turnover than choline. The methylation of phosphatidylaminoethanol was shown to occur stepwise by a process involving *S*-adenosylmethionine. Gibson *et al.* (565) studied the incorporation of radioactivity from methyl-labeled *S*-adenosylmethionine in homogenates of rat liver. The activity was entirely associated with subcellular particles, and monomethylaminoethanol and dimethyl-aminoethanol were identified as constituents of microsomal phospho-lipid after incubation with C^{14}-*S*-adenosylmethionine. Lecithin-containing radioactive choline was isolated from a similar incubation mixture. Scheme 5 is based on these observations. It should be stated,

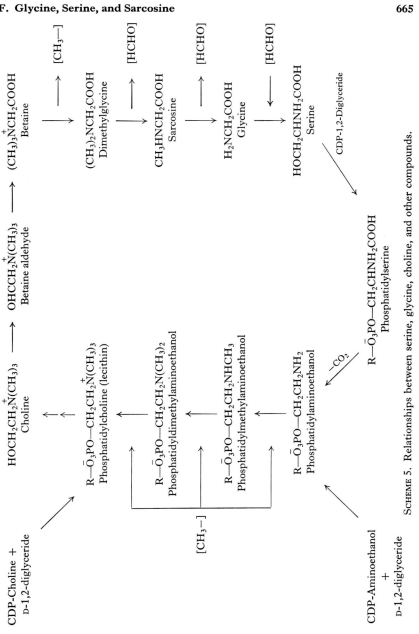

SCHEME 5. Relationships between serine, glycine, choline, and other compounds.

however, that there may be significant species differences in the relative importance of the various reactions of the "cycle." For example, the major pathway of lecithin formation in mammals is via cytidine 5'-diphosphate choline and D-1,2-diglyceride, and the conversion of serine to phosphatidylserine is probably a relatively minor pathway in mammals.

The formation of phosphatidyl-L-serine takes place by an exchange reaction between phosphatidylaminoethanol and L-serine as described above. Phosphatidylaminoethanol is formed by the decarboxylation of phosphatidyl-L-serine, and can be formed directly by the following reactions (566):

Cytidine 5'-triphosphate + phosphoaminoethanol ⇌
                    cytidine diphosphate aminoethanol + pyrophosphate

Cytidine diphosphate aminoethanol + D-1,2-diglyceride ⇌
                    cytidine monophosphate + phosphatidylaminoethanol

Phosphatidylcholine is formed from phosphatidylaminoethanol as indicated in the scheme above, but can also be formed from phosphoryl-choline by reactions analogous to those leading to phosphatidylamino-ethanol formation from phosphoaminoethanol. The direct synthesis of phosphatidylserine has been shown to take place as follows in extracts of *E. coli* (567):

Cytidine diphosphate diglyceride + L-serine →
                    phosphatidyl-L-serine + cytidine monophosphate

The incorporation of serine into phosphatidylserine catalyzed by rat liver microsomes was found to require cytidine 5'-triphosphate, coenzyme A, adenosine triphosphate, glutathione, and α-glycerophosphate. Calcium ions stimulate incorporation, but the mechanism of the reaction is not yet clear (568).

The conversion of choline to betaine and transmethylation of the latter to dimethylglycine is considered below (see p. 764). The oxidation of sarcosine and dimethylglycine to formaldehyde by a washed liver particle preparation was first observed in 1941 by Handler *et al.* (569). Dimethylglycine is converted in two oxidative steps to glycine; in experiments with rat liver mitochondria, both methyl groups furnished stoichiometric quantities of "active formaldehyde" (i.e., one-carbon units capable of forming the β-carbon atom of serine) (570). Similar results had been obtained earlier in experiments in which methyl-deuterated sarcosine was incubated with mitochondrial preparations;

the deuterium content of the β-carbon atom indicated that the one-carbon unit formed from sarcosine was at the same oxidation level as formaldehyde (571). Hoskins and MacKenzie (572) succeeded in solubilizing the sarcosine and dimethylglycine dehydrogenases by sonic treatment of liver mitochondria; both enzymes appeared in the same fraction on ammonium sulfate precipitation, and required an electron transfer flavoprotein for the reduction of 2,6-dichlorophenolindophenol. Subsequent studies by Frisell and MacKenzie (573) led to separation by chromatography of the two enzymes, which were found to contain tightly bound flavin and nonheme iron. Succinate dehydrogenase was separated from sarcosine and dimethylglycine dehydrogenases by the procedures employed. Sarcosine oxidase was fractionated into two components after sonic disruption and centrifugation; one of these was soluble sarcosine dehydrogenase that lacked respiratory activity but was active with 2,6-dichlorophenolindophenol, and the other was a particulate electron transfer system that lacked sarcosine dehydrogenase activity. When the fractions were combined, electron flow from the dehydrogenase to molecular oxygen was reestablished. The soluble sarcosine dehydrogenase was fractionated to yield a dehydrogenase which was inactive toward indophenol, and an enzyme that transferred electrons from the primary dehydrogenase to the dye. The latter enzyme was activated by addition of flavin adenine dinucleotide. Frisell and his colleagues (574) concluded that the mitochondrial oxidation of the N-methyl groups of dimethylglycine and sarcosine requires an electron transfer flavoprotein that accepts electrons from the substrate specific flavoprotein dehydrogenases. The electron-transferring flavoprotein of the sarcosine dehydrogenase system of rat liver substituted for the electron-transferring flavoprotein of the fatty acyl coenzyme A dehydrogenase system of pig liver, and vice versa; these enzymes are probably identical or very similar (575).

Klain and Johnson (576) observed that when C^{14}-aminoethanol is administered by intraperitoneal injection to chicks, the urinary uric acid was highly labeled, mainly in carbon atoms 4 and 5 (those supplied by glycine; see p. 630). These observations are consistent with conversion of aminoethanol via choline to glycine. However, although considerable radioactivity was found in choline, there was little labeling of tissue glycine or serine. Administration of labeled glycine led to labeling of liver glycine and also carbon atoms 4 and 5 of uric acid. It is possible that there is a pathway to carbon atoms 4 and 5 of purine that does not involve free glycine or that there are separate glycine pools. Klain and Johnson also obtained evidence for a pathway from arginine to uric acid that does not involve glycine.

Degradation of Serine

Several attempts have been made to determine the fate of isotopically labeled L- and D-serine in intact animals and in tissue slices; the somewhat divergent results obtained can probably be ascribed to differences in experimental technique. Thus Nadkarni et al. (577) examined the incorporation of radioactivity into the blood glucose, muscle and liver glycogen, and respiratory carbon dioxide after administration of D- and L-serine-3-C^{14} and glycine-2-C^{14} in fasted rats and in rats fed glucose simultaneously. Both D- and L-serine were converted to carbon dioxide at about the same rate, but D-serine was more extensively incorporated into glucose and glycogen than was L-serine. The data suggest that D-serine was metabolized via hydroxypyruvate and that L-serine yielded pyruvate. In experiments carried out by Minthorn et al. (578), the isotope distribution patterns in liver and muscle glycogen were determined in fed and fasted rats after administration of D- and L-serine-3-C^{14}. The results of these studies also suggested conversion of L-serine to pyruvate; approximately 10% of the radioactivity of the administered D-serine was found in an acidic urinary metabolite. This was not identified; perhaps it was hydroxypyruvate formed by D-amino acid oxidase. In contrast to these results, Elwyn et al. (579) found evidence that L-serine was mainly converted to glycine in liver slices from fed and fasted rats. Their data suggest that D-serine is metabolized predominantly via hydroxypyruvate.

Studies on cell-free preparations have revealed several enzymes that act on serine, including serine transhydroxymethylase (see p. 654), serine transaminase (see p. 661), and L- and D-serine dehydrases. The anaerobic deamination of serine has been studied with several biological preparations; the over-all reaction can be represented as follows (580):

$$\text{L-serine} \rightarrow \text{pyruvate} + \text{ammonia}$$

An L-serine dehydrase has been obtained from *Neurospora crassa*, which seems to require pyridoxal phosphate; this preparation also deaminated L-threonine (581) (see p. 679). A D-serine dehydrase was obtained from *E. coli* which was activated by pyridoxal phosphate (582, 583), but an

L-serine dehydrase from this organism was activated by glutathione and adenylic acid and not by pyridoxal phosphate (584); this enzyme also attacked L-threonine. L-Serine deaminase of *Streptococcus rimosus* catalyzes deamination of β-chloroalanine to yield pyruvate (585). The conversion of β-chloroalanine to pyruvate, ammonia, chloride, and hydrogen ion is also catalyzed by rat liver preparations (586).

$$\underset{\underset{Cl}{|}\;\underset{+NH_3}{|}}{CH_2CHCOO^-} + H_2O \longrightarrow \underset{\underset{O}{\|}}{CH_3CCOO^-} + NH_4^+ + H^+ + Cl^-$$

The L-serine and L-threonine dehydrases of sheep liver have been obtained in essentially separate form, and both require pyridoxal phosphate (587). A much more active L-serine dehydrase has been isolated from rat liver (588). This enzyme preparation also catalyzes the synthesis of cystathionine (see p. 760); the two activities are probably properties of the same enzyme. It is of interest that a number of vitamin B_6-enzymes can catalyze the deamination of serine; in addition to cystathionine synthetase, the B protein of tryptophan synthetase (588a), and crystalline tryptophanase (see p. 879) deaminate serine (see p. 319). The deamination of homoserine is catalyzed by the cystathionine-cleaving enzyme (see p. 760). A mechanism based on the formation of a Schiff base between substrate and enzyme-bound pyridoxal phosphate has been proposed for the deamination of serine (see p. 402).

The reported conversion of DL-serine to alanine by liver preparations (589) may probably be ascribed to dehydration of L-serine to yield pyruvate followed by transamination to alanine. Some degradation of serine probably takes place by transamination leading to the formation of β-hydroxypyruvate. Hydroxypyruvate (590) readily undergoes both oxidation and decarboxylation enzymatically and nonenzymatically (591). Injection of labeled hydroxypyruvate into fasting rats led to formation of labeled liver glycogen. Incorporation of hydroxypyruvate carbon into glucose was also shown in studies with rat liver slices, and it appears that all three carbon atoms of hydroxypyruvate are incorporated into the glucose molecule via intermediates not identical with L-serine or pyruvate (592).

The formation of xylulose from hydroxypyruvate, dihydroxyfumarate, or tartronic acid semialdehyde in the presence of glyceraldehyde and rat liver transketolase was shown, and evidence was obtained for the enzymatic decarboxylation of dihydroxyfumarate to tartronic acid semialdehyde. The following sequence of reactions provides a pathway for conversion of serine carbon to carbohydrate (593, 594):

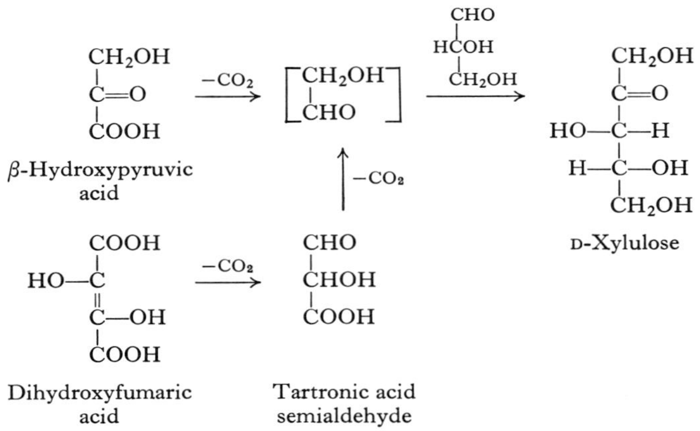

Sphingosine

Brady and colleagues (595) obtained cell-free preparations from rat brain that catalyze incorporation of labeled serine into sphingosine. Their data confirm earlier findings (596, 597) which showed that carbon atoms 3 and 2 of serine are the precursors of carbon atoms 1 and 2 of sphingosine, respectively, and that the nitrogen atom of serine becomes the nitrogen atom of sphingosine. Synthesis of sphingosine from serine and palmityl-coenzyme A required addition of reduced triphosphopyridine nucleotide, pyridoxal 5'-phosphate, and manganese ions. An activity present in the enzyme preparation catalyzed reduction of palmityl-coenzyme A by reduced triphosphopyridine nucleotide to palmitylaldehyde, and the latter substituted for reduced pyridine nucleotide and palmityl-coenzyme A in sphingosine synthesis. The extensive decarboxylation of serine observed in these studies in the presence of pyridoxal phosphate was probably nonenzymatic. Aminoethanol did not replace serine in the reaction. Dihydrosphingosine was the primary product of synthesis and enzymatic conversion of the latter compound to sphingosine was observed with enzyme preparations fortified with diphosphopyridine nucleotide, triphosphopyridine nucleotide, and phenazine methosulfate in an atmosphere of oxygen. The findings suggest that the reaction involves addition of palmitylaldehyde to carbon atom 2 of serine (activated by Schiff base formation with enzyme-bound pyridoxal phosphate); the over-all reaction may be represented as follows:

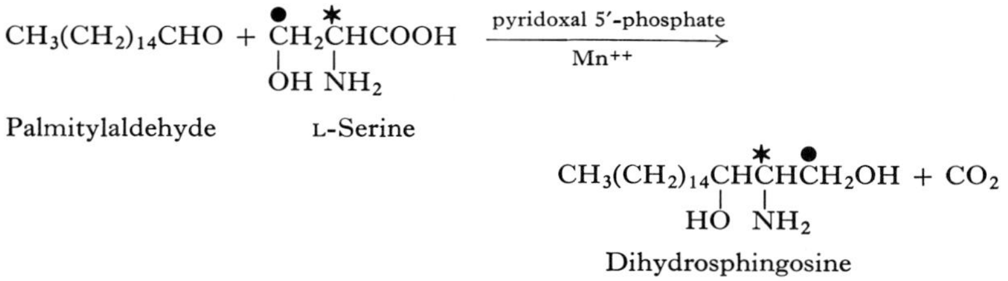

$$CH_3(CH_2)_{14}CHO + \overset{\bullet}{C}H_2\overset{*}{C}HCOOH \xrightarrow[\text{Mn}^{++}]{\text{pyridoxal 5'-phosphate}}$$

with OH and NH$_2$ substituents

Palmitylaldehyde   L-Serine

$$CH_3(CH_2)_{14}\overset{*}{C}H\overset{\bullet}{C}HCH_2OH + CO_2$$

with HO and NH$_2$ substituents

Dihydrosphingosine

Recent studies of Weiss (597a) have shown that the α-hydrogen atom of serine is retained during sphingosine biosynthesis. This observation excludes a mechanism suggested earlier (595) in which loss of a proton from the α-carbon atom of serine was postulated. Decarboxylation of serine may occur prior to or simultaneously with condensation of palmityl-aldehyde.

The sphingolipids of animal tissues contain dihydrosphingosine and sphingosine possessing a D-configuration at carbon atom 2 and the erythro-configuration at carbon atom 3. The enzymatically formed products (in the rat brain system) have been shown to possess the erythro-configuration (598).

Lombricine and Serine-Aminoethanol Phosphodiester

The O-phosphodiester of L-serine and aminoethanol has been isolated from turtle muscle (599), and there is evidence for its occurrence in the muscle of dystrophic chickens (599a). D-Serine-aminoethanol phosphodiester (600), D-serine (601), and lombricine (2-amino-2-carboxyethyl-2-guanidinoethyl hydrogen phosphate) (602–604) have been found in the earthworm. Administration of labeled aminoethanol and serine to earthworms led to labeling of serine-aminoethanol phospho-diester and lombricine (605); aminoethanol was mainly incorporated into the guanidinoethanol moiety of lombricine while serine was incorporated into the serine portion of this molecule. When amidine-labeled C^{14}-arginine was administered virtually all of the radioactivity was in the guanidinoethanol moiety. The specific radioactivity of serine-aminoethanol phosphodiester was greater than that of lombricine, and in similar experiments with P^{32}-inorganic phosphate, the phosphodiester became more rapidly labeled than did lombricine; this suggests that the phosphodiester is the precursor of lombricine, which could be formed by transamidination:

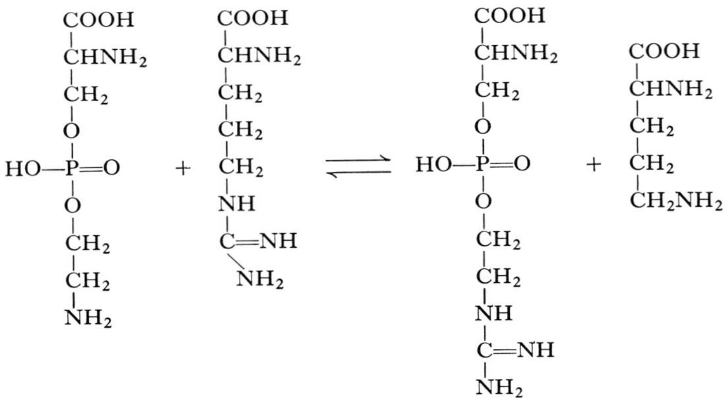

$$
\begin{array}{c}
\text{COOH} \\
| \\
\text{CHNH}_2 \\
| \\
\text{CH}_2 \\
| \\
\text{O} \\
| \\
\text{HO—P=O} \\
| \\
\text{O} \\
| \\
\text{CH}_2 \\
| \\
\text{CH}_2 \\
| \\
\text{NH}_2
\end{array}
\;+\;
\begin{array}{c}
\text{COOH} \\
| \\
\text{CHNH}_2 \\
| \\
\text{CH}_2 \\
| \\
\text{CH}_2 \\
| \\
\text{CH}_2 \\
| \\
\text{NH} \\
| \\
\text{C=NH} \\
\diagdown \\
\text{NH}_2
\end{array}
\;\rightleftharpoons\;
\begin{array}{c}
\text{COOH} \\
| \\
\text{CHNH}_2 \\
| \\
\text{CH}_2 \\
| \\
\text{O} \\
| \\
\text{HO—P=O} \\
| \\
\text{O} \\
| \\
\text{CH}_2 \\
| \\
\text{CH}_2 \\
| \\
\text{NH} \\
| \\
\text{C=NH} \\
| \\
\text{NH}_2
\end{array}
\;+\;
\begin{array}{c}
\text{COOH} \\
| \\
\text{CHNH}_2 \\
| \\
\text{CH}_2 \\
| \\
\text{CH}_2 \\
| \\
\text{CH}_2\text{NH}_2
\end{array}
$$

Serine-   Arginine   Lombricine   Ornithine
aminoethanol
phosphodiester

Phospholombricine has also been isolated from earthworms (601), and there is evidence that the formation of this phosphagen is catalyzed by a phosphoryl-transferase (606, 607, 607a).

Other Reactions of Glycine and Serine

Although there now seems to be no evidence for the natural occurrence of L-serine-O-sulfate, when this compound labeled with radioactive sulfur was administered to rats, most of the radioactivity appeared in the urine within one day. About 92% of the radioactivity was present in the inorganic sulfate fraction, and evidence for the formation of a number of additional compounds was obtained. A substantial portion of the sulfate ester was probably metabolized by the intestinal flora, since administration of antibacterial agents reduced the formation of inorganic sulfate (608). On the other hand, the O-sulfate esters of L-serine, L-threonine and L-hydroxyproline were hydrolyzed by a rat liver preparation (609).

Glycine and serine participate in a number of reactions not considered in this section. These include formation of hippuric acid (see p. 442), glycocholic acid (see p. 445), tryptophan (see p. 847), cystathionine (see p. 759), and cysteine (see pp. 789 and 793).

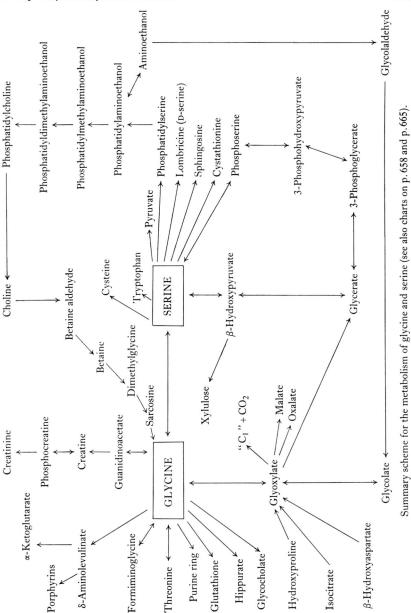

Summary scheme for the metabolism of glycine and serine (see also charts on p. 658 and p. 665).

G. Threonine

Biosynthesis

Information concerning the synthesis of threonine has come from studies on several microorganisms. The first evidence that homoserine was a precursor of threonine arose from investigations of a mutant of *Neurospora crassa* which required both methionine and threonine for growth; homoserine replaced both methionine and threonine for the growth of this mutant (610). Homoserine and threonine were found to accumulate in cultures of a mutant which required only methionine for growth (611). Yeast and *Escherichia coli*, when grown on labeled acetate, produced threonine and aspartate exhibiting similar isotope distributions (158, 160). Isotope competition studies were also consistent with the belief that homoserine was a precursor of threonine (339, 612).

Further progress in the elucidation of the biosynthetic route to threonine was made by Cohen and collaborators (613–615) and by Black (616, 617). Suspensions of a threonineless mutant of *E. coli* were found capable of converting aspartate to homoserine, and *E. coli* suspensions were able to use homoserine for the synthesis of threonine (613, 614). Black and Wright discovered two new intermediates in the aspartic acid–threonine pathway, namely, β-aspartyl phosphate and aspartic acid β-semialdehyde, and demonstrated the intermediate reactions with purified enzyme preparations obtained from yeast. The conversion of L-aspartate to L-β-aspartyl phosphate takes place in the presence of adenosine triphosphate, magnesium ions, and the enzyme β-aspartokinase (616–619):

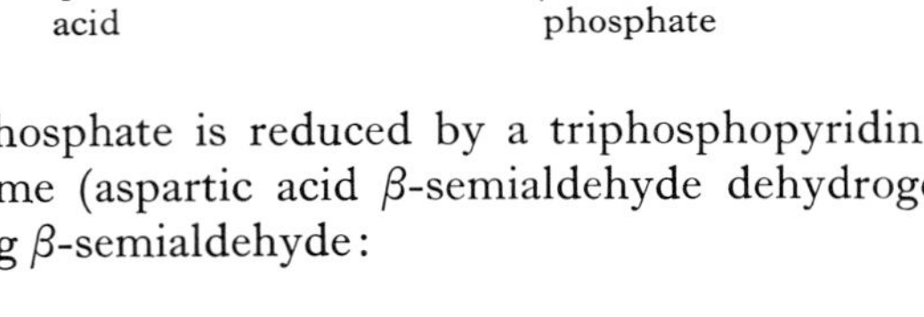

$$
\begin{array}{c}
\text{COOH} \\
| \\
\text{CH}_2 \\
| \\
\text{CHNH}_2 \\
| \\
\text{COOH}
\end{array}
+ \text{ATP}
\underset{\xrightarrow{\text{Mg}^{++}}}{\rightleftharpoons}
\begin{array}{c}
\text{O} \quad\quad \text{OH} \\
\| \quad\quad / \\
\text{C—O—P=O} \\
| \quad\quad \text{OH} \\
\text{CH}_2 \\
| \\
\text{CHNH}_2 \\
| \\
\text{COOH}
\end{array}
+ \text{ADP}
$$

Aspartic acid β-Aspartyl phosphate

β-Aspartyl phosphate is reduced by a triphosphopyridine nucleotide-specific enzyme (aspartic acid β-semialdehyde dehydrogenase) to the corresponding β-semialdehyde:

$$\begin{array}{c} \overset{O}{\underset{\parallel}{C}}-O-\overset{OH}{\underset{\parallel}{P}}\overset{O}{\underset{\parallel}{}} \\ \overset{|}{CH_2} \\ \overset{|}{CHNH_2} \\ \overset{|}{COOH} \end{array} + \text{TPNH} + \text{H}^+ \rightleftharpoons \begin{array}{c} \overset{O}{\underset{\parallel}{C}}-H \\ \overset{|}{CH_2} \\ \overset{|}{CHNH_2} \\ \overset{|}{COOH} \end{array} + \text{TPN}^+ + \text{H}_3\text{PO}_4$$

β-Aspartyl   Aspartic acid
phosphate   β-semialdehyde

This reaction is analogous to that catalyzed by 3-phosphoglyceraldehyde dehydrogenase; in both reactions there is reversible oxidation of an aldehyde to an acyl phosphate in the presence of inorganic phosphate and pyridine nucleotide. Both enzymes are inhibited by iodoacetate and catalyze arsenolysis of acyl phosphate; however, in contrast to the arsenolysis catalyzed by 3-phosphoglyceraldehyde dehydrogenase, arsenolysis of β-aspartyl phosphate did not require addition of pyridine nucleotide. L-β-Aspartic acid semialdehyde is reduced by a diphospho-pyridine nucleotide-dependent enzyme, homoserine dehydrogenase (which is also somewhat active with triphosphopyridine nucleotide), to L-homoserine (617, 620):

$$\begin{array}{c} \overset{O}{\underset{\parallel}{C}}-H \\ \overset{|}{CH_2} \\ \overset{|}{CHNH_2} \\ \overset{|}{COOH} \end{array} + \text{DPNH} + \text{H}^+ \rightleftharpoons \begin{array}{c} CH_2OH \\ \overset{|}{CH_2} \\ \overset{|}{CHNH_2} \\ \overset{|}{COOH} \end{array} + \text{DPN}^+$$

Aspartic acid   Homoserine
β-semialdehyde

Cohen and associates (613) observed some increase in aspartic acid β-semialdehyde formation upon addition of coenzyme A to extracts of *E. coli*; although this suggests that β-aspartyl-coenzyme A might be an intermediate in the initial reaction, additional studies on this point have apparently not been reported, and further work with mutants of *E. coli* support the reaction sequence as described above (621). Both β-aspartyl phosphate (see p. 42) and aspartic acid β-semialdehyde are relatively unstable and have thus far been prepared only in solution. Black and Wright prepared aspartic acid β-semialdehyde by passing ozone through a solution of allylglycine hydrochloride at 0°. Neuberger and Tait (622) have prepared crystalline N-carbobenzyloxy-L-aspartic acid β-semi-aldehyde, which can readily be converted to free L-aspartic acid β-semialdehyde by hydrogenolysis in dilute acid.

Early studies on the conversion of homoserine to threonine in *E. coli* demonstrated that adenosine triphosphate and pyridoxal phosphate were required; however, although both cofactors were needed for threonine formation, only adenosine triphosphate was required for the disappearance of homoserine, suggesting an intermediate between homoserine and threonine. Watanabe and collaborators showed that (at least) two separate enzyme fractions are needed for the conversion of homoserine to threonine in yeast (623). One of these is homoserine kinase, which catalyzes the phosphorylation of homoserine according to the following reaction:

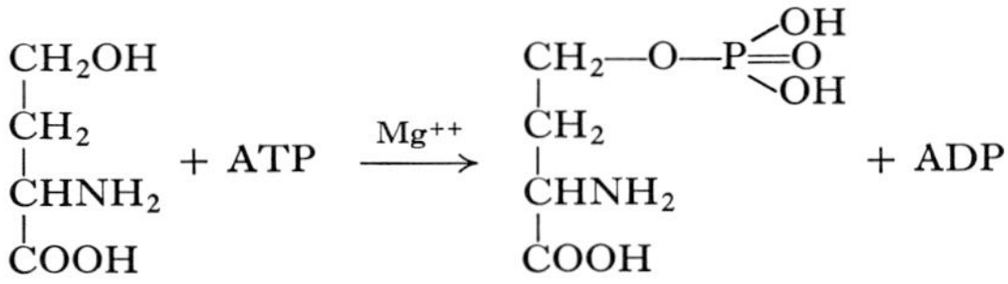

$$
\begin{array}{ccc}
\begin{array}{l}
\text{CH}_2\text{OH} \\
|\\
\text{CH}_2 \\
|\\
\text{CHNH}_2 \\
|\\
\text{COOH}
\end{array}
+ \text{ATP}
\xrightarrow{\text{Mg}^{++}}
&
\begin{array}{l}
\text{CH}_2\!-\!\text{O}\!-\!\text{P}{\overset{\diagup\text{OH}}{\underset{\diagdown\text{OH}}{=\!\text{O}}}} \\
|\\
\text{CH}_2 \\
|\\
\text{CHNH}_2 \\
|\\
\text{COOH}
\end{array}
& + \text{ADP}
\end{array}
$$

Homoserine   *O*-Phosphohomoserine

The final step in the biosynthesis of threonine is catalyzed by the enzyme threonine synthetase, which has been purified from yeast and from *Neurospora*, and shown to require pyridoxal phosphate (623, 624). Flavin and colleagues (624, 625), who purified threonine synthetase about 500-fold from *N. crassa*, carried out some elegant studies on the reaction mechanism. When *O*-phosphohomoserine was incubated with the enzyme in H_2O^{18}, 1 atom of oxygen was incorporated into threonine but none into phosphate, indicating that phosphate is eliminated non-hydrolytically with cleavage at the C—O bond of the phosphate ester group. When the reaction was carried out in 100% D_2O, the threonine formed contained 2 atoms of deuterium, one of which was in the α-position. Flavin and Slaughter (624) suggested a mechanism for the threonine synthetase reaction based on an extension of the model γ-elimination reaction of homoserine (see p. 403). According to this proposal, a β-hydrogen atom of *O*-phosphohomoserine adjacent to a conjugated series of double bonds is labilized and eliminated as a proton along with the phosphate group leading to formation of the vinyl glycine derivative. A proton from the solvent adds to the γ-position and addition of water to the α,β-double bond introduces a second solvent hydrogen atom in the α-position and a solvent oxygen atom in the β-hydroxyl position (see Scheme 6).

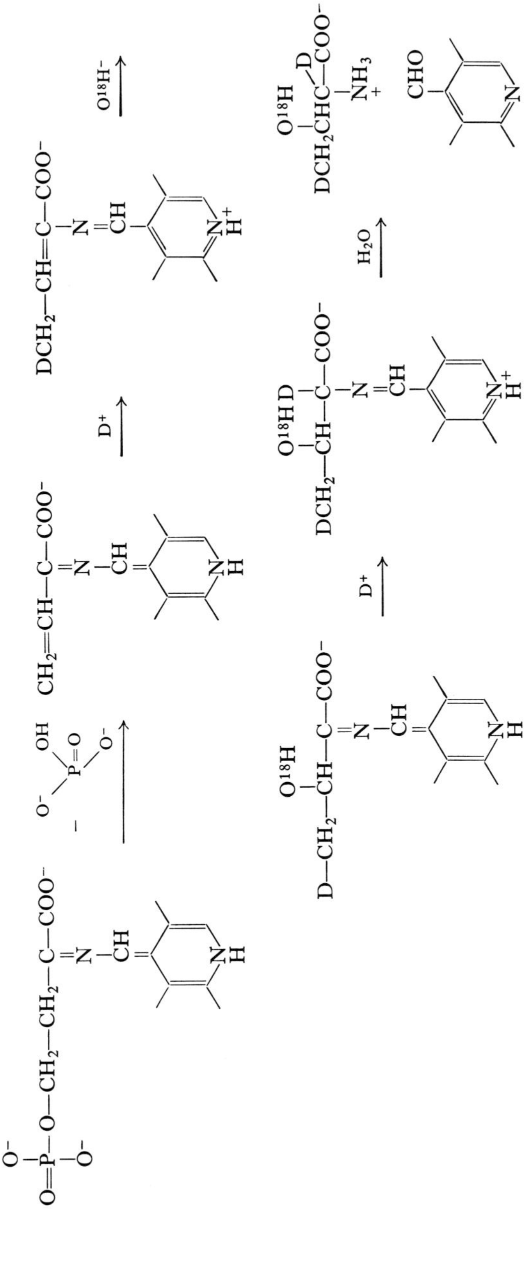

SCHEME 6. Mechanism of reaction catalyzed by threonine synthetase (624).

Homoserine occurs free in a number of plants (see p. 94), and in certain plants (e.g., pea seedlings) it is formed in relatively large quantities. Sasaoka (626) observed formation of radioactive homoserine when pea seedlings were incubated in a medium containing C^{14}-aspartic acid; however, as would be expected, radioactivity was also found in glutamate and other amino acids. The findings that pea seedlings contain considerable quantities of homoserine dehydrogenase and aspartic acid β-semialdehyde dehydrogenase are consistent with the existence of the same pathway that has been found in microorganisms. Studies on the distribution of C^{14} in glutamate, aspartate, and threonine after administration to plants of acetate-1-C^{14} and acetate-2-C^{14} also indicate conversion of aspartate to threonine (627).

Although there is no evidence that homoserine is a threonine precursor in mammalian metabolism, it is interesting to note that the formation of its α-keto acid analog, α-keto-γ-hydroxybutyric acid, has been observed from pyruvate and formaldehyde in preparations of beef liver (628). Transamination of this α-keto acid has been observed (629).

$$
\begin{array}{l}
\text{CH}_3 \\
| \\
\text{C}=\text{O} \quad + \quad \text{H—C}=\text{O} \\
| \qquad\qquad\quad \text{H} \\
\text{COOH}
\end{array}
\longrightarrow
\begin{array}{l}
\text{CH}_2\text{OH} \\
| \\
\text{CH}_2 \\
| \\
\text{C}=\text{O} \\
| \\
\text{COOH}
\end{array}
\longrightarrow
\begin{array}{l}
\text{CH}_2\text{OH} \\
| \\
\text{CH}_2 \\
| \\
\text{CHNH}_2 \\
| \\
\text{COOH}
\end{array}
$$

There are several important interrelationships between the pathway from aspartate to threonine described above and those leading to the biosynthesis of certain other amino acids. Thus, aspartic acid β-semialdehyde is an intermediate in lysine formation via the diaminopimelate pathway (see p. 932), homoserine is an intermediate in methionine formation (see p. 761), and threonine contributes to the biosynthesis of isoleucine (see p. 736). The early observation that threonine could partially replace the growth requirement for aspartate of several bacteria (630) is explained by the aspartate-threonine pathway described above.

Stadtman and colleagues (631) have made the highly interesting discovery that extracts of *E. coli* contain at least two different and separable aspartokinases. One enzyme is specifically and noncompetitively inhibited by L-lysine and is not formed when the organism is grown on a medium containing lysine. Another aspartokinase is specifically and competitively inhibited by L-threonine; there is also evidence for the existence of a third aspartokinase which is specifically inhibited by L-homoserine. It is evident that adequate metabolic control of the formation of a common intermediate such as aspartic acid β-semialdehyde by simple repression or feedback inhibition would not be possible. Thus, the production of an excess of one amino acid product could conceivably result in dangerously reduced formation of the intermediate that is common to the biosynthesis of other essential amino acids. The existence of multiple enzymes catalyzing the formation of common precursors each of which is subject only to control by a single end product is therefore a plausible biological control mechanism. It is of interest in this connection that yeast apparently contains only a single aspartokinase which is sensitive to threonine and homoserine inhibition and repression (632); in yeast, aspartyl phosphate is not a precursor of lysine (see p. 934). It has frequently been observed that tissues and organisms contain more than one enzyme capable of catalyzing the same reaction. The studies on the aspartokinases suggest that at least certain "isozymes" may function as part of physiological control systems.

Evidence of "multivalent repression" has come from studies on *Salmonella typhimurium* and *E. coli*; in these studies, both threonine and isoleucine were required in excess to repress the synthesis of "threonine aspartokinase" (determined in the presence of lysine), homoserine dehydrogenase, and threonine synthetase (633). Synthesis of homoserine dehydrogenase of *Micrococcus glutamicus* is repressed by methionine; the aspartokinase of this organism is not repressed by methionine, but is inhibited by threonine (634). Synthesis of the homoserine dehydrogenase of yeast is repressed by methionine (and ethionine) (635). Threonine has been reported to inhibit formation of O-phosphohomoserine in *E. coli* (636). The studies summarized above indicate that several types of control phenomena exist, and that there are significant species differences.

Degradation

The degradative metabolism of threonine has been studied in animals and microorganisms. In the rat, these reactions are irreversible; threonine does not participate in the general exchange of amino acid nitrogen. Thus, administration of N^{15}-amino acids to rats does not result in appreciable labeling of threonine (637, 638). Threonine is converted to α-ketobutyrate, which is used for isoleucine biosynthesis in microorganisms (see p. 737).

Threonine Dehydrases. The anaerobic deamination of threonine catalyzed by threonine dehydrase is analogous to the serine dehydrase reaction (see p. 668), and the over-all reaction can be represented as follows:

$$\text{Threonine} \rightarrow \alpha\text{-ketobutyrate} + \text{ammonia}$$

As stated above (see p. 669), preparations have been obtained from various sources that catalyze this reaction. The conversion of DL-threonine by rat liver preparations to L-α-aminobutyric acid (639) is probably due to a reaction of this type followed by L-specific transamination of the α-ketobutyric acid formed to L-α-aminobutyric acid. Deamination of D-threonine might give a similar result. A purified threonine dehydrase, shown to be pyridoxal phosphate-dependent, was obtained from sheep liver by Nishimura and Greenberg (640). The enzyme deaminated L-threonine, L-allothreonine, and L-serine, and it is of interest that L-serine strongly inhibited the reaction with L-threonine; the D-isomers of these amino acids were not substrates. Treatment of the enzyme with hydroxylamine and L-serine led to dissociation of the prosthetic group and reactivation of the resolved enzyme was achieved by incubation with pyridoxal phosphate. A number of these findings were confirmed by Davis and Metzler (641), who also studied a partially purified sheep liver L-threonine dehydrase. These workers carried out a study of the pH dependence of the Michaelis constant and maximal velocity; their findings suggest that the uncharged amino group of the substrate anion combines with the enzyme and that the enzyme undergoes reversible inactivation at about a pH value of 9.1. Goldstein et al. (642), who have summarized data in the literature on the threonine and serine dehydrase activities of preparations from sheep liver, rat liver, and microorganisms, found that assay in the presence of relatively high concentrations of L-threonine and pyridoxal phosphate gave activity values that were much greater than those previously reported. They found that high protein intake or cortisol administration for 2 days led to a significant increase in threonine dehydrase activity of male rats. Sayre et al. (643) previously reported that the liver threonine dehydrase activity of rats was increased to about four times the normal value after intraperitoneal injection of threonine; similar results were obtained in perfusion experiments. Pitot and Peraino (644) found that feeding rats a 90% casein diet for 7 days resulted in a large increase in hepatic threonine dehydrase and that this response was markedly accelerated by tube-feeding protein-depleted animals an enzymatic casein hydrolyzate at 6-hour intervals. The increase in enzymatic activity varied between

50- and 100-fold as compared to the controls. Such responses were almost completely inhibited when puromycin was injected intraperitoneally, and no enzyme induction was observed when glucose was included in the intubation mixture. Similar results were obtained with ornithine transaminase. These studies indicate that certain hepatic enzymes can be induced by dietary amino acids and that such induction can be prevented by administration of glucose or by inhibiting protein synthesis. The analogy with control mechanisms in bacteria is evident, but full understanding of the need for a control mechanism for threonine metabolism in animals will require further study.

Threonine dehydrase of *E. coli* (and presumably certain other microorganisms) has the biosynthetic function of producing α-ketobutyric acid for isoleucine formation; certain mutants of *E. coli* that respond to either isoleucine or α-ketobutyrate were found to lack threonine dehydrase activity (see p. 738). An adaptive enzyme is formed by *E. coli* that catalyzes the deamination of both L-threonine and L-serine (584). A constitutive L-threonine dehydrase from *Streptomyces rimosus* was reported to be activated by adenosine 5'-phosphate (645); the nature of this activation, which has also been observed with certain serine dehydrases (see p. 669), is not yet clear. However, the activation of *Clostridium tetanomorphum* L-threonine dehydrase by very low concentrations of adenosine diphosphate is associated with a marked decrease in the K_m value for substrate. The increased activity produces more substrate for formation of propionyl phosphate, which can react with adenosine diphosphate to form adenosine triphosphate; thus, the deaminase seems to be part of a regulatory mechanism that responds to adenosine diphosphate (646, 646a).

Hydroxyamino Acid Aldolases. Another pathway of threonine degradation was discovered by Braunstein and Vilenkina, who observed formation of glycine and acetaldehyde from threonine in preparations of the livers and kidneys of several species (647):

$$\underset{\text{Threonine}}{\underset{\displaystyle \quad\ \ \ \underset{\text{HO}}{|}\ \ \underset{\text{NH}_2}{|}}{\text{CH}_3\text{CHCHCOOH}}} \longrightarrow \underset{\text{Acetaldehyde}}{\text{CH}_3\text{CHO}} + \underset{\text{Glycine}}{\underset{\displaystyle \underset{\text{NH}_2}{|}}{\text{CH}_2\text{COOH}}}$$

It is curious that allothreonine is a more active substrate for this system than is threonine (466, 647, 648). Apparently the enzymatic reaction is reversible to a slight extent, although the configuration of the product formed in the reverse reaction has not been established (649). The enzyme that catalyzes cleavage of threonine to glycine and acetaldehyde has been designated "glycinogenase" (647) and "hydroxyamino acid aldolase" (650). The mechanism of the threonine cleavage reaction has been considered by Snell and collaborators, who demonstrated non-enzymatic reversible cleavage of threonine in the presence of pyridoxal and metal salts (651).

Karasek and Greenberg (652) purified hydroxyamino acid aldolase from sheep liver and found that their most active preparation as well as the crude homogenate cleaved allothreonine more rapidly than threonine. On the other hand, they concluded that two distinct enzymes were present in sheep liver, since the ratios of the two activities varied during fractionation and different values were obtained with different concentrations of enzyme. Definite activation by pyridoxal phosphate was observed, and the reaction was demonstrated to be reversible. Whether or not the two activities are due to different proteins, it is difficult at this time to explain the relatively high allothreonine aldolase activity present in mammalian liver.

The enzymatic cleavage of the L-isomers of β-phenylserine by a purified fraction of rat liver has been described (653). The *erythro*-isomer was cleaved nine times more rapidly than the *threo*-isomer of β-phenylserine and at a rate seven times that observed for cleavage of allothreonine. Benzaldehyde and glycine were shown to be the products of the enzymatic cleavage of *erythro*-β-phenyl-L-serine. Another phenylserine aldolase, which is present in the liver and kidney of several mammalian species, was reported to be specific for the L-*threo*-isomer (654), and it was suggested that different β-phenylserine aldolases exist for the L-*threo*- and L-*erythro*- forms of this amino acid. It is of interest that Knoop in 1914 reported excretion of extra hippuric acid in the urine after feeding β-phenylserine to dogs; on the basis of this observation, he postulated cleavage of β-phenylserine to glycine and benzoic acid (655).

In experiments with N^{15}- and C^{14}-methyl-labeled threonine, it was shown in the rat that about one fifth to one third of dietary threonine is cleaved to glycine and acetate (638); the latter compound presumably arose by oxidation of acetaldehyde. In agreement with earlier findings, it was observed in the same study that only a small amount of N^{15} was found in threonine after administration of N^{15}-leucine. However, the fact that some leucine nitrogen found its way into threonine suggests that there is a small amount of synthesis or a partial reversal of the degradative reactions; on the other hand, it is possible that the activity of the intestinal flora was responsible for the observed incorporation.

Conversion of Threonine to Aminoacetone. Elliott (656) found that when *Staphylococcus aureus* was incubated aerobically in the presence of either glycine and glucose or threonine, aminoacetone accumulated in the medium. Neuberger and Tait (657) observed aminoacetone accumulation in cultures of *Rhodopseudomonas spheroides* incubated aerobically in the dark or anaerobically in the light in a medium containing α-ketoglutarate, fumarate, and glycine. Extracts of the organism were shown to contain an L-threonine dehydrogenase capable of converting threonine to amino-acetone according to the following reaction:

$$\text{L-Threonine} + \text{DPN}^+ \rightarrow \text{aminoacetone} + \text{DPNH} + \text{H}^+ + \text{CO}_2$$

Either α-amino-β-ketobutyric acid or 1-aminopropan-2-ol could be formed as intermediates in the conversion of threonine to aminoacetone. Since 1-aminopropan-2-ol is not converted to aminoacetone, intermediate formation of α-amino-β-ketobutyric acid seems more probable; further-more, this β-keto acid decarboxylates very readily nonenzymatically (half-life less than 1 minute at pH 7). Decarboxylation could occur simultaneously with dehydrogenation on the surface of the enzyme by a concerted reaction. The enzyme acts on L-threonine and D-allothreonine, but not their enantiomorphs, suggesting that a β-carbon atom possessing a D-configuration is essential for enzymatic activity; the possibility that the enzyme preparation contains a threonine epimerase must also be considered. Aminoacetone is also formed by condensation of acetyl coenzyme A and glycine, as described above (see p. 646). The subsequent metabolism of aminoacetone remains to be investigated; however, deamination would yield methylglyoxal, which might be converted by glyoxalase to D-lactic acid. The discovery of this pathway indicates, at last, a plausible explanation for the existence of glyoxalase.

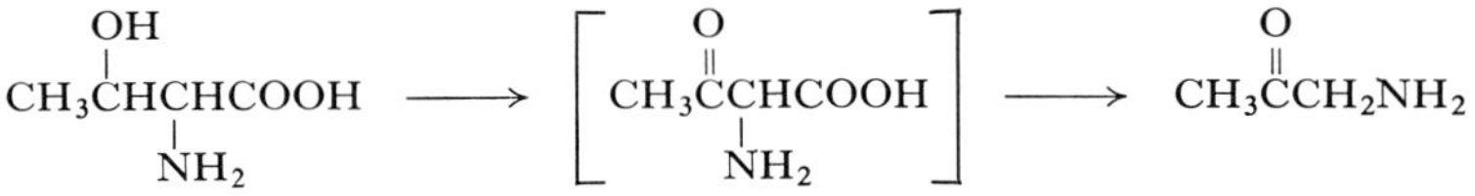

$$\underset{\text{Threonine}}{\underset{\underset{\text{NH}_2}{|}}{\overset{\overset{\text{OH}}{|}}{\text{CH}_3\text{CHCHCOOH}}}} \longrightarrow \left[\underset{\substack{\alpha\text{-Amino-}\beta\text{-ketobutyric}\\\text{acid}}}{\underset{\underset{\text{NH}_2}{|}}{\overset{\overset{\text{O}}{\parallel}}{\text{CH}_3\text{CCHCOOH}}}}\right] \longrightarrow \underset{\text{Aminoacetone}}{\overset{\overset{\text{O}}{\parallel}}{\text{CH}_3\text{CCH}_2\text{NH}_2}}$$

$$\underset{\text{Aminoacetone}}{\overset{\overset{\text{O}}{\parallel}}{\text{CH}_3\text{CCH}_2\text{NH}_2}} \longrightarrow \underset{\text{Methylglyoxal}}{\overset{\overset{\text{O}}{\parallel}}{\text{CH}_3\text{CCHO}}} \longrightarrow \underset{\text{D-Lactic acid}}{\underset{\underset{\text{OH}}{|}}{\text{CH}_3\text{CHCOOH}}}$$

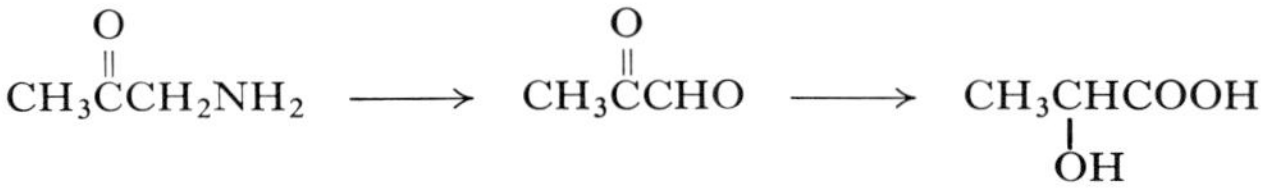

Incorporation of Threonine Carbon into Vitamin B_{12}. Evidence that threonine is the precursor of the D_g-1-amino-2-propanol moiety of vitamin B_{12} was obtained by examining the biosynthesis of the vitamin in the presence of L-threonine labeled with N^{15} (658). After growth of a strain of *Streptomyces griseus* on a medium containing the labeled threonine, the vitamin was isolated and the aminopropanol was separated.

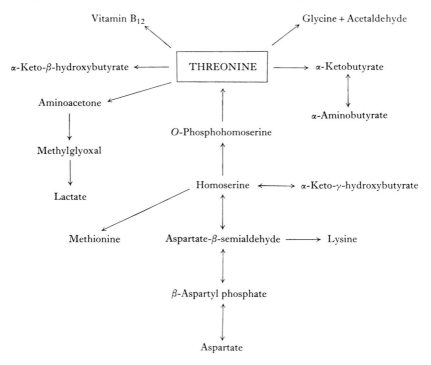

Summary scheme for the metabolism of threonine.

Threonine nitrogen was effectively incorporated into aminopropanol; indeed its utilization for this fragment was almost ten times higher than that for other portions of the vitamin. In the absence of an unforeseen specific nitrogen transfer reaction, the data provide substantial evidence for the decarboxylation of threonine to the corresponding amine. Although a large number of amino acid decarboxylation reactions have been studied (see p. 331), and it has been known for some time that the closely related amino acid serine undergoes decarboxylation (see p. 664), this seems to be the first evidence concerning decarboxylation of threonine.

H. Arginine, Ornithine, and Citrulline; Urea Synthesis

General Considerations

In 1932, Krebs and Henseleit proposed a cyclic series of reactions to explain the formation of urea (659):

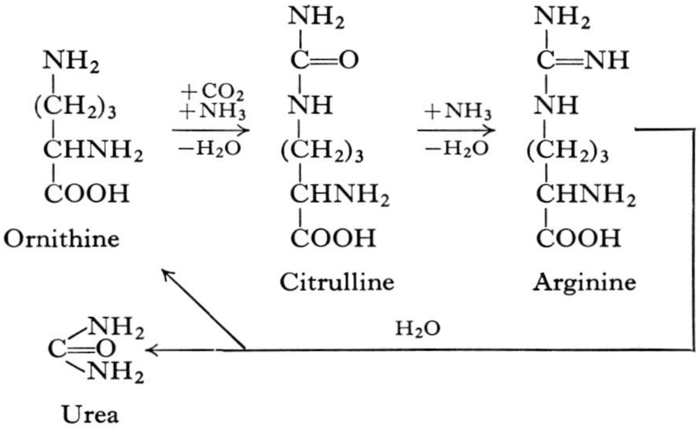

This formulation was suggested by the observation that the rate of urea formation by liver slices was greatly accelerated by the addition of ornithine. Since addition of 1 mole of ornithine led to production of approximately thirty times as much urea, it was postulated that an intermediate was formed from ornithine, ammonia, and carbon dioxide which would yield urea and also regenerate ornithine. It was subsequently found that citrulline (discovered only 2 years earlier in watermelon by Wada; see p. 98) also has a catalytic effect on urea synthesis.

Studies with isotopically labeled compounds on intact animals (660–662) confirmed the general mechanism proposed by Krebs and Henseleit. There is now evidence for all or most of the reactions of this cycle in *Neurospora, Escherichia coli, Penicillium,* several lactic acid bacteria (612, 663–667), invertebrates (668), and plants (669, 670), as well as vertebrates.

Arginase, which has been known since 1904 (671), occurs in many animal tissues, in particular liver and mammary tissue (672–678). Arginase is activated by certain divalent metal ions (Co^{++}, Ni^{++}, Fe^{++},

Mn^{++}) (677, 679). The enzyme also exhibits some activity toward octopine (680), α-N-benzoylarginine (681), L-α-uramido-δ-guanidinovaleric acid (682), agmatine (683), and canavanine (684), but does not attack α-keto-δ-guanidinovaleric acid (685), ϵ-guanidinocaproic acid (686), δ-N-methylarginine (687), γ-guanidinobutyric acid (687), and arginine phosphate (688). The hydrolysis of canavanine yields canaline and urea (see p. 70). Several highly purified preparations of arginase have been obtained (689–692) including a crystalline preparation of relatively low activity (689). Although the enzymatic hydrolysis of arginine to urea and ornithine catalyzed by arginase was observed before the work of Krebs and Henseleit, understanding of the other reactions of the urea cycle was achieved much later and even at this time several points remain unsettled.

Formation of Arginine

The formation of arginine from citrulline was demonstrated in liver and kidney preparations (693, 694), and this conversion was found to be stimulated by either aspartate or glutamate. Studies by Ratner and her colleagues (695–700) showed that arginine formation from citrulline specifically requires aspartate as well as adenosine triphosphate, and that the reaction occurs in two steps involving the intermediate formation of a compound identified as argininosuccinic acid (700–702). Enzymatic cleavage of the latter compound gives arginine and fumaric acid. The sequence of events is as follows:

$$
\begin{array}{ccc}
\underset{\text{Citrulline}}{
\begin{array}{l}
\text{NH} \\
\|\\
\text{C—OH} \\
|\\
\text{NH} \\
|\\
(\text{CH}_2)_3 \\
|\\
\text{CHNH}_2 \\
|\\
\text{COOH}
\end{array}}
+
\underset{\text{Aspartic acid}}{
\begin{array}{l}
\text{COOH} \\
|\\
\text{H}_2\text{N—CH} \\
|\\
\text{CH}_2 \\
|\\
\text{COOH}
\end{array}}
+ \text{ATP} \longrightarrow
\underset{\text{Argininosuccinic acid}}{
\begin{array}{l}
\text{NH}\qquad\ \text{COOH} \\
\|\qquad\qquad |\\
\text{C—NH—CH} \\
|\qquad\qquad\ |\\
\text{NH}\qquad\ \ \text{CH}_2 \\
|\qquad\qquad\ |\\
(\text{CH}_2)_3\ \ \ \text{COOH} \\
|\\
\text{CHNH}_2 \\
|\\
\text{COOH}
\end{array}}
+ \text{AMP} + \text{H}_4\text{P}_2\text{O}_7
\end{array}
$$

$$
\underset{\text{Argininosuccinic acid}}{
\begin{array}{l}
\text{NH}\qquad\ \text{COOH} \\
\|\qquad\qquad |\\
\text{C—NH—CH} \\
|\qquad\qquad\ |\\
\text{NH}\qquad\ \ \text{CH}_2 \\
|\qquad\qquad\ |\\
(\text{CH}_2)_3\ \ \ \text{COOH} \\
|\\
\text{CHNH}_2 \\
|\\
\text{COOH}
\end{array}}
\rightleftharpoons
\underset{\text{Arginine}}{
\begin{array}{l}
\text{NH} \\
\|\\
\text{C—NH}_2 \\
|\\
\text{NH} \\
|\\
(\text{CH}_2)_3 \\
|\\
\text{CHNH}_2 \\
|\\
\text{COOH}
\end{array}}
+
\underset{\text{Fumaric acid}}{
\begin{array}{l}
\text{COOH} \\
|\\
\text{CH} \\
\|\\
\text{HC} \\
|\\
\text{COOH}
\end{array}}
$$

Davison and Elliott (701) found that incubation of extracts of pea seedlings with arginine and fumarate gave a compound which they identified as argininosuccinate; similar observations were made by Walker (702) with algal cells. The cleavage of argininosuccinate is readily reversible and this reaction has been utilized for the large-scale biosynthetic preparation of argininosuccinate. Argininosuccinic acid can undergo spontaneous reversible conversion to a product which is enzymatically inactive (697). When argininosuccinic acid is boiled with mineral acid, a mixture of two cyclic compounds is formed:

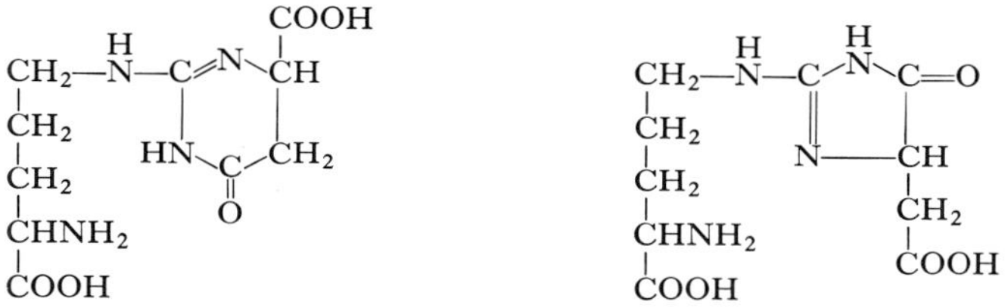

A   B

These have been separated by chromatography; one cyclic compound (probably A) is more resistant to opening by alkali and, in contrast to the other form, does not give a Jaffé reaction. Both anhydride forms yield aspartate and ornithine on prolonged alkaline hydrolysis, and after shorter treatment with weak alkali arginine, citrulline, and other products are formed (703). The enzyme that catalyzes the cleavage of argininosuccinate (argininosuccinase) occurs in a number of cells and has been purified from mammalian liver (700). The urinary excretion of argininosuccinate is associated with a human inborn error of metabolism (see p. 1042).

The condensation of citrulline and aspartate, catalyzed by argininosuccinate synthetase, was first thought to require two separate enzymes; subsequently, Petrack and Ratner (704) found that one of these was inorganic pyrophosphatase. In the absence of the latter, formation of argininosuccinate proceeds extremely slowly, but on addition of excess pyrophosphatase the rate of condensation is increased by more than 5-fold. It is possible that pyrophosphate inhibits the condensation reaction, but the position of the equilibrium of the condensation reaction does not favor synthesis. Values of 0.89 and 8.9 were found for the equilibrium constants at pH 7.0 and 7.5, respectively; the free-energy change at 37° and pH 7.5 is 2100 calories (705). From data obtained in these studies (and certain assumptions) a value of $-10,300$ calories was calculated for the free-energy change associated with the hydrolysis of adenosine 5′-triphosphate to adenosine 5′-monophosphate and inorganic pyrophosphate (at 37° and pH 7.5 in the presence of excess magnesium ions); this is somewhat greater than the corresponding value for the hydrolysis of adenosine 5′-triphosphate to adenosine 5′-diphosphate and orthophosphate (see p. 447). Rochovansky and Ratner (706) have carried out studies on the mechanism of the reaction using a purified steer liver enzyme free of adenylate kinase and inorganic pyrophosphatase. In this work, it was demonstrated that O^{18} is transferred from the ureido group of citrulline to adenosine monophosphate in the course of argininosuccinate synthesis. This interesting observation suggests the possibility that an enzyme-bound adenyl-citrulline intermediate is involved; it might be possible to demonstrate such an intermediate directly in experiments with relatively large quantities of enzyme. Argininosuccinate synthetase has been found in mammalian liver, kidney, and brain as well as in yeast, *Neurospora*, *Chlorella*, *Escherichia coli*, jackbeans, and pea seeds (699, 700).

Formation of Carbamyl Phosphate and Citrulline

The synthesis of citrulline from ornithine was first observed by Borsook and Dubnoff in liver homogenates (707). Cohen and collaborators (708–712) carried out an extensive study of this conversion and demonstrated citrulline synthesis in a soluble liver system containing adenosine triphosphate, magnesium ions, carbon dioxide, ammonia, and an α-N-acyl derivative of glutamic acid. The reaction was shown to take place in two steps, the first of which gave rise to an intermediate, possessing a carbamyl group (713, 714).

Jones and her associates made an important step forward by successfully carrying out the chemical synthesis of carbamyl phosphate from dihydrogen phosphate and cyanate (129). The synthetic material was active in citrulline formation from ornithine with enzyme preparations from bacteria and liver. It was also demonstrated that chemically synthesized carbamyl phosphate could serve as the carbamyl donor in the formation of carbamyl aspartate. Subsequent work showed that the intermediate formed in the mammalian citrulline-synthesizing system was identical with carbamyl phosphate (715). It is interesting that prior to the work of Jones *et al.* carbamyl phosphate had been considered as a possible intermediate, but it was generally thought that the compound was extremely unstable and that its chemical synthesis would be difficult if not impossible.

Several enzymes are now known that catalyze the synthesis of carbamyl phosphate. Carbamate kinase, which is found in a number of microorganisms and plants (716–720), catalyzes the following reaction:

$$NH_2COO^- + ATP \underset{}{\overset{Mg^{++}}{\rightleftharpoons}} NH_2COOPO_3^{--} + ADP$$

The formation of carbamic acid from ammonium ion and bicarbonate takes place nonenzymatically (719):

$$NH_4^+ + HCO_3^- \rightleftharpoons NH_2COO^- + H_3O^+$$

The equilibrium of the carbamate kinase reaction favors adenosine triphosphate formation. Decomposition of carbamyl phosphate at values of pH below 6 yields carbamate and phosphate, while cyanate and phosphate are formed at values of pH from 6 to 9 (720, 721). Although carbamyl phosphate synthesized by carbamate kinase is utilized for citrulline formation, this reaction is also of importance in the utilization of arginine and citrulline for adenosine triphosphate formation by microorganisms (see p. 693).

The synthesis of carbamyl phosphate catalyzed by carbamyl phosphate synthetase takes place according to the following over-all reaction:

$$NH_4^+ + HCO_3^- + 2ATP \xrightarrow[\text{N-acetylglutamate}]{Mg^{++}} NH_2COOPO_3^{--} + 2ADP + HPO_4^{--}$$

In contrast to the synthesis of carbamyl phosphate catalyzed by carbamate kinase, this reaction is not reversible and 2 moles of adenosine triphosphate are needed. In addition catalytic amounts of an N-acyl glutamate derivative are required. This enzyme has been found in the liver of many ureotelic animals, but elasmobranchs appear to have little or no activity (720). The possibility must be considered that another type of carbamyl phosphate synthesis occurs in elasmobranchs, which possess relatively high blood urea concentrations. It is of interest that the carbamyl phosphate synthetase activity of the tadpole begins to increase at the onset of metamorphosis, at which time there is also an increase in the activities of the other liver enzymes of the urea cycle (722). Thyroxine increases the activity of tadpole liver, and this is associated with a parallel increase in the amount of apparent enzyme protein as determined by an immunological procedure (723, 724). The activity of hepatic carbamyl phosphate synthetase and other enzymes of the urea cycle in the rat is influenced by dietary protein intake and starvation (725). Increased enzymatic activity followed feeding a diet high in protein. Conditions leading to degradation of protein, i.e., starvation, corticosteroid administration, led to an increase in enzymatic activity.

Carbamyl phosphate synthetase has been purified from dog liver (726) and from frog liver (727). Although highly purified, the enzyme from frog liver was not homogeneous by physical criteria; nevertheless, an estimate of the molecular weight (315,000) was achieved. The enzyme was inhibited by sulfhydryl reagents, and inhibition was reversed by 2-mercaptoethanol and prevented by preincubation of the enzyme with N-acetylglutamate. A large number of N-acyl glutamate derivatives (e.g., N-chloroacetyl, N-carbamyl-, N-formyl-) are active in the carbamyl phosphate synthetase system (728). However, the isolation and characterization of N-acetylglutamate from mammalian liver (729) suggests (but does not prove) that this derivative is the natural cofactor. The function of N-acyl glutamate, as well as the mechanism of this reaction, is still largely a mystery. O^{18}-Oxygen is not transferred from water or from the terminal phosphate group of adenosine triphosphate to N-acetylglutamate during carbamyl phosphate synthesis (730), and 1 atom of O^{18} from water is transferred to both inorganic phosphate and the phosphate group of carbamyl phosphate (731). The possibility that acetylglutamate functions to stabilize the active site of the enzyme must also be considered. Metzenberg et al. (732) have suggested that the reaction takes place in two steps as follows:

$$ATP + CO_2 \xrightarrow{\text{acyl glutamate}} ADP + \text{``active } CO_2\text{''} + \text{phosphate}$$

$$ATP + \text{``active } CO_2\text{''} + NH_3 \xrightleftharpoons{\text{acyl glutamate}} ADP + \text{carbamyl phosphate}$$

This formulation is supported in part by experimental data. Thus, when relatively large amounts of the enzyme were incubated with adenosine triphosphate, orthophosphate formation was observed in the absence of added ammonium ions; however, in these experiments (which were carried out in the presence of ornithine transcarbamylase) some citrulline was formed even when ammonia was not added. In other experiments the enzyme was incubated with P^{32}-carbamyl phosphate and adenosine diphosphate; under these conditions the disappearance of carbamyl phosphate was essentially equivalent to adenosine triphosphate formation, and these observations therefore suggest partial reversal (i.e., of the second step) of the reaction. As stated above, synthesis of carbamyl phosphate in O^{18}-water led to labeling of both carbamyl phosphate and inorganic orthophosphate. Jones and Spector (733) carried out similar experiments with O^{18}-labeled water and bicarbonate under conditions where exchange between these was very slight. These studies indicated that the oxygen atoms of water are not the immediate precursors of inorganic phosphate or carbamyl phosphate oxygen, but that orthophosphate oxygen is derived from bicarbonate. Thus, during the enzymatic synthesis of citrulline an oxygen atom is transferred from carbonate to both orthophosphate molecules formed. One of these transfers results from the cleavage of carbamyl phosphate between the carbon and oxygen atoms during carbamylation of ornithine. The other transfer must occur at an earlier stage in the synthesis of carbamyl phosphate, and it would be most interesting to learn the nature of this reaction. Evidence that an "active carbon dioxide" is formed prior to enzymatic reaction of ammonia arose from the studies of Metzenberg *et al.* (732). Jones and Spector (733) have suggested possible structures for "active carbon dioxide" involving *N*-acetylglutamate:

The data obtained with O^{18}-labeled compounds would be consistent with initial formation of carbonic-phosphoric anhydride according to the following reaction:

$$ATP + HOCO_2^- \rightarrow ADP + {}^-OCOOPO_3^{--}$$

The anhydride might then react with *N*-acetylglutamate to yield a carboxy derivative as illustrated above and orthophosphate. The second step would then involve reaction of carboxy-*N*-acetylglutamate with ammonia and adenosine triphosphate to yield adenosine diphosphate and carbamyl phosphate essentially as proposed by Metzenberg *et al.* (732). The latter reaction might involve an enzyme-bound phosphorylated carboxy-*N*-acetylglutamate intermediate. The recent observation by

Schooler *et al.* (734) that 2-acetoxyglutarate can replace N-acetylgluta-
mate as an activator of carbamyl phosphate synthetase argues against
carboxy-N-acetylglutamate intermediates of the type suggested by Jones
and Spector (733).

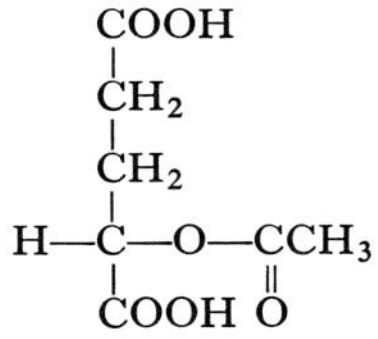

$$
\begin{array}{c}
\text{COOH} \\
| \\
\text{CH}_2 \\
| \\
\text{CH}_2 \\
| \\
\text{H—C—O—CCH}_3 \\
|\qquad \| \\
\text{COOH} \ \ \text{O}
\end{array}
$$

2-Acetoxyglutarate

In view of the latter finding, and the very low specificity of the acyl
glutamate requirement in this system, it appears more reasonable that
N-acyl glutamate protects the enzyme or perhaps affects the steric or
electronic configuration of the enzyme in such a manner as to permit
binding of substrate. If this is the case, a simpler mechanism can be
visualized. The first step in carbamyl phosphate synthesis might involve
reaction of adenosine triphosphate with carbon dioxide to yield enzyme-
bound carboxy phosphate; such an intermediate would be stabilized by
binding to the enzyme. It is possible that adenosine diphosphate is also
involved in the enzyme-bound activated carbon dioxide derivative as in
the case of glutamine synthetase (see p. 446). In a subsequent reaction,
ammonia would react with enzyme-bound carboxyl phosphate to yield
enzyme-bound carbamate and free inorganic phosphate. In the final
stage, enzyme-bound carbamate would react with adenosine triphosphate
to yield adenosine diphosphate and carbamyl phosphate. These postulated
steps may be represented as follows:

$$\text{Enzyme} + \text{ATP} + \text{CO}_2 \ \rightarrow \ \text{enzyme-}[^-\text{OCOOPO}_3{}^{--}] + \text{ADP}$$
$$\text{Enzyme-}[^-\text{OCOOPO}_3{}^{--}] + \text{NH}_3 \ \rightarrow \ \text{enzyme-}[\text{NH}_2\text{COO}^-] + \text{HPO}_4{}^{--}$$
$$\text{Enzyme-}[\text{NH}_2\text{COO}^-] + \text{ATP} \ \rightarrow \ \text{enzyme} + \text{ADP} + \text{NH}_2\text{COOPO}_3{}^{--}$$

Other mechanisms that lead to synthesis of carbamyl phosphate
include a reaction in which carbamyl phosphate is formed from the amide
nitrogen of glutamine and various carbamyl transfer reactions (735, 736);
these are considered below. It is possible that the synthesis of carbamyl
aspartate in pigeon liver does not utilize free carbamyl phosphate (737),
but further studies on this system are needed.

The formation of citrulline from ornithine takes place according to the following reaction, catalyzed by ornithine transcarbamylase (ornithine carbamyl transferase):

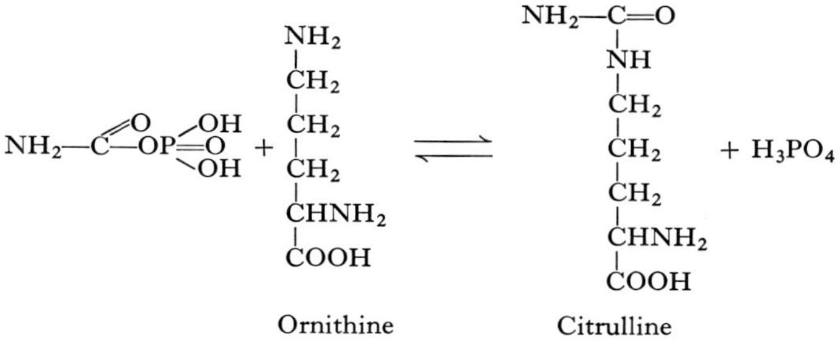

$$NH_2-\overset{\displaystyle O}{\underset{\displaystyle OH}{C}}-O\overset{\displaystyle O}{P}\overset{\displaystyle OH}{=}O \quad + \quad \begin{array}{c} NH_2 \\ | \\ CH_2 \\ | \\ CH_2 \\ | \\ CH_2 \\ | \\ CHNH_2 \\ | \\ COOH \end{array} \quad \rightleftharpoons \quad \begin{array}{c} NH_2-C=O \\ | \\ NH \\ | \\ CH_2 \\ | \\ CH_2 \\ | \\ CH_2 \\ | \\ CHNH_2 \\ | \\ COOH \end{array} \quad + \ H_3PO_4$$

Ornithine   Citrulline

This enzyme has been found in the liver of ureotelic animals, including the elasmobranch fishes (735, 738–740). The enzyme is not present in the livers of other fish, birds, and reptiles. It is present in a variety of microorganisms and plants (716–718, 735, 741–744).

Ornithine transcarbamylase has been purified from rat liver (745), bovine liver (746, 747), and *Streptococcus lactis* (744). Ornithine transcarbamylase also catalyzes the conversion of citrulline to ornithine, carbon dioxide, and ammonia in the presence of high concentrations of orthophosphate or arsenate (716–718, 741–743, 745, 748). The breakdown of citrulline in this manner (citrulline phosphorylase reaction) involves reversal of the reaction catalyzed by ornithine transcarbamylase to yield ornithine and carbamyl phosphate. In microorganisms the presence of carbamate kinase provides a mechanism for the synthesis of adenosine triphosphate. Several microorganisms possess arginine desimidase which catalyzes conversion of arginine to citrulline. Thus, the bacterial degradation of citrulline, and of arginine in those organisms possessing arginine desimidase, provides a mechanism for adenosine triphosphate formation. In earlier work, the identity of ornithine transcarbamylase and the enzyme involved in the breakdown of citrulline was not fully appreciated, and the latter reaction was given the separate designation "citrulline phosphorylase." Prior to the demonstration that carbamyl phosphate was the intermediate, both carbamyl phosphate and citrulline phosphate were considered as possible intermediates by several workers (741–743). An important finding which contributed significantly to the development of this area was the observation that bacterial preparations catalyzed the formation of O^{18}-labeled carbon dioxide in the presence of citrulline, adenosine monophosphate, and O^{18}-orthophosphate (749).

Shive and collaborators (750, 751) found that biotin-deficient lacto-bacilli exhibit significantly lower ornithine transcarbamylase and aspartate transcarbamylase activities than nondeficient cells, and that enzymatic activity is restored on addition of biotin. Subsequent studies (744) showed that ornithine transcarbamylase of *Streptococcus lactis* does not contain appreciable quantities of biotin; however, an enzymatic digest of purified ornithine transcarbamylase replaces the biotin require-ment for the synthesis of ornithine transcarbamylase in *S. lactis* (752). Similar stimulation was obtained, however, with enzymatic hydrolyzates of casein and with a mixture of synthetic peptides. Peptides containing aspartic acid and asparagine residues replace the biotin requirement for enzyme synthesis, and the data therefore suggest that biotin functions in the synthesis of a four-carbon compound, which can be synthesized by the organism in the presence of biotin or be provided by externally supplied aspartate derivatives.

Grisolia and his colleagues have made the interesting observation that several enzymes that catalyze reactions involving carbamyl phosphate can also utilize acetyl phosphate (753–755). Thus, carbamate kinase catalyzes the synthesis of acetyl phosphate from acetate and adenosine triphos-phate, and acetyl phosphate is utilized for δ-N-acetylornithine synthesis by both animal and bacterial preparations of ornithine transcarbamylase. Frog liver carbamyl phosphate synthetase is also active with acetyl phosphate and forms adenosine triphosphate and acetate from acetyl phosphate and adenosine diphosphate in the presence of acetylglutamate and magnesium ions. Aspartate transcarbamylase catalyzes N-acetyl aspartate formation from aspartate and acetyl phosphate. The carbamyl phosphate synthetases of rat and frog liver catalyze adenosine triphosphate synthesis from formyl phosphate as well as acetyl phosphate and carb-amyl phosphate; the synthesis of formyl phosphate was also demonstrated with carbamyl phosphate synthetase. In all of these studies, the rates of reaction were considerably lower with acetyl phosphate than with carbamyl phosphate. Purified horse muscle phosphatase hydrolyzes carbamyl phosphate as well as acetyl phosphate; the latter is more rapidly cleaved (756). Studies on the carbamate and acetyl kinases of *E. coli* and *S. faecalis* by Thorne and Jones (757) are in general consistent with the findings described above. Thus, two protein fractions exhibiting acetyl kinase activity were obtained from *S. faecalis*; one of these appears to be identical with carbamate kinase. Carbamate kinase of *E. coli* also exhibits acetyl kinase activity. In the course of these studies, it was found that the wild strain of *E. coli* and a mutant requiring arginine and uracil exhibited about the same level of carbamate kinase activity. Subsequent work indicates that carbamyl phosphate formation in *E. coli* takes place by a reaction involving glutamine (see p. 698). It is clearly of interest that acetyl phosphate can serve as an analog of carbamyl phosphate in several enzymatic reactions, but the significance of this phenomenon is not yet clear. It is conceivable that the reactions leading to the formation of *N*-acetylaspartic acid and δ-*N*-acetylornithine function in the physiological formation of these compounds, which are known to occur in nature. The synthesis of formyl phosphate by carbamyl phosphate synthetase would appear to be analogous to the first step postulated to occur in the synthesis of carbamyl phosphate (see p. 692). Further study of this reaction could well be of value in the elucidation of the mechanism of action of carbamyl phosphate synthetase.

As indicated above, the physiological significance of carbamyl phosphate formation by bacterial carbamate kinase differs from that catalyzed by carbamyl phosphate synthetase of animal tissues, and indeed there are important differences in the catalytic systems involved. Carbamyl phosphate synthetase of mammalian liver functions effectively with very low concentrations of ammonia, and carbamyl phosphate synthesis represents one of several enzymatic reactions that function in removal of ammonia. In contrast, relatively higher concentrations of ammonia are required for carbamyl phosphate synthesis by carbamate kinase. The more effective utilization of ammonia by the mammalian system is associated with enzymatic cleavage of 2 moles of adenosine triphosphate for each mole of ammonia utilized; this additional adenosine triphosphate requirement contributes to the irreversibility of carbamyl phosphate synthesis in ureotelic animals. *E. coli*, the mushroom, and probably animal tissues also possess a mechanism for the utilization of glutamine amide nitrogen for carbamyl phosphate synthesis (see below).

The synthesis of arginine in microorganisms and in animals is subject to repression control. In certain strains of *Escherichia coli* arginine represses the formation of enzymes leading to its biosynthesis. For example, ornithine transcarbamylase of *E. coli* is markedly increased when the organism is grown on media containing a very low concentration of arginine. End-product inhibition of arginine biosynthesis has also been observed (see p. 711). Similar phenomena occur in mammalian tissues.

Thus, arginine represses the synthesis of the enzymes that catalyze argininosuccinate synthesis and cleavage (758). During active regeneration following partial hepatectomy, ornithine transcarbamylase activity decreases but aspartate transcarbamylase activity increases (759). During regeneration, increased aspartate transcarbamylase activity would probably be required to provide additional precursors for nucleic acid synthesis. It is of interest that enzyme activity returns to normal levels upon completion of regeneration.

The capacity of the mammalian liver to synthesize citrulline and arginine is very great, but the kidney also contains the enzymatic activities required for synthesis of urea from carbon dioxide and ammonia (739). Plasma arginine probably arises mainly from the kidney, which can synthesize arginine from citrulline, but which exhibits relatively little arginase compared to the liver. The presence of arginase in the brain is indicated by direct assay and by studies in which guanido-labeled arginine was administered to rats via the cerebral circulation (760). Mammalian brain, including that of man, can catalyze the synthesis and cleavage of argininosuccinic acid (761). There seems to be no evidence for the synthesis of citrulline in the brain, and it appears unlikely that the formation of urea in this tissue offers a substantial contribution to the total urea production of the animal. It is conceivable that this pathway is needed to produce arginine that is used for transamidination with γ-aminobutyric acid to yield γ-guanidinobutyric acid, which is present in brain (see pp. 91 and 642). Brain arginase might serve to regulate the concentration of arginine available for γ-guanidinobutyrate formation. The importance of a normal pattern of metabolism of argininosuccinate is indicated by the existence of a type of human mental deficiency associated with urinary excretion of argininosuccinate. These patients also accumulate argininosuccinate in the cerebrospinal fluid (see p. 1042).

As stated above (see p. 204), arginine is required in the diet of chicks, and citrulline but not ornithine can replace dietary arginine. The nutritional observations have been elucidated by enzymatic studies which showed that ornithine transcarbamylase, the argininosuccinate synthetase and cleavage enzymes, and arginase, but not carbamyl phosphate synthetase, are present in chick kidney (761a). The liver, pancreas, spleen, and intestinal tract exhibit relatively little or none of these activities. Experiments with C^{14}-citrulline provided direct evidence for conversion of this amino acid to arginine. On the other hand, no label was found in tissue arginine after administration of labeled carbonate,

C^{12}-citrulline, and a low arginine diet, indicating that the chick cannot convert ornithine to citrulline. When C^{14}-carbonate or C^{14}-glutamate was given with unlabeled benzoate, there was no label in the excreted ornithuric acid, indicating that the chick does not synthesize ornithine, except by hydrolysis or transamidination of arginine. The absence of carbamyl phosphate synthetase in the chick indicates that this animal utilizes another mechanism for producing carbamyl phosphate for pyrimidine biosynthesis. Utilization of citrulline for this purpose is conceivable since the chick possesses ornithine transcarbamylase; however, other possibilities exist. Data suggesting that the synthesis of carbamyl aspartate by avian liver does not use free carbamyl phosphate (737) indicate the possibility of a carbamyl group transfer reaction.

Alternate Pathways of Urea Formation

From time to time various authors have proposed that alternative pathways for urea biosynthesis exist in animals (762–766). In a recent study, α-methylaspartic acid (which inhibits argininosuccinate synthetase) was injected into rats; although synthetase activity could not be detected in *in vitro* assays on liver homogenates, excretion of urea was normal (766). The published findings are provocative, but additional study of this phenomenon is needed since it was not proved that all activity *in vivo* was inhibited. A number of investigators have considered the possibility that glutamine amide nitrogen rather than free ammonia is the immediate precursor of carbamyl phosphate nitrogen. Such a possibility certainly cannot be dismissed; however, at this time there is no direct enzymatic evidence for the participation of glutamine in mammalian urea biosynthesis. On the other hand, studies with N^{15}-labeled glutamine have provided evidence that the synthesis of arginine in *Lactobacillus arabinosus* utilizes glutamine rather than ammonia. Furthermore, this organism cannot synthesize arginine in the absence of glutamine even though ammonia is supplied. Citrulline, but not ornithine, is capable of replacing glutamine (767). Levenberg (768) has discovered that extracts of the mushroom, *Agaricus bisporus*, contain an enzyme activity that utilizes L-glutamine in the presence of bicarbonate, ornithine, adenosine triphosphate, and a divalent cation (Mg^{++} or Co^{++}) as a specific source of the carbamyl nitrogen atom of citrulline. Ammonia is not active in place of glutamine and evidence was obtained for the formation of carbamyl phosphate as an intermediate in citrulline synthesis in this system. Levenberg could not demonstrate reversibility of carbamyl phosphate synthesis, so that this synthesis of carbamyl phosphate is similar to that observed in animal liver. Since carbamyl phosphate is synthesized in the mushroom at the expense of adenosine triphosphate cleavage and conversion of glutamine to glutamate, the synthesis of carbamyl phosphate is thermodynamically analogous to the reaction observed in animal tissues which requires 2 molecules of adenosine triphosphate for each molecule of carbamyl phosphate formed. It is probable, though not yet experimentally demonstrated, that carbamyl phosphate is formed in animal tissues from glutamine. The presence of aspartate transcarbamylase activity in tissues that lack carbamyl phosphate synthetase suggests that there is an alternative pathway for carbamyl phosphate formation (739). It is possible that carbamyl phosphate formation for the pyrimidine pathway and arginine formation in extrahepatic tissues utilizes glutamine amide nitrogen, and that the ammonia-utilizing carbamyl phosphate synthetase of liver (and possibly also a glutamine-requiring enzyme) produce arginine used for urea formation.

Recent studies suggest that glutamine is utilized for carbamyl group formation in the pathways of arginine and pyrimidine biosynthesis in *E. coli* (739a). Thus, it was found that extracts of a strain of this organism used glutamine rather than ammonia for citrulline formation [i.e., in a manner analogous to that observed in the mushroom (768)], and that this reaction was not catalyzed by "one-step" mutants that require both arginine and uracil. Arginine and uracil repressed the glutamine-dependent reaction in other mutants.

Other Pathways of Carbamyl Phosphate Formation

In addition to its function in the metabolism of citrulline and the pyrimidines, carbamyl phosphate is formed in the degradation of creatinine and allantoin. Thus, the breakdown of creatinine has been examined in *Eubacterium sarcosinogenum* (769); creatinine in the presence of phosphate is converted to 1 mole of sarcosine, 2 moles of ammonia, 1 mole of carbon dioxide, and less than 1 mole of inorganic polyphosphate. The available data indicate the following pathway:

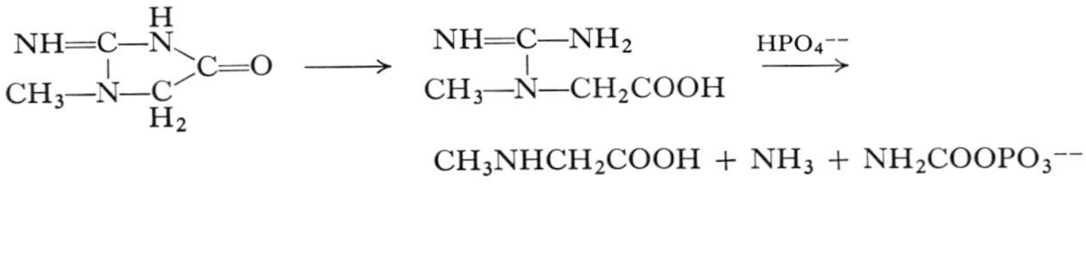

$$NH{=}C{-}N(H){<}{>}C{=}O \quad\text{with}\quad CH_3{-}N{-}C(H_2) \longrightarrow NH{=}C{-}NH_2,\ CH_3{-}N{-}CH_2COOH \xrightarrow{HPO_4^{--}}$$

$$CH_3NHCH_2COOH + NH_3 + NH_2COOPO_3^{--}$$

The degradation of creatinine in this organism is analogous to that of arginine in certain microorganisms; carbamyl phosphate formation is linked to adenosine triphosphate formation and the organism is thus able to utilize creatinine as a source of energy.

The degradation of allantoin by *Streptococcus allantoicus* is thought to lead to glyoxylurea, which can be converted directly to urea and glyoxylate or be oxidized to carbamyl oxamate. The latter compound undergoes phosphorolysis to carbamyl phosphate and oxamic acid (770, 770a), as shown in Scheme 7.

Extracts of *Streptococcus allantoicus* catalyze the phosphorolytic cleavage of urea by an indirect pathway involving glyoxylate; diphosphopyridine nucleotide, magnesium ions, and phosphate (or arsenate) are required (771):

$$H_2NCONH_2 + HCOCOOH \rightleftharpoons H_2NCONHCHOHCOOH$$

$$H_2NCONHCHOHCOOH \xrightleftharpoons{DPN} H_2NCONHCOCOOH$$

$$H_2NCONHCOCOOH \xrightleftharpoons{H_3PO_4} H_2NCOOPO_3H_2 + H_2NCOCOOH$$

It is of interest that *Candida flareri* utilizes urea as the sole nitrogen source, but this organism does not contain urease. Preliminary studies have led to the suggestion that urea combines with a two-carbon fragment to yield hydantoic acid, which is cleaved to carbamyl phosphate and glycine (772).

As discussed elsewhere (see p. 603), carbamyl-β-alanine is an intermediate in the degradation of pyrimidines, and evidence has been presented for the enzymatic carbamylation of β-alanine by carbamyl phosphate (41).

Arginine Desimidase

The degradation of arginine by a pathway not involving arginase is catalyzed by several microorganisms. The first step in the degradation of arginine is catalyzed by arginine desimidase (670, 773–776):

$$\text{Arginine} + H_2O \rightarrow \text{citrulline} + NH_3$$

Arginine desimidase has been separated from the enzyme that catalyzes the degradation of citrulline in these organisms (ornithine transcarbamylase).

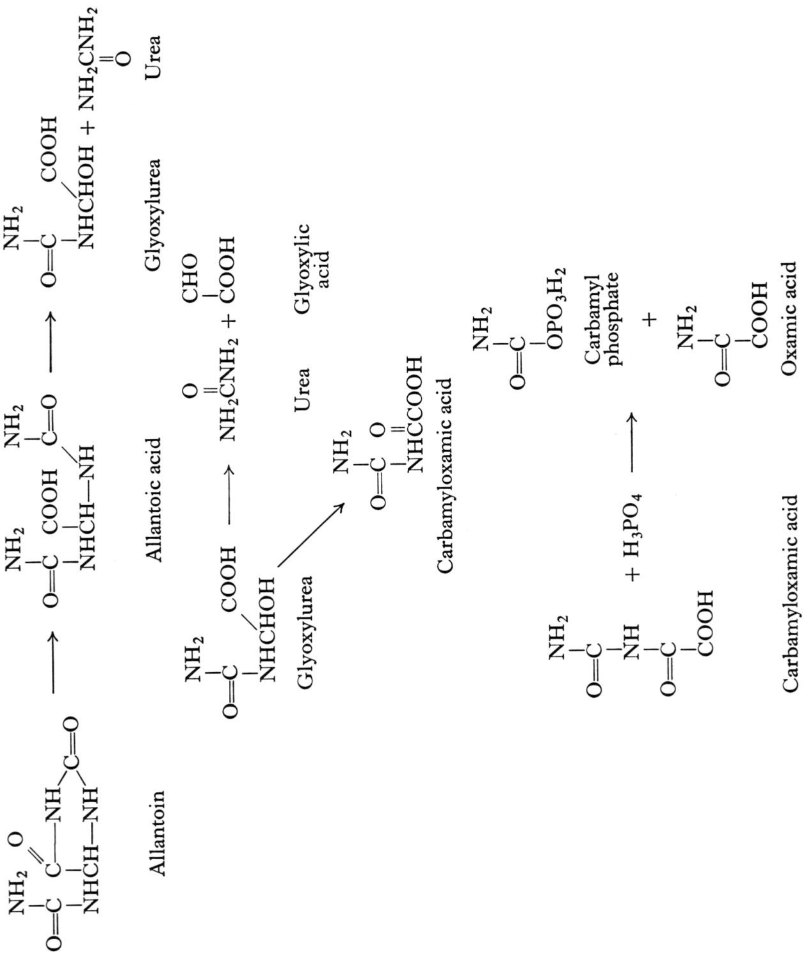

$$\begin{array}{c}
\text{NH}_2 \quad \text{O} \\
\text{O=C} \quad \text{C—NH—C=O} \\
\quad \text{NHCH—NH}
\end{array}$$

Allantoin

$$\longrightarrow$$

$$\begin{array}{c}
\text{NH}_2 \qquad \text{NH}_2 \\
\text{O=C COOH C=O} \\
\quad \text{NHCH—NH}
\end{array}$$

Allantoic acid

$$\longrightarrow$$

$$\begin{array}{c}
\text{NH}_2 \\
\text{O=C} \quad \text{COOH} \\
\quad \text{NHCHOH} + \text{NH}_2\text{CNH}_2 \text{ (=O)}
\end{array}$$

Glyoxylurea Urea

$$\begin{array}{c}
\text{NH}_2 \\
\text{O=C} \quad \text{COOH} \\
\quad \text{NHCHOH}
\end{array}$$

Glyoxylurea

$$\longrightarrow$$

$$\begin{array}{c}
\text{O} \\
\text{NH}_2\text{CNH}_2 + \\
\text{CHO—COOH}
\end{array}$$

Urea Glyoxylic acid

$$\begin{array}{c}
\text{NH}_2 \quad \text{O} \\
\text{O=C} \\
\quad \text{NHCCOOH}
\end{array}$$

Carbamyloxamic acid

$$\begin{array}{c}
\text{NH}_2 \\
\text{O=C—NH—C—COOH} \\
\qquad \text{O=C}
\end{array}$$

Carbamyloxamic acid

$$+ \text{H}_3\text{PO}_4 \longrightarrow$$

$$\begin{array}{c}
\text{NH}_2 \\
\text{O=C} \quad \text{OPO}_3\text{H}_2
\end{array}$$

Carbamyl phosphate

$$+$$

$$\begin{array}{c}
\text{NH}_2 \\
\text{O=C} \quad \text{COOH}
\end{array}$$

Oxamic acid

SCHEME 7. The degradation of allantoin.

There is no evidence for the occurrence of the arginine desimidase reaction in mammalian tissues. Stetten and Bloom (777) fed rats L-arginine labeled with N^{15} and C^{14} in the amidine moiety. The $N^{15}:C^{14}$ ratio was higher in the isolated tissue arginine than in the arginine fed. The isotope ratio in the urinary urea rose with time; these data are consistent with conversion of urea to ammonia and carbon dioxide by urease of the gastrointestinal bacteria. Ammonia formed in this process would be reutilized for urea and arginine synthesis, while much of the carbon dioxide formed would be lost. These data are in accord with other studies (see p. 209) which indicate utilization of urea in the mammal by the action of bacterial urease; they do not exclude the desimidation of arginine since a small change in the isotope ratio in the opposite direction could have been obscured by loss of carbon dioxide.

Canavanine

Canavanine is reductively cleaved by an enzyme present in *Streptococcus faecalis* and *S. equinus* to yield guanidine and homoserine (778). Preparations of *S. faecalis* catalyze the hydrolytic desimidation of canavanine to *O*-ureidohomoserine and ammonia (779); this activity is probably identical with arginine desimidase (see above). Another hydrolytic reaction involving canavanine catalyzed by bacterial preparations yields homoserine and hydroxyguanidine (780).

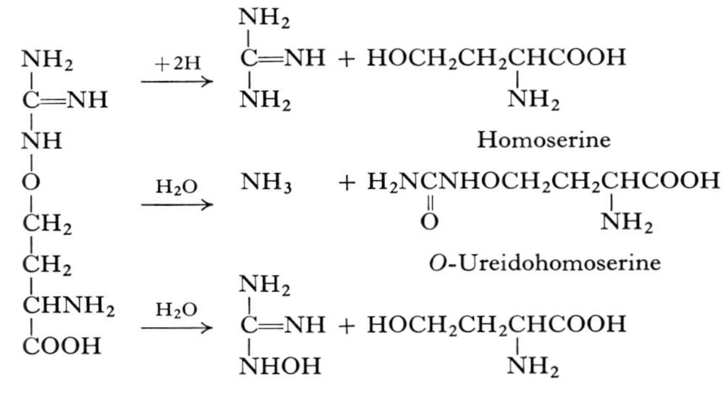

The formation of hydroxyguanidine is also catalyzed by trans-amidinases (see p. 642); thus, incubation of transamidinase with arginine and hydroxylamine yields ornithine and hydroxyguanidine. The finding that injection of hydroxyguanidine sulfate into rats was followed by urinary excretion of guanidine led to the subsequent *in vitro* demonstration of hydroxyguanidine reductase activity with a guinea pig liver particulate preparation. The enzyme can utilize riboflavin phosphate as the electron donor. Hydroxyguanidine reductase activity has also been found in mammalian kidney, pigeon liver, and in microorganisms (781).

Canavanosuccinic acid, the canavanine analog of argininosuccinic acid, has been found in *Chlorella* (702). Canavanosuccinic acid is formed by reactions analogous to those leading to argininosuccinic acid; mammalian systems can synthesize as well as cleave canavanosuccinic acid (782, 783). Both canavanine and canaline are substrates for kidney transamidination; thus, canavanine can replace arginine in the formation of guanidinoacetic acid (see p. 641).

Other Reactions of Arginine and Ornithine

Streptomyces griseus, which can utilize L-arginine (and γ-guanidinobutyric acid) as the sole source of carbon and nitrogen, converts arginine by oxidative decarboxylation to γ-guanidinobutyramide (see p. 324). The latter compound is enzymatically hydrolyzed to γ-guanidinobutyric acid. There is also evidence for the conversion by transamidination of γ-guanidinobutyric acid to γ-aminobutyric acid (see p. 642). Arginine is oxidatively deaminated to the corresponding α-keto acid by an L-amino acid oxidase of turkey liver which is relatively specific for the basic L-amino acids (see p. 310). Enzymatic synthesis of arginine phosphate (783a) was shown by Lohmann with extracts of crab muscle (784); arginine phosphokinase, which exhibits properties similar to those of creatine phosphokinase (adenosine triphosphate-creatine transphosphorylase), has been purified from tail muscle of sea crayfish (784a).

The decarboxylation of ornithine to putrescine (see p. 332) is catalyzed by bacterial preparations, and no evidence has yet been obtained for the occurrence of this reaction in animal tissues. It is of interest that potassium-deficient barley plants accumulate putrescine as well as agmatine, the decarboxylation product of arginine. Both agmatine and putrescine have been found in various plants; the concentration of putrescine in barley seedlings was increased by feeding agmatine, ornithine, or arginine. Accumulation of agmatine was increased by feeding arginine. The observations, though indirect, support the existence of the corresponding amino acid decarboxylases in higher plants. The function of potassium ions in apparently inhibiting amine formation is not yet clear (785). The participation of putrescine in the biosynthesis of spermine and spermidine is considered elsewhere (see p. 787). Putrescine can be converted to γ-aminobutyric acid by a pathway involving oxidative deamination to γ-aminobutyraldehyde. The latter compound is oxidized by a diphosphopyridine nucleotide-dependent enzyme which was isolated from a strain of *Pseudomonas* that can utilize either pyrrolidine or putrescine for growth (786) (see, also, transamination of putrescine, p. 358):

$$
\begin{array}{ccc}
CH_2NH_2 & CHO & COOH \\
| & | & | \\
CH_2 & CH_2 & CH_2 \\
| \quad\longrightarrow & | \quad\longrightarrow & | \\
CH_2 & CH_2 & CH_2 \\
| & | & | \\
CH_2NH_2 & CH_2NH_2 & CH_2NH_2 \\
\text{Putrescine} & \text{γ-Aminobutyr-} & \text{γ-Aminobutyric} \\
& \text{aldehyde} & \text{acid}
\end{array}
$$

When arginine, ornithine, and putrescine are administered to *Atropa* and *Datura* plants, there is an increase in the formation of tropan alkaloids, and administration of C^{14}-ornithine to *Datura stramonium* gave labeled hyoscyamine (787). When ornithine-2-C^{14} was given, the label was shown to be present in only one of the bridgehead carbon atoms (e.g., carbon atom 1) of the tropine moiety of hyoscyamine (788). Studies on the biosynthesis of hyoscyamine from acetate-1-C^{14} also indicated asymmetric incorporation of ornithine (789). The available data suggest that ornithine is the precursor of the pyrrolidine rings of other alkaloids of this type, e.g., cocaine, hygrine.

Although ornithine-2-C^{14} was not incorporated into stachydrine (790, 791; see p. 106) in alfalfa plants (792), it was later found that these plants do not accumulate stachydrine until mature, and evidence that both proline-1-C^{14} and ornithine-2-C^{14} are incorporated into stachydrine was subsequently obtained (793). There is evidence that the methyl group of methionine is the precursor of the methyl groups of stachydrine (794). Hygric acid, labeled in the carboxyl group, is also utilized (795); these observations support the biosynthetic pathway shown on p. 704.

Ornithine (796, 797), putrescine (798), and glutamate (799) are incorporated into nicotine by plants capable of synthesizing this alkaloid. Studies with ornithine-2-C^{14} and acetate-1-C^{14} (800) led to labeling of both carbon atoms 2 and 5 of the pyrrolidine moiety of nicotine; the data therefore indicate utilization of a symmetrical intermediate for the

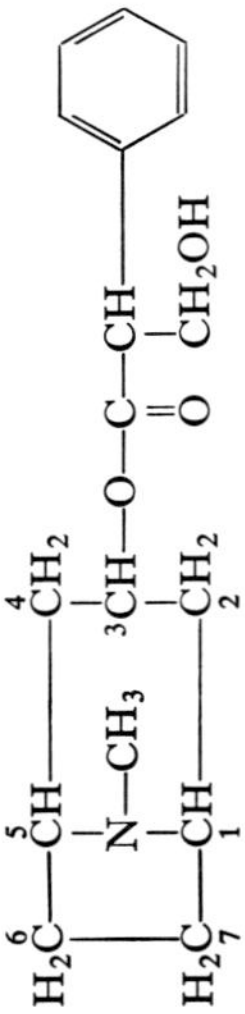

Hyoscyamine

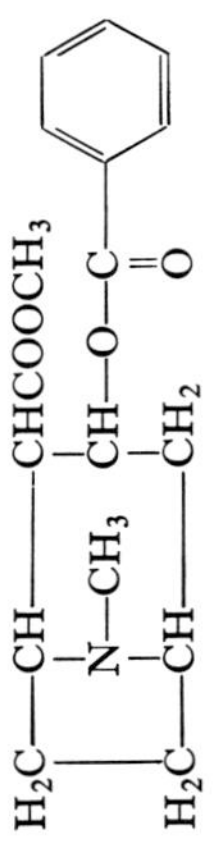

Cocaine

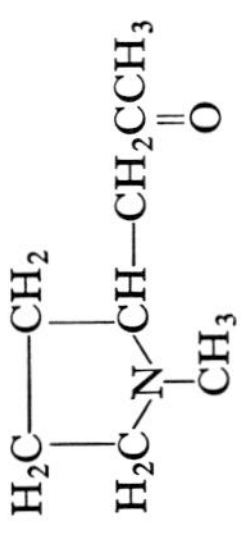

Hygrine

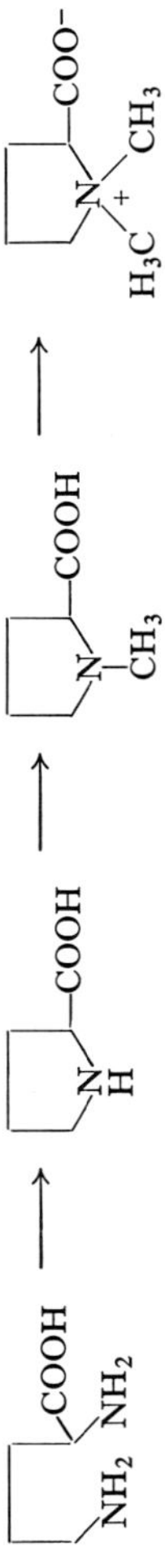

Ornithine → Proline → Hygric acid → Stachydrine

pyrrolidine ring of nicotine. It is possible that Δ^1-pyrroline, formed by cyclization of the product of diamine oxidase on putrescine, is an intermediate in nicotine biosynthesis (801–805; see p. 863).

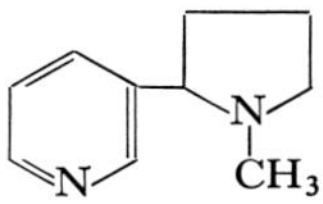

Nicotine

Thoai and Robin (806) have investigated the biosynthesis of octopine, which occurs in the muscle of certain invertebrate forms (see p. 104). Evidence was obtained for enzymatic reduction of the Schiff base formed from pyruvate and L-arginine. Presumably the Schiff base forms non-enzymatically, although its formation may be catalyzed; the reduction was demonstrated in the presence of reduced diphosphopyridine nucleotide:

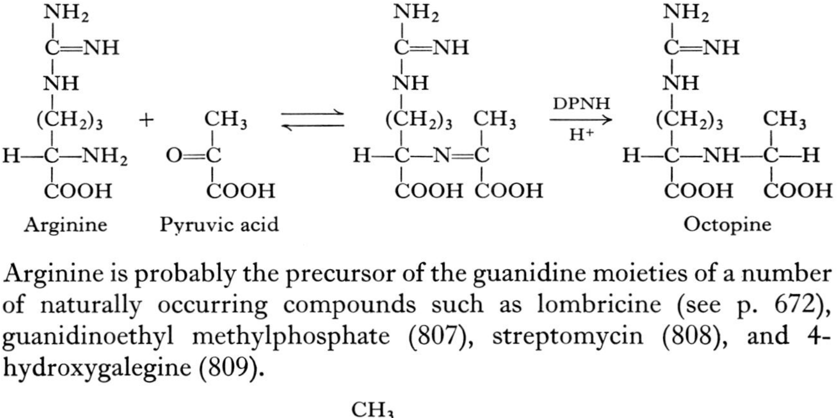

$$
\begin{array}{ccc}
\text{NH}_2 & \text{NH}_2 & \text{NH}_2 \\
| & | & | \\
\text{C}{=}\text{NH} & \text{C}{=}\text{NH} & \text{C}{=}\text{NH} \\
| & | & | \\
\text{NH} & \text{NH} & \text{NH} \\
| & | & | \\
(\text{CH}_2)_3 \quad + \quad \text{CH}_3 & (\text{CH}_2)_3 \quad \text{CH}_3 & (\text{CH}_2)_3 \quad \text{CH}_3 \\
| \qquad\quad | & | \qquad | & | \qquad\qquad | \\
\text{H}{-}\text{C}{-}\text{NH}_2 \quad \text{O}{=}\text{C} & \text{H}{-}\text{C}{-}\text{N}{=}\text{C} & \text{H}{-}\text{C}{-}\text{NH}{-}\text{C}{-}\text{H} \\
| \qquad\quad | & | \qquad | & | \qquad\qquad | \\
\text{COOH} \quad \text{COOH} & \text{COOH} \quad \text{COOH} & \text{COOH} \quad \text{COOH}
\end{array}
$$

Arginine   Pyruvic acid   (DPNH, H+)   Octopine

Arginine is probably the precursor of the guanidine moieties of a number of naturally occurring compounds such as lombricine (see p. 672), guanidinoethyl methylphosphate (807), streptomycin (808), and 4-hydroxygalegine (809).

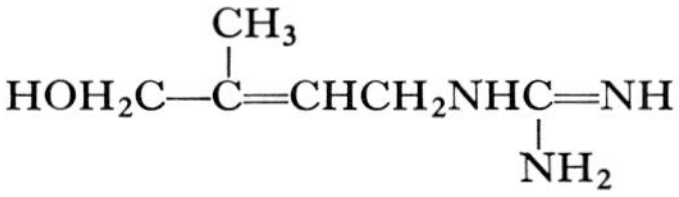

$$
\begin{array}{c}
\text{CH}_3 \\
| \\
\text{HOH}_2\text{C}{-}\text{C}{=}\text{CHCH}_2\text{NHC}{=}\text{NH} \\
| \\
\text{NH}_2
\end{array}
$$

4-Hydroxygalegine

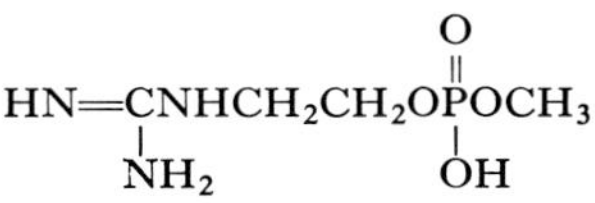

$$
\begin{array}{c}
\qquad\qquad\qquad \text{O} \\
\qquad\qquad\qquad \| \\
\text{HN}{=}\text{CNHCH}_2\text{CH}_2\text{OPOCH}_3 \\
| \qquad\qquad\quad | \\
\text{NH}_2 \qquad\qquad \text{OH}
\end{array}
$$

Guanidinoethyl methylphosphate

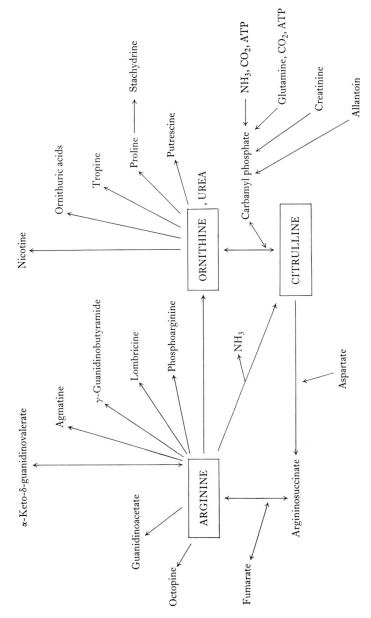

Summary schemes for the metabolism of arginine, ornithine, and citrulline.

In addition to its role in the urea cycle, ornithine participates in other metabolic reactions, including conversion to proline (see p. 714) and conjugation with benzoic acid (see p. 444). The conversion of glutamic acid to ornithine is considered in the next section of this chapter.

I. Proline

A discussion of the intermediary metabolism of proline must necessarily consider interrelationships between this amino acid, ornithine, and glutamic acid. This section will therefore include certain aspects of the synthesis and degradation of the latter two amino acids; other metabolic reactions of glutamate and ornithine are considered in the appropriate sections of this chapter.

Biosynthesis of Proline in Microorganisms

The synthesis of proline in *Escherichia coli* was studied by Vogel and Davis, who employed mutant strains of this organism blocked at different steps of biosynthesis (810). Mutants which responded to (*a*) proline only, (*b*) proline or glutamic acid-γ-semialdehyde, and (*c*) proline, glutamic acid-γ-semialdehyde, or glutamate were isolated. Mutant (*a*) accumulated glutamic acid-γ-semialdehyde, which was isolated and also obtained by hydrolysis of γ,γ-dicarbethoxy-γ-acetamidobutyraldehyde (811). Glutamic acid-γ-semialdehyde was suggested earlier (812) as an intermediate between glutamate and proline on the basis of tracer studies in animals; it exists in solution in equilibrium with its cyclic form, Δ^1-pyrroline-5-carboxylic acid. The pathway from glutamic acid to proline discovered in *E. coli* also occurs in *Neurospora crassa* (813), *Torula utilis* (814), and other organisms; it may be represented as follows:

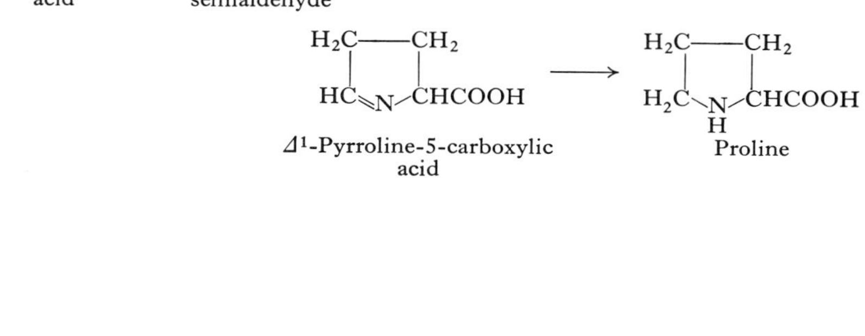

Glutamic acid · Glutamic acid-γ-semialdehyde · Δ^1-Pyrroline-5-carboxylic acid · Proline

Δ^1-Pyrroline-5-carboxylic acid, first obtained by chemical synthesis in solution (810), was subsequently prepared as a white solid of about 80% purity (815). The enzymatic conversion of glutamic acid to Δ^1-pyrroline-5-carboxylic acid has been investigated with preparations of resting cells of *E. coli* (816). Although formation of Δ^1-pyrroline-5-carboxylic acid was demonstrated, the details of this enzymatic transformation are not yet known. The γ-aldehyde may be formed by reactions analogous to those shown earlier by Black for the conversion of aspartic acid to aspartic acid-β-semialdehyde (see p. 675). The reduction of Δ^1-pyrroline-5-carboxylic acid to L-proline was studied in preparations of *N. crassa* and *E. coli*; either diphosphopyridine nucleotide or triphosphopyridine nucleotide is required (817). Δ^1-Pyrroline-5-carboxylate reductase was partially purified from *N. crassa* (818), and ω-hydroxy-α-amino acid dehydrogenase, which also occurs in this organism, was obtained in partially purified form. The latter enzyme catalyzes the reversible conversion of α-amino-δ-hydroxyvaleric acid to Δ^1-pyrroline-5-carboxylate. The reaction requires either diphosphopyridine nucleotide or triphosphopyridine nucleotide (which is less active), and the enzyme also acts on α-amino-ϵ-hydroxycaproic acid, reversibly converting it to α-aminoadipic acid-δ-semialdehyde (Δ^1-piperideine-6-carboxylate) (818, 819). The enzymatic transformations of the latter compound are considered in relation to the metabolism of lysine (see p. 940).

Enzyme preparations obtained from a mutant of *N. crassa* genetically blocked in the reduction of Δ^1-pyrroline-5-carboxylic acid to proline, as well as the corresponding parent wild strain, were capable of catalyzing the reduction of Δ^1-pyrroline-2-carboxylic acid and Δ^1-piperideine-2-carboxylic acid to L-proline and L-pipecolic acid, respectively (820). This *N. crassa* mutant and a proline-requiring mutant of *Aerobacter aerogenes* were able to grow when supplied with Δ^1-pyrroline-2-carboxylic acid. These observations indicate that the intact microorganisms can convert Δ^1-pyrroline-2-carboxylic acid to L-proline. It is evident, however, that this pyrroline compound is not on the major pathway of proline biosynthesis. Certain glutamate-requiring mutants of *E. coli* grow when supplied with proline. The formation of glutamate from proline is catalyzed by enzymes that are different from those which catalyze the conversion of glutamate to proline. Δ^1-Pyrroline-5-carboxylate reductase does not catalyze oxidation of proline; a separate enzyme, perhaps similar to the proline oxidase of animal tissues, may be involved. Δ^1-Pyrroline-2-carboxylate reductase and ω-hydroxy-α-amino acid dehydrogenase activities do not seem to function in biosynthesis, and the physiological significance of these enzymes is not yet clear. Δ^1-Pyrroline-2-carboxylate might be formed from proline or ornithine by reactions similar to those catalyzed by L-amino acid oxidase (see p. 304).

Biosynthesis of Ornithine in Microorganisms

The pathway from glutamic acid to ornithine involves a series of N-acetylamino acid derivatives. Vogel found that an ornithine-requiring mutant of *E. coli* accumulated N-acetylglutamic acid-γ-semialdehyde, and it was shown that the latter compound transaminates with glutamate to yield α-N-acetylornithine, which is hydrolyzed to ornithine (821–824). Studies with isotopically labeled compounds supported the belief that acetylation of glutamate is the first step in the biosynthetic sequence, which may be described as follows:

$$
\begin{array}{ccccc}
\text{COOH} & & \text{COOH} & & \text{CHO} \\
| & & | & & | \\
\text{CH}_2 & & \text{CH}_2 & & \text{CH}_2 \\
| & & | & & | \\
\text{CH}_2 & \longrightarrow & \text{CH}_2 & \longrightarrow & \text{CH}_2 & \longrightarrow \\
| & & | & & | \\
\text{CHNH}_2 & & \text{CHNHCOCH}_3 & & \text{CHNHCOCH}_3 \\
| & & | & & | \\
\text{COOH} & & \text{COOH} & & \text{COOH}
\end{array}
$$

Glutamic	N-Acetylglutamic	N-Acetylglutamic
acid	acid	acid-γ-semialdehyde

$$
\begin{array}{ccc}
\text{CH}_2\text{NH}_2 & & \text{CH}_2\text{NH}_2 \\
| & & | \\
\text{CH}_2 & & \text{CH}_2 \\
| & & | \\
\text{CH}_2 & \longrightarrow & \text{CH}_2 \\
| & & | \\
\text{CHNHCOCH}_3 & & \text{CHNH}_2 \\
| & & | \\
\text{COOH} & & \text{COOH}
\end{array}
$$

α-N-Acetylornithine	Ornithine

There is evidence that N-acetylglutamate is formed by a mechanism involving reaction of acetyl-coenzyme A and glutamate (825, 826); it can also be formed by transacetylation from acetylornithine (see below). The synthesis of N-acetylglutamic acid-γ-semialdehyde from N-acetyl-glutamic acid has been studied in preparations of *Micrococcus glutamicus*; adenosine triphosphate and reduced triphosphopyridine nucleotide were required. Enzymatic formation of a hydroxamate was observed when hydroxylamine was added, and reduction of triphosphopyridine nucleotide was demonstrated when the enzyme preparation was incubated with this coenzyme, N-acetylglutamic acid-γ-semialdehyde and inorganic orthophosphate (827). These reactions have also been carried out with preparations from *E. coli* (828). The data suggest intermediate formation of N-acetyl-γ-glutamyl phosphate, and its conversion to the corresponding aldehyde by a pathway analogous to that demonstrated for the formation of aspartic acid-β-semialdehyde (see p. 675). Transamination between N-acetylglutamic acid-γ-semialdehyde and glutamate yields α-N-acetylornithine (see p. 355). α-N-Acetylornithine is hydrolyzed by an acylase which is activated by Co^{++} ions. Mutants blocked between α-N-acetylornithine and ornithine lack acylase activity. Enzymatic studies on preparations of *Bacillus subtilis* have provided evidence that this organism uses the same biosynthetic pathway as *E. coli* (829). However, *Micrococcus glutamicus* lacks acetylornithine acylase, and has been reported to possess an enzymatic activity that transfers the acetyl group from acetylornithine to glutamate (827). There is then a cyclic pathway in which the acetyl group is preserved:

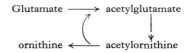

Glutamate ⟶ acetylglutamate

ornithine ⟵ acetylornithine

It has been concluded that the pathways of ornithine biosynthesis in *N. crassa* and *T. utilis* do not involve N-acetylglutamic acid-γ-semialdehyde. This compound is not able to support the growth of mutants of these organisms, and there is evidence that glutamate and glutamic acid-γ-semialdehyde can be precursors of ornithine in these organisms (824). *Neurospora* extracts can reversibly transaminate glutamic acid-γ-semialdehyde with glutamic acid to yield α-ketoglutarate and ornithine (see p. 355). If this were the sole pathway of ornithine formation in *Neurospora*, an ornithine-requiring mutant which does not need proline should fail to exhibit ornithine transaminase activity; examination of such a mutant revealed an active transaminase, suggesting that this pathway is probably not of major biosynthetic importance (830). These considerations lead logically to the conclusion that another pathway for ornithine biosynthesis must exist in *Neurospora*. It has been suggested (813) that a mechanism exists in *Neurospora* for the channeling of glutamic acid-γ-semialdehyde to either proline or ornithine. According to this hypothesis, glutamic acid-γ-semialdehyde destined to be converted to ornithine is separated in some way from that which is to be converted to proline.

Studies with labeled compounds gave results that were considered to be consistent with the channeling idea (831), but other interpretations of these data are possible. Channeling might conceivably be effected by a physical separation of the two forms of glutamic acid-γ-semialdehyde; on the other hand, a "chemical channeling" (e.g., conversion of some of the compound to the N-acetyl derivative) seems to be a reasonable solution to the problem. Evidence has recently been obtained that preparations of yeast cells can catalyze the reduction of N-acetylglu-tamic acid; L-arginine strongly inhibits the reaction, indicating a feedback type inhibition. The additional finding that yeast cells possess α-N-acetylornithinase suggests that yeast catalyzes a pathway of ornithine biosynthesis similar to that found in $E.\ coli$ (832). It would seem of importance now to reexamine the pathway of ornithine biosynthesis in $Neurospora$; although N-acetylglutamic acid-γ-semialdehyde was not active in supporting the growth of mutants of $Neurospora$ and $T.\ utilis$, it is possible that the aldehyde did not enter the cell because of a barrier to permeation. Recent work by Vogel and Vogel (832a) has demonstrated the presence of acetylornithinase and ornithine-glutamate transacetylase in $N.\ crassa$. It would be interesting to determine whether the other enzymes involved in the N-acetylglutamic acid-α-N-acetylornithine pathway of $E.\ coli.$ are also present in $Neurospora$ and $T.\ utilis$. On the basis of present evidence, it would seem that ornithine transaminase does not have major biosynthetic significance. However, this enzyme can function in the conversion of ornithine to proline and glutamate, and thus provide a metabolic link between proline and ornithine which does not involve the intermediate formation of glutamic acid.

Several investigators have examined the mechanisms of regulation of arginine biosynthesis in $E.\ coli$ (833–839). There is general agreement that arginine represses the synthesis of all of the enzymes involved in the conversion of acetylglutamate to arginine. Although these can be repressed together, there are differences in the degree of repression (or derepression) in various experiments; this is in contrast to the "coordinate" repression observed in studies on the enzymes involved in the biosynthesis of histidine (see p. 824). A further difference between the enzymes of the arginine and histidine pathways is that the latter but not the former are controlled by genes that are located next to each other on the chromosome. The biosynthesis of arginine is also controlled by end-product inhibition; thus, acetylglutamate synthetase of $E.\ coli$ is inhibited by arginine, which also can repress the synthesis of this enzyme (826). Another finding of interest is that acetylornithine transaminase can be induced in a mutant of *E. coli*, while the other enzymes in the pathway are repressed. An explanation of this effect postulates a close connection between the mechanisms for inducing and repressing enzyme synthesis; thus, it appears that the same substance, arginine, can both induce and repress, and that the same gene that normally governs repressibility controls inducibility in the mutant (840).

Metabolism in Mammals

The proline-glutamate-ornithine interrelationships of mammalian tissues are somewhat similar to those elucidated for microorganisms. Although these were suggested by nutritional studies (see p. 203), investigations in which isotopes were employed provided direct proof. Thus, rats fed labeled glutamic acid were found to contain labeled proline and arginine (841, 842). When N^{15}-proline was fed, isotope was found in glutamate, arginine, and ornithine (843), and the conversion of deuterium-labeled ornithine to proline and glutamic acid was also shown (844). Experiments with slices of kidney and liver demonstrated conversion of proline to glutamate (845, 846).

Several possible intermediates in these reactions have been considered, including α-keto-δ-aminovaleric acid (or its cyclized form, Δ^1-pyrroline-2-carboxylic acid), glutamic acid-γ-semialdehyde (Δ^1-pyrroline-5-carboxylic acid), 2-pyrrolidone-5-carboxylic acid, and α-amino-δ-hydroxyvaleric acid. Studies with kidney slices and *E. coli* suggested that α-amino-δ-hydroxyvaleric acid was probably not metabolized, and, although it was utilized by *Neurospora*, there was a lag period prior to growth; this suggests conversion to a more active intermediate, probably glutamic acid-γ-semialdehyde (810, 846, 847). There is no evidence that 2-pyrrolidone-5-carboxylic acid is an intermediate in these interconversions, although the L-isomer of this compound is rapidly metabolized by the rabbit and will substitute for glutamate in certain microorganisms (848); in contrast, D-pyrrolidone-carboxylic acid is excreted in the urine when this compound or D-glutamic acid is fed to animals (see p. 619.)

α-Keto-δ-aminovaleric acid, identified as its 2,4-dinitrophenylhydrazone, is the product of oxidative deamination of D-proline and D-ornithine by D-amino acid oxidase (849); the same hydrazone was isolated after oxidation of L-proline by the L-amino acid oxidase of rat kidney (850). Preparation of the free α-keto acid was achieved by oxidative deamination (using snake venom L-amino acid oxidase) of δ-N-carbo-benzyloxy-L-ornithine; after removal of the blocking group, the resulting α-keto-δ-aminovaleric acid was found to be in equilibrium with its intramolecular cyclization product, Δ^1-pyrroline-2-carboxylic acid (685).

The latter compound has also been prepared by chemical synthesis (851, 852). There is good evidence that Δ^1-pyrroline-2-carboxylic acid is not in spontaneous equilibrium with Δ^1-pyrroline-5-carboxylic acid. These compounds and their derivatives can be separated by chromatography and electrophoresis, and the latter compound (but not the former) supports the growth of certain proline-requiring mutants of *E. coli* (685). Enzymatic catalysis of interconversion of these pyrroline compounds has not been reported. There is now no evidence for the belief that Δ^1-pyrroline-2-carboxylic acid is an intermediate in the proline-ornithine-glutamate transformation in animals. Nevertheless, it is of interest that an enzyme activity exists in many rat tissues, in plants, and also in microorganisms that is capable of catalyzing the conversion of Δ^1-pyrroline-2-carboxylic acid to L-proline (820). This activity might conceivably function in a pathway from ornithine (perhaps by α-oxidation) to proline, or it may reflect lack of specificity of the enzyme that catalyzes pipecolic acid formation (see p. 944).

In a study in which N^{15}-glycine was fed to rats, equivalent concentrations of isotope were found in the α- and δ-amino groups of ornithine (812). This result may be explained by a shift of the α-amino group of ornithine to the δ-position, or interpreted to mean that both amino groups arose originally from the same nitrogenous precursor. Stetten fed DL-ornithines labeled in the α- or δ-positions with N^{15} to rats for 9 days (853). The δ-amino group of ornithine contributed very little isotope to the α-amino group of tissue arginine. Proline derived much less isotope from the δ- than the α-amino group of ornithine, whereas most of the glutamate amino group arose from the δ-amino group of ornithine. These results are perhaps somewhat influenced by the fact that racemic ornithines were used; however, considerable quantities of D-ornithine were recovered in the urine, suggesting that much of the D-ornithine was not metabolized. The findings were considered to be consistent with initial conversion of ornithine to glutamic acid-γ-semialdehyde, with loss of the δ-amino group to the labile pool of nitrogen, which was presumably in equilibrium with glutamate. This interpretation is compatible with the observation that the α-amino group of ornithine was the predominant precursor of proline nitrogen.

Early observations indicated that preparations of rabbit kidney can oxidize L-proline to a compound exhibiting the properties of glutamic acid-γ-semialdehyde (854, 855). Johnson and Strecker (856) demonstrated that rat liver mitochondria oxidize L-proline to Δ^1-pyrroline-5-carboxylic acid stoichiometrically. The reaction requires oxygen and cytochrome C and is inhibited by cyanide, antimycin A, and azide, and these authors concluded that the proline oxidase system consists of a dehydrogenase linked to the cytochrome-containing respiratory chain. It is of interest that the same preparation oxidizes hydroxy-L-proline.

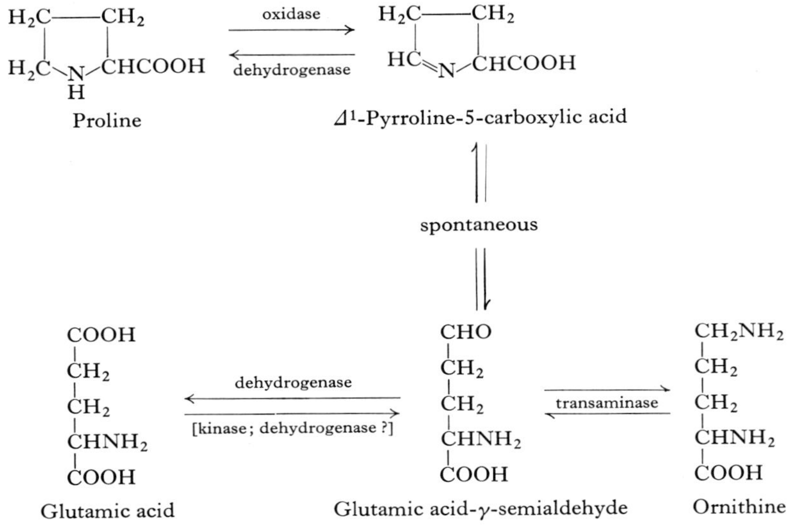

The subsequent transformations of glutamic acid-γ-semialdehyde include oxidation to glutamic acid, transamination to ornithine, and reduction to proline. Another enzymatic reaction referred to above (see p. 708) is reversible conversion to α-amino-δ-hydroxyvaleric acid catalyzed by *Neurospora* preparations. Reduction of glutamic acid-γ-semialdehyde to proline has been demonstrated with preparations from various animal tissues and microorganisms (820, 857, 858). The enzyme was purified approximately 160-fold from calf liver and found to be specific for the L-isomer of Δ^1-pyrroline-5-carboxylic acid (858). It requires either diphosphopyridine nucleotide or triphosphopyridine nucleotide; no evidence for reversibility of the reaction was obtained.

The latter observation indicates that the conversion of proline to glutamate is probably catalyzed by proline oxidase. Kinetic data suggest that
although the reductase preparation is active with Δ^1-pyrroline-3-
hydroxy-5-carboxylic acid, reduction of this substrate is catalyzed by a
separate enzyme. DL-Δ^1-Pyrroline-5-carboxylic acid is oxidized to
DL-glutamic acid by an enzyme present in ox liver (859). Both diphosphopyridine nucleotide and triphosphopyridine nucleotide are active and
several other aldehydes are also oxidized, including Δ^1-pyrroline-3-
hydroxy-5-carboxylate, Δ^1-pyrroline, Δ^1-piperideine, and glutaric
dialdehyde. Transamination of ornithine with a number of α-keto acids to
yield glutamic acid-γ-semialdehyde has been demonstrated with rat
liver preparations (see p. 355). Thus, each of the reactions indicated in
the metabolic scheme shown has been demonstrated enzymatically.
There is as yet no evidence suggesting or excluding the participation of
N-acetyl (or other N-acyl) derivatives of glutamate, glutamic acid-γ-
semialdehyde, or ornithine in mammalian metabolism.

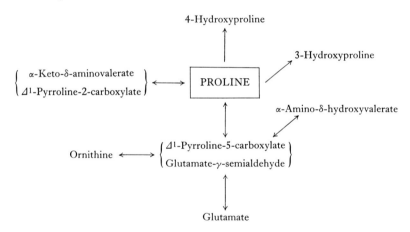

Summary scheme for the metabolism of proline.

J. 4-Hydroxyproline

General Considerations

4-Hydroxy-L-proline has been found in hydrolyzates of a limited
number of proteins, in particular collagen and to a lesser extent elastin;

its distribution in animal proteins therefore appears to be restricted to the connective tissue proteins. The significance of hydroxyproline as a constituent of collagen has been reviewed by Gustavson (860). 4-Hydroxyproline has been found in acid hydrolyzates of the proteins of carrot tissue grown in tissue culture (861), and it occurs in peptide linkage in higher plants where it appears to be localized in the primary cell wall (862–864). A recent report describes the occurrence of hydroxyproline in a collagen-like protein of hydra nematocysts (865), and it seems probable that as time goes on hydroxyproline will be found in still other proteins. A protein obtained from the cuticle of the earthworm was found to contain more than ten times as many hydroxyproline residues as proline residues (866), and it would appear that the class of proteins designated as collagen is a fairly heterogeneous group. Collagens frequently studied, such as that isolated from ox hide, contain similar concentrations of proline and hydroxyproline. Allo-4-hydroxy-L-proline is known to occur in the free state in the sandal tree, and this imino acid is also present in acid hydrolyzates of phalloidine (see p. 87). Allo-4-hydroxy-D-proline has been found in hydrolyzates of the antibiotic etamycin (see p. 135). Collagen also contains relatively small amounts of *trans*-3-hydroxy-L-proline, and both the *cis*- and *trans*-isomers of 3-hydroxyproline have been isolated from hydrolyzates of the antibiotic telomycin (see p. 87). At the time of writing, there is no information available concerning the metabolism of 3-hydroxyproline, and the present discussion will therefore be concerned only with the intermediary metabolism of 4-hydroxyproline (hereinafter referred to as hydroxyproline), usually the L-isomer. As yet, no organism has been shown to require hydroxyproline for growth. Hydroxyproline accumulates in the cells and culture media of *Sarcina lutea* when this microorganism is grown in media containing peptides or proteins that contain hydroxyproline (867).

Conversion of Proline to Collagen Hydroxyproline

Stetten and Schoenheimer (843) found that when proline labeled with N^{15} and deuterium was administered to rats for 3 days, hydroxyproline became the most highly labeled carcass amino acid except for proline itself. The N^{15}-to-deuterium ratio of the isolated hydroxyproline indicated that between 1 and 2 atoms of deuterium were lost during conversion of proline to hydroxyproline. These results suggest direct conversion of proline to hydroxyproline, but they do not exclude the existence of other pathways of hydroxyproline biosynthesis. When racemic N^{15}-hydroxy-proline was fed to rats, only about 0.1% of the carcass hydroxyproline became labeled (868). Although this result is consistent with the known low rate of turnover of collagen, when labeled proline was administered, much more incorporation of isotope into body hydroxyproline occurred than when hydroxyproline itself was fed. The N^{15} of dietary hydroxyproline was found widely distributed in the other amino acids, especially in glutamic and aspartic acids, suggesting that hydroxyproline is readily metabolized. On the basis of these studies with isotopically labeled hydroxyproline, Stetten suggested that most of the hydroxyproline of animal tissue protein does not arise from free hydroxyproline but from a bound form of proline, possibly proline in peptide linkage. It is of interest that Womack and Rose (869) found that dietary hydroxyproline did not affect the growth rate of rats fed diets deficient in proline, arginine, or glutamate. On the other hand, it is known that arginine, proline, and glutamate increase the rate of growth of young rats (see p. 203). Another pertinent early observation is that of Pederson and Lewis (870), who found that dietary hydroxyproline is largely excreted unchanged in the urine. Hydroxyproline does not support the growth of proline-requiring mutants of *Escherichia coli* (871); the report that hydroxyproline competes with glucose in the synthesis of proline in *E. coli* (612) may be explained readily by the presence of a small amount of proline in the hydroxyproline preparation employed. (Virtually all currently available commercial preparations of hydroxyproline contain small amounts of proline.)

The important observation of Stetten that proline rather than hydroxyproline is the precursor of collagen hydroxyproline has been amply confirmed by studies in other laboratories, and analogous observations have been made on the origin of collagen hydroxylysine (see p. 949). Thus, Green and Lowther (872) observed that incubation of C^{14}-proline with guinea pig granuloma slices led to labeling of the collagen proline and hydroxyproline, while incubation with C^{14}-hydroxyproline failed to label the collagen. Mitoma *et al.* (873) reported that the specific activity of the bound hydroxyproline in chick embryos after administration of labeled hydroxyproline was only one-tenth of that observed in similar experiments with labeled proline. Prockop *et al.* (874) found that after injection of C^{14}-L-proline into chick embryos the specific activity of the free hydroxyproline was lower than that of the protein-bound hydroxyproline, indicating again that free hydroxyproline cannot be a significant source of collagen hydroxyproline. The latter studies also demonstrated that the protein-bound hydroxyproline with the highest specific activity was in the microsomal fraction, and this result suggests that collagen is probably synthesized by mechanisms similar to those used in the synthesis of other proteins. A number of attempts have been made to determine the mechanism of the conversion of proline to hydroxyproline by administering labeled proline to animals or incubating it with tissue preparations and subsequently isolating the collagen imino acids and determining their specific radioactivities. A specific activity ratio of hydroxyproline to proline of 1.0 would be consistent with the occurrence of hydroxylation in peptide linkage. A ratio of less than 1.0 could be reconciled with such a mechanism, but ratios larger than unity might be more difficult to explain in this way. This approach suffers from several difficulties, such as the possibility that the collagen isolated might be contaminated with noncollagen proteins. Other troubles include those due to effects of different pool sizes and side reactions. Hausmann and Neuman (875) determined the specific activities of proline and hydroxyproline obtained from sodium chloride-soluble skin collagen after injection of C^{14}-L-proline into guinea pigs. The specific activity ratios of collagen hydroxyproline to proline varied between 0.94 and 1.20. Other workers (872, 876–878), using various systems for the study of collagen formation, observed ratios significantly different than unity. Green and Lowther (872) found a ratio of 1.6 after incubation of guinea pig granuloma slices with C^{14}-proline.

It is well known that collagen synthesis takes place at a reduced rate in ascorbic acid deficiency (879–887). Thus, granulation tissue induced by wounding or by injecting a foreign substance (e.g., a polysaccharide, polyvinyl sponge) generally contains much less collagen when such procedures are carried out with ascorbic acid-deficient guinea pigs. The function of ascorbic acid in the synthesis of collagen is not yet clear; it has been suggested that ascorbic acid is needed for the maintenance of collagen (888), that it is required for the hydroxylation of proline, that it is needed for the maturation of fibroblasts (877), and that it functions in relation to a hormonally induced systemic effect. Ascorbic acid can function nonenzymatically in the hydroxylation of proline (889, 890). It has been found that D-ascorbic acid replaces the L-isomer in preventing the decrease in collagen formation that occurs in granulomas grown in scorbutic guinea pigs (891); the low optical specificity of the ascorbate effect suggests that other compounds might also serve in place of L-ascorbate. Robertson and Schwartz (880) found that carrageenin-induced tumors in scorbutic guinea pigs developed rapidly on administration of ascorbic acid to the deficient animals. Gould and Woessner (881) found that collagen synthesis did not occur in the healing wounds of scorbutic guinea pigs, but began immediately after administration of ascorbate. Robertson *et al.* (882) and Gould *et al.* (885) carried out kinetic studies on collagen proline and hydroxyproline formation in normal and scorbutic guinea pigs; although these studies provided no evidence for a mechanism of collagen synthesis involving proline-rich polypeptide precursors, they did not exclude it. In other experiments (878), granuloma minces from normal and scorbutic guinea pigs were incubated with labeled proline, and the specific activity of the collagen proline subsequently isolated from deficient granulomas was found to be only moderately reduced as compared to normals. In contrast, the specific activity of the collagen hydroxyproline was greatly reduced in deficiency. These observations suggest accumulation of precursors of collagen hydroxyproline in the scorbutic granuloma, and support a mechanism of collagen formation in which there are two types of proline-containing pools: one of these contains proline destined to become collagen proline and the other contains proline that will become collagen hydroxyproline. The latter is oxidized to a hydroxyproline intermediate not in equilibrium with free hydroxyproline and not yet in peptide linkage. Proof of such a mechanism will probably require separation of the hydroxylation steps from protein synthesis, and obviously acceptance of any mechanism will depend upon characterization of the intermediate compounds involved. In summary, two types of mechanisms have been suggested for the conversion of proline to hydroxyproline. According to one, proline is converted to a proline-rich collagen precursor and hydroxylation takes place in peptide linkage. The alternative mechanism involves conversion of proline to hydroxyproline in a bound form which is not protein.

A useful method for following the hydroxylation of proline during collagen synthesis has been devised in which proline containing tritium is incubated with collagen-forming tissues (878). Under these circumstances, it has been found, in the case of the carrageenin granuloma of the guinea pig, that the formation of tritiated water parallels the formation of collagen hydroxyproline. This procedure is not satisfactory for following collagen synthesis in chick embryo since there is considerable metabolism of proline to other products in this tissue.

Several studies on collagen formation indicate that free hydroxyproline is formed in tissues that catalyze collagen synthesis. Daughaday and Mariz (892) incubated segments of costal cartilage from rapidly growing rats in a medium containing C^{14}-proline. They found that the free hydroxyproline present after incubation exhibited a specific activity considerably higher than that of collagen hydroxyproline, and concluded that the free hydroxyproline was not derived from soluble collagen, but arose from an activated hydroxyproline intermediate. Free hydroxyproline has also been observed in similar experiments on collagen synthesis in chick embryos, but its specific activity was much lower than that of collagen hydroxyproline; it was thought that such free hydroxyproline arises from the degradation of collagen (874, 893). The observation that ultrafilterable material containing hydroxyproline is formed in collagen-synthesizing systems has been interpreted to mean that these relatively low-molecular-weight materials are collagen precursors (894). Lindstedt and Prockop (895) injected C^{14}-proline into rats and followed the changes in specific activity of urinary hydroxyproline as an index of collagen metabolism. The results suggest the presence of three hydroxyproline pools in young rats. Two of these exhibit half-lives of 1 and 5 days, and a third a half-life of 50 to 100 days. These findings indicate that in young animals some collagen must be synthesized and degraded rapidly and suggest that the highly labeled free hydroxyproline in collagen-synthesizing systems is a product of collagen breakdown rather than of the degradation of an activated hydroxyproline intermediate.

The major portion of urinary hydroxyproline is not free, and a considerable literature has accumulated on the urinary excretion of hydroxyproline-containing peptides (896–902). There is a relationship between growth rate and the excretion of urinary hydroxyproline; thus, excretion of hydroxyproline is greater in children than in adults. A number of peptides have been found that exhibit sequences known to occur in collagen and it seems then that the excretion of hydroxyproline-containing peptides reflects an aspect of the metabolism of soluble collagen in the tissues.

Attempts have been made to obtain information about the chemical mechanism of hydroxylation of proline during collagen biosynthesis by carrying out experiments with C^{14}-proline, tritiated proline, and O^{18}. Ebert and Prockop (903) incubated chick embryos with C^{14}- and $3,4$-H^3-proline; from the ratios of specific activities of the isolated imino acids they concluded that there is a loss of only 1 of the 4 tritium atoms of proline during hydroxylation; see also (903a). Unfortunately, it is not certain that the tritiated proline used in these studies was randomly labeled in the 3- and 4-positions only. However, it is of interest to note that in the experiments of Stetten and Schoenheimer (843) with N^{15}- and deuterium-labeled proline, the isotope ratios for the isolated hydroxyproline indicate a loss of between 1 and 2 deuterium atoms per molecule of proline during hydroxylation. Other experiments (904–907) indicate that the hydroxylation of proline in chick embryo is associated with the incorporation of atmospheric oxygen into the hydroxyl group of hydroxyproline. The data also indicate that the oxygen of water is not utilized. Similar results have been obtained in experiments on the formation of the hydroxyproline of plant cell-wall protein (908). These data indicate that the conversion of proline to hydroxyproline probably takes place by an oxygenase mechanism, perhaps similar to those which occur in aromatic and steroid hydroxylation. Such a mechanism would be consistent with a loss of only 1 hydrogen atom in the conversion of proline to hydroxyproline. These considerations argue against the possibility that such compounds as 4-ketoproline and 3,4-dehydroproline are intermediates in the hydroxylation reaction. These compounds and other proline and hydroxyproline derivatives have been synthesized by Witkop and collaborators (909–914). It is of interest that administration of 4-ketoproline to chick embryos led to an increase in free hydroxyproline. This was shown to be due to the presence of an enzyme activity, designated 4-ketoproline reductase, that catalyzes the diphosphopyridine nucleotide-dependent reduction of ketoproline to hydroxyproline. This enzyme activity, which has been found in rat kidney and a number of other mammalian tissues, does not appear to be identical with other known dehydrogenase systems (915). It is difficult to see how this enzyme could be involved in the conversion of proline to collagen hydroxyproline, unless it also acts on a bound form of 4-ketoproline. The possibility that it functions in the formation of free hydroxyproline must be considered.

$$O=C\text{------}CH_2$$
$$H_2C\diagdown_{\underset{H}{N}}\diagup CHCOOH$$

4-Ketoproline

Peterkofsky and Udenfriend (916) have demonstrated the conversion of C^{14}-proline to peptide-bound C^{14}-hydroxyproline in a cell-free system obtained from 9–10-day-old chick embryos. These studies were carried out with microsomal preparations which were incubated with labeled proline, adenosine triphosphate, and creatine phosphate.

Although proline incorporation began immediately, radioactive hydroxyproline was not detected until about 20 minutes had elapsed. Studies in which puromycin and ribonuclease were added initially and at various times during the experiment were interpreted to indicate that conversion of proline to hydroxyproline takes place after proline is incorporated into peptide linkage. Similarly, anaerobic incubation had little effect on incorporation of proline, but formation of protein-bound hydroxyproline was reduced. The interpretation of these experiments is complicated by the fact that considerable noncollagen protein is formed; therefore, the major proportion of isotope incorporated is not incorporated into collagen. Other studies (917–919) have provided evidence consistent with the formation of hydroxyprolyl-RNA in a similar chick embryo system. It is evident that additional studies are needed to clarify the mechanism of collagen hydroxyproline formation. Such studies will be of importance in order to distinguish between a mechanism in which there is a specific ribonucleic acid code for hydroxyproline and one in which hydroxylation occurs after the peptide chain has been formed. In either case, the experimental data (916, 920) indicate that hydroxylation is catalyzed by a system associated with the ribosome fraction.

Several of the actinomycin antibiotics contain imino acids (see pp. 136 and 465). Thus, actinomycin I contains L-proline and hydroxy-L-proline; other actinomycins contain only proline or both proline and 4-ketoproline. Studies with labeled proline indicate that proline can serve as the precursor of antibiotic proline, hydroxyproline, and ketoproline. Labeled hydroxyproline is incorporated directly into actinomycin I, but is not significantly incorporated into actinomycin proline or ketoproline (921).

Degradation

Early investigations revealed that hydroxyproline was glucogenic (922, 923), and *in vitro* studies suggested metabolism to glutamic acid and glutamine (845). The studies of Stetten and Schoenheimer (843, 868; see p. 716) also provided evidence for conversion of hydroxyproline to glutamate. Gianetto and Bouthillier (924) administered hydroxy-DL-proline-2-C^{14} to rats, and found that of the tissue amino acids subsequently isolated, glutamic acid exhibited the highest specific radioactivity, while aspartic acid and hydroxyproline contained approximately the same amounts of isotope; proline contained very little radioactivity. The isolated glutamic acid was most heavily labeled in the α-carbon atom, indicating conversion of hydroxyproline to glutamate. Wolf *et al.* (925)

carried out similar experiments with hydroxy-DL-proline-2-C^{14} and observed that the principal labeled amino acid in the liver protein was alanine, but considerable radioactivity was also found in glutamic and aspartic acids. In subsequent experiments with hydroxy-L-proline-2-C^{14}, the specific activities of the isolated free hydroxyproline from the liver and the urine showed approximately 6-fold dilution of the administered hydroxyproline, suggesting the presence of a small pool of free hydroxyproline. The apparent size of this pool was increased about 10-fold after feeding unlabeled proline, indicating that some free hydroxyproline is synthesized from proline. Very little hydroxyproline radioactivity was incorporated into protein, and, as in previous experiments, most of the label was present in aspartic acid, alanine, and glutamic acid. Pyrrole-2-carboxylic acid was found to be the major urinary metabolite (except for urea) after administration of either hydroxy-L-proline or hydroxy-DL-proline. Although labeled urinary pyrrole-2-carboxylic acid would be expected after administration of hydroxy-DL-proline or hydroxy-D-proline (see below, p. 728), its formation from hydroxy-L-proline suggests a mechanism for conversion of hydroxyproline to Δ^1-pyrroline-4-hydroxy-2-carboxylic acid, a transformation which has not yet been observed enzymatically.

The proline oxidase system of liver and kidney also attacks hydroxy-L-proline, and its oxidation leads to the accumulation of a product, the 2,4-dinitrophenylosazone of which was considered to be that of γ-hydroxyglutamic acid-γ-semialdehyde (854, 926). The latter compound, which exists in solution in equilibrium with Δ^1-pyrroline-3-hydroxy-5-carboxylic acid, was isolated after its production by enzymatic oxidation from hydroxy-L-proline by Adams and Goldstone (927). Their evidence strongly supported the proposed structure and showed that the cyclic form predominated in solution; they also showed that the configuration about the 4-carbon atom was L_g. Additional support for these conclusions came from the observation that preparations of beef liver catalyze the reduction of this compound to hydroxy-L-proline; the enzymatic activity involved appears to be identical with Δ^1-pyrroline-5-carboxylate reductase (928, 929). Adams and Goldstone (930) subsequently isolated an enzyme from beef liver that catalyzes the pyridine nucleotide dependent conversion of Δ^1-pyrroline-3-hydroxy-5-carboxylate to γ-hydroxyglutamate according to the following equation:

$$\Delta^1\text{-Pyrroline-3-hydroxy-5-carboxylate} + DPN^+ + H_2O \rightarrow$$
$$\gamma\text{-hydroxyglutamate} + DPNH + H^+$$

The product of the reaction was isolated in crystalline form, compared with the chemically synthesized isomers of γ-hydroxyglutamic acid (see p. 148), and identified as *erythro*-γ-hydroxy-L-glutamic acid. The enzyme that catalyzes the formation of γ-hydroxyglutamic acid is probably identical with that which oxidizes Δ^1-pyrroline-5-carboxylate to glutamate (859). γ-Hydroxyglutamate was proposed as an intermediate in hydroxyproline metabolism on the basis of earlier studies in which C^{14}-hydroxyproline was administered to animals (924); evidence for its formation in rat liver slices was also reported (931). Benoiton and Bouthillier (932) administered γ-hydroxyglutamic acid-1-C^{14} to rats and observed an amino acid-labeling pattern similar to that found after administration of hydroxyproline.

The further metabolism of *erythro*-γ-hydroxy-L-glutamic acid has been clarified by independent observations in several laboratories. Transamination of both L-isomers of γ-hydroxyglutamate is catalyzed by rat liver preparations; the enzyme activity is probably identical with glutamate-aspartate transaminase. Both isomers of α-keto-γ-hydroxyglutarate were obtained and characterized by Goldstone and Adams (933). Dekker and Maitra (934, 935) and Kuratomi and Fukunaga (936) obtained evidence for the reversible formation of glyoxylate and alanine from γ-hydroxyglutamate catalyzed by liver preparations. Bouthillier *et al.* (937) observed conversion in the rat and in liver homogenates of racemic-labeled γ-hydroxyglutamic acid to glycine (and glyoxylate) and alanine. In the conversion of γ-hydroxyglutamate to glyoxylate and alanine studied by Maitra and Dekker (938), either α-ketoglutarate or α-ketoglutaramate serve in catalytic quantities to effect the formation of α-keto-γ-hydroxyglutarate:

γ-Hydroxyglutamate + α-ketoglutarate ⇌ α-keto-γ-hydroxyglutarate + glutamate
            (α-ketoglutaramate)   (glutamine)

α-Keto-γ-hydroxyglutarate ⇌ pyruvate + glyoxylate

Pyruvate + glutamate ⇌ α-ketoglutarate + alanine
   (glutamine)   (α-ketoglutaramate)

Sum: γ-Hydroxyglutamate ⇌ glyoxylate + alanine

Although conversion of α-ketoglutaramate to glutamine is postulated, it seems more likely that the effect of this keto acid is due to α-ketoglutarate formed by enzymatic deamidation (see p. 349). α-Keto-γ-hydroxyglutarate is the substrate for the cleavage reaction, which is reversible, i.e., formation of α-keto-γ-hydroxyglutarate from glyoxylate and pyruvate has been demonstrated (936). The transformations leading to the conversion of hydroxyproline to glyoxylate and pyruvate are shown in Scheme 8.

When γ-hydroxy-2-C^{14}-glutamate (mixture of 4 isomers) was administered to leaves of *Phlox decussata*, evidence for conversion to alanine and other amino acids was obtained (938a). It is not yet clear whether this plant, which contains the *threo* form of γ-hydroxyglutamate (see p. 148), uses the same pathway found in the rat. Homogenates of these leaves catalyze transamination between α-ketoglutarate and γ-hydroxyglutamate (937a). α-Keto-γ-hydroxyglutarate has been found in *Oxalis pes-caprae* (938b).

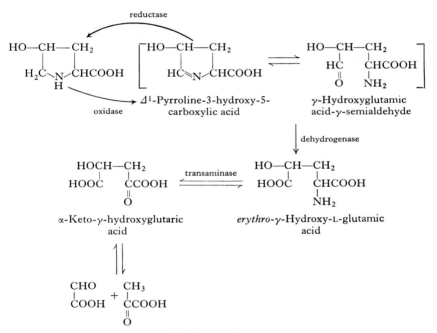

SCHEME 8. Conversion of hydroxyproline to glyoxylate and pyruvate.

All of the steps in the conversion of hydroxy-L-proline to glyoxylate and pyruvate are reversible except the oxidation leading to the formation of γ-hydroxyglutamic acid. Conversion of γ-hydroxyglutamic acid to the corresponding γ-aldehyde might take place by a mechanism analogous to that shown for aspartate, and postulated for glutamate. If this reaction can occur the enzymatic synthesis of hydroxy-L-proline from glyoxylate and pyruvate is possible [see p. 1048, and also (939a)]. Although virtually all of the collagen hydroxyproline is derived from proline, our knowledge concerning the origin of free hydroxyproline is still incomplete, and it is possible that some free hydroxyproline is formed by the reactions discussed above. 4-Ketoproline might also be a precursor of hydroxyproline (see p. 721), but information about the formation of 4-ketoproline is lacking. Direct hydroxylation of free proline to hydroxyproline is a possibility worth considering.

The metabolism of hydroxyproline by an adapted strain of *Pseudomonas* has been investigated by Adams (939–941). It was found initially that soluble extracts obtained from this organism converted both hydroxy-L-proline and allohydroxy-D-proline to L-glutamate; hydroxy-D-proline and allohydroxy-L-proline were not attacked at a significant rate. Subsequent study of the intermediates involved in this transformation led to the interesting finding that the metabolism of hydroxy-L-proline requires obligatory conversion to allohydroxy-D-proline. The latter reaction, catalyzed by hydroxyproline-2-epimerase (see p. 375), involves inversion of configuration at the α-carbon atom only. Allohydroxy-D-proline undergoes oxidation to Δ^1-pyrroline-4-hydroxy-2-carboxylate, which is in spontaneous equilibrium with the open-chain form, 2-keto-4-hydroxy-5-aminovaleric acid. The utilization of hydroxyproline by extracts of this organism occurs only when the organism has been grown on this substrate. Allohydroxy-D-proline oxidase is an inducible enzyme associated with a particulate fraction of the cell. The reaction it catalyzes is analogous to that catalyzed by mammalian D-amino acid oxidase (see below); however, formation of hydrogen peroxide could not be detected, and the evidence suggests that the reaction is linked to reduction of cytochrome. The enzyme exhibits some activity toward other D-amino acids. The formation of pyrrole-2-carboxylic acid was also demonstrated in these studies (see below). The further metabolism of the pyrroline intermediate is not yet known in detail, but it is clear that either α-ketoglutarate or glutamate is ultimately formed. The pathway described below postulates conversion of the pyrroline compound to α-ketoglutaric acid-γ-semialdehyde. Recently, enzymes have been obtained from pseudomonas that catalyze the deamination of Δ^1-pyrroline-4-hydroxy-2-carboxylate to α-ketoglutaric acid-γ-semialdehyde, and oxidation of the latter compound (in the presence of triphosphopyridine nucleotide) to α-ketoglutarate (950).

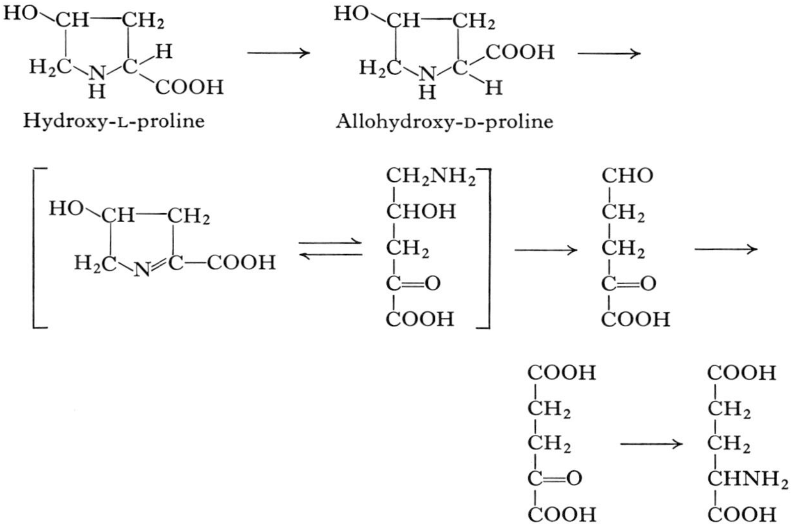

$$\text{Hydroxy-L-proline} \longrightarrow \text{Allohydroxy-D-proline} \longrightarrow$$

$$\begin{bmatrix} \text{HO--CH---CH}_2 \\ \text{H}_2\text{C---N---C---COOH} \end{bmatrix} \rightleftharpoons \begin{bmatrix} \begin{array}{l} \text{CH}_2\text{NH}_2 \\ \text{CHOH} \\ \text{CH}_2 \\ \text{C=O} \\ \text{COOH} \end{array} \end{bmatrix} \longrightarrow \begin{array}{l} \text{CHO} \\ \text{CH}_2 \\ \text{CH}_2 \\ \text{C=O} \\ \text{COOH} \end{array} \longrightarrow$$

$$\begin{array}{l} \text{COOH} \\ \text{CH}_2 \\ \text{CH}_2 \\ \text{C=O} \\ \text{COOH} \end{array} \longrightarrow \begin{array}{l} \text{COOH} \\ \text{CH}_2 \\ \text{CH}_2 \\ \text{CHNH}_2 \\ \text{COOH} \end{array}$$

Mammalian D-amino acid oxidase catalyzes the conversion of allo-hydroxy-D-proline and hydroxy-D-proline (in the presence of catalase) to pyrrole-2-carboxylic acid (942). The oxidation of D-proline yields α-keto-δ-aminovaleric acid, and in the absence of catalase, proline and hydroxy-proline are converted, respectively, to γ-aminobutyric and β-hydroxy-γ-aminobutyric acids. The formation of pyrrole-2-carboxylic acid from the immediate product of oxidation is nonenzymatic and acid-catalyzed. Evidence for the formation of Δ^1-pyrroline-4-hydroxy-2-carboxylic acid (in equilibrium with 2-keto-4-hydroxy-5-aminovaleric acid) includes spectrophotometric and chromatographic studies, conversion by cata-lytic hydrogenation to hydroxyproline, and oxidative decarboxylation to β-hydroxy-γ-aminobutyric acid. The same intermediate is formed in the course of nonenzymatic oxidation of hydroxyproline by hydrogen peroxide, and pyrrole-2-carboxylic acid is also formed during enzymatic transamination between γ-hydroxyornithine and several α-keto acids. Although the color reaction with p-dimethylaminobenzaldehyde (Ehrlich's reagent) has often been used for the identification and quantitative determination of pyrrole-2-carboxylic acid, pyrrole-2-carboxylic acid reacts slowly, if at all, with p-dimethylaminobenzalde-hyde at 26°; the color formed when pyrrole-2-carboxylic acid is treated with this reagent appears to be due to pyrrole formed by decarboxylation

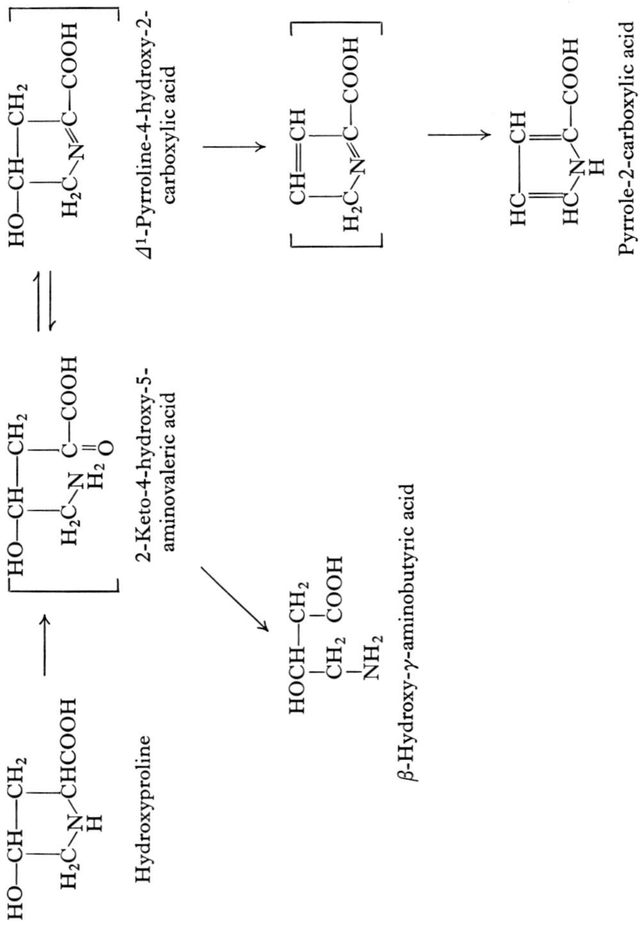

$$HO-CH-CH_2$$
$$H_2C\diagdown N\diagup CHCOOH$$
$$H$$

Hydroxyproline

$\longrightarrow$

$$\left[HO-CH-CH_2 \atop H_2C\diagdown N{-} \underset{H_2\,O}{\overset{C-COOH}{\underset{\|}{C}}}{=}O \right]$$

2-Keto-4-hydroxy-5-aminovaleric acid

$\rightleftharpoons$

$$\left[HO-CH-CH_2 \atop H_2C\diagdown N{=}C{-}COOH \right]$$

Δ1-Pyrroline-4-hydroxy-2-carboxylic acid

$\longrightarrow$

$$\left[CH{=}CH \atop H_2C\diagdown N{=}C{-}COOH \right]$$

$\longrightarrow$

$$HC{=}CH \atop HC\diagdown N{-} \underset{H}{\overset{C-COOH}{}}$$

Pyrrole-2-carboxylic acid

$$HOCH-CH_2 \atop {-}CH_2\;COOH \atop {-}NH_2$$

β-Hydroxy-γ-aminobutyric acid

(943). Pyrrole-2-carboxylic acid has also been found as a degradation product of sialic acid (944).

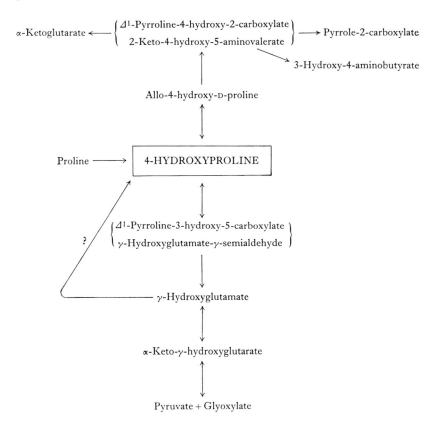

Summary scheme for the metabolism of 4-hydroxyproline.

K. Valine, Isoleucine, and Leucine

The metabolism of the three branched-chain amino acids may conveniently be discussed together. The first step in degradation and the last step in biosynthesis of these amino acids are transamination reactions (see p. 338); this discussion is concerned principally with the metabolism of the carbon skeletons of the amino acids.

Biosynthesis of Valine and Isoleucine

The isolation of a mutant of *Neurospora crassa* which required iso-leucine and valine by Bonner and associates (945) was the starting point for studies on the biosynthesis of these amino acids. Since that time the application of mutant, isotopic, and enzymatic techniques has resulted in a good understanding of the major steps in the biosynthesis of valine and isoleucine, and also of leucine.

Early studies on mutants of *Neurospora* and *Escherichia coli* suggested that α-ketoisovaleric and α-keto-β-methylvaleric acids were the immediate precursors of valine and isoleucine, respectively (946–949). Mutants were obtained which exhibit an absolute growth requirement for isoleucine and a partial requirement for valine. These organisms do not grow when supplied with the corresponding α-keto acids, and in fact accumulate the α-keto acid analogs of isoleucine and valine when grown on media con-taining minimal quantities of valine and isoleucine (949, 950). That such mutants were blocked at the stage of transamination of isoleucine was suggested by the growth studies and proved by enzymatic work which showed that the mutants lacked the transaminase that catalyzes isoleucine formation from α-keto-β-methylvalerate (951). Absence of this enzyme also explains the partial valine requirement; however, mutant and wild strain cells can form some valine by transamination between α-ketoiso-valeric acid and alanine or α-aminobutyric acid. The transaminase for this reaction is not sufficiently active to provide enough valine for maximal growth (951, 952). However, mutants grown for several transfers on media containing low concentrations of valine exhibit increased valine–alanine activity and then require little or no supplementation with valine for maximal growth (952). After these enzyme systems had been elucidated, it was found that either alanine or α-aminobutyric acid could support the growth of the "valine-requiring" mutants used in these studies, a finding that agreed with the proposed scheme (951, 952). Similar transaminases have been found in *N. crassa* (953, 954). Other aspects of the transaminase systems concerned in the biosynthesis of the branched-chain amino acids are considered elsewhere in this treatise (see p. 360).

α-Keto-β-methylvaleric and α-ketoisovaleric acids arise from the α,β-dihydroxy acid precursors, α,β-dihydroxy-β-methylvaleric acid, and α,β-dihydroxyisovaleric acid, respectively, which are accumulated by certain mutants that are blocked immediately prior to the transamination step (955–957). Such mutants grow when supplied with the α-keto compounds, and an enzyme (dihydroxy acid dehydrase) that catalyzes the dehydration of the dihydroxy acids to the corresponding α-keto acids has been found in a number of microorganisms (958–962). The enzyme has been looked for in tissues of the rat and in several lactobacilli, but it has not been found. The data indicate that the same enzyme catalyzes the formation of α-ketoisovaleric and α-keto-β-methylvaleric acids.

Isotopic studies on *Neurospora crassa* and *Torula utilis* provided important clues to the origin of the carbon skeletons of the dihydroxy acid precursors of α-ketoisovaleric and α-keto-β-methylvaleric acids. Studies with C^{14}-acetate suggested that the four-carbon straight chains of valine and isoleucine have a common origin (963). Subsequent work in two laboratories showed that the carbon skeletons of valine and isoleucine have different origins, although the reactions involved are similar. Thus, Strassman and associates (964, 965) studied the incorporation of lactate carbon into valine in *T. utilis*. The carboxyl carbon of lactate appeared exclusively in the carboxyl of valine, while the α- and β-carbon atoms of lactate proved to be the precursors of valine carbon atoms 2 and 3, and of the methyl carbons, respectively. A most significant observation was that both carbon atoms 2 and 3 arose from the α-carbon atom of lactate, a finding which suggested a coupling of the α-carbon atoms of two molecules of lactate. A formulation based on these observations is given below:

$$
\begin{array}{c}
c\ CH_3 \\
b\ C{=}O \\
a\ COOH
\end{array}
+
\begin{array}{c}
e\ CH_3 \\
d\ CHO
\end{array}
\longrightarrow
\begin{array}{c}
e\ CH_3 \\
d\ C{=}O \\
c\ CH_3{-}C{-}OH \\
b\ | \\
a\ COOH
\end{array}
\longrightarrow
$$

$$
\begin{array}{c}
e\ CH_3 \\
{\to}\,d\ C{=}O \\
c\ CH_3{-}C{-}OH \\
b\ | \\
a\ COOH
\end{array}
\longrightarrow
\begin{array}{c}
e\ CH_3 \\
c\ CH_3{-}_d CH \\
b\ C{=}O \\
a\ COOH
\end{array}
\longrightarrow
\begin{array}{c}
e\ CH_3 \\
c\ CH_3{-}_d CH \\
b\ CHNH_2 \\
a\ COOH
\end{array}
$$

According to this proposal, pyruvic acid and acetaldehyde condense to yield α-acetolactic acid, followed by migration of a methyl group from the α- to the β-position, a pinacol-type rearrangement. Rearrangement of α-acetolactic acid could also give α-keto-β-hydroxyisovaleric acid, which might serve as a precusor of valine. Adelberg (959), on the basis of studies on *Neurospora*, suggested a similar intramolecular rearrangement of α-acetolactic acid. His scheme accounts for formation of the dihydroxy acid precursor of valine, but does not involve intermediate formation of α-keto-β-hydroxyisovaleric acid. Both schemes are compatible with the known derivations of valine and pyruvic acid from acetic acid and carbon dioxide (966–968).

Although the findings of Strassman and associates (964, 965) were in substantial agreement with those of Adelberg (959), the latter author also considered the possibility that the initial step in valine biosynthesis is an aldol condensation of 2 molecules of pyruvate to form γ-hydroxy-γ-methyl-α-ketoglutarate. The postulated steps involve enolization, hydration, pinacol rearrangement, and decarboxylation. An analogous pathway was postulated for isoleucine biosynthesis. Findings consistent with this mechanism were obtained later by Willson and Adelberg (969), who studied a *Neurospora* mutant that required both isoleucine and valine for growth. This organism, which grew when supplied with the α-keto acid analogs of isoleucine and valine, did not respond to the dihydroxy acids nor did it accumulate them; however, it accumulated a large number of organic acids, two of which were identified as citramalic acid and α,β-

$$
\begin{array}{ccccc}
\underset{\substack{\mathrm{COOH} \\ | \\ \mathrm{O}\!=\!\mathrm{C}\!-\!\mathrm{CH_3} \\ + \\ \mathrm{CH_3} \\ | \\ \mathrm{C}\!=\!\mathrm{O} \\ | \\ \mathrm{COOH}}}{} & \longrightarrow &
\underset{\substack{\mathrm{COOH} \\ | \\ \mathrm{HO}\!-\!\mathrm{C}\!-\!\mathrm{CH_3} \\ | \\ \mathrm{CH_2} \\ | \\ \mathrm{C}\!=\!\mathrm{O} \\ | \\ \mathrm{COOH}}}{} & \longrightarrow &
\underset{\substack{\mathrm{COOH} \\ | \\ \mathrm{HO}\!-\!\mathrm{C}\!-\!\mathrm{CH_3} \\ | \\ \mathrm{CH_2} \\ | \\ \mathrm{COOH}}}{} \\[4em]
& & \substack{\gamma\text{-Hydroxy-}\gamma\text{-} \\ \text{methyl-}\alpha\text{-} \\ \text{ketoglutaric acid}} & & \text{Citramalic acid}
\end{array}
$$

$$
\begin{array}{ccccc}
\underset{\substack{\mathrm{COOH} \\ | \\ \mathrm{O}\!=\!\mathrm{C}\!-\!\mathrm{CH_3} \\ + \\ \mathrm{CH_3} \\ | \\ \mathrm{CH_2} \\ | \\ \mathrm{C}\!=\!\mathrm{O} \\ | \\ \mathrm{COOH}}}{} & \longrightarrow &
\underset{\substack{\mathrm{COOH} \\ | \\ \mathrm{HO}\!-\!\mathrm{C}\!-\!\mathrm{CH_3} \\ | \\ \mathrm{CH}\!-\!\mathrm{CH_3} \\ | \\ \mathrm{C}\!=\!\mathrm{O} \\ | \\ \mathrm{COOH}}}{} & \longrightarrow &
\underset{\substack{\mathrm{COOH} \\ | \\ \mathrm{HO}\!-\!\mathrm{C}\!-\!\mathrm{CH_3} \\ | \\ \mathrm{CH}\!-\!\mathrm{CH_3} \\ | \\ \mathrm{COOH}}}{} \\[4em]
& & \substack{\gamma\text{-Hydroxy-}\beta,\gamma\text{-} \\ \text{dimethyl-}\alpha\text{-} \\ \text{ketoglutaric acid}} & & \substack{\alpha,\beta\text{-Dimethylmalic} \\ \text{acid}}
\end{array}
$$

dimethylmalic acid. These compounds are, respectively, the expected decarboxylation products of γ-hydroxy-γ-methyl-α-ketoglutaric acid (known to be formed by condensation of 2 molecules of pyruvic acid; see p. 64), and the analogous product of condensation of α-ketobutyric acid and pyruvic acid, γ-hydroxy-β,γ-dimethyl-α-ketoglutaric acid. These relationships are shown above.

Although these compounds are probably formed in the manner postulated, subsequent studies failed to show that γ-hydroxy-γ-methyl-α-ketoglutaric acid is a precursor of valine. On the other hand, there is now excellent evidence that the first compounds formed in the biosynthesis of valine and isoleucine are α-acetolactate and α-aceto-α-hydroxybutyrate, respectively.

There are several lines of evidence indicating that α-acetolactate is an intermediate in valine biosynthesis. Umbarger et al. (970) and Umbarger and Brown (971) found that α-acetolactate was accumulated by a mutant of E. coli grown on media containing low concentrations of valine. It was also observed that C^{14}-acetolactate was incorporated into valine (as well as leucine; see below, p. 739), and that extracts of the wild strain organism catalyzed the formation of α-acetolactate from pyruvate; activity was stimulated by magnesium ions and a high concentration of thiamine pyrophosphate. The formation of this enzyme was repressed by valine, and valine also acted as an inhibitor (competitive with pyruvate) of the enzyme. Other studies (972, 973) demonstrated that extracts of yeast catalyzed the conversion of α-acetolactate to α-ketoisovalerate and to valine.

It has long been known that certain microorganisms can synthesize acetoin; Juni (974) showed that Aerobacter aerogenes formed acetoin only from pyruvate and that α-acetolactate is an intermediate in its formation:

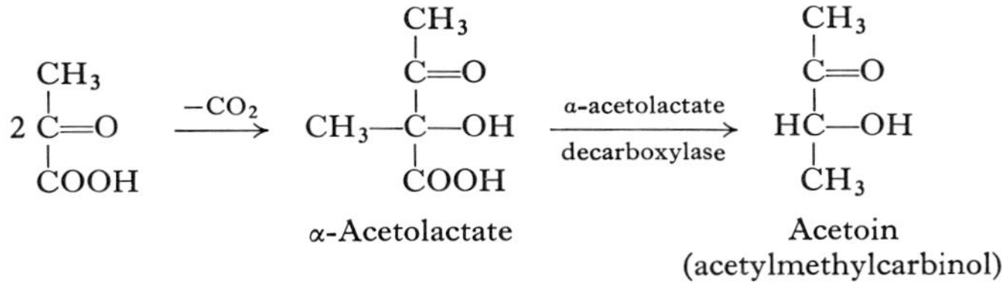

$$
2\ \begin{array}{c} CH_3 \\ | \\ C{=}O \\ | \\ COOH \end{array}
\xrightarrow{-CO_2}
CH_3{-}\begin{array}{c} CH_3 \\ | \\ C{=}O \\ | \\ C{-}OH \\ | \\ COOH \end{array}
\xrightarrow[\text{decarboxylase}]{\alpha\text{-acetolactate}}
\begin{array}{c} CH_3 \\ | \\ C{=}O \\ | \\ HC{-}OH \\ | \\ CH_3 \end{array}
$$

α-Acetolactate   Acetoin
(acetylmethylcarbinol)

The α-acetolactate-forming enzyme was separated from α-acetolactate decarboxylase; the latter was shown to be specific for the d-isomer of α-acetolactate. The formation of acetoin and α-acetolactate also occurs by other mechanisms in certain microbial and animal tissue systems which are able to utilize free acetaldehyde; the α-acetolactate formed by pyruvic oxidase is racemic (974, 975).

Halpern and Umbarger (976) showed that *A. aerogenes* can form two enzymes capable of synthesizing α-acetolactate; one of these catalyzes acetoin formation and acts predominantly at about pH 6, while the other synthesizes α-acetolactate for valine biosynthesis. The latter enzyme is inhibited noncompetitively by valine and its formation is repressed by valine. However, since *A. aerogenes* grows well in minimal medium at pH 5.8, the acetoin-forming enzyme may also function in valine biosynthesis. The mechanism of α-acetolactate synthesis probably involves the intermediate formation of "active acetaldehyde," whose structure has been elucidated by the work of Krampitz, Brown, and their collaborators (977, 978).

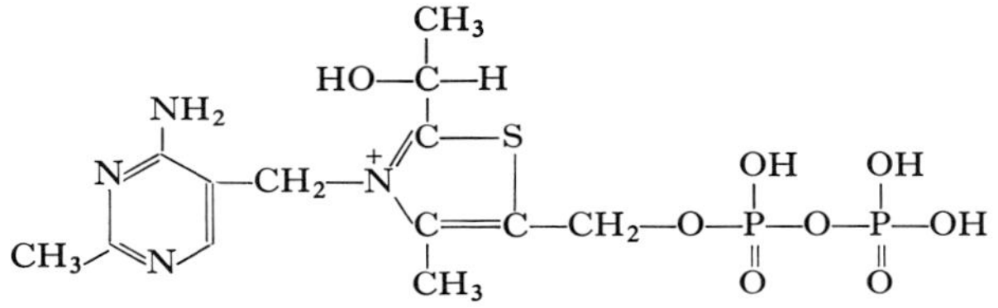

α-Hydroxyethyl thiamine pyrophosphate

Demonstration of the conversion of α-aceto-α-hydroxybutyric acid to α,β-dihydroxy-β-methylvaleric acid (979) is consistent with earlier experiment and thought concerning the biosynthesis of isoleucine. Additional evidence that α-acetolactate and α-aceto-α-hydroxybutyrate are intermediates was obtained in studies on a mutant of *N. crassa* which requires both isoleucine and valine for growth and accumulates both acetylmethylcarbinol (acetoin) and acetylethylcarbinol (980).

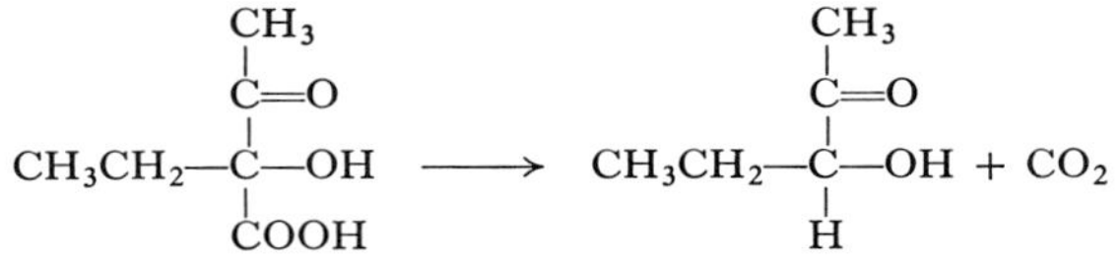

α-Aceto-α-hydroxybutyric   Acetylethylcarbinol
acid

These compounds, which are derived by decarboxylation of their respective precursors, accumulate only after the isoleucine and valine present in the medium are largely consumed. Extracts of *E. coli* catalyze the condensation of pyruvate and α-ketobutyrate to α-aceto-α-hydroxybutyrate in the presence of magnesium ions and thiamine pyrophosphate, and the enzyme activity involved is probably the same as that which catalyzes α-acetolactate formation (981, 982). Chemically synthesized α-aceto-α-hydroxybutyrate is converted to isoleucine by extracts of *E. coli* (983). It has been known for some time that growth of the K12 strain of *E. coli* is inhibited by valine and that inhibition is reversed by isoleucine. Leavitt and Umbarger (984) found that the synthesis of α-aceto-α-hydroxybutyrate and α-acetolactate in extracts of *E. coli* K12 was inhibited by valine. Less sensitivity to valine was observed with a valine-resistant mutant of strain K12 and *E. coli*, strain W.

Conversion of α-acetolactate and α-aceto-α-hydroxybutyrate to valine and isoleucine, respectively, via intermediate formation of the corresponding α,β-dihydroxy acids was independently demonstrated in several laboratories in experiments on *N. crassa*, *E. coli*, *A. aerogenes*, and yeast (979, 981, 985–987). Thus, the incorporation of α-aceto-α-hydroxybutyrate into isoleucine, and that of α-acetolactate into valine (and leucine) was shown, and certain isoleucine-requiring mutants were found able to utilize α-aceto-α-hydroxybutyrate for growth. The conversion of α-acetolactate and α-aceto-α-hydroxybutyrate to the corresponding α,β-dihydroxy acids was accomplished with extracts of microorganisms in the presence of reduced triphosphopyridine nucleotide and magnesium ions. Such extracts also catalyze conversion of α-keto-β-hydroxy-β-methylvalerate and α-keto-β-hydroxyisovalerate to the respective dihydroxy acids under similar conditions (979), and small amounts of α-keto-β-hydroxyisovalerate and α-keto-β-hydroxy-β-methylvalerate were found in the culture medium of a mutant of *N. crassa* (986). Although these observations are consistent with a pathway involving intermediate formation of the α-keto-β-hydroxy acids, enzyme preparations were obtained that catalyzed formation of the dihydroxy acids directly from α-acetolactate and α-aceto-α-hydroxybutyrate. No evidence could be obtained that the α-keto-β-hydroxy acids are intermediates in these reactions, and enzymatic formation of the α-keto-β-hydroxy acids was not demonstrated (986). The activity capable of converting the α-keto acids to the corresponding dihydroxy acids (reductase) was separated from that which catalyzes direct conversion of the α-aceto compounds to the dihydroxy acids (reductoisomerase). Armstrong and Wagner (988) purified the α-hydroxy-β-keto acid reductoisomerase from *Salmonella typhimurium*, and found that under certain conditions the activity could be partially destroyed with concomitant appearance of α-keto-β-hydroxy acid reductase activity. They therefore considered the possibility that the reductase was a modified form of the reductoisomerase. It is significant that mutants of *S. typhimurium* blocked at the reductoisomerase step (i.e., unable to grow on the α-hydroxy-β-keto acids) had low reductoisomerase activity, but exhibited much more reductase activity than did the wild type. Purification by starch gel electrophoresis gave a single band with reductoisomerase activity and three bands with reductase activity. Similar results were obtained by electrophoresis of a preparation of purified reductoisomerase that was initially free of reductase activity. The data taken together indicate that the reductoisomerase is the biosynthetically important enzyme rather than the reductase. It should also be mentioned that beef heart lactic dehydrogenase (and certain other preparations of lactic dehydrogenase) (989) catalyze the reduction of a wide variety of α-keto acids, including α-keto-β-hydroxypropionate and α-keto-β-hydroxybutyrate (see p. 167). The "reductase" might be identical with lactic dehydrogenase, and in this connection the observation that several reductase bands were found on electrophoresis recalls studies demonstrating the multiplicity of lactic dehydrogenases in various biological materials (990). Finally, it may be noted that Radhakrishnan *et al.* (986) found that α-keto-β-hydroxyisovalerate was reduced by preparations of animal tissues including the liver of the rat, guinea pig, mouse, and rabbit. Nevertheless, the findings are consistent with the possibility that the action of the reductoisomerase involves formation of an enzyme-bound α-keto-β-hydroxy acid; reduction of added α-keto acid might be catalyzed under certain conditions by the same enzyme, and alteration of the enzyme might change its catalytic properties.

The role of threonine as a precursor of isoleucine was indicated by studies which showed that threonine carbon appears in isoleucine [(959, 991–993), see also (160)]. Threonine furnishes carbon for positions 1, 2, 5, and 6 of isoleucine; positions 1 and 2 of threonine contribute carbon for the corresponding atoms of isoleucine:

Isoleucine

Threonine

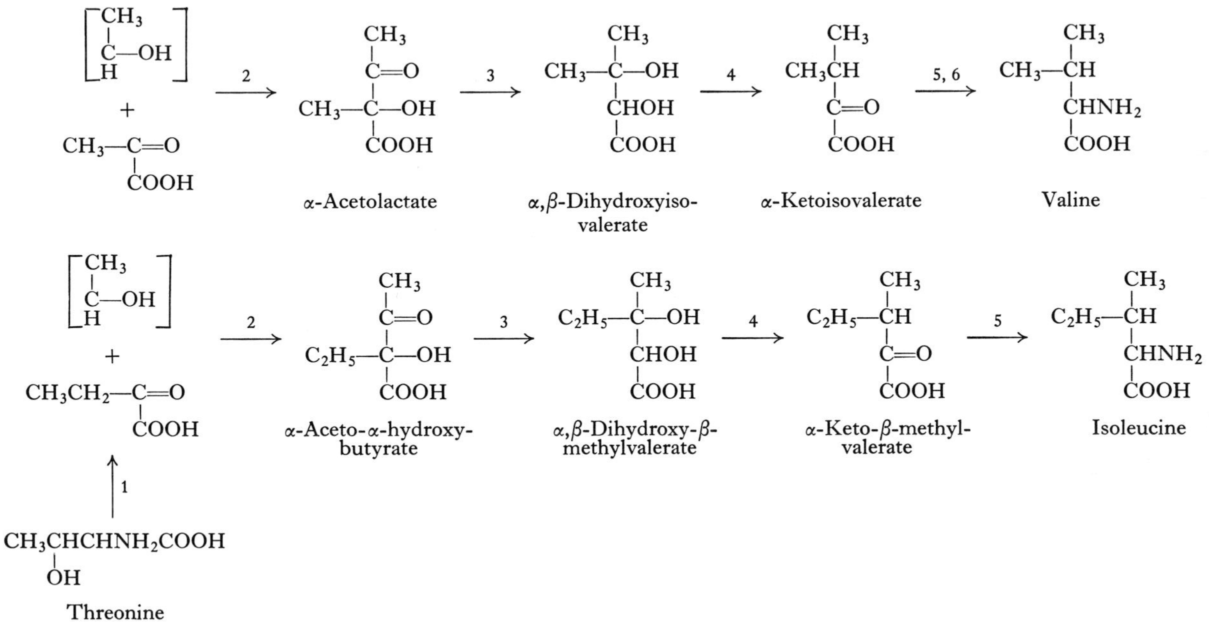

SCHEME 9. Biosynthesis of valine and isoleucine. 1, Threonine dehydrase. 2, α-Keto acid-"active acetaldehyde"-condensing enzyme. 3, Reductoisomerase. 4, α,β-Dihydroxy acid dehydrase. 5, Transaminase B (see p. 360). 6, Transaminase C (see p. 366).

These findings are consistent with conversion of threonine to α-keto-butyrate, and with the intramolecular rearrangement considered above. Threonine has been shown to be a precursor of isoleucine in *E. coli*, and mutants have been isolated that exhibit growth responses to either isoleucine or α-ketobutyrate; such mutants lack threonine dehydrase, which is inhibited by threonine and isoleucine (994). There is evidence that *E. coli* contains two types of threonine dehydrases, one of which serves a biosynthetic function and the other a degradative one. Under certain conditions, the activity of the latter may permit growth of mutants blocked in the formation of the biosynthetic dehydrase. Isoleucine spares the threonine requirement of a threonineless mutant of *E. coli* and inhibits accumulation of α-keto-β-methylvaleric acid by a mutant blocked at the transamination step. Isoleucine was found to inhibit threonine dehydrase much more effectively than threonine; thus, isoleucine inhibits the first step in its synthesis, and there is also evidence that isoleucine represses overproduction of threonine dehydrase (994).

Scheme 9 summarizes the pathways of biosynthesis of isoleucine and valine. The available data indicate that the same enzymes are involved in steps 2–4.

Although threonine is an obligatory intermediate in the formation of isoleucine in *E. coli* under "normal" conditions, other precursors of α-ketobutyrate (e.g., α-aminobutyrate, homoserine) can replace threonine as a source of isoleucine carbon. The discovery that β-methylaspartic acid could serve as a precursor of isoleucine arose from experiments designed to determine whether β-methylaspartic acid was converted to thymine. Evidence for the latter conversion was not obtained, but when *E. coli* was grown on media containing C^{14}-methyl-labeled β-methylaspartate, the proteins contained isoleucine labeled in a methyl group (995). A consider-able portion of isoleucine was derived from β-methylaspartic acid, since the specific radioactivity of the isolated isoleucine was about 30% of that of the β-methylaspartic acid added to the medium. The ability of certain organisms to convert glutamic acid to β-methylaspartic acid (see p. 618) suggests a pathway from glutamic acid to isoleucine. (See p. 739.)

Several observations indicate that the pathway of valine and isoleucine biosynthesis discovered in microorganisms exists also in higher plants. A dihydroxy acid dehydrase has been purified from spinach leaf, which requires added magnesium ions for maximal activity. The enzyme is more active toward the *threo-* than the *erythro*-isomer of DL-α,β-dihydroxy-butyric acid (996). Preparations of the dehydrase from microorganisms

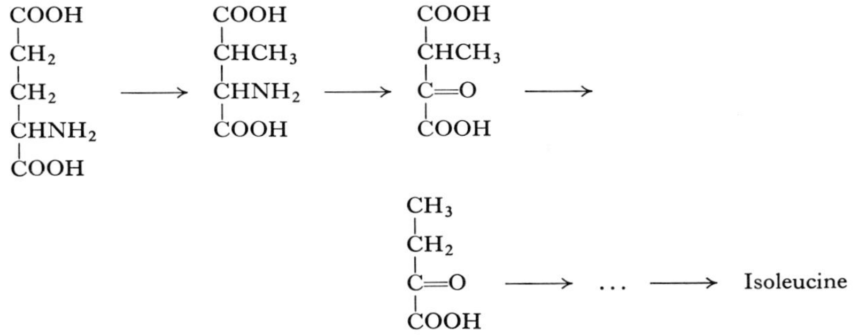

$$
\begin{array}{l}
\text{COOH} \\
\text{CH}_2 \\
\text{CH}_2 \\
\text{CHNH}_2 \\
\text{COOH}
\end{array}
\longrightarrow
\begin{array}{l}
\text{COOH} \\
\text{CHCH}_3 \\
\text{CHNH}_2 \\
\text{COOH}
\end{array}
\longrightarrow
\begin{array}{l}
\text{COOH} \\
\text{CHCH}_3 \\
\text{C=O} \\
\text{COOH}
\end{array}
\longrightarrow
$$

$$
\begin{array}{l}
\text{CH}_3 \\
\text{CH}_2 \\
\text{C=O} \\
\text{COOH}
\end{array}
\longrightarrow \; \ldots \; \longrightarrow \text{Isoleucine}
$$

exhibit a similar specificity. It is probable that only one of the four possible isomers of each of the natural substrates is acted upon by the enzyme, but definitive studies on this point have not yet been done. Satyanarayana and Radhakrishnan (997) demonstrated the presence of dihydroxy acid dehydrase in the germinated seeds of green gram (*Phaseolus radiatus*), preparations of which also catalyze formation of α-acetolactate, conversion of this compound and α-aceto-α-hydroxybutyrate to the corresponding α,β-dihydroxy acids, and transamination of the α-keto analogs of isoleucine and valine to the corresponding amino acids. Kretovich and collaborators (998, 999) carried out studies in which the α-keto acid analogs of valine and isoleucine were introduced into ripening wheat ears through the transpiration current of the stem; this procedure led to the accumulation of considerable amounts of valine and isoleucine. Similar results were obtained with the dihydroxy acid analog of isoleucine in experiments on green seedlings of wheat, pea, and sunflower.

Biosynthesis of Leucine

Early studies on the biosynthesis of leucine in *Torula utilis* with labeled acetate and lactate indicated that leucine was synthesized from acetate and the isobutyryl moiety of valine (1000). Isotopic competition studies with *E. coli* (339, 814) had previously suggested that α-ketoisovaleric acid was a precursor of leucine. These observations and data from experiments with isotopes (160, 1001, 1002) were consistent with a scheme for the biosynthesis of leucine proposed by Strassman and associates (1002). These investigators suggested condensation between α-ketoisovaleric acid and the methyl carbon atom of acetyl-coenzyme A to give α-hydroxy-α-isopropylsuccinic acid (α-isopropylmalic acid, β-carboxy-β-hydroxy-isocaproic acid), a reaction analogous to the formation of citric acid from

oxaloacetic acid and acetyl-coenzyme A. The other postulated transformations also followed the pattern of the citric acid cycle to yield in
sequence isopropylmaleic acid, α-hydroxy-β-carboxyisocaproic acid
(β-isopropylmalic acid), α-keto-β-carboxyisocaproic acid, and α-ketoisocaproic acid. This pathway has been substantiated by later study.
Thus, β-carboxy-β-hydroxyisocaproic acid was isolated from the culture
media of several leucine-requiring mutants of *Neurospora crassa* (1003,
1004), *Salmonella typhimurium* (1003), *Aspergillus fumigatus*, *Streptomyces erythreus*, and *Nocardia lurida* (1005); it was also formed by
Corynebacterium sp., which does not exhibit an amino acid requirement
for growth (1005). Extracts of *N. crassa* and *S. typhimurium* catalyze the
formation of β-carboxy-β-hydroxyisocaproic acid from α-ketoisovaleric
acid and acetyl-coenzyme A, and the conversion of β-carboxy-β-
hydroxyisocaproic acid to α-ketoisocaproic acid was demonstrated with
an extract of *S. typhimurium* in the presence of diphosphopyridine
nucleotide (1003). Evidence was obtained that the isolated compound is
identical with the levorotatory isomer of synthetic β-carboxy-β-hydroxyisocaproic acid (1005, 1006). The conversion of C^{14}-valine to β-carboxy-
β-hydroxyisocaproic acid has also been demonstrated with extracts of
E. coli in the presence of acetyl-coenzyme A and other cofactors (1004).
The enzymatic synthesis of β-carboxy-β-hydroxyisocaproic acid catalyzed
by yeast preparations requires coenzyme A, adenosine triphosphate,
magnesium ions, acetate, and α-ketoisovalerate (1007). Acetyl-coenzyme
A replaces coenzyme A, adenosine triphosphate, and acetate, and the
disappearance of acetyl-coenzyme A in the presence of α-ketoisovalerate
and enzyme is associated with formation of product. Incubation of the
isolated β-carboxy-β-hydroxyisocaproic acid with yeast extracts led to an
increase in absorbancy at 240 mμ, offering presumptive evidence for the
formation of an α,β-unsaturated acid; however, similar studies with
racemic β-carboxy-β-hydroxyisocaproic acid showed no change in
absorbancy, suggesting that the unnatural *d*-isomer inhibits the reaction
(1007). The observation that α-isopropylmaleate supports the growth of
S. typhimurium mutants, while isopropylfumaric acid does not (1003),
suggests that the dehydration of β-carboxy-β-hyroxyisocaproic acid
yields the *cis*-α,β-unsaturated acid. The enzyme that catalyzes conversion
of β-carboxy-β-hydroxyisocaproate to α-hydroxy-β-carboxyisocaproate
was partially purified from *N. crassa*; this reversible reaction is accompanied by formation of an unsaturated compound, probably α-isopropylmaleic acid (dimethylcitraconic acid) (1008). The latter reaction appears

to be analogous to that catalyzed by aconitase, and the final reaction in the biosynthesis of α-ketoisocaproic acid is also analogous to the corresponding reaction of the citric acid cycle. An enzyme activity capable of converting α-hydroxy-β-carboxyisocaproic acid to α-ketoisocaproic acid in the presence of diphosphopyridine nucleotide was partially purified from *S. typhimurium* (1009). α-Keto-β-carboxyisocaproic acid may be an enzyme-bound intermediate in this reaction.

The similarity of the pathway of leucine biosynthesis to the reactions of the citric acid cycle has served usefully in directing experiments. Undoubtedly, different enzymes are involved, but it would be of interest to determine whether the enzymes of the two pathways overlap in specificity. In contrast to the condensation of oxaloacetate and acetyl-coenzyme A, the first step in leucine biosynthesis leads to a product that is asymmetric in the classical sense. Although the α-carboxyl group of the keto acid is lost as carbon dioxide in both pathways, the position of the double bond formed by dehydration of the condensation product is different. Another reaction analogous to the first step in leucine biosynthesis is that catalyzed by malate synthetase, which catalyzes the condensation of acetyl-coenzyme A and glyoxylate to yield malate (see p. 640). A pathway similar to that of leucine biosynthesis has been proposed for the biosynthesis of α-ketoadipic acid, which is a precursor of lysine (see p. 936). The formation of α-ketobutyrate, α-ketovalerate, and α-ketocaproate from the respective next-lower α-keto acids in yeast may take place by substantially the same mechanism (1010). Thus, if one replaces α-ketoisovalerate by pyruvate in the scheme for leucine biosynthesis (Scheme 10), the product would be α-ketobutyrate.

There is evidence that the carboxyl carbon atom of α-ketoisovalerate is converted to a one-carbon unit in *A. aerogenes* (1011). Culture of this organism in the presence of aminopterin led to accumulation of valine (as well as alanine and 5-amino-4-imidazolecarboxamide ribonucleotide). On recovery from aminopterin inhibition, both alanine and valine were utilized; the data suggest that alanine (via pyruvate and acetyl-coenzyme A) provides the two-carbon unit added to the α-ketoisovalerate carbon chain during leucine synthesis and that folic acid is required for utilization of the carboxyl carbon atom of α-ketoisovalerate. The details of the latter reaction require study at the enzyme level.

Studies on higher plants have shown conversion of C^{14}-valine to leucine, suggesting that the pathway of leucine biosynthesis is similar to that of *E. coli* and the other microorganisms studied (1012). However,

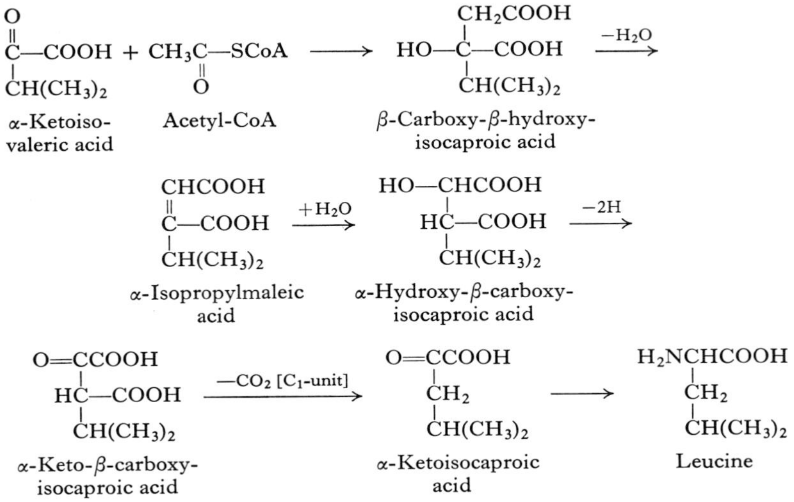

$$
\begin{array}{c}
\underset{\text{CH(CH}_3)_2}{\overset{\overset{\displaystyle O}{\parallel}}{\underset{|}{C}}\text{—COOH}} + \underset{\overset{\displaystyle O}{\parallel}}{\text{CH}_3\text{C}}\text{—SCoA} \longrightarrow \underset{\text{CH(CH}_3)_2}{\overset{\text{CH}_2\text{COOH}}{\underset{|}{\text{HO—C—COOH}}}} \xrightarrow{-\text{H}_2\text{O}}
\end{array}
$$

α-Ketoiso-   Acetyl-CoA   β-Carboxy-β-hydroxy-
valeric acid   isocaproic acid

$$
\underset{\text{CH(CH}_3)_2}{\overset{\text{CHCOOH}}{\underset{|}{\overset{\parallel}{C}\text{—COOH}}}} \xrightarrow{+\text{H}_2\text{O}} \underset{\text{CH(CH}_3)_2}{\overset{\text{HO—CHCOOH}}{\underset{|}{\text{HC—COOH}}}} \xrightarrow{-2\text{H}}
$$

α-Isopropylmaleic   α-Hydroxy-β-carboxy-
acid   isocaproic acid

$$
\underset{\text{CH(CH}_3)_2}{\overset{\text{O=CCOOH}}{\underset{|}{\text{HC—COOH}}}} \xrightarrow{-\text{CO}_2 \,[\text{C}_1\text{-unit}]} \underset{\text{CH(CH}_3)_2}{\overset{\text{O=CCOOH}}{\underset{|}{\text{CH}_2}}} \longrightarrow \underset{\text{CH(CH}_3)_2}{\overset{\text{H}_2\text{NCHCOOH}}{\underset{|}{\text{CH}_2}}}
$$

α-Keto-β-carboxy-   α-Ketoisocaproic   Leucine
isocaproic acid   acid

SCHEME 10. Biosynthesis of leucine.

Ruminococcus flavefaciens appears to have a different pathway of leucine biosynthesis. Thus, it was reported that in this organism isovaleric acid labeled in the carboxyl group was converted to leucine, which was labeled in carbon atom 2 (1013).

The formation of isoamyl alcohol by yeast seems to take place by a pathway similar to that for leucine biosynthesis; thus, α-ketoisocaproic acid is decarboxylated to isovaleraldehyde, which is reduced to isoamyl alcohol (1010). Other higher alcohols produced by yeasts are probably formed by analogous reactions from the corresponding α-keto acids. The conversion of α-ketobutyric acid to active amyl alcohol (1013a) appears to take place via the pathway described above for synthesis of α-keto-β-methylvaleric acid.

Degradation of Leucine

The degradative pathways of valine, isoleucine, and leucine have been studied in mammalian tissues and the initial steps follow a similar pattern, i.e., transamination to the respective α-keto acids, followed by irreversible oxidative decarboxylation to the corresponding acyl-coenzyme A derivatives.

It was recognized in early studies that the metabolism of leucine and isovaleric acid in mammals gives rise to ketone bodies (1014–1016). The steps involved in the conversion of leucine to acetoacetic acid were elucidated by isotope experiments and later by enzymatic studies. Studies with isotopic carbon demonstrated that carbon atoms 1 and 2 of isovaleric acid (corresponding to the α- and β-carbon atoms of leucine) give rise to two-carbon fragments capable of condensing to form aceto-acetate (1017–1020), that the methyl group carbon atoms of the isopropyl residue become the methyl and methylene carbon atoms of acetoacetic acid, and that the γ-carbon atom of leucine (or carbon atom 3 of iso-valeric acid) becomes the carbonyl carbon of acetoacetic acid. These studies also showed that carbon dioxide is incorporated into the carboxyl group of acetoacetic acid (1019, 1021). Enzymatic studies by Coon and associates (1022–1025) and others demonstrated the intermediates and reactions involved (see Scheme 11).

The decarboxylation of α-ketoisocaproic acid yields isovaleryl-coenzyme A (in analogy with the conversion of pyruvate to acetyl-coenzyme A), which is oxidized to senecioyl-coenzyme A (β-methyl-crotonyl-coenzyme A), again by analogy with the reactions involved in metabolism of the straight-chain fatty acids (1026, 1027). It has been suggested that isovaleraldehyde is an intermediate between α-ketoiso-caproic acid and isovaleryl-coenzyme A. Although decarboxylation to the aldehyde is catalyzed by preparations of *Proteus vulgaris*, the following postulated reaction has not yet been demonstrated (1028):

$$(CH_3)_2CHCH_2CHO + CoA\!-\!SH + DPN^+ \rightleftharpoons$$
$$(CH_3)_2CHCH_2\underset{\underset{O}{\|}}{C}\!-\!S\!-\!CoA + DPNH + H^+$$

Evidence for the conversion of isovaleryl-coenzyme A to β-methyl-crotonyl-coenzyme A was obtained by anaerobic incubation of the former compound with triphenyltetrazolium chloride, methylene blue, and a rat liver preparation; reduction of the triphenyltetrazolium dye was observed, and paper chromatographic evidence for the formation of β-hydroxy-isovaleryl-coenzyme A was obtained. Extracts of heart and liver as well as crystalline crotonase from ox liver catalyze the reversible hydration of β-methylcrotonyl-coenzyme A to β-hydroxyisovaleryl-coenzyme A. Although it was originally thought that β-hydroxyisovaleryl-coenzyme A was carboxylated, later work showed that β-methylcrotonyl-coenzyme A was the actual substrate for the carboxylation reaction. The possibi-lity that β-methylvinylacetyl-coenzyme A was carboxylated was also

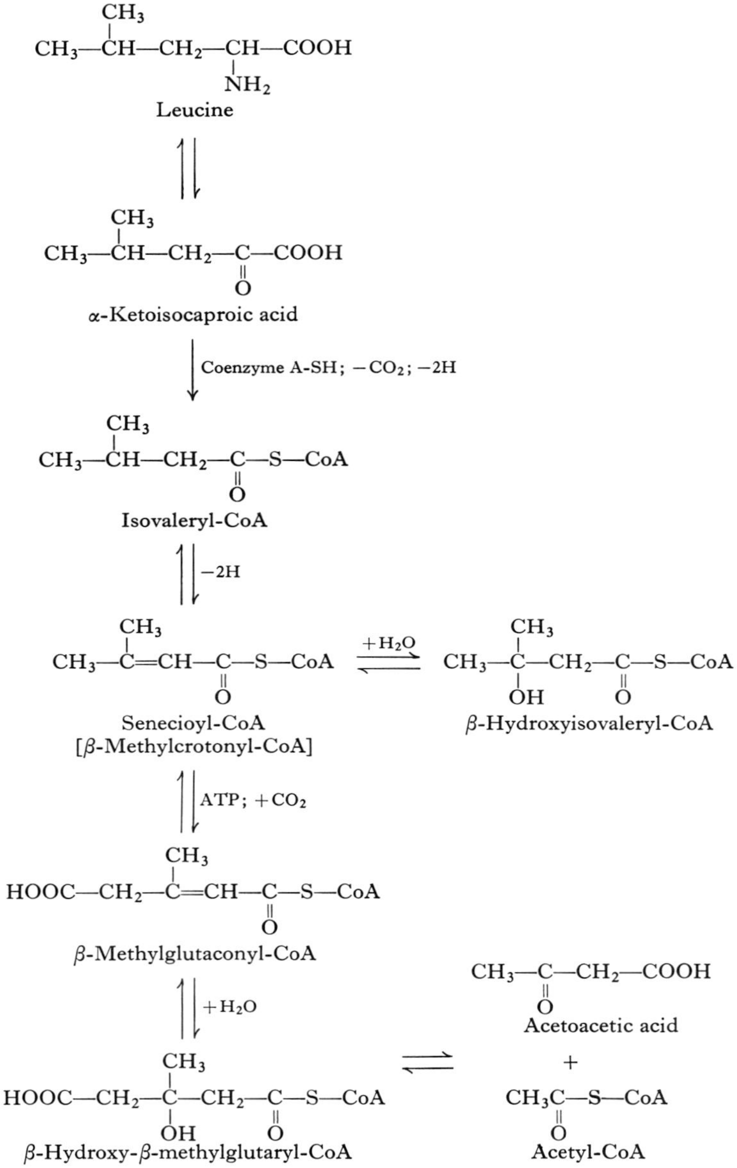

$$CH_3-\overset{\overset{\displaystyle CH_3}{\displaystyle |}}{CH}-CH_2-\overset{\overset{\displaystyle |}{\displaystyle NH_2}}{CH}-COOH$$

Leucine

$$CH_3-\overset{\overset{\displaystyle CH_3}{\displaystyle |}}{CH}-CH_2-\overset{\overset{\displaystyle |}{\displaystyle \underset{O}{\|}}}{C}-COOH$$

α-Ketoisocaproic acid

Coenzyme A-SH; $-CO_2$; $-2H$

$$CH_3-\overset{\overset{\displaystyle CH_3}{\displaystyle |}}{CH}-CH_2-\overset{\overset{\displaystyle |}{\displaystyle \underset{O}{\|}}}{C}-S-CoA$$

Isovaleryl-CoA

$-2H$

$$CH_3-\overset{\overset{\displaystyle CH_3}{\displaystyle |}}{C}=CH-\overset{\overset{\displaystyle |}{\displaystyle \underset{O}{\|}}}{C}-S-CoA \quad \overset{+H_2O}{\rightleftharpoons} \quad CH_3-\overset{\overset{\displaystyle CH_3}{\displaystyle |}}{\underset{OH}{C}}-CH_2-\overset{\overset{\displaystyle |}{\displaystyle \underset{O}{\|}}}{C}-S-CoA$$

Senecioyl-CoA   β-Hydroxyisovaleryl-CoA
[β-Methylcrotonyl-CoA]

ATP; $+CO_2$

$$HOOC-CH_2-\overset{\overset{\displaystyle CH_3}{\displaystyle |}}{C}=CH-\overset{\overset{\displaystyle |}{\displaystyle \underset{O}{\|}}}{C}-S-CoA$$

β-Methylglutaconyl-CoA

$+H_2O$

$$CH_3-\overset{\overset{\displaystyle }{\displaystyle \underset{O}{\|}}}{C}-CH_2-COOH$$
Acetoacetic acid

$\rightleftharpoons$

$+$

$$HOOC-CH_2-\overset{\overset{\displaystyle CH_3}{\displaystyle |}}{\underset{OH}{C}}-CH_2-\overset{\overset{\displaystyle }{\displaystyle \underset{O}{\|}}}{C}-S-CoA \qquad CH_3\overset{\overset{\displaystyle }{\displaystyle \underset{O}{\|}}}{C}-S-CoA$$

β-Hydroxy-β-methylglutaryl-CoA   Acetyl-CoA

SCHEME 11. Conversion of leucine to acetoacetic acid and acetyl-coenzyme A.

excluded, and this compound was shown to be converted to β-methyl-crotonyl-coenzyme A by the enzyme vinyl acetyl isomerase, which was purified from ox liver (1029). The carboxylation of β-methylcrotonyl-coenzyme A is associated with the cleavage of adenosine triphosphate to adenosine diphosphate and orthophosphate, and the formation of β-methylglutaconyl-coenzyme A (1030–1032). Lynen and his colleagues have proposed that the reaction takes place in two steps as shown below:

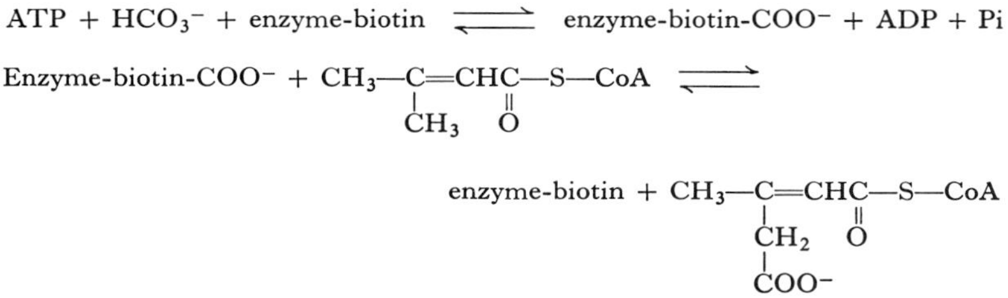

$$\text{ATP} + \text{HCO}_3^- + \text{enzyme-biotin} \; \rightleftharpoons \; \text{enzyme-biotin-COO}^- + \text{ADP} + \text{Pi}$$

$$\text{Enzyme-biotin-COO}^- + \text{CH}_3\text{—C}\!\!=\!\!\text{CHC—S—CoA} \; \rightleftharpoons$$
$$\overset{|}{\underset{\text{CH}_3}{}} \quad \overset{\|}{\underset{\text{O}}{}}$$

$$\text{enzyme-biotin} + \text{CH}_3\text{—C}\!\!=\!\!\text{CHC—S—CoA}$$
$$\overset{|}{\underset{\text{CH}_2}{}} \quad \overset{\|}{\underset{\text{O}}{}}$$
$$\overset{|}{\underset{\text{COO}^-}{}}$$

These investigations, which were carried out with a purified bacterial preparation of the enzyme, showed that the enzyme carboxylated free biotin when it was incubated with biotin, adenosine triphosphate, and potassium bicarbonate. β-Methylcrotonyl-coenzyme A carboxylase is apparently the only carboxylase that catalyzes carboxylation of free biotin; such carboxylated biotin was isolated by Lynen and collaborators as the methyl ester and shown to be identical with $1'$-N-carboxy-($+$)-biotin (1033). When stoichiometric quantities of the enzyme were in-cubated with adenosine triphosphate, labeled bicarbonate, and magnesium ions and then passed through a column of Sephadex, radio-activity was found associated with the protein. After incubation of the labeled protein with β-methylcrotonyl-coenzyme A and hydrolysis of the coenzyme A derivatives, radioactivity was detected in β-methylglutaconic acid as well as in β-hydroxy-β-methylglutaric acid. The finding of radioactivity in the latter compound is due to the presence of β-methyl-glutaconase in the enzyme preparation. Degradation of $C^{14}O_2$-β-methylcrotonyl carboxylase with trypsin, followed by esterification with diazomethane and hydrolysis with biotinidase gave $1'$-N-carboxymethyl-($+$)-biotin which contained virtually all of the radioactivity originally present in the enzyme (1034). Similar studies and results were obtained with propionyl carboxylase (1035), and there is now substantial evidence that biotin is linked to propionyl carboxylase and the other carboxylases through peptide linkage with an ϵ-amino group of a protein lysine (1036) (see p. 446).

Analogous mechanisms of carboxylation have been proposed for propionyl-coenzyme A carboxylase (1037–1040) and pyruvic carboxylase (1041). However, in contrast to these observations, Waite and Wakil (1042) have reported that C^{14}-bicarbonate was incorporated into acetyl-coenzyme A carboxylase in the presence of adenosine triphosphate to yield a labeled enzyme, which on hydrolysis with strong acid or alkali gave free biotin containing more than 85% of the radioactivity originally bound to the protein. The label was located only in the ureido carbon atom of the isolated biotin. Although these workers found that the carboxylase gave biotin on hydrolysis, after treatment of the enzyme with acetyl-coenzyme A or adenosine diphosphate and phosphate, a biotin derivative tentatively identified as "diaminobiotin" was obtained. These observations were interpreted to indicate that the "decarboxylated" enzyme possessed a "diaminobiotin" coenzyme, which could be converted to the biotin-enzyme in the presence of bicarbonate, adenosine triphosphate, and Mn^{++}. These observations on acetyl-coenzyme A carboxylase are quite different from those made on the other carboxylases. Although it is possible that the mechanism of acetyl-coenzyme A carboxylase differs from those of the other enzymes of this group, this would be surprising, and it is evident that further investigation is needed. Although the weight of evidence supports the mechanism proposed by Lynen and his collaborators for those enzymes studied by them, it is possible that an independent mechanism exists for incorporation of carbon dioxide into the ureido carbon atom of biotin.

It was originally believed that the carboxylation reaction involved enzymatic formation of an activated form of carbon dioxide by an enzyme designated "hydroxylamine kinase"; this enzyme, also known as "carbon dioxide activating enzyme," was shown to be identical with pyruvic kinase (1043, 1044). The cleavage of β-hydroxy-β-methylglutaryl-coenzyme A to acetoacetic acid and acetyl-coenzyme A is catalyzed by extracts of liver, kidney, and heart (1024). The enzyme activity was purified from pig heart and shown to require magnesium or manganese ions and a thiol compound. β-Hydroxy-β-methylglutaryl-coenzyme A is hydrolyzed by an enzyme that has been demonstrated in mammalian liver, kidney, and brain and also in several microorganisms; it was partially purified from chicken liver (1045). β-Hydroxy-β-methylglutaryl-coenzyme A is also formed from acetoacetyl-coenzyme A and acetyl-coenzyme A (1046).

Conversion of Leucine to Isoprenoid Compounds

β-Hydroxy-β-methylglutaryl-coenzyme A is reduced to mevalonic acid by an enzyme that has been purified from yeast and shown to require reduced triphosphopyridine nucleotide (1047, 1048). Mevalonic acid is a precursor of cholesterol, carotenes, rubber, compounds of the coenzyme Q group, and other compounds (1049, 1050). Thus, β-hydroxy-β-methylglutaryl-coenzyme A is an intermediate at the branching point between the metabolism of leucine, fatty acids, and isoprenoid compounds. The incorporation of leucine carbon into cholesterol (1051, 1052) and carotenes (1053, 1054) had been observed in a number of earlier studies.

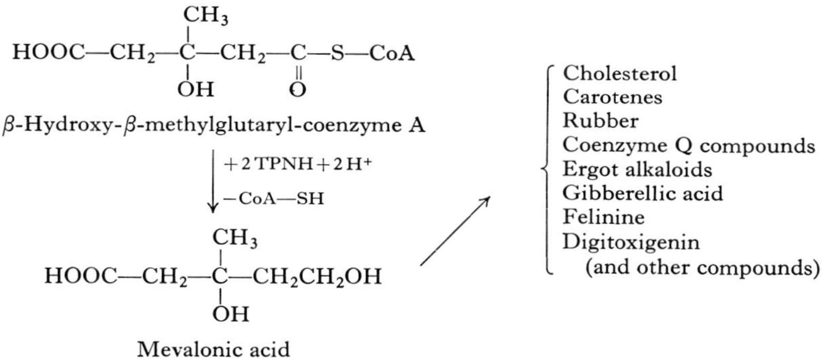

$$\overset{\displaystyle CH_3}{\underset{\displaystyle OH \quad\quad O}{HOOC-CH_2-\overset{|}{\underset{|}{C}}-CH_2-\overset{\|}{C}-S-CoA}}$$

β-Hydroxy-β-methylglutaryl-coenzyme A

$$\downarrow \begin{array}{l} +2\,TPNH+2\,H^+ \\ -CoA-SH \end{array}$$

$$\overset{\displaystyle CH_3}{\underset{\displaystyle OH}{HOOC-CH_2-\overset{|}{\underset{|}{C}}-CH_2CH_2OH}}$$

Mevalonic acid

Cholesterol
Carotenes
Rubber
Coenzyme Q compounds
Ergot alkaloids
Gibberellic acid
Felinine
Digitoxigenin
(and other compounds)

Degradation of Valine

Although the degradation of valine involves several reactions similar to those that occur in leucine metabolism, the end products are quite different. It has, in fact, been known for some time that valine is glycogenic (1055–1058). Evidence derived from isotopic tracer experiments suggested that valine is metabolized to a three-carbon acid which is utilized for glycogen synthesis (1057, 1058). Early studies with labeled valine and other work (1057–1060) provided data that were of considerable significance in guiding subsequent investigations of the enzymatic transformations involved; present knowledge of the steps involved in the degradation of valine may be summarized as shown in Scheme 12.

Isobutyryl-coenzyme A was shown to be converted to methacrylyl-coenzyme A by an experimental procedure analogous to that used for

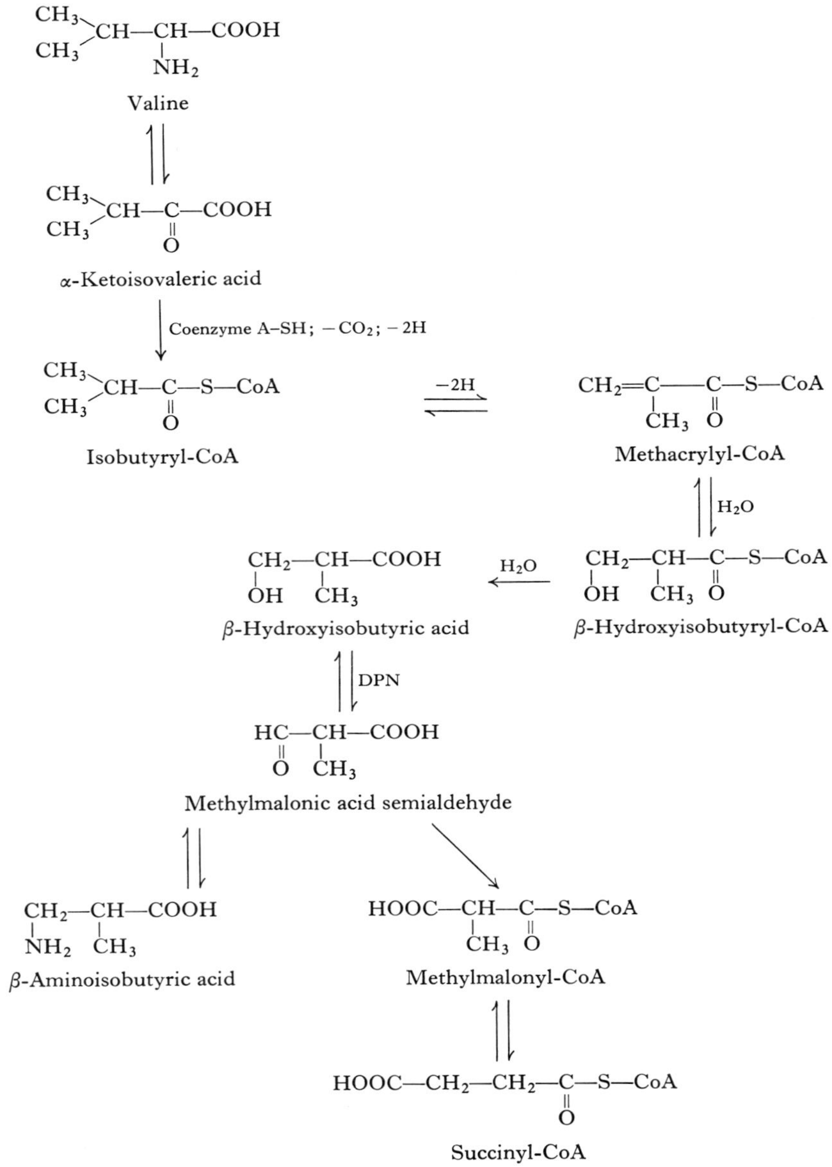

$$\begin{matrix} CH_3 \\ CH_3 \end{matrix} \!\!> \!\! CH\!\!-\!\!CH\!\!-\!\!COOH$$
$$\underset{NH_2}{|}$$

Valine

$$\begin{matrix} CH_3 \\ CH_3 \end{matrix} \!\!> \!\! CH\!\!-\!\!C\!\!-\!\!COOH$$
$$\underset{O}{\parallel}$$

α-Ketoisovaleric acid

Coenzyme A–SH; $-CO_2$; $-2H$

$$\begin{matrix} CH_3 \\ CH_3 \end{matrix} \!\!> \!\! CH\!\!-\!\!C\!\!-\!\!S\!\!-\!\!CoA$$
$$\underset{O}{\parallel}$$

Isobutyryl-CoA

$$\xrightarrow{-2H}$$

$$CH_2\!\!=\!\!C\!\!-\!\!\!\underset{CH_3}{\overset{}{|}}\!\!\!-\!\!C\!\!-\!\!S\!\!-\!\!CoA$$
$$CH_3 \quad O$$

Methacrylyl-CoA

H_2O

$$CH_2\!\!-\!\!CH\!\!-\!\!COOH$$
$$\underset{OH}{|} \quad \underset{CH_3}{|}$$

β-Hydroxyisobutyric acid

$$\xleftarrow{H_2O}$$

$$CH_2\!\!-\!\!CH\!\!-\!\!C\!\!-\!\!S\!\!-\!\!CoA$$
$$\underset{OH}{|} \quad \underset{CH_3}{|} \quad \underset{O}{\parallel}$$

β-Hydroxyisobutyryl-CoA

DPN

$$HC\!\!-\!\!CH\!\!-\!\!COOH$$
$$\underset{O}{\parallel} \quad \underset{CH_3}{|}$$

Methylmalonic acid semialdehyde

$$CH_2\!\!-\!\!CH\!\!-\!\!COOH$$
$$\underset{NH_2}{|} \quad \underset{CH_3}{|}$$

β-Aminoisobutyric acid

$$HOOC\!\!-\!\!CH\!\!-\!\!C\!\!-\!\!S\!\!-\!\!CoA$$
$$\underset{CH_3}{|} \quad \underset{O}{\parallel}$$

Methylmalonyl-CoA

$$HOOC\!\!-\!\!CH_2\!\!-\!\!CH_2\!\!-\!\!C\!\!-\!\!S\!\!-\!\!CoA$$
$$\underset{O}{\parallel}$$

Succinyl-CoA

SCHEME 12. Degradation of valine.

the dehydrogenation of isovaleryl-coenzyme A to β-methylcrotonyl-coenzyme A (1061); the reaction is also catalyzed by butyryl-coenzyme A dehydrogenase (1062). The hydration of methacrylyl-coenzyme A to β-hydroxyisobutyryl-coenzyme A is catalyzed by pig heart preparations and by crystalline crotonase. β-Hydroxyisobutyryl-coenzyme A is converted to β-hydroxyisobutyric acid by a deacylase, which has been found in pig heart, liver, brain, and kidney, and also in *N. crassa* (46). The formation of methylmalonic acid semialdehyde from β-hydroxyiso-butyric acid is catalyzed by a pyridine nucleotide-dependent dehydrogen-ase, which has been purified from pig kidney and which has been found in other animal tissues and in microorganisms (1063). The enzyme does not oxidize β-hydroxyisobutyryl-coenzyme A. Methylmalonic acid semialdehyde transaminates with glutamate to give β-aminoisobutyrate and α-ketoglutarate in the presence of an enzyme purified from pig kidney. The enzyme also catalyzes transamination between β-alanine and α-ketoglutarate to yield malonic acid semialdehyde and glutamate (45). These reactions and the formation of β-aminoisobutyrate and β-alanine from thymine and uracil, respectively, are discussed elsewhere in this volume (see p. 601). Additional metabolic fates of methylmalonic acid semialdehyde include conversion to methylmalonic acid and methyl-malonyl-coenzyme A. The latter compound is an intermediate in the conversion of propionate to succinate. The carboxylation of propionyl-coenzyme A catalyzed by propionyl carboxylase takes place in accordance with the following reaction:

$$\text{ATP} + \text{CO}_2 + \text{propionyl—CoA} \underset{}{\overset{}{\rightleftharpoons}}$$
$$\text{ADP} + \text{inorganic phosphate} + \text{methylmalonyl—CoA}$$

This enzyme has been purified from pig heart and from other sources and shown to contain biotin (1035–1040, 1064). The reversible conversion of methylmalonyl-coenzyme A to succinyl-coenzyme A is catalyzed by the vitamin B_{12}-dependent methylmalonyl-coenzyme A isomerase, which has been found in several animal tissues (1065–1067). The carboxylation of propionyl-coenzyme A yields a specific isomer of methylmalonyl-coenzyme A, and only 50% of chemically synthesized methylmalonyl-coenzyme A is utilized by the isomerase (1065). The isomer of methyl-malonyl-coenzyme A ("form a") formed by the carboxylation of propionyl-coenzyme A is converted to the racemic methylmalonyl derivative of coenzyme A by the enzyme, methylmalonyl racemase (1065a), and methylmalonyl-coenzyme A ("form b") is the substrate for the isomerase. Recently, the absolute configurations of the methyl-malonyl-coenzyme A isomers have been established (1065b, 1065c). The isomerization reaction involves an intramolecular shift of the coenzyme A-carboxyl group (1068–1072):

$$
\begin{array}{ccc}
\text{COOH} & & \text{COOH} \\
| & & | \\
\text{CH}_2 & & \text{CH—C—S—CoA} \\
| & \rightleftharpoons & | \quad \| \\
*\text{CH}_2 & & *\text{CH}_3 \ \ \text{O} \\
| & & \\
\text{C}{=}\text{O} & & \\
| & & \\
\text{S—CoA} & & \\
\end{array}
$$

Succinyl-   Methylmalonyl-
coenzyme A   coenzyme A

The early suggestion by Marston (1073) that the primary metabolic lesion in vitamin B_{12}-deficient sheep is inability to metabolize propionic acid has been borne out by subsequent investigations (1074–1078). Both dimethylbenzimidazolyl and benzimidazolyl cobamide coenzymes, but not adenyl cobamide coenzyme (see p. 774), activated apo-methylmalonyl coenzyme A isomerase from sheep kidney; all three coenzymes activated isomerase preparations obtained from *Propionibacterium shermanii* (1076).

Propionyl-coenzyme A, which also arises in the course of isoleucine metabolism, is formed from propionate by a reaction analogous to that for acetate activation (see p. 442). Propionyl-coenzyme A is dehydro-genated to acrylyl-coenzyme A, which undergoes hydration catalyzed by crotonase to β-hydroxypropionyl-coenzyme A. The deacylase that acts on β-hydroxyisobutyryl-coenzyme A also hydrolyzes β-hydroxypro-pionyl-coenzyme A; dehydrogenation by a specific diphosphopyridine nucleotide-dependent enzyme present in kidney yields malonate semi-aldehyde (46, 1079). Malonate semialdehyde is converted by trans-amination to β-alanine (see p. 603). The conversion of propionate to β-hydroxypropionate has also been observed in mitochondria obtained from peanut cotyledons (1080). These reactions may be represented as follows:

$$\text{Propionate} + \text{CoA—SH} + \text{ATP} \rightleftharpoons \text{propionyl—S—CoA} + \text{AMP} + \text{PP}$$

$$\text{Propionyl-CoA} \rightleftharpoons \text{acrylyl-CoA} + 2\text{H}$$

$$\text{Acrylyl CoA} + \text{H}_2\text{O} \rightleftharpoons \beta\text{-hydroxypropionyl-CoA}$$

$$\beta\text{-Hydroxypropionyl-CoA} + \text{H}_2\text{O} \rightleftharpoons \beta\text{-hydroxypropionate} + \text{CoA—SH}$$

$$\beta\text{-Hydroxypropionate} + \text{DPN}^+ \rightleftharpoons \text{malonate semialdehyde} + \text{DPNH} + \text{H}^+$$

Preparations of *Clostridium kluyveri*, which catalyze the oxidation of propionic acid, also catalyze the hydration of acrylyl-coenzyme A to β-hydroxypropionyl-coenzyme A. However, the latter compound is oxidized directly to malonyl semialdehyde-coenzyme A, which is subsequently oxidized to malonyl-coenzyme A (1081).

Degradation of Isoleucine

Isoleucine is ketogenic under certain conditions, but under other conditions leads to formation of carbohydrate (1082–1084). The studies of Coon and associates established that in liver slices both two- and three-carbon fragments arise from the degradation of isoleucine (1022, 1025, 1085–1087). Further work suggested the scheme given on p. 752.

Isoleucine is converted to its α-keto analog, which in turn is oxidatively decarboxylated to yield α-methylbutyryl-coenzyme A. Coon and associates found that the coenzyme A derivative of tiglic acid (*cis*-2-methyl-2-butenoic acid) undergoes hydration catalyzed by preparations of liver, heart, or of purified crotonase. Conversion of tiglyl-coenzyme A to acetyl-coenzyme A was suggested by the observation of citrate formation in systems supplemented with oxaloacetate and diphosphopyridine nucleotide. The last two steps of the scheme are plausible by analogy with the reactions demonstrated for the oxidation of straight-chain fatty acids (1088), and have been demonstrated (1087). A purified coenzyme A transferase which catalyzes the following reaction was obtained from pig heart:

α-Methylacetoacetyl-coenzyme A + succinate ⇌
α-methylacetoacetate + succinyl-coenzyme A

Degradation of Straight-Chain Amino Acids

The metabolism of α-aminobutyric acid, norvaline, and norleucine in animal tissues was examined by Greenberg and his colleagues (1089–1091). Incubation of DL-α-aminobutyric acid-3-C^{14} with homogenates of rat liver gave products that included the corresponding α-keto acid and propionic acid (1091). Similar experiments with DL-norvaline-3-C^{14} gave α-ketovaleric acid, β-hydroxybutyric acid, butyric acid, acetic acid, and acetoacetic acid (1090). Studies with DL-norleucine-3-C^{14} indicated conversion to α-ketocaproic acid, valeric acid, and β-hydroxyvaleric acid (1091). These findings suggest pathways involving transamination and oxidative decarboxylation to the corresponding acyl-coenzyme A derivatives followed by β-oxidation.

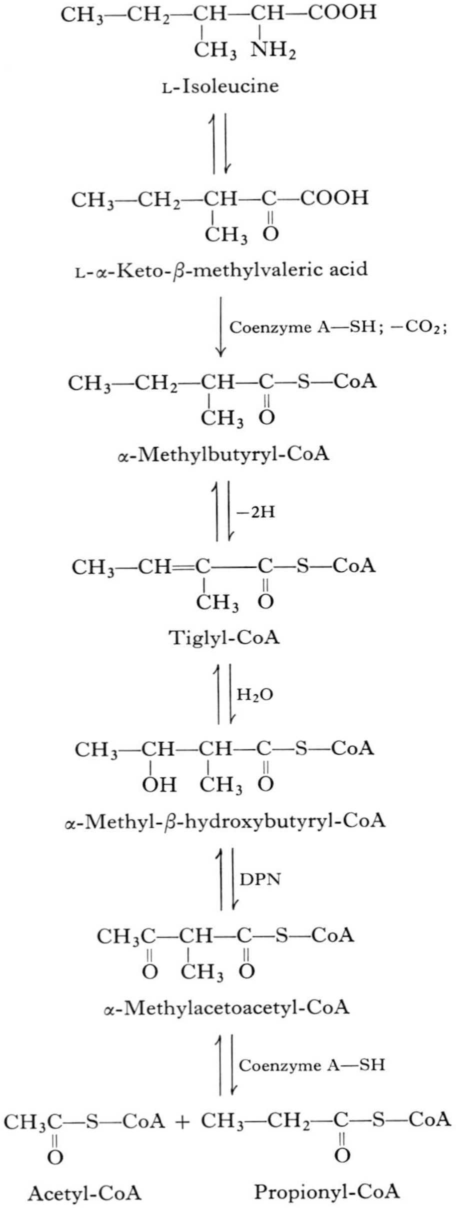

$$CH_3-CH_2-CH-CH-COOH$$
$$CH_3 \ \ NH_2$$

L-Isoleucine

$$CH_3-CH_2-CH-C-COOH$$
$$CH_3 \ \ O$$

L-α-Keto-β-methylvaleric acid

Coenzyme A—SH; $-CO_2$; $-2H$

$$CH_3-CH_2-CH-C-S-CoA$$
$$CH_3 \ \ O$$

α-Methylbutyryl-CoA

$-2H$

$$CH_3-CH=C-\!\!-\!\!-C-S-CoA$$
$$CH_3 \ \ O$$

Tiglyl-CoA

H_2O

$$CH_3-CH-CH-C-S-CoA$$
$$OH \ \ \ CH_3 \ O$$

α-Methyl-β-hydroxybutyryl-CoA

DPN

$$CH_3C-CH-C-S-CoA$$
$$O \ \ \ CH_3 \ O$$

α-Methylacetoacetyl-CoA

Coenzyme A—SH

$$CH_3C-S-CoA \ + \ CH_3-CH_2-C-S-CoA$$
$$O O$$

Acetyl-CoA   Propionyl-CoA

Conversion of Valine, Leucine, and Isoleucine to Other Products

The branched-chain amino acids are precursors of a number of structurally related compounds found in nature. As stated previously (p. 747), leucine is a precursor of mevalonic acid, which accounts for the incorporation of leucine carbon into various compounds derived from mevalonic acid. The occurrence of β-methylbutyric acid and d-α-methylbutyric acid in dog hair grease suggests that these acids arise from leucine and isoleucine, respectively (1092). Valine is one of the precursors of penicillin and cephalosporin (see p. 461). Pantoic acid arises from α-ketoisovaleric acid in *E. coli* (1093, 1094), and the available data suggest that a one-carbon unit is added as follows:

$$
\begin{array}{ccc}
\begin{array}{c}
CH_3 \quad CH_3 \\
\diagdown \diagup \\
CH \\
| \\
C{=}O \\
| \\
COOH
\end{array}
&
\xrightarrow[\text{tetrahydrofolic acid}]{\text{``C-1'' unit}}
&
\begin{array}{c}
CH_3 \quad CH_2OH \\
\diagdown \diagup \\
C{-}CH_3 \\
| \\
C{=}O \\
| \\
COOH
\end{array}
\end{array}
$$

α-Ketoiso-valeric acid → α-Keto-β,β-dimethyl-γ-hydroxybutyric acid (ketopantoic acid) → Pantoic acid

$$
\begin{array}{c}
CH_3 \quad CH_2OH \\
\diagdown \diagup \\
C{-}CH_3 \\
| \\
CHOH \\
| \\
COOH
\end{array}
$$

An enzyme that catalyzes the condensation of α-ketoisovaleric acid and formaldehyde to a compound exhibiting the properties of α-keto-β,β-dimethyl-γ-hydroxybutyric acid (ketopantoic acid) was purified from extracts of *E. coli*. No evidence for the participation of a folic acid coenzyme was obtained. However, in nutritional studies on a strain of *Bacterium linens* which required either pantothenate or *p*-aminobenzoate for growth, *p*-aminobenzoate abolished the pantothenate requirement, and pantothenate, pantoate, and ketopantoate (but not α-ketoisovalerate) reversed inhibition by sulfanilamide noncompetitively. Cells grown on *p*-aminobenzoate contained pantothenate, and although pantoate and ketopantoate replaced pantothenate for growth, α-ketoisovalerate did not (1095).

The formation of pantothenic acid has been studied with a purified preparation obtained from *E. coli* that catalyzes pantothenate formation from adenosine triphosphate, pantoate, and β-alanine (see p. 456). At this point it may be noted that at least six amino acids contribute to the structure of coenzyme A (1096). See top of page 754.

The antibiotic hydroxyaspergillic acid, which is synthesized by *Aspergillus flavus*, is derived from both leucine and isoleucine. Studies in which this organism was grown in a medium containing labeled

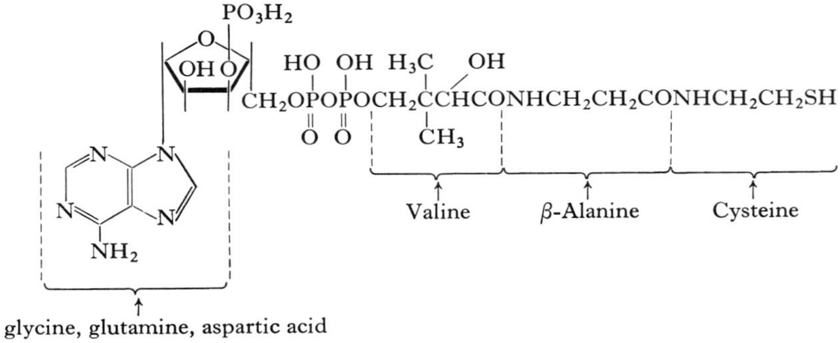

$$PO_3H_2$$

$$\underset{NH_2}{\text{(purine-ribose structure)}} \quad CH_2OPOPOCH_2CCHCONHCH_2CH_2CONHCH_2CH_2SH$$

HO OH H$_3$C OH

$$CH_2OPOPOCH_2\underset{\underset{O\ O}{||\ ||}}{C}\underset{CH_3}{CHCONHCH_2CH_2CONHCH_2CH_2SH}$$

Valine   β-Alanine   Cysteine

glycine, glutamine, aspartic acid

leucine or isoleucine showed that both aspergillic and hydroxyaspergillic acids became labeled. It is possible that aspergillic acid is formed by dehydrogenation of the mixed diketopiperazine of leucine and isoleucine. The available data indicate that hydroxyaspergillic acid is formed from aspergillic acid (1097).

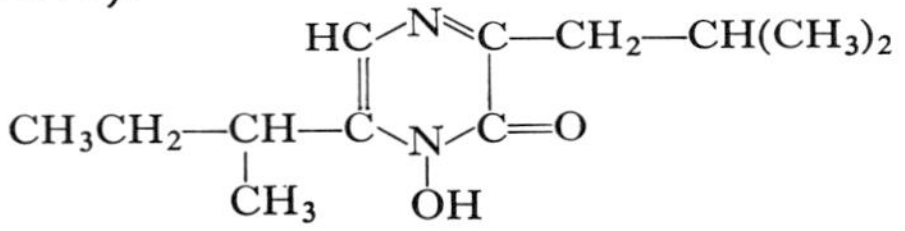

$$CH_3CH_2-CH-C\underset{CH_3}{\overset{HC\diagup N\diagdown C-CH_2-CH(CH_3)_2}{||}}\underset{\underset{OH}{N}}{C}=O$$

Aspergillic acid

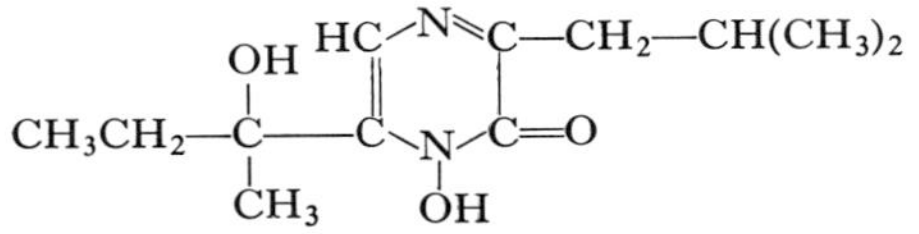

$$CH_3CH_2-\underset{CH_3}{\overset{OH}{C}}-C\underset{OH}{\overset{HC\diagup N\diagdown C-CH_2-CH(CH_3)_2}{N}}C=O$$

Hydroxyaspergillic acid

Incorporation of isoleucine into the C_{15}-branched chain fatty acid (12-methyltetradecanoic acid) of *Micrococcus lysodeikticus* was shown in studies in which this organism was grown on media containing labeled isoleucine or α-methylbutyric acid (1098). The probable mechanism of incorporation involves successive addition of two carbon units (via malonyl-coenzyme A) to α-methylbutyryl-coenzyme A. Leucine may also be incorporated into fatty acids of this type, and recent studies on *Bacillus subtilis* indicate a similar pathway for incorporation of valine into iso-fatty acids containing 14–17 carbon atoms (1099).

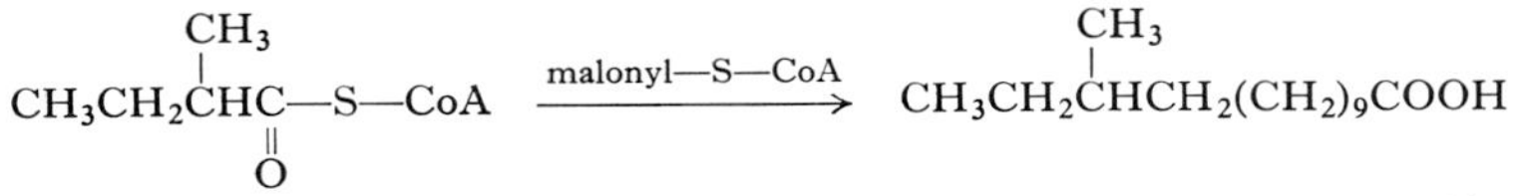

$$\underset{\underset{O}{||}}{CH_3CH_2\overset{CH_3}{\overset{|}{C}}HC}-S-CoA \xrightarrow{\text{malonyl—S—CoA}} CH_3CH_2\overset{CH_3}{\overset{|}{C}}HCH_2(CH_2)_9COOH$$

α-Methylbutyryl-coenzyme A   12-Methyltetradecanoic acid

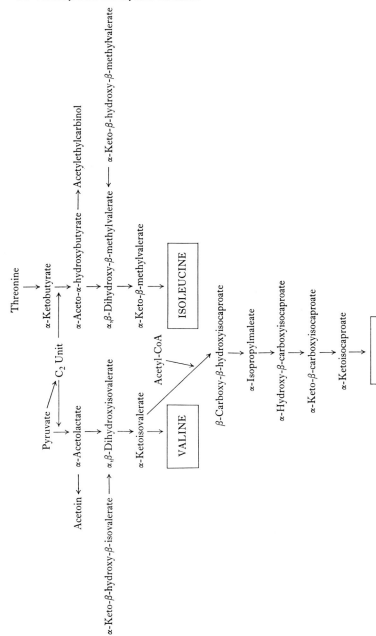

Summary scheme for the biosynthesis of valine, isoleucine, and leucine.

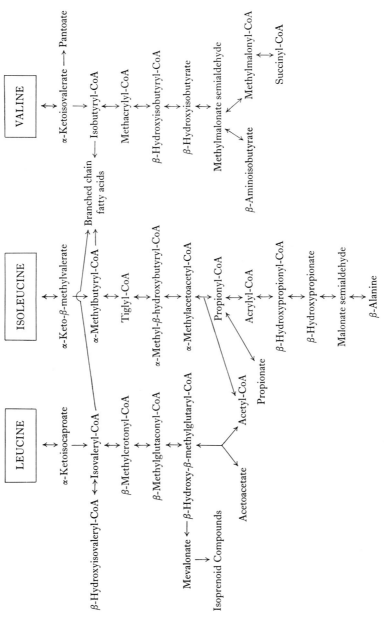

Summary scheme for the degradation of leucine, isoleucine, and valine.

Several new metabolites have been isolated from cultures of *Alternaria tenuis*, including tenuazonic acid. Studies in which the organism was grown on media containing acetate-1-C^{14} suggest that this compound is synthesized from 2 molecules of acetate and 1 of L-isoleucine (1100).

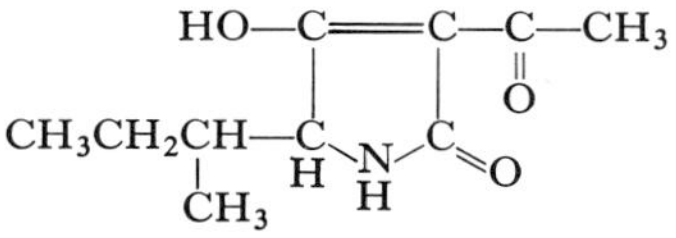

$$HO—C{=\!=}C—C—CH_3$$

Tenuazonic acid

L. Methionine and Cysteine

General Considerations

The metabolism of methionine includes reactions in which its sulfur atom and methyl group are transferred to other molecules. Trans-sulfuration involves the formation of cystathionine, which is an intermediate in both degradative and synthetic pathways. *S*-Adenosyl-methionine, representative of a large group of sulfonium compounds, is the key compound in transmethylation which leads to the formation of the methyl groups of *N*-methylnicotinamide, methylhistamine, creatine, choline, anserine, epinephrine, metanephrine, ergosterol, certain purines, alkaloids, and other compounds. Methionine is synthesized from homocysteine by transmethylation and by a mechanism in which a one-carbon unit is utilized by reactions involving folic acid and vitamin B_{12}. These and additional reactions of methionine carbon and sulfur are considered in this section.

The synthesis of cysteine (by transsulfuration or from inorganic forms of sulfur) utilizes serine. The degradative metabolism of cysteine involves reactions in which its sulfur atom is oxidized, as well as deamination and decarboxylation reactions. Cysteine is converted to cysteinesulfinic acid, hypotaurine, taurine, and a large number of additional compounds.

The Cystathionine Pathway

It was learned from nutritional studies on the rat that cysteine (or cystine) is a dispensable component of the diet, that the need for cysteine can be met by dietary methionine, and that part of the dietary methionine requirement can be fulfilled by cystine (see p. 207). Thus, it is apparent that the rat is able to convert methionine sulfur to cystine sulfur. Further evidence of such conversion is the increase in excretion of cystine after methionine administration in human cystinuria (1101), and the increased formation of mercapturic acids (see p. 815) when methionine and halogenated benzenes are administered together (1102, 1103). Direct demonstration of the conversion of methionine sulfur to cystine sulfur in the rat was shown by Tarver and Schmidt (1104), using methionine labeled with S^{35}. It was shown by Stetten that when serine labeled with N^{15} is administered to rats, highly labeled cystine is formed in the tissues (555). Brand and associates (1105) observed that homocysteine administered to a patient with cystinuria led to formation of extra urinary cystine, and suggested (1106) that the transfer of sulfur from homocysteine to cysteine takes place via the intermediate *S*-(β-amino-β-carboxyethyl)-homocysteine (later named cystathionine). du Vigneaud and associates (551, 1107–1112) provided the evidence for this mechanism and found that serine is the sulfur acceptor. The four diastereoisomers of cystathionine were prepared and tested in nutritional experiments on rats (1107). Of these, the D-isomers were inactive, L-cystathionine

D-Homocysteine

L-Serine

L-Allocystathionine

L-Homoserine

L-Cysteine

L-Cystathionine

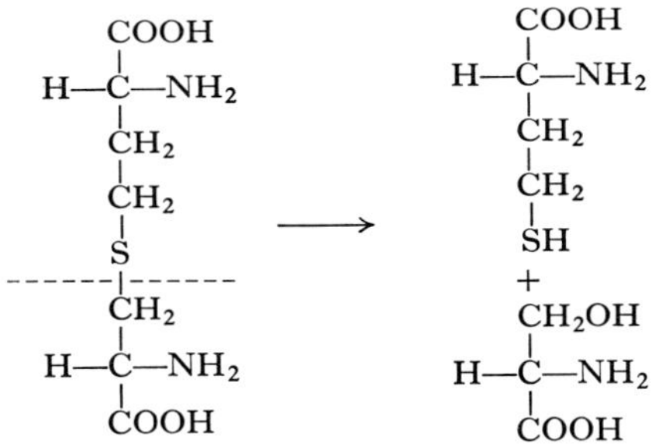

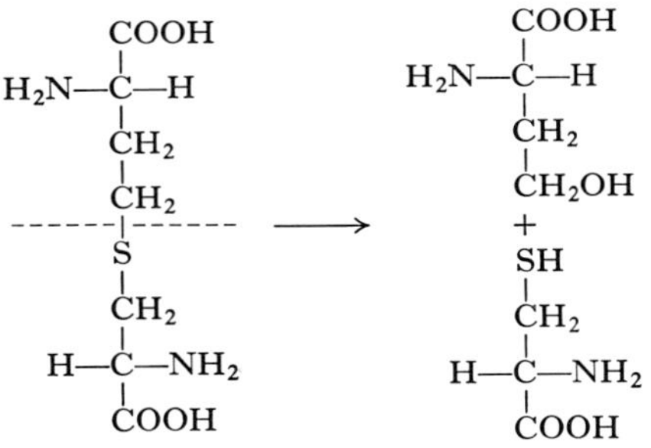

supported the growth of rats in place of cysteine, and L-allocystathionine promoted growth in the absence of methionine but in the presence of choline. It was therefore concluded that L-cystathionine is cleaved to cysteine and homoserine, whereas L-allocystathionine is cleaved to homocysteine and serine. This was also indicated by *in vitro* studies with liver preparations by Anslow *et al.* (1113).

Further evidence of the cystathionine pathway came from studies in which a cystinuric patient was given S^{35}-methionine; the isotope was found in the urinary cystine (1114). A number of other compounds can contribute sulfur to cystine. Thus, L-lanthionine supports the growth of rats on a cystine-deficient diet (1115); the sulfur atoms of homolanthionine (1116) and of ethionine (1117) are also converted to cystine sulfur. Sulfur-labeled L-cystathionine was converted to labeled cystine (1112), and, in *in vitro* studies with a rat liver preparation, cystathionine was converted to cysteine and α-ketobutyric acid (1108, 1110, 1118). Homoserine added to such digests gave rise to keto acid. Apparently some of the keto acid is aminated to form α-aminobutyric acid (1119); this amino acid is found in greater than usual amounts in the urine of humans who have ingested methionine (1120).

Cystathionine has been isolated from cultures of certain methionine-requiring mutant microorganisms (see below), from the urine of vitamin B_6-deficient rats (1121), from the urine of rats fed methionine and serine

$$
\begin{array}{c}
\text{CH}_3 \\
| \\
\text{S} \\
| \\
\text{CH}_2 \\
| \\
\text{CH}_2 \\
| \\
\text{CHNH}_2 \\
| \\
\text{COOH}
\end{array}
\qquad
\begin{array}{c}
\text{CH}_2\text{SH} \\
| \\
\text{CH}_2 \\
| \\
\text{CHNH}_2 \\
| \\
\text{COOH}
\end{array}
\qquad
\begin{array}{c}
\text{HOCH}_2 \\
| \\
\text{CHNH}_2 \\
| \\
\text{COOH} \\
\text{Serine}
\end{array}
\qquad
\begin{array}{c}
\text{CH}_2-\text{S}-\text{CH}_2 \\
| \qquad\quad | \\
\text{CH}_2 \qquad \text{CHNH}_2 \\
| \qquad\quad | \\
\text{CHNH}_2 \quad \text{COOH} \\
| \\
\text{COOH}
\end{array}
$$

Methionine   Homocysteine   Cystathionine

$$
\begin{array}{c}
\text{CH}_3 \\
| \\
\text{CH}_2 \\
| \\
\text{CHNH}_2 \\
| \\
\text{COOH}
\end{array}
\xleftarrow{\qquad}
\begin{array}{c}
\text{CH}_3 \\
| \\
\text{CH}_2 \\
| \\
\text{C}=\text{O} \\
| \\
\text{COOH}
\end{array}
\xleftarrow{-\text{NH}_3}
\left[
\begin{array}{c}
\text{CH}_2\text{OH} \\
| \\
\text{CH}_2 \\
| \\
\text{CHNH}_2 \\
| \\
\text{COOH}
\end{array}
\right]
\begin{array}{c}
\text{CH}_2\text{SH} \\
+ \; | \\
\text{CHNH}_2 \\
| \\
\text{COOH}
\end{array}
$$

α-Amino-   α-Keto-   Homo-   Cysteine
butyric acid   butyric acid   serine

(1122, 1123), and from the body fluid of the silkworm *Bombyx mori* 1123a). L-Cystathionine has also been isolated from human brain, where it is present in concentrations of 22.5–56.6 mg. per 100 g. of wet weight of tissue (1124). The presence of cystathionine in brain may have special significance in relation to the function of this organ, which apparently has the enzymatic equipment necessary for the conversion of methionine to cystine (1125). Human cell lines grown in tissue culture also catalyze conversion of methionine sulfur to cysteine (1126). The cystathionine pathway may be represented as shown on p. 759.

Braunstein and Goryachenkova (1127) found that liver preparations obtained from vitamin B_6-deficient rats do not catalyze cysteine formation from homocysteine and serine unless pyridoxal phosphate is added; this observation foreshadowed later findings that both the cystathionine-forming and cystathionine-cleaving enzymes contain pyridoxal phosphate (1128, 1129). As noted above, cystathionine has been found in the urine of vitamin B_6-deficient rats, suggesting that these enzymes exhibit different affinities for pyridoxal phosphate. Binkley (1130) was able to separate the cleaving from the condensing activity since the latter is more rapidly inactivated by heating at 50°. Later, Selim and Greenberg (1131) purified cystathionine synthetase about 35-fold from rat liver, and showed that the enzyme contains pyridoxal phosphate. Their purified preparation catalyzes both the synthesis of cystathionine from serine and homocysteine, and the deamination of L-serine (see serine dehydrase, p. 668). No cystathionine-cleaving activity (cystathionase) was found in the preparation, which was also free from homocysteine and cysteine desulfhydrase activities.

Binkley and Olson (1132) obtained enzyme preparations from rat liver that catalyzed both cleavage of cystathionine and deamination of homoserine; heat inactivation studies suggested that the two activities were due to separate enzymes (1130, 1132), but later work (see below) does not confirm this. In addition to L-cystathionine, the enzyme cleaved djenkolic acid, L-allocystathionine, and lanthionine (1133). Matsuo and Greenberg (1134) purified an enzyme from rat liver that catalyzes conversion of homoserine to ammonia and α-ketobutyric acid. It was discovered subsequently that this enzyme, isolated in crystalline form, also cleaves L-cystathionine to cysteine, ammonia, and α-ketobutyric acid. The crystalline enzyme deaminates homoserine and cleaves cystathionine at rates of about the same order of magnitude; the ratio of these activities during purification remained essentially constant. The enzyme (molecular weight, about 190,000) contains 4 moles of pyridoxal phosphate per mole of protein. The crystalline enzyme exhibits an absorbancy maximum at pH 7.5 at 427 mμ; relatively little change in absorbancy was observed over the pH range 4.0 to 8.4. In order to determine whether homoserine is formed in the course of cystathionine cleavage, C^{14}-labeled cystathionine was incubated with the enzyme in the presence of homoserine as a trapping agent; no radioactivity was detected in the homoserine subsequently isolated. This indicates that free homoserine is not a product of cleavage, although it is probable that enzyme-bound homoserine is formed during the reaction, since the enzyme catalyzes the incorporation of C^{14}-homoserine into cystathionine in the presence of L-cysteine. A mechanism for the reaction of substrates with enzyme-pyridoxal phosphate has been proposed (see p. 403). Crystalline cystathionase also cleaves djenkolic acid, lanthionine, and L-cysteine; the latter is converted to keto acid and hydrogen sulfide (see cysteine desulfhydrase, p. 795). Since cystathionase does not form free homoserine, the earlier observation of the formation of labeled homoserine from methionine-2-C^{14} (1119) must be ascribed to another enzyme. On the other hand, previous reports of the conversion of homoserine to α-ketobutyrate (1118, 1135) can be attributed to this enzyme, "cystathionase-homoserine deaminase." The action of the enzyme on djenkolic acid (see p. 74) yields equimolar quantities of pyruvate, cysteine, hydrogen sulfide, formaldehyde, and ammonia; S-thiomethylcysteine, an intermediate in this reaction, decomposes spontaneously (1135a).

The synthesis of methionine from cysteine in microorganisms occurs by a reaction sequence which is essentially the reversal of the reactions indicated above. Some organisms, e.g., *Neurospora*, can catalyze these reactions in both directions. Studies on methionine synthesis in *N. crassa* have been carried out with several mutants, each blocked at a different point in the biosynthetic sequence (610, 611, 1136, 1137). Thus, mutants which grew on media containing (*a*) methionine, (*b*) methionine or cysteine, (*c*) methionine, homocysteine, or cystathionine were isolated, and mutants unable to catalyze homoserine synthesis and condensation of cysteine and homoserine were identified. Analogous mutants of *E. coli* have been studied, and there are isotopic and enzymatic data for the cystathionine pathway from cysteine to methionine (1138–1144). Cystathionine has been isolated from cultures of methionine-requiring mutants of *Neurospora* and *Aerobacter aerogenes* that exhibit growth response to homocysteine (1136, 1142).

Although the pathway of homocysteine biosynthesis in microorganisms appears to represent a reversal of the cystathionine transsulfuration pathway in animal tissues, the reactions leading to the synthesis and cleavage of cystathionine are different. Thus, the pathway in animals involves formation of cystathionine from serine and homocysteine; cleavage of cystathionine yields cysteine, α-ketobutyrate, and ammonia. The methionine-biosynthetic pathway involves formation of cystathionine from homoserine and cysteine, and cleavage of cystathionine to homocysteine, pyruvate, and ammonia. Therefore, it is probable that four separate enzymes are involved. The cleavage reaction in microorganisms involves a β-elimination mechanism, while the animal cleavage enzyme catalyzes a γ-elimination reaction (see p. 403). It is conceivable that there is some overlapping in specificity of each of these enzymes and that some or all of them may catalyze the respective reactions to some extent in the reverse direction. Flavin (1143) purified an enzyme from *N. crassa* that catalyzes cystathionine cleavage via γ-elimination to yield cysteine and α-ketobutyrate; this reaction is therefore the same as that which occurs in animal tissues. The organism from which the enzyme was obtained was a mutant that required either methionine or homocysteine for growth, but did not grow when supplied with cystathionine, which it accumulated. For this reason, the mutant was expected to lack the enzyme that cleaved cystathionine to homocysteine and pyruvate, but it was found to catalyze this reaction to some extent. The explanation for this finding is not entirely clear, but the fact that the organism required homocysteine or methionine for growth indicates that the amount of β-elimination activity present was insufficient to supply the needed amino acid. The enzyme, which required pyridoxal phosphate, was purified about 400-fold and found to cleave (in addition to cystathionine, lanthionine, and homoserine) the L and *meso* forms of cystine and homocystine. Anaerobic incubation of the enzyme with cystine for short periods led to the appearance of equimolar quantities of pyruvate, ammonia, cysteine, and elemental sulfur. A number of experiments were carried out which indicate that the enzymatic decomposition of cystine involved β-elimination of disulfide from its mono-Schiff base with pyridoxal phosphate, followed by hydrolysis of the aminoacrylate Schiff base to pyruvate and ammonia (see p. 796).

In recent studies evidence has been obtained that the synthesis of cystathionine in *E. coli* and certain other microorganisms involves reaction of cysteine with O-succinyl homoserine (formed by reaction of succinyl-coenzyme A and homoserine) (1143a, 1143b).

In addition to the formation of homocysteine, complete consideration of methionine biosynthesis includes conversion of homocysteine to methionine (see p. 778), biosynthesis of cysteine (see p. 789), and biosynthesis of homoserine (see p. 674).

Transmethylation

The demethylation of methionine to homocysteine and the reversal of this process are important metabolic reactions. Nutritional studies on the rat showed that both the D- and L-isomers of homocysteine could support growth in the absence of methionine (551, 1144). However, with certain methionine-deficient diets, homocysteine was not effective in promoting growth unless choline or another methyl donor was incorporated in the diet (1145–1147). The concept of transmethylation, originally suggested in 1894 by Hofmeister (1148), received experimental support from investigations which developed from these nutritional observations. The conversion of methionine to homocysteine was considered to result in the formation of a labile methyl group capable of methylating a compound such as guanidinoacetic acid to form creatine (1149). Transmethylation from choline to homocysteine to form methionine, and from methionine to carnosine to form anserine (1150), represent other examples of this process. du Vigneaud and collaborators demonstrated that the methyl group is transferred intact, i.e., there was no loss of deuterium from a carbon-labeled methyl group during transfer (1151). On the other hand, the concept of the dietary indispensability of the methyl group has been modified by the observation that diets devoid of methionine (and other methyl donors) but containing homocysteine and optimal amounts of vitamin B_{12} and folic acid could support the growth of rats (1147, 1152–1156). It became evident that the diets used in the earlier studies were probably deficient in vitamin B_{12} and folic acid, and that these vitamins promote the synthesis of methyl groups. Conclusive proof that the synthesis of methyl groups was carried out in the tissues rather than in the intestinal flora was obtained in experiments with germ-free rats (1156); see also (1157–1162). In these studies, germ-free rats maintained on a diet devoid of choline were given D_2O for 10 to 23 days. The concentration of deuterium in the methyl groups of the body choline was significantly higher than the mean level of body deuterium, indicating that methyl groups were synthesized by the tissues (1156). In other studies it was shown that when rat liver slices were incubated with C^{14}-formate there was appreciable incorporation of radioactivity into the methyl groups of methionine and choline (1156a).

The formation of methionine from homocysteine can occur by transfer of the labile methyl groups of several compounds, including choline, betaine, and dimethyl propiothetin. Transmethylation from choline to homocysteine was studied in liver preparations by Borsook and Dubnoff, who found that betaine was superior to choline as a methyl donor (1163). Under anaerobic conditions, betaine, but not choline, was active in methyl transfer (1164), and the reaction with choline was shown to require the presence of choline oxidase (1165). Choline is not itself a methyl donor, but is converted, via betaine aldehyde, to betaine, which serves as the methyl donor (1166). When choline and homocysteine were incubated with rat liver preparations, the formation of dimethylglycine was demonstrated rather than dimethylaminoethanol (1165). There is also evidence that the synthesis of betaine in higher plants takes place by oxidation of choline (1167, 1168):

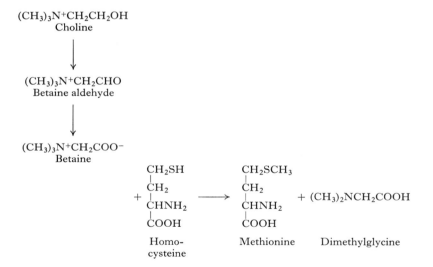

$(CH_3)_3N^+CH_2CH_2OH$
Choline

$(CH_3)_3N^+CH_2CHO$
Betaine aldehyde

$(CH_3)_3N^+CH_2COO^-$
Betaine

In studies with N^{15}-betaine, the nitrogen atom of this compound was shown to be the precursor of glycine, indicating that complete demethylation occurs (1169) (see p. 665).

$$CH_3 \diagdown \overset{+}{\underset{CH_3 \diagup}{S}}CH_2CH_2COO^-$$

Dimethyl-β-propiothetin

$$CH_3 \diagdown \overset{+}{\underset{CH_3 \diagup}{S}} - CH_2CH_2\underset{\underset{NH_3^+}{|}}{CHCOO^-}$$
$$OH^-$$

S-Methylmethionine

Transmethylation involving thetins such as dimethyl-β-propiothetin, dimethylthetin (1170–1171), and S-methylmethionine (1172–1174) has been observed. S-Methylmethionine can replace methionine in promoting the growth of the rat and several microorganisms (1172–1174). Transmethylation between dimethylthetin and homocysteine yields methionine according to the following reaction:

$$CH_3 \diagdown \overset{+}{\underset{CH_3 \diagup}{S}}CH_2COO^- + HSCH_2CH_2\underset{\underset{NH_3^+}{|}}{CHCOO^-} \longrightarrow$$

Dimethylthetin   Homocysteine

$$CH_3SCH_2CH_2\underset{\underset{NH_3^+}{|}}{CHCOO^-} + CH_3SCH_2COO^- + H^+$$

Methionine S-Methylthioglycolic
acid

There is evidence that this and other reactions involving transmethylation of thetins are catalyzed by a separate enzyme (1170). In general, thetins are excellent methyl donors and can replace choline in supporting the growth of rats receiving homocystine and diets deficient in folic acid and vitamin B_{12}. Dimethylpropiothetin has been found in certain marine algae (1175, 1176) and α-aminodimethyl-γ-butyrothetin (S-methylmethionine; see p. 786) also occurs naturally (see p. 80). An enzyme obtained from the marine alga *Polysiphonia lanosa* catalyzes the breakdown of dimethylpropiothetin to dimethylsulfide, acrylic acid, and hydrogen ions (1177). Studies with labeled methionine have shown that the methyl group and sulfur atom of methionine are incorporated into both methyl groups and the sulfur of dimethylpropiothetin, and the α-carbon atom of methionine is converted to the carboxyl carbon of the thetin (1178). Durell *et al.* (1179) have purified a thetin-homocysteine methylpherase from horse liver and demonstrated that dimethyl-β-propiothetin is a substrate. Thetin-homocysteine methylpherase undergoes reversible polymerization due to formation and cleavage of intermolecular disulfide bonds; homocysteine causes the enzyme to depolymerize, but the state of aggregation appears not to be related to enzymatic activity (1180).

The observation that transmethylation reactions involving "onium" compounds such as betaine and dimethylthetin do not require adenosine triphosphate, and the recognition that adenosine triphosphate is required for transmethylation reactions involving methionine (1181) indicated that transfer of the methyl group of methionine required activation. The activation of methionine was shown by Cantoni to proceed according to the following equation (1182–1187):

L-Methionine + ATP → "active methionine" + pyrophosphate + orthophosphate

The structure of "active methionine" was shown to be:

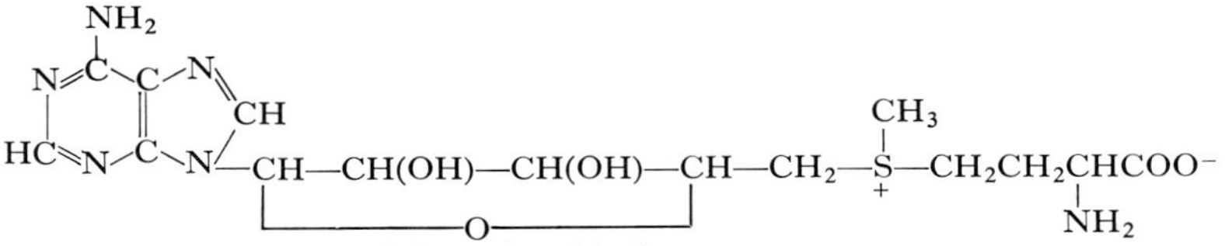

S-Adenosylmethionine

The structure was proved by total synthesis by Baddiley and Jamieson (1188). Purified enzyme preparations that catalyze the activation of methionine were obtained, and it was shown that S-adenosylmethionine serves as methyl donor in the absence of adenosine triphosphate. Thus, the methylation of guanidinoacetic acid to creatine takes place as follows (1189–1192):

Guanidinoacetic acid + S-adenosylmethionine$^+$ →
$\qquad\qquad\qquad\qquad\qquad\qquad$ S-adenosylhomocysteine + creatine + H$^+$

This reaction is catalyzed by the enzyme, guanidinoacetic acid methylpherase (guanidinoacetate methyltransferase). Methylation of nicotinamide to N-methylnicotinamide (1193, 1194), which takes place in analogous fashion, is catalyzed by nicotinamide methylpherase. Hydrogen ion formation accompanies the formation of creatine from guanidinoacetic acid, but does not occur in the methylation of nicotinamide; in the methylation of guanidinoacetic acid, a tertiary amine is formed (I), while methylation of nicotinamide yields a new onium compound (II) containing a methyl pyridinium bond:

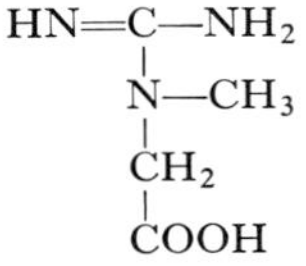

(I) 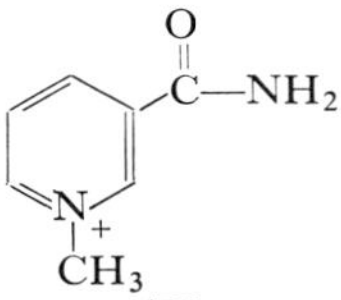   (II)

The enzyme that catalyzes the activation of methionine has been purified from rabbit liver (1187) and from baker's yeast (1195, 1196). Experiments with P^{32}-adenosine triphosphate showed that the α- and β-phosphorus atoms of adenosine triphosphate are the precursors of pyrophosphate, and that the orthophosphate liberated arises from the terminal phosphate group (1187). Studies with H_2O^{18} demonstrated that no oxygen is introduced into pyrophosphate and that 1 atom of oxygen is incorporated into orthophosphate. No evidence was obtained for the participation of 3',5'-cycloadenosine, adenosine 2'-phosphate-5'-pyrophosphate, and adenosine 3'-phosphate-5'-pyrophosphate. Direct evidence for the binding of S-adenosylmethionine was obtained by a gel filtration procedure. In experiments in which large amounts of enzyme were incubated with labeled adenosine triphosphate, it was shown that inorganic triphosphate was formed on the enzyme. The enzyme catalyzes the formation of inorganic triphosphate from adenosine triphosphate in the presence of methionine, and under the conditions of these experiments the amount of inorganic triphosphate bound to the enzyme was less than one equivalent relative to the enzyme. The enzyme exhibits triphosphatase activity, which is markedly stimulated by S-adenosylmethionine. These data suggest that adenosine triphosphate and methionine condense on the enzyme to yield enzyme-bound S-adenosylmethionine and enzyme-bound triphosphate; the latter is cleaved on the enzyme with subsequent liberation of products. The enzyme also catalyzes a slow reversal of S-adenosylmethionine synthesis which requires triphosphate. A value of -6700 calories per mole was calculated for the free energy change associated with the hydrolysis of adenosine triphosphate to adenosine and triphosphate (1196, 1197).

An enzyme was obtained from rat liver that catalyzes the reversible cleavage of S-adenosyl-L-homocysteine:

$$\text{Adenosine} + \text{L-homocysteine} \rightleftharpoons S\text{-adenosyl-L-homocysteine}$$

The position of the equilibrium is distinctly in favor of synthesis, and the reaction is therefore useful for the preparation of S-adenosyl-L-homocysteine (1198). This reaction also takes place in yeast (1199). Studies in which S-adenosyl-L-homocysteine was methylated nonenzymatically gave a preparation of S-adenosyl-L-methionine that was only 50% as active in creatine formation as enzymatically synthesized S-adenosyl-L-methionine, indicating that only one of the 2 sulfonium diastereoisomers is enzymatically utilized. The unreactive sulfonium diastereoisomer of

S-adenosyl-L-methionine was obtained after prolonged action of guanidinoacetate methylpherase. Studies on several enzymes showed that the dextrorotatory isomer of S-adenosyl-L-methionine is the enzymatically susceptible form (1200). Another useful procedure for the preparation of S-adenosylmethionine involves culture of *Torula utilis* in media containing L-methionine; S-adenosyl-L-methionine accumulates in quantity in the vacuoles and can be readily isolated (1201). It is remarkable that when *T. utilis* is cultured in the presence of D-methionine, a product consisting of 80 to 90% S-adenosyl-D-methionine is formed.

S-Adenosylmethionine is the precursor of 5′-methylthioadenosine, a compound known for many years to occur in various microorganisms including yeasts (1202–1206). 5′-Methylthioadenosine as well as S-ribosylmethionine can arise from S-adenosylmethionine by non-enzymatic degradation (1207, 1208). Enzyme preparations that catalyze the cleavage of S-adenosylmethionine have been obtained from *Aerobacter aerogenes* (1208) and baker's yeast (1209). The reaction involves formation of 5′-methylthioadenosine and α-amino-γ-butyrolactone, and hydrolysis of the latter yields homoserine; this reaction could be responsible for the reported conversion of methionine to homoserine (1119) rather than the cystathionase-catalyzed reaction, which does not yield free homoserine (see p. 761).

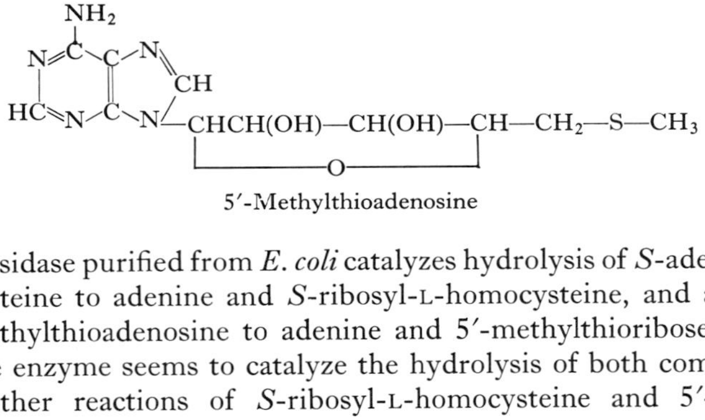

5′-Methylthioadenosine

A nucleosidase purified from *E. coli* catalyzes hydrolysis of S-adenosyl-L-homocysteine to adenine and S-ribosyl-L-homocysteine, and also that of 5′-methylthioadenosine to adenine and 5′-methylthioribose (1210); the same enzyme seems to catalyze the hydrolysis of both compounds. The further reactions of S-ribosyl-L-homocysteine and 5′-methyl-thioribose remain to be explored.

There is now much evidence that the methyl group of methionine is the precursor of the methyl groups of many other compounds, and that the actual methyl donor is S-adenosyl-L-methionine. S-Adenosyl-L-methionine is active in all *in vitro* systems in which S-methylmethionine functions as a methyl donor, and S-adenosylmethionine is more active than S-methylmethionine. The latter compound is probably formed from methionine (see p. 786).

S-Adenosyl-L-methionine is present in a number of rat tissues (adrenal, liver, heart, spleen, kidney, lung, brain) in concentrations ranging from 10–48 μg. per gram (1211). There is evidence that administration of large doses of methionine increases liver and brain S-adenosylmethionine, while administration of pyrogallol decreases the concentration of S-adenosylmethionine. Pyrogallol is methylated by catechol-O-methyltransferase (1212; see p. 913). S-Adenosylmethionine-homocysteine transmethylase activity has been found in rat liver (1213), pigeon liver (1214), microorganisms, and plants (1215). In this reaction (reaction A), S-adenosylmethionine provides only a source of methyl groups and is not cleaved to yield free methionine (1213, 1216, 1217).

(Reaction A)

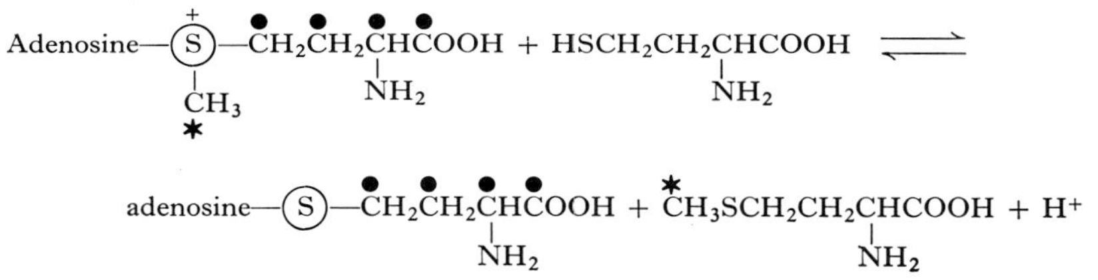

Adenosine—$\overset{+}{(S)}$—CH$_2$CH$_2$CHCOOH + HSCH$_2$CH$_2$CHCOOH $\rightleftharpoons$
    | | |
    CH$_3$ NH$_2$ NH$_2$
    *

adenosine—(S)—CH$_2$CH$_2$CHCOOH + CH$_3$SCH$_2$CH$_2$CHCOOH + H$^+$
    | |
    NH$_2$ NH$_2$

(Reaction B)

Adenosine—$\overset{+}{(S)}$—CH$_2$CH$_2$CHCOOH + HSCH$_2$CH$_2$CHCOOH $\rightleftharpoons$
    | | |
    CH$_3$ NH$_2$ NH$_2$
    *

adenosine—S—CH$_2$CH$_2$CHCOOH + CH$_3$$(S)CH_2CH_2$CHCOOH + H$^+$
    | |
    NH$_2$ NH$_2$

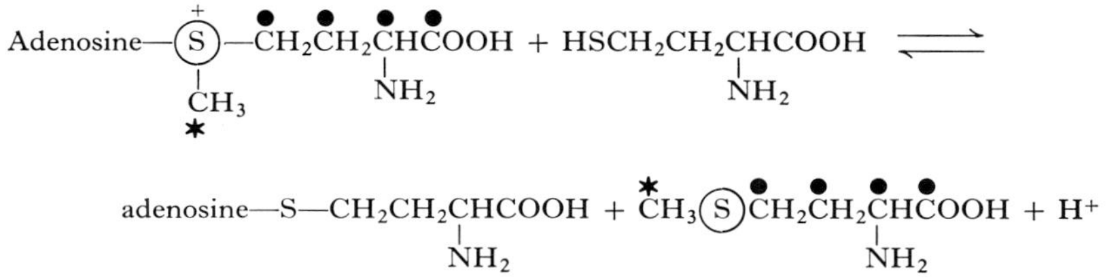

Studies on mutants of A. aerogenes (1218) and E. coli (1219) have shown that certain organisms can utilize S-adenosylmethionine for growth and that both methyl and sulfur moieties of S-adenosylmethionine are utilized for methionine synthesis. The utilization of S-adenosylmethionine sulfur for methionine biosynthesis cannot be explained by reaction A (see above), but would be consistent with a mechanism involving transadenosylation as indicated in reaction B. At present there is no direct evidence for the occurrence of reaction B, and the observation that carbon atom 2 of the methionine moiety of S-adenosylmethionine is not utilized for methionine biosynthesis in *A. aerogenes* (1218) is inconsistent with it. An alternative explanation for the experimental findings is that there is transmethiolation, but data in support of this possibility are also lacking.

As stated above, the methyl group of methionine is utilized in a large number of enzymatic reactions leading to the formation of compounds that differ widely in their chemical and biological properties. A number of examples of transmethylation reactions are considered below, and a list of some of the compounds whose methyl groups are derived from methionine is given in Table II.

Imidazole-*N*-methyltransferase, an enzyme that catalyzes transmethylation from S-adenosyl-L-methionine to histamine to yield *N*-methylhistamine has been obtained from guinea pig brain (1220) and from mouse liver (1221). As discussed elsewhere (see p. 835), methylation of the imidazole ring of histamine is a significant metabolic pathway of histamine in mammals. There is evidence that this enzymatic activity is widely distributed in animal tissues. The methylation of carnosine to anserine is catalyzed by an enzyme (carnosine-*N*-methyltransferase) present in chick pectoral muscle (1222, 1223). Carnosine appears to be a specific acceptor of the methyl group of S-adenosylmethionine; similar enzymatic activity was detected in skeletal muscle obtained from several mammals, but these tissues exhibit much less activity than chick pectoral muscle. The direct synthesis of anserine from N^1-methylhistidine and β-alanine has also been demonstrated (see p. 454). The methylation of norepinephrine (1224) also requires S-adenosylmethionine *in vitro* (1225; see p. 911) as do the methylation of dimethylaminoethanol, guanidinoacetic acid, and nicotinamide, which have been discussed above.

7-Methylguanine was reported as a constituent of urine in 1898 (1226), and investigations much later revealed the presence of other methylated purines in normal human urine; these include 1-methylguanine, 6-hydroxy-2-methylaminopurine, 1-methylhypoxanthine, and 8-hydroxy-7-methylguanine (1227). Small amounts of *N*-methylated purines have also been found in hydrolyzates of nucleic acids (1228, 1229); thus, 6-methylaminopurine, 6-hydroxy-2-methylaminopurine, and 1-methylguanine were found in hydrolyzates of yeast ribonucleic acid (1229). There is also evidence for the occurrence of all four of the 2'-*O*-methylribonucleosides in ribonucleic acid obtained from the

Table II

SOME COMPOUNDS WHOSE METHYL GROUPS ARE DERIVED FROM
THAT OF METHIONINE

Anserine	Metanephrine
Bacteriochlorophyll	6-Methoxy-5-hydroxyindole
Betaine	3-Methoxytyramine
Carnitine	N^3-Methyladenine
Colchicine	2-Methylamino-6-aminopurine
Choline	N-Methylaminoethanol
Codeine	N-Methylhistamine
Creatine	ϵ-N-Methyllysine
Dimethylaminoethanol	S-Methylmethionine
Dimethylglycine	N-Methylnicotinamide
Dimethylpropiothetin	N-Methyltyramine
Dimethylselenide	Morphine
Epinephrine	Nicotine
Ergosterol	Normetanephrine
Ergothioneine	Nucleic acids
Fumigatin	Oripavine
Gramine	Pectin
Hercynine	Protopectin
Homostachydrine	Protopine [b]
Hordenine	Ricinine
Hygric acid	Sarcosine
Hygrine	Stachydrine
Isothebaine	Thebaine
N-Isovanillyltyramine	Trigonelline
Lactobacillic acid [a]	Trimethylarsine
Lignin	N-Vanillyltyramine
Melatonin	Vitamin B_{12}

[a] Methylene bridge.
[b] Methylenedioxy and methyl groups.

microsomal and soluble fractions of mammalian tissues and from the
soluble fraction of *E. coli* (1230, 1231). Extracts of several microorganisms including *E. coli* catalyze methylation of 2,6-diaminopurine to 2-
methylamino-6-aminopurine (1232). Enzymatic transmethylation from
S-adenosylmethionine to adenine to yield N^3-methyladenine was
demonstrated with an enzyme preparation obtained from rabbit lung
(1233); this enzyme preparation also catalyzes methylation of 2,6-

diaminopurine, 7-methyladenine, and 6-methylaminopurine. Recently, evidence has been obtained for the N-methylation of nucleic acid adenine and guanine in several species (1234–1241). The available data indicate that S-adenosylmethionine is the methyl donor and that the substrate is polynucleotide. Although several studies have been carried out with transfer ribonucleic acid, other types of ribonucleic acid and deoxyribonucleic acid are also methylated. The methyl group of ribonucleic acid thymine (1235) arises from the methyl group of methionine, and in the same experiments (as expected) the methyl group of the thymine of deoxyribonucleic acid was shown not to arise from this source. There is evidence suggesting that the methylation of nucleic acids does not occur in a random manner, that there are several enzymes capable of catalyzing such methylation, and that there is species variation in their activity and specificity. The biological function of N-methylation of nucleic acids is not yet known; several ideas have been considered including the suggestion that N-methylation reduces the number of hydrogen-bonding sites.

S-Adenosyl-L-methionine is required for the enzymatic synthesis of gramine, N-methyltyramine, and hordenine (1242) (see p. 925). Tyramine methylpherase, obtained from germinating barley roots, catalyzes N-methylation of tyramine by S-adenosyl-L-methionine (1243, 1244). The participation of S-adenosylmethionine or of methionine in the synthesis of the methyl groups of various alkaloids is considered in other sections of this chapter.

Carnitine, the betaine of β-hydroxy-γ-aminobutyric acid, has been found in the muscle of vertebrates and invertebrates and occurs also in certain microorganisms (1245; see p. 106). There is evidence that the methyl groups of carnitine arise from methionine (1246, 1247). Rat liver preparations catalyze the hydroxylation of γ-butyrobetaine to carnitine in the presence of oxygen, reduced triphosphopyridine nucleotide, and ascorbate (1248). The biosynthesis of γ-butyrobetaine seems not yet to have been studied, but a plausible pathway would be stepwise methylation of γ-aminobutyric acid. Carnitine can be reversibly acetylated by mitochondrial preparations obtained from several animal tissues (1249, 1250). Several fatty acylcarnitines have been prepared; these are completely oxidized by mitochondrial preparations in the presence of catalytic amounts of succinate. The finding that fatty acylcarnitines behave like activated fatty acids is of interest in relation to the earlier finding that carnitine stimulates oxidation of fatty acids.

$$(CH_3)_3\overset{+}{-}N-CH_2CH_2CH_2COO^- \longrightarrow (CH_3)_3\overset{+}{-}N-CH_2\overset{OH}{\underset{|}{C}}HCH_2COO^-$$

γ-Butyrobetaine   Carnitine

The methyl group of methionine is also the precursor of the N-methyl moiety of ε-N-methyllysine. After methyl-labeled methionine was injected into rabbits, hydrolyzates of the kidney, liver, and pancreas histones were found to contain labeled ε-N-methyllysine (see p. 106). ε-N-Methyllysine also occurs in the flagellar protein of certain strains of *Salmonella*, but is absent from other cellular proteins. The presence of ε-N-methyllysine in flagellar proteins is genetically determined (1251), but it is not yet known whether methylation of lysine occurs before, during, or after protein synthesis. Administration of C^{14}-methyl-labeled nicotine and cotinine to the dog, and of the latter compound to man led to the urinary excretion of isomethylnicotinium ion and cotinine methonium ion (1252). It is probable that these and the N-methyl groups of other compounds are introduced by transmethylation from S-adenosyl-L-methionine; studies at the enzyme level have not yet been reported. There is also evidence for the formation of sarcosine by direct N-methylation of glycine (1252a) (see also p. 466).

The first demonstration of transmethylation to a carbon atom came from studies on the synthesis of ergosterol (1253–1255); incorporation of the methyl group of methionine into the side-chain C-28 methyl group of ergosterol was observed in studies with cell-free preparations of yeast. Subsequent work showed utilization of S-adenosyl-L-methionine.

The function of methionine as precursor of some of the methyl groups of vitamin B_{12} was shown in experiments in which *Actinomyces* was grown on a medium containing C^{14}-methyl-labeled methionine. All of the radioactivity incorporated into vitamin B_{12} was found in the porphyrin-like moiety, and the data are consistent with the conclusion that the six "extra" methyl groups of vitamin B_{12} arise from methionine (1256). Earlier studies demonstrated that δ-aminolevulinic acid and porphobilinogen are precursors of vitamin B_{12} carbon (see pp. 645 and 774).

An enzyme activity present in *Rhodopseudomonas spheroides* and *Rhodospirillum rubrum* catalyzes the formation of magnesium protoporphyrin monomethyl ester from S-adenosylmethionine and magnesium protoporphyrin. The enzyme (S-adenosylmethionine-magnesium protoporphyrin methyltransferase) also catalyzes methyl group transfer to zinc protoporphyrin, calcium protoporphyrin, magnesium mesoporphyrin, and magnesium deuteroporphyrin. These studies indicate that methionine plays a specific role in the formation of bacteriochlorophyll (1259). The observation that O-methylation of epinephrine and other catechols

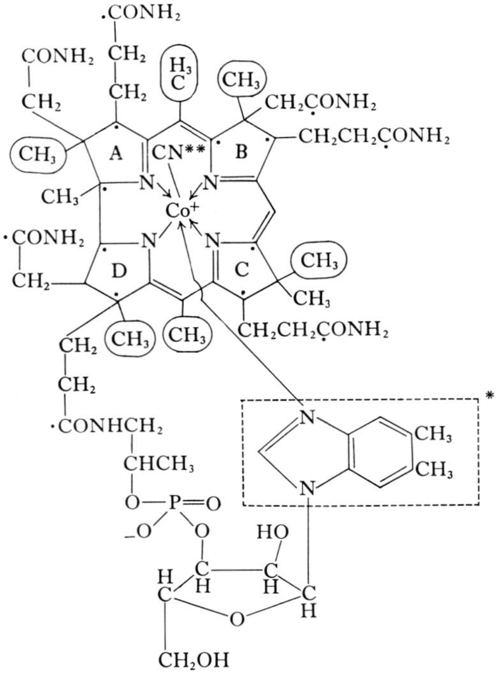

Vitamin B_{12} [cyanocobalamin; α-(5,6-dimethylbenzimidazolylcobamide) cyanide] (1257, 1258, 1258a)

* Replaced by adenine in pseudovitamin B_{12} (adenylcobamide cyanide); absent in cobamide.

** Replaced by adenosine in cobamide coenzymes (the 5′-carbon atom of adenosine is linked to cobalt); replaced by —CH_3 in methylcobalamin.

Encircled methyl groups: from methionine.

· From δ-aminolevulinic acid carbon atoms 1 and 4.

occurs *in vivo* (see p. 913) suggested the existence of catechol O-methyltransferase, which was found in the liver, kidney, and other tissues of several mammals including man. Enzymatic transfer of a methyl group from S-adenosyl-L-methionine to the 3-hydroxy group of epinephrine and other catechols was demonstrated (1260). The rat liver enzyme also catalyzes the methylation of norbelladine, but the major product is the *m-O*-methylated derivative (*N*-vanillyltyramine); on the other hand, an enzyme obtained from flowering bulbs of *Nerine bowdenii* catalyzed mainly *p*-methylation of norbelladine to yield *N*-isovanillyltyramine (1261).

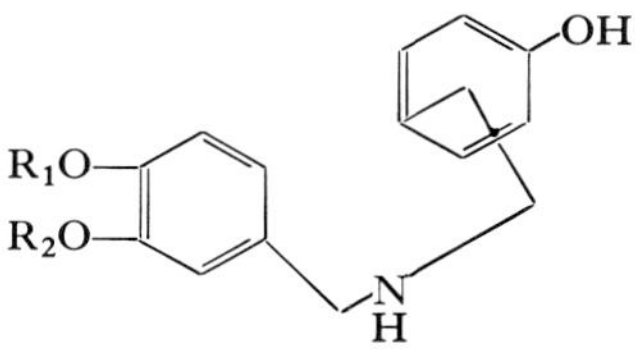

$R_1 = R_2 = H$: norbelladine
$R_1 = H$; $R_2 = CH_3$: *N*-vanillyltyramine
$R_2 = H$; $R_1 = CH_3$: *N*-isovanillyltyramine

The synthesis of pectinic acid in radish plants utilizes the methyl group of methionine; thus, when methyl-labeled methionine was administered to plants, radioactivity appeared in the methyl ester carbon atom and this represented 90% of the total isotope incorporated (1262). Subsequent studies showed that *S*-methylmethionine is an active methyl source for formation of pectin and protopectin, but this methyl donor is less active than either methionine or methionine sulfoxide (1263). The methyl group of methionine is also a precursor of the methoxyl groups of barley and tobacco lignin (1264), the methyl group of nicotine (1265, 1266), and the methyl and methoxy carbon atoms of ricinine (1267) (see p. 863) and fumigatin (1269). The *N*-methyl and methylenedioxy carbon atoms of protopine, synthesized by *Dicentra* plants, also come from methionine-methyl. The methylenedioxy groups are apparently formed by oxidation of *O*-methyl groups followed by ring closure with an adjacent hydroxyl group (1268).

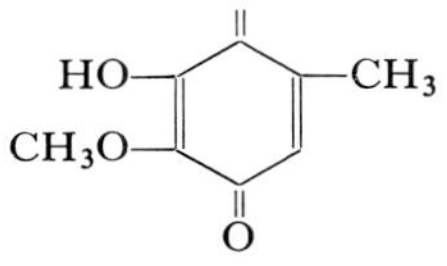

Fumigatin

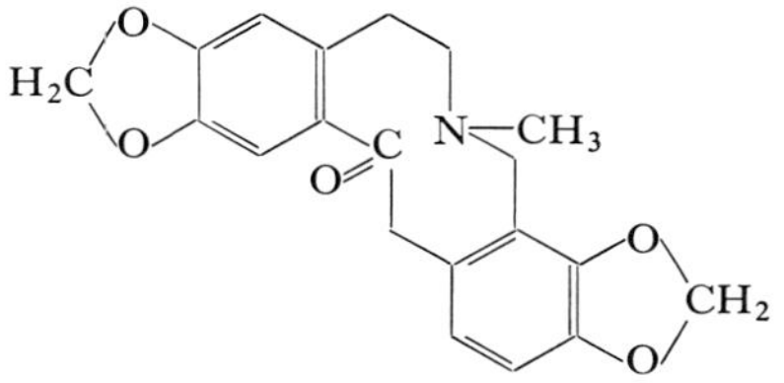

Protopine

The methyl groups of trimethylarsine [$(CH_3)_3As$] and dimethyl-selenide [$(CH_3)_2Se$] arise from the methyl group of methionine in cultures of *Aspergillus niger* and *Scopulariopsis brevicaulis* (1270, 1271).

Challenger (1272) has reviewed several interesting cases of poisoning in man caused by trimethylarsine, which was released to the atmosphere by the action of molds on arsenic-treated wall-paper. It was suggested long ago (1148) that dimethyl telluride $[(CH_3)_2Te]$ and the corresponding selenium compound were formed in animals treated with inorganic tellurium and selenium. Excretion of dimethyl selenide has been detected after administration of inorganic selenium to rats (1273).

The ability of selenium to replace sulfur in methionine and cystine has been discussed elsewhere in this treatise (see pp. 106 and 243). Mudd and Cantoni (1274) made the interesting observation that DL-selenomethionine was utilized as well as, or better than, methionine when incubated with methionine-activating enzyme. The Se-adenosyl compound was isolated from the reaction mixture and incubated with guanidinoacetic acid in the presence of creatine methylpherase. Its activity with this enzyme was also of the same order of magnitude as found with S-adenosylmethionine. In studies in which *E. coli* was grown in media containing trace amounts of radioactive selenite, incorporation of radioactive selenium into selenomethionine was demonstrated (1275).

A novel type of transmethylation is suggested by recent studies on the biosynthesis of bacterial cyclopropane fatty acids. Liu and Hofmann (1276) found that labeled *cis*-vaccenic acid is converted to lactobacillic acid by growing cultures of *Lactobacillus arabinosus*. When methyl-labeled methionine or C^{14}-formate was present in the medium, radioactivity was incorporated almost exclusively into the methylene bridge carbon of lactobacillic acid. O'Leary (1277) grew several strains of *Aerobacter aerogenes* on media containing methyl-labeled L-methionine and S-adenosyl-L-methionine, and found that isotope from both precursors was incorporated into the C_{17}-cyclopropane acid of this organism. Similar results were obtained in studies on the wild strain and on a mutant whose growth requirement was satisfied by either methionine or S-adenosyl-L-methionine. In the mutant that specifically required S-adenosyl-L-methionine, there was little uptake of L-methionine carbon, although label from S-adenosyl-L-methionine was incorporated; the reverse occurred with a methionine-requiring mutant that did not utilize S-adenosyl-L-methionine. These studies indicate that the cyclopropane fatty acids arise from the corresponding unsaturated fatty acids and that S-adenosyl-L-methionine provides the carbon atom of the methylene bridge. The mechanism of this interesting reaction is clearly different from those involved in other transmethylation reactions, since in addition to methyl group transfer, reduction of the double bond and formation of a methylene bridge take place. The carbon and hydrogen

$$CH_3(CH_2)_5CH = CH(CH_2)_9COOH$$

Vaccenic acid
(*cis*-11,12-octadecenoic acid)

$\downarrow$ C_1 unit

$$CH_3(CH_2)_5CH-CH(CH_2)_9COOH$$
$$\diagdown CH_2 \diagup$$

Lactobacillic acid
(*cis*-11,12-methyleneoctadecenoic acid)

atoms of the methyl group of methionine are also used for the synthesis of the cyclopropane ring of the lipids of *E. coli*, *Agrobacterium tumefaciens*, and *Serratia marcescens* (1277a). In studies on *E. coli* with *S*-adenosyl-methionine labeled in the methyl group with deuterium, 2 atoms of deuterium were incorporated into the product, presumably in the methylene bridge (1277b). There is recent evidence that cyclopropane fatty acid synthesis requires a phospholipid as well as *S*-adenosyl-methionine (1277c). In studies with a purified cyclopropane fatty acid synthetase from *Clostridium butyricum*, the methyl group of *S*-adenosyl-methionine was transferred to a monounsaturated fatty acid chain of phosphatidylaminoethanol to yield a cyclopropane-fatty acid chain (1277d).

In addition to transmethylation to homocysteine, it is now known that there are other types of methyl group transfer to sulfur atoms. Thus, an enzymatic activity present in kidney and other mammalian tissues catalyzes the *S*-methylation of 2-thiol-substituted pyrimidines and 6-thiol-substituted purines. The enzyme is apparently not identical with other known sulfhydryl transmethylases (1278).

S-Adenosylethionine has been isolated from yeast grown on a medium containing ethionine by Parks (see p. 242). Enzymatic transfer of the ethyl group of *S*-adenosylethionine to homocysteine and transethylation from *S*-adenosylethionine to carnosine (1223) and guanidinoacetic acid (1279) has been observed. As discussed above, the ethyl group of ethionine has been recovered in the ethyl analogs of creatine and choline (see p. 242).

Synthesis of Methionine

Methionine is formed from homocysteine by incorporation of a one-carbon unit. That synthesis of methyl groups takes place in the tissues of the rat was conclusively demonstrated in studies on germ-free animals (see p. 763), and evidence was obtained that such synthesis involves the participation of vitamin B_{12} and folic acid. Both vitamin B_{12} and folic acid exert a sparing action on choline in protecting rats against renal damage and chicks against perosis (1156, 1159). It was also found that certain methionine-requiring mutants of *Escherichia coli* could grow when supplied with either methionine or vitamin B_{12} (1280). These observations made it clear that a pathway other than transmethylation is involved in the incorporation of one-carbon units into methionine.

Berg (1281) showed that cell-free extracts of pigeon liver catalyze the anaerobic incorporation of labeled formate into methionine, and that homocysteine stimulates this reaction. An enzyme preparation from sheep liver catalyzed incorporation of isotope from serine-3-C^{14} and formaldehyde-C^{14} into methionine methyl, and incorporation was stimulated by adenosine triphosphate, tetrahydrofolate, and pyridine nucleotides (1282). Methionine methyl group formation from one-carbon units (or precursors of one-carbon units) was also demonstrated in studies with preparations of chicken liver (1283). In the synthesis of methionine from formaldehyde catalyzed by a pig liver fraction, *S*-adenosylhomocysteine replaced homocysteine, but adenosine triphosphate was still required (1284). Other studies on methionine biosynthesis in mammalian tissues are considered below; however, more detailed information is available about its synthesis in *E. coli*.

Woods and collaborators (1285–1289) observed that cell suspensions of *E. coli* catalyze the synthesis of methionine from homocysteine; cell extracts fortified with hexose diphosphate, pyridoxal phosphate, adenosine triphosphate, magnesium ions, and pyridine nucleotide synthesized methionine from homocysteine and serine. Evidence for a folic acid derivative was obtained, but the folate requirement could not be fulfilled by tetrahydrofolate or N^5-formyltetrahydrofolate; in fact, tetrahydrofolate inhibited the natural folic acid coenzyme (1289), which could be partially replaced by an *N*-formyltetrahydrofolate derivative obtained from *Clostridium cylindrosporum* (1288). However, extracts of acetone-dried cells grown on media containing cobalamin were activated by tetrahydrofolate (1289), and cobalamin stimulated methionine synthesis by extracts of a mutant of *E. coli* that can grow on either methionine or cobalamin when this mutant was grown on media devoid of cobalamin (1285, 1290). Thus, the natural form of folic acid can be replaced by tetrahydrofolate in methionine biosynthesis provided that cobalamin is present. Studies on extracts of another *E. coli* mutant (requiring either serine or glycine for growth) showed that cobalamin is not needed for methionine synthesis if the natural folic acid derivative is provided, and again that tetrahydrofolate can be used if cobalamin is present. Subsequent work (1291, 1292) showed that tetrahydropteroyltriglutamate, its N^5 or N^{10}-formyl derivative, or an extract of heated *E. coli* was each able to serve as a source of folic acid cofactor for methionine synthesis by extracts of a mutant of *E. coli* that requires either glycine or serine for growth. Extracts of the latter organism (when grown on media containing cobalamin) contain a heat-labile factor which enables tetrahydrofolate to be used in place of the natural folic acid derivative. This factor proved to be an enzyme containing cobalamin (B_{12}-enzyme), which could be released by heating, extraction with hydrogen cyanide, or digestion with papain (1293).

In other studies with *E. coli* mutants (1294–1297) it was found that synthesis of methionine from serine and homocysteine required several enzymes including serine hydroxymethyltransferase and an enzyme containing a cobalamin prosthetic group. The formation of methionine from N^5,N^{10}-methylenetetrahydrofolate and homocysteine required reduced diphosphopyridine nucleotide, flavin adenine dinucleotide, adenosine triphosphate, and magnesium ions. Extracts that catalyzed methionine formation were found to catalyze the following reaction:

$$N^5,N^{10}\text{-Methylenetetrahydrofolate} + \text{DPNH} + \text{H}^+ \rightarrow$$
$$N^5\text{-methyltetrahydrofolate} + \text{DPN}^+$$

The enzymatic synthesis of N^5-methyltetrahydrofolate [identical with prefolic A (1298)] was also shown with preparations obtained from pig liver (1298, 1299). The reversal of this conversion, formation of N^5,N^{10}-methylenetetrahydrofolate from N^5-methyltetrahydrofolate, takes place in the presence of the electron acceptor menadione (1298). The enzyme that catalyzes the reduction of N^5,N^{10}-methylenetetrahydrofolate to N^5-methyltetrahydrofolate (N^5,N^{10}-methylenetetrahydrofolate reductase), and that which catalyzes the oxidation of prefolic A are identical; the flavoprotein catalyzes the reaction in either direction, depending upon whether an electron acceptor is present. Only one isomer of *dl*-L-

N^5-methyltetrahydrofolate is enzymatically active; thus, when N^5-methyltetrahydrofolate was prepared by chemical reduction of a mixture of formaldehyde and tetrahydrofolate which contained both C_6 isomers, only 50% of the N^5-methyltetrahydrofolate product was utilized for

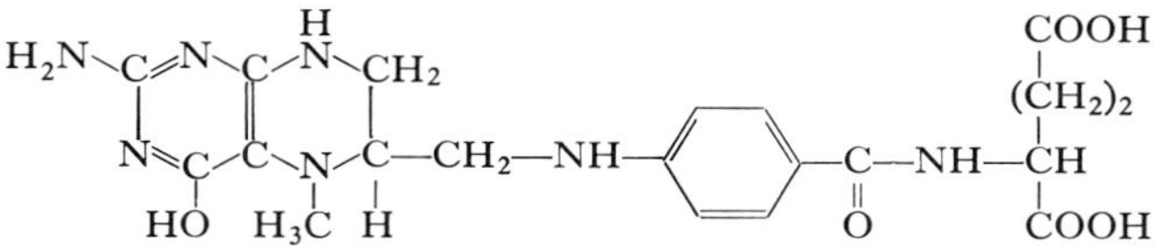

N^5-Methyltetrahydrofolic acid
(see p. 651 for structures of other folic compounds)

enzymatic synthesis of methionine (1300). N^5-Methyltetrahydrofolate has been found in certain leukemic cells of the mouse, in mouse liver (1301), and in human blood serum (1302), and it appears that much of the folic acid present in animals occurs in this form.

Kisliuk (1303, 1304) examined the synthesis of methionine by *E. coli* preparations in the presence of tetradeuterofolate. No deuterium appeared in the isolated methionine, but methionine synthesis in D_2O led to incorporation of 2 atoms of deuterium per mole of methionine. One atom of deuterium was attached to the α-carbon atom (an observation consistent with the presence of transaminase), and the other was found in the methyl group of methionine. Earlier studies (457) showed that the two β-hydrogen atoms of serine are incorporated into methionine, and the studies of Kisliuk indicate therefore that the third atom of hydrogen comes from water. In experiments on the formation of methionine from N^5-methyltetrahydrofolate containing tritium and C^{14} in the methyl group, there was no loss of tritium from the methyl group during methionine synthesis. Similar observations were reported by Buchanan *et al.* (1305) who found that the conversion of N^5,N^{10}-methylenetetrahydrofolate labeled with tritium in positions 6 and 7 to N^5-methyltetrahydrofolate is not associated with loss of isotope. [Earlier conclusions that a dihydrofolate compound is involved in this reaction and that the third hydrogen atom of the methyl group of methionine arose from hydrogen attached to carbon atom 6 of dihydrofolate were withdrawn (1306, 1307)].

The studies of Woods and his collaborators (1308; see also above) have led to the conclusion that there are two pathways of methionine biosynthesis in *E. coli*. One is present in wild-strain organisms and in various mutants, but absent from mutants that require either cobalamin or methionine for growth. Methionine synthesis by this pathway requires tetrahydropteroyltriglutamate:

N^5-Methyltetrahydropteroyltriglutamate + homocysteine $\rightarrow$
methionine + tetrahydropteroyltriglutamate

N^5-Methyltetrahydrofolate is not utilized in this pathway, and cobalamin, flavin adenine dinucleotide, adenosine triphosphate, and S-adenosylmethionine are not required.

The second pathway is the only one present in mutant organisms that require either methionine or cobalamin for growth, but can be induced in other strains by addition of cobalamin to the media or to extracts. Extracts of organisms that do not exhibit a requirement for cobalamin or methionine when grown in the absence of cobalamin catalyze synthesis of methionine from N^5-methyltetrahydrofolate only in the presence of B_{12}-enzyme. These extracts can catalyze methionine biosynthesis in the presence of B_{12}-enzyme with either tetrahydrofolate or tetrahydropteroyltriglutamate. Ultrasonic extracts of such organisms contain apo-B_{12}-enzyme, which combines with cobalamin. Extracts of acetone-dried cells, which do not contain apo-B_{12}-enzyme, catalyze methionine synthesis with N^5-methyltetrahydrofolate provided that B_{12}-enzyme is added. Extracts of strains that require cobalamin or methionine for growth contain B_{12}-enzyme when grown on media containing cobalamin; when grown in its absence extracts of such cells contain apo-B_{12}-enzyme.

The activity of apo-B_{12}-enzyme is only partly restored by addition of dimethylbenzimidazolylcobamide coenzyme (169). The spectrum of B_{12}-enzyme does not resemble that of cobalamin (1309), and treatment of B_{12}-enzyme with 80% ethanol releases a cobamide derivative that is not identical with cobalamin.

The conversion of homocysteine to methionine by the B_{12}-pathway requires reduced diphosphopyridine nucleotide, flavin adenine dinucleotide, and adenosine triphosphate, in addition to N^5-methyltetrahydrofolate. S-Adenosylmethionine can replace adenosine triphosphate in this reaction (1310), and since the methyl group of S-adenosylmethionine is not transferred to homocysteine (1303), it may be concluded that S-adenosylmethionine acts catalytically. In addition, S-adenosylmethionine is effective in very low concentrations and does not become labeled when C^{14}-labeled N^5-methyltetrahydrofolate is used (1311). Since tritium is not lost from the methyl group of N^5-methyltetrahydrofolate during conversion to methionine, incorporation of deuterium from the medium must occur during formation of N^5-methyltetrahydrofolate from N^5,N^{10}-methylenetetrahydrofolate, a reaction that requires flavin adenine dinucleotide.

Recent experiments by Guest *et al.* (1312) indicate that the methyl analog of dimethylbenzimidazolylcobamide coenzyme may participate in methionine synthesis. These workers treated fully reduced hydroxocobalamin with dimethyl sulfate or methyl iodide to obtain methylcobalamin (see p. 774; the adenosine moiety is replaced by a methyl group). This compound reacted nonenzymatically with homocysteine in the presence of 2-mercaptoethanol to yield methionine. The rate of methionine formation was increased considerably when B_{12}-enzyme was added. Methylcobalamin labeled with C^{14} in the methyl moiety gave methyl-labeled methionine of similar specific activity. Methylcobalamin was much more effective than a number of other cobalamin derivatives in the formation of B_{12}-enzyme from a crude source of apoenzyme in the absence of a reducing system, but when the latter was present methylcobalamin and hydroxocobalamin were equally active. Although these findings suggest intermediate formation of methylcobalamin in methionine biosynthesis, the mechanism by which added methylcobalamin acts is not clear. It is possible that the enzyme preparation contains some apoenzyme, that methyl group transfer involves dissociation of the apoenzyme from the enzyme, or that methyl transfer occurs between added methylcobalamin and the enzyme-bound cobamide prosthetic group.

The demonstration that methylcobalamin functions enzymatically should stimulate and direct further research on methionine biosynthesis. At this time there are a number of unanswered questions. What is the nature of the catalytic role of S-adenosylmethionine ? Why is a reducing system required ? An explanation is needed for the observation that both tetrahydrofolate and tetrahydropteroyltriglutamate function in the presence of B_{12}-enzyme, and that only tetrahydropteroyltriglutamate is active in its absence. The possible relationship of the bacterial B_{12}-pathway to the methionine-synthesizing system of animal tissues remains to be explored. The mammalian system utilizes N^5-methyltetrahydrofolate and requires catalytic amounts of S-adenosylmethionine, but at this time there is no direct evidence for the participation of vitamin B_{12}. It would seem that the mammal is analogous to the *E. coli* mutant whose growth requires either methionine or vitamin B_{12}.

Other findings and considerations may be pertinent to the problem of methionine biosynthesis. Thus, it has been reported that a mutant of

E. coli that requires either methionine or cobalamin for growth contained approximately as much vitamin B_{12} as did the wild type when grown on media containing methionine (1313). Vitamin B_{12} production by certain strains of *E. coli* is stimulated by methionine, and it may be significant that the biosynthesis of cobalamin requires methionine (1256). Floyd and Whitehead (1314) suggested that an *E. coli* mutant capable of growth on either methionine or cobalamin might be inhibited in methionine synthesis or utilization rather than in cobalamin synthesis, and these investigators questioned the conclusion that cobalamin functions directly in methionine synthesis. A possibly related finding is the observation that methionine sulfoxide supports the growth of certain methionine mutants of coliform bacteria anaerobically, while methionine does not; both methionine and methionine sulfoxide promote growth in the presence of oxygen. When growth was stimulated by addition of vitamin B_{12} to the medium, there was no oxygen requirement for growth (1315). These observations seem to represent pieces of a puzzle which, hopefully, will fall into place when the mechanism of methionine biosynthesis is understood.

In addition to its function in methionine biosynthesis, vitamin B_{12} is involved in the isomerization of β-methylaspartate (see p. 609) and methylmalonyl coenzyme A (see p. 750). Evidence has also been put forth for the participation of vitamin B_{12} in deoxyribose synthesis (1316), anaerobic degradation of lysine (see p. 947), dehydration of glycols (1317), and other reactions including protein synthesis (see p. 564). Not all of the suggested functions of vitamin B_{12} have been supported by further study. For example, the possible role of vitamin B_{12} in the interconversion of one-carbon units at the formate and formaldehyde levels of oxidation, and in the utilization of formate for synthesis of the methyl group of thymine (1318) has not been confirmed (1319). Definite evidence for its function in protein synthesis is also lacking. The ability of vitamin B_{12} derivatives in the presence of reducing agents to protect enzymes against oxidation (1320) may conceivably be of significance in some of the reported studies in which vitamin B_{12} effects have been observed, including methionine biosynthesis.

Other Reactions of Methionine

From the foregoing discussion it is evident that a major metabolic pathway of methionine is conversion to homocysteine, followed by transfer of the sulfur atom of this amino acid to the carbon chain of serine.

There is evidence (see p. 751) that the α-ketobutyrate formed from the homocysteine carbon chain in this reaction is converted to propionate. Such a pathway was suggested by the studies of Kisliuk *et al.* (1321), who studied the conversion of labeled methionine to liver glycogen in the fasting rat; their data indicate that propionate is a major intermediate of methionine catabolism in the rat.

Alternative pathways for the degradation of homocysteine are conceivable. In addition to oxidation to homocystine or homocysteic acid (1322), homocysteine can undergo desulfhydration to yield hydrogen sulfide, ammonia, and α-ketobutyric acid. An enzyme activity capable of catalyzing this reaction (homocysteine desulfhydrase) was found in mammalian liver, kidney, and pancreas, and in *Proteus morganii* (1323, 1324). The bacterial enzyme, which requires pyridoxal phosphate, exhibits some activity toward D-homocysteine, but the L-isomer is more rapidly attacked (1325). Highly purified preparations of this enzyme have apparently not yet been obtained, and therefore detailed studies of its properties are not available. The possibility that the desulfhydration of homocysteine is catalyzed by one of the enzymes that acts on cystathionine (see p. 760) must be considered.

$$
\begin{array}{ccc}
\text{SH} & & \text{CH}_3 \\
| & & | \\
\text{CH}_2 & & \text{CH}_2 \\
| & & | \\
\text{CH}_2 & \longrightarrow & \text{C}\!=\!\text{O} \quad + \text{H}_2\text{S} + \text{NH}_3 \\
| & & | \\
\text{CHNH}_2 & & \text{COOH} \\
| & & \\
\text{COOH} & & \\
\text{Homo-} & & \text{α-Keto-} \\
\text{cysteine} & & \text{butyric acid}
\end{array}
$$

Methionine is also susceptible to the action of the general amino acid oxidases; the product is α-keto-γ-methiolbutyric acid. The reaction occurs with both isomers of methionine (see p. 298). Oxidation of D-methionine followed by transamination of the resulting α-keto acid to L-methionine probably accounts for the ability of the rat and man to utilize D-methionine for growth. α-Keto-γ-methiolbutyrate may undergo degradative metabolism to yield methyl mercaptan (see below).

The degradation of methionine in certain strains of *Pseudomonas* leads to the anaerobic formation of ammonia, α-ketobutyric acid, and methyl mercaptan. The enzyme activity ("methionase") responsible for this reaction has been studied in cell-free extracts; pyridoxal phosphate appears to be the coenzyme (1328). Extracts of these organisms also possess L-amino acid oxidase (see p. 309) and methionine racemase activities (see p. 369).

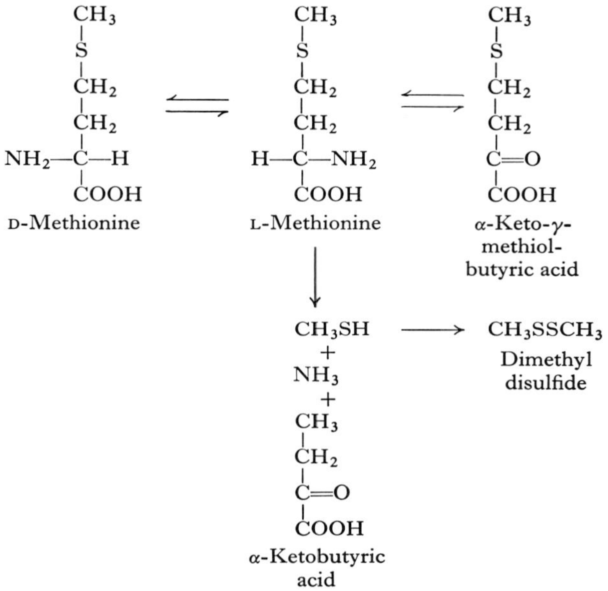

$$
\begin{array}{ccc}
\text{CH}_3 & \text{CH}_3 & \text{CH}_3 \\
| & | & | \\
\text{S} & \text{S} & \text{S} \\
| & | & | \\
\text{CH}_2 & \text{CH}_2 & \text{CH}_2 \\
| & | & | \\
\text{CH}_2 & \text{CH}_2 & \text{CH}_2 \\
| & | & | \\
\text{NH}_2\text{—C—H} & \text{H—C—NH}_2 & \text{C=O} \\
| & | & | \\
\text{COOH} & \text{COOH} & \text{COOH} \\
\text{D-Methionine} & \text{L-Methionine} & \alpha\text{-Keto-}\gamma\text{-} \\
& & \text{methiol-} \\
& & \text{butyric acid}
\end{array}
$$

$$
\begin{array}{cc}
\text{CH}_3\text{SH} & \longrightarrow \quad \text{CH}_3\text{SSCH}_3 \\
+ & \text{Dimethyl} \\
\text{NH}_3 & \text{disulfide} \\
+ & \\
\text{CH}_3 & \\
| & \\
\text{CH}_2 & \\
| & \\
\text{C=O} & \\
| & \\
\text{COOH} & \\
\alpha\text{-Ketobutyric} & \\
\text{acid} &
\end{array}
$$

Another bacterial system, which converts methionine to α-amino-butyric acid and methyl mercaptan (1329), present in *E. coli*, requires the presence of adenosine triphosphate and pyridoxal. The mechanism of the reaction may be similar to that of the *Pseudomonas* system, α-amino-butyric acid being formed by transamination.

The formation of methyl mercaptan from methionine in preparations of rat liver has also been reported; in this system, α-keto-γ-methiol-butyric acid is apparently the precursor of methyl mercaptan, since the keto acid yields methyl mercaptan much more rapidly than does methionine (1326, 1327):

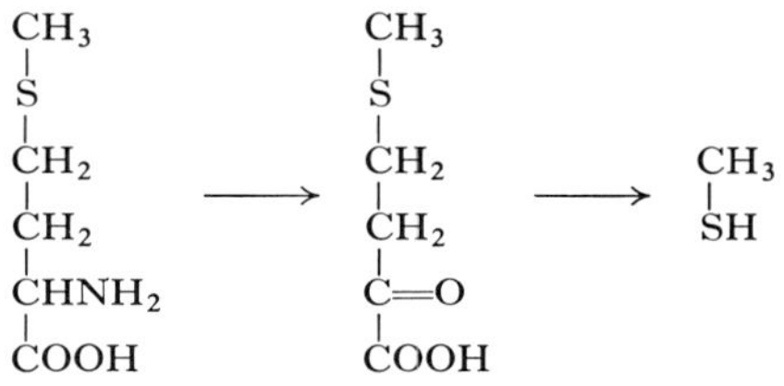

$$
\begin{array}{ccc}
\text{CH}_3 & \text{CH}_3 & \\
| & | & \\
\text{S} & \text{S} & \\
| & | & \\
\text{CH}_2 & \text{CH}_2 & \text{CH}_3 \\
| & | & | \\
\text{CH}_2 \xrightarrow{} & \text{CH}_2 \xrightarrow{} & \text{SH} \\
| & | & \\
\text{CHNH}_2 & \text{C=O} & \\
| & | & \\
\text{COOH} & \text{COOH} &
\end{array}
$$

The characteristic musty odor of the breath ("fetor hepaticus") of patients with severe liver disease may be due to methyl mercaptan formed by degradation of methionine; methyl mercaptan has been found in the urine of patients with advanced hepatic disease (1330). When C^{14}- and S^{35}-labeled methyl mercaptan are administered to rats, the sulfur and the carbon of methyl mercaptan appear as sulfate and carbon dioxide, respectively (1327).

Methionine sulfoxide as well as S-methylmethionine support the growth of the rat and certain microorganisms (1172–1174). While S-methylmethionine seems to be utilized for transmethylation without intermediate formation of methionine (1331), methionine sulfoxide is probably reduced to methionine (1332). There is evidence suggesting that methionine sulfoxide can serve as a methyl donor in oat seedling sections without prior conversion to methionine (1263), but studies at the enzyme level have apparently not been carried out. Formation of S-methylmethionine from methionine and methionine sulfoxide has been reported in intact sections and homogenates of oat seedlings. Other studies suggest that methionine sulfoxide (but not methionine) can support growth of coliform bacteria under anaerobic conditions (see p. 783); this suggests a specific function for the sulfoxide, but additional study is needed.

Black and colleagues (1333) have carried out an elegant study of the enzymatic reduction of L(−)methionine sulfoxide to methionine. They isolated three enzymes, all of which are required for the reduction of methionine sulfoxide in the presence of reduced triphosphopyridine nucleotide. A combination of two of these enzymes catalyzes nonspecific reduction of disulfides to thiols, which is inhibited by arsenite and iodoacetate. Susceptible disulfides are: hydroxyethyl disulfide, L- and D-cystine, homocystine, DL-lipoic acid, oxidized glutathione, oxytocin, and the three disulfide bonds of insulin. Although the purified enzyme system is active only with L-(−)methionine sulfoxide, crude extracts of yeast catalyze the reduction of the L(+) and D(+) isomers, indicating the existence of other systems that reduce methionine sulfoxide. Black and colleagues postulated that the transfer of hydrogen or electrons from reduced triphosphopyridine nucleotide takes place by two successive enzyme transfers to a disulfide or by three enzymes in succession to L(−)methionine sulfoxide. The physiological significance of methionine sulfoxide and of the enzymes that catalyze its reduction to methionine is not yet clear. The system may function to regenerate methionine oxidized nonenzymatically; although nonenzymatic oxidation might be expected to give both L-methionine sulfoxide isomers, another "protective" reductive system may exist that acts on the other sulfoxide isomer. It is possible that methionine residues of proteins can undergo reversible oxidation to methionine sulfoxide; the activity toward protein disulfide bonds may clearly be of physiological significance.

Studies on the biosynthesis of spermidine revealed a new function of S-adenosylmethionine. Tabor et al. (1334) found that C^{14}-N^{15}-putrescine is incorporated as a unit in the bacterial synthesis of spermidine and spermine, and it was also found (1335) that methionine-2-C^{14} is incorporated into spermidine. The observation that adenosine triphosphate was required for incorporation of methionine into spermidine by a cell-free extract of a *Neurospora* mutant suggested the participation of S-adenosylmethionine. The biosynthesis of spermidine by cell-free extracts of *E. coli* was subsequently shown to require adenosine triphosphate in addition to putrescine and methionine, and S-adenosylmethionine replaced adenosine triphosphate and methionine in this system. Evidence was obtained for the formation of the postulated decarboxylation product, S-adenosyl(5')-3-methylmercaptopropylamine. The data therefore indicate the following pathway for the biosynthesis of spermidine and spermine:

$$\underset{\overset{|}{CH_3}}{Adenosine—\overset{+}{S}}—CH_2CH_2CHCOOH \longrightarrow$$
$$\hspace{4cm} \overset{|}{NH_2}$$
S-Adenosylmethionine

$$\hspace{4cm}\underset{\overset{|}{CH_3}}{adenosine—\overset{+}{S}}—CH_2CH_2CH_2NH_2 + CO_2$$
S-Adenosyl(5')-3-methylmercapto-
propylamine

$$\underset{\overset{|}{CH_3}}{Adenosine—\overset{+}{S}}—CH_2CH_2CH_2NH_2 + NH_2(CH_2)_4NH_2 \longrightarrow$$
Putrescine

$$adenosine—S—CH_3 + H_2N(CH_2)_3NH(CH_2)_4NH_2$$
5'-Methylthio-   Spermidine
adenosine

$$\underset{\overset{|}{CH_3}}{Adenosine—\overset{+}{S}}—CH_2CH_2CH_2NH_2 + H_2N(CH_2)_3NH(CH_2)_4NH_2 \longrightarrow$$

$$H_2N(CH_2)_3NH(CH_2)_4NH(CH_2)_3NH_2 + adenosine—S—CH_3$$
Spermine

The metabolism of spermidine and spermine has been studied in a number of microorganisms. In certain organisms (e.g., *E. coli*) these amines are acetylated (1336), while others cleave the polyamines to products that include propane-1,3-diamine (1337–1340). Some microorganisms can oxidize propane-1,3-diamine to β-alanine (see p. 603), and convert the 4-carbon chain of spermidine to γ-aminobutyric acid (1338). A purified spermidine oxidase from spermidine-adapted cells of *Serratia marcescens* oxidizes spermidine to $Δ^1$-pyrroline and propane-1,3-diamine (1337); the enzyme exhibits no activity toward spermine, propane-1,3-diamine, and several other amines.

Another reaction in which the carbon chain of methionine is used is involved in the formation of the thiazole moiety of thiamine in yeast (1337a). Experiments with labeled methionine indicate the following pathway:

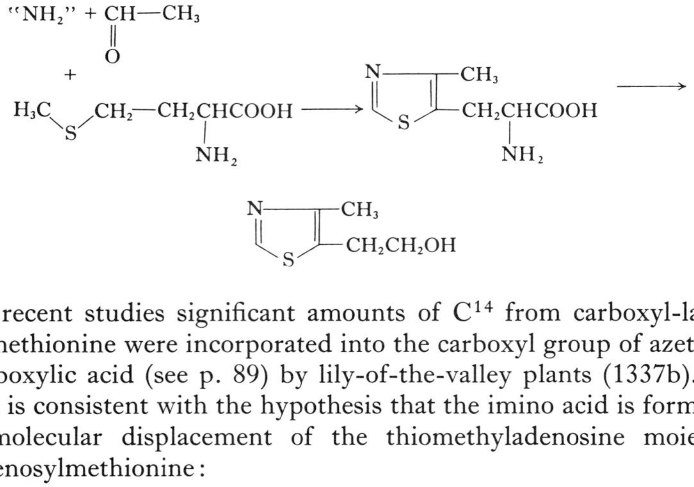

In recent studies significant amounts of C^{14} from carboxyl-labeled C^{14}-methionine were incorporated into the carboxyl group of azetidine-2-carboxylic acid (see p. 89) by lily-of-the-valley plants (1337b). This result is consistent with the hypothesis that the imino acid is formed by intramolecular displacement of the thiomethyladenosine moiety of *S*-adenosylmethionine:

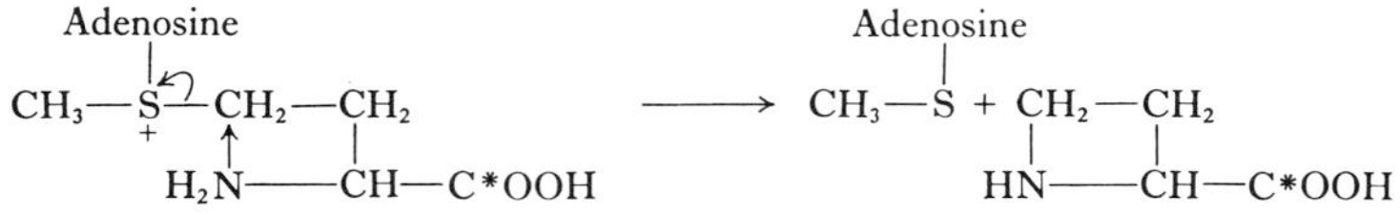

S-Methylcysteine

The next lower homolog of methionine, *S*-methylcysteine, has been found in *Neurospora crassa* and in higher plants (see p. 77). The corresponding sulfoxide and the peptide γ-glutamyl-S-methylcysteine have also been obtained from plants. An enzyme was found in yeast that catalyzes the synthesis of S-methylcysteine from methyl mercaptan and L-serine (1341). No activity was observed with homoserine, suggesting that methionine is not formed in this way.

An investigation of the metabolism of methyl-labeled S-methylcysteine in the intact rat revealed that the oxidation of the methyl group to carbon dioxide was much slower than that of the methyl group of methionine, and the incorporation of radioactivity into tissue choline and creatine was also considerably smaller than observed with methionine (1342). S-Methylcysteine is not activated by the methionine-activating enzyme (1182). The data suggest that the methyl group of S-methylcysteine undergoes oxidation to the level of formate or formaldehyde, and that there is much dilution with other one-carbon units, before reduction and incorporation into choline or creatine.

Biosynthesis of Cysteine

The synthesis of cysteine in animals and in certain microorganisms takes place by transsulfuration from homocysteine to serine as discussed above. Serine also provides the carbon chain for cysteine synthesized from inorganic sulfur by many microorganisms and plants. The incorporation of sulfate into cysteine is considered in this section.

Studies on the growth requirements of several mutant microorganisms suggest the following pathway for the incorporation of sulfate into cysteine (1343–1345):

$$(SO_4^{--}) \longrightarrow (SO_3^{--}) \longrightarrow (S^{--} \text{ or } S_2O_3^{--}) \xrightarrow{\text{serine}} \text{cysteine}$$

Isotopic competition studies in *E. coli* showed that unlabeled serine competes extensively with labeled glucose as a precursor of protein cystine (339). There is also evidence that sulfite, sulfide, and thiosulfate compete with labeled sulfate for incorporation into sulfur-containing amino acids.

Activation of sulfate for formation of phenolsulfate and other compounds was found by DeMeio *et al.* (1346) to involve adenosine triphosphate, and the activated form of sulfate was subsequently identified as adenosine 3′-phosphate-5′-phosphosulfate (1347). The latter compound was shown to react with nitrophenol to yield nitrophenolsulfate and 3′,5′-diphosphoadenosine. The following reactions were elucidated in studies with enzyme preparations from liver and yeast (1347–1351):

Adenosine 5′-triphosphate + sulfate → adenosine 5′-phosphosulfate + pyrophosphate

Adenosine 5′-phosphosulfate + adenosine triphosphate →
                adenosine diphosphate + adenosine 3′-phosphate-5′-phosphosulfate

The first of these reactions is catalyzed by adenosine triphosphate sulfurylase, and the second by adenosine 5′-phosphosulfate-3′-phosphokinase. The structure of "active" sulfate is given below:

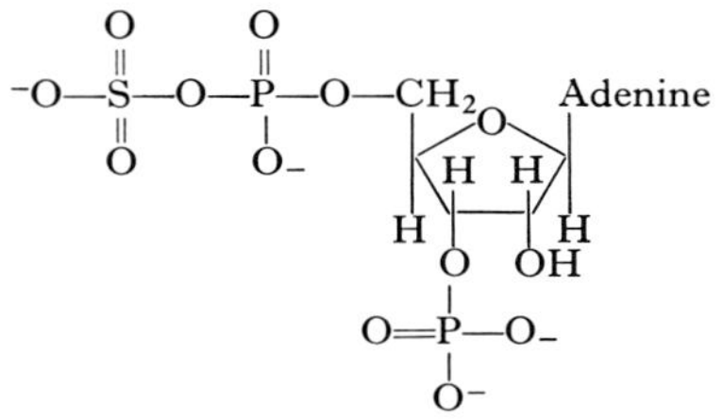

$$\begin{array}{c} \overset{O}{\underset{O}{\overset{\|}{\underset{\|}{-O-S}}}} -O- \overset{O}{\underset{O_-}{\overset{\|}{\underset{|}{P}}}} -O-CH_2 \quad Adenine \end{array}$$

Both enzymes are normally present in the wild strain of *Neurospora crassa* and in other microorganisms that can reduce sulfate. A mutant of *N. crassa* that is unable to reduce sulfate was found to lack adenosine triphosphate sulfurylase activity (1352). Other studies showed that incorporation of labeled sulfate by growing cultures of *E. coli* and *B. subtilis* is prevented or reduced by cysteine, a finding that suggests repression of the synthesis of an enzyme or enzymes required for utilization of sulfate. Observations consistent with the participation of active sulfate in the pathway from sulfate to cysteine sulfur arose from the discovery of mutants of *Salmonella typhimurium* that are blocked at several steps of incorporation (1353). Wilson *et al.* (1354) obtained a soluble preparation from yeast that catalyzes reduction of sulfate to sulfite; adenosine triphosphate and magnesium ions are required, and glucose-6-phosphate plus triphosphopyridine nucleotide (or reduced triphosphopyridine nucleotide) serve as the hydrogen donor. The reduction of active sulfate was shown to require at least two heat-labile enzymes and one heat-stable, nondialyzable, low-molecular-weight protein. A dithiol group of the latter protein may function as the reductant for active sulfate in accordance with the following equation:

Protein—$(SH)_2$ + adenosine 3′-phosphate-5′-phosphosulfate $\rightleftharpoons$
          protein—SS + 3′,5′-diphosphoadenosine + SO_3^{--}

The reaction may not lead to free sulfite but to a bound form of sulfite possibly involving a protein sulfhydryl group (1354a). There is evidence that reduced triphosphopyridine nucleotide or lipoic acid can function in the formation of sulfite from adenosine 3'-phosphate-5'-phosphosulfate by reduction of the protein disulfide (1355, 1356):

$$\text{Protein—SS} \xrightarrow[\text{Lipoic—(SH)}_2]{\text{TPNH+H}^+} \text{Protein—(SH)}_2$$

The pathway described above is apparently not the only mechanism for sulfate incorporation. Thus, extracts of *Desulfovibrio desulfuricans* catalyze formation of adenosine 5'-phosphosulfate, and reduction of this compound to sulfite and adenosine monophosphate. Adenosine 5'-phosphosulfate reductase exhibits no activity toward adenosine 3'-phosphate-5'-phosphosulfate (1357).

Desulfovibrio desulfuricans, an organism which utilizes sulfate reduction for energy production, catalyzes sulfide formation from sulfite (1358). This organism, as well as yeast (1359), can also convert thiosulfate to sulfide, possibly by a reaction of the following type:

$$[2H] + S\text{—}SO_3^{--} \rightarrow SO_3^{--} + H_2S$$

A sulfite reductase has been purified from *E. coli* (1360, 1361); the formation of this enzyme is repressed by cysteine (and cystine). The enzyme, which appears to be a flavoprotein, catalyzes the reduction of sulfite in the presence of reduced triphosphopyridine nucleotide. The same enzyme also catalyzes reduction of nitrite and hydroxylamine, but sulfite seems to be the physiological substrate. All three activities are repressed by cysteine, and genetic, kinetic, and other data support the conclusion that a single enzymatic entity is involved.

Sulfide is utilized for cysteine formation by a yeast enzyme (serine sulfhydrase) that catalyzes the following reaction (1362, 1363):

$$\underset{\overset{|}{\text{OH}}\ \overset{|}{\text{NH}_2}}{\text{CH}_2\text{CHCOOH}} + H_2S \rightleftharpoons \underset{\overset{|}{\text{SH}}\ \overset{|}{\text{NH}_2}}{\text{CH}_2\text{CHCOOH}} + H_2O$$

Isotopic competition studies indicated that utilization of sulfate by yeast cells involves both sulfite and hydrogen sulfide as intermediates; serine sulfhydrase was purified about 50-fold and found to be specific for L-serine. The reaction catalyzed by serine sulfhydrase is analogous to that previously shown in yeast extracts in which S-methyl-L-cysteine is formed from methylmercaptan and L-serine (see p. 78). Rat and chicken liver (1363b) and the vitellin sac and liver of the chick embryo also catalyze synthesis of cysteine from sulfide and serine (1363a) (see also p. 797).

Nakamura and Sato (1364) have followed up earlier evidence (1343) suggesting that thiosulfate reacts with serine to form S-sulfocysteine (cysteine sulfonate). A mutant of *Aspergillus nidulans* was found to accumulate radioactive S-sulfocysteine when grown in the presence of

$$HO_3S—S—CH_2—CHCOOH$$
$$|$$
$$NH_2$$

S-Sulfocysteine
(cysteine sulfonate)

S^{35}-sulfate. This organism requires cysteine (or cystine, methionine) for growth, but cannot use S-sulfocysteine or inorganic sulfur. An enzyme preparation from extracts of the organism catalyzed the conversion of labeled thiosulfate to S-sulfocysteine in the presence of serine, pyridoxal phosphate, adenosine triphosphate, and magnesium ions. The thiosulfate-incorporating activity was extremely low in preparations obtained from a mutant that required S-sulfocysteine, cysteine, or methionine for growth; on the other hand, a mutant blocked in the conversion of S-sulfocysteine to cysteine and the wild-type strain exhibited high activity. Nakamura and Sato also showed that the two sulfur atoms of sulfocysteine are equally labeled, a finding which excludes occurrence of nonenzymatic reactions [cf. (1365)] between labeled thiosulfate and unlabeled cysteine present in the cells. The nature of the reaction in which S-sulfocysteine is converted to cysteine is not yet known. Other reactions of thiosulfate (see p. 811) and cysteine sulfonate (see p. 811) are considered below.

The available information indicates that the conversion of sulfate to cysteine-sulfur takes place in several ways in different organisms. The scheme on page 793 summarizes these observations.

Alternative pathways have been suggested including reversal of the cysteine desulfhydrase reaction (see p. 793). The possibility that cysteine-sulfinic acid is an intermediate in cysteine formation has also been considered, but definitive enzymatic studies have not been done (see pp. 797 and 813).

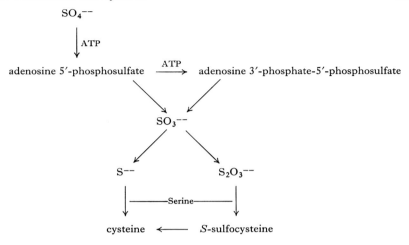

The Cysteine Desulfhydrase Reaction

The enzymatic conversion of cysteine to pyruvate, hydrogen sulfide, and ammonia was first observed by Tarr (1366) and by Fromageot and his collaborators (1367–1370) in preparations of mammalian liver, kidney, and pancreas, and also in certain microorganisms. The overall reaction is described by the following equation (1371):

$$Cysteine + H_2O \rightarrow pyruvate + H_2S + NH_3$$

There is some evidence for its reversibility; thus, incorporation of S^{35}-sulfide into cysteine has been observed with preparations that catalyze the reaction above (1372). Until relatively recently, the reaction was studied only in crude enzyme preparations that also possessed transaminase and other enzymatic activities. For this reason, early studies of the reaction were undoubtedly complicated by the occurrence of competing reactions for cysteine and pyruvate; in some experiments, alanine was formed, due probably to transamination between pyruvate and cysteine or other free amino acids such as glutamic acid, present in the enzyme preparation. Pyridoxal phosphate activates enzyme preparations obtained from the tissues of vitamin B_6-deficient animals (1324, 1373–1378). A mechanism of the desulfhydrase reaction, based on Schiff base formation between pyridoxal phosphate and cysteine, has been proposed and studied in nonenzymatic model systems (see p. 402). Recent studies indicate that there are a number of enzymatic mechanisms that can lead to the desulfhydration of cysteine in a manner essentially in accord with the equation given above. One of these is catalyzed by cystathionase (see p. 796) and another involves several reactions including desulfuration of β-mercaptopyruvate.

Transamination of cysteine with an α-keto acid yields β-mercapto-pyruvic acid (1379). A variety of preparations of animal and bacterial origin catalyze the desulfuration of β-mercaptopyruvate to pyruvate (1379–1381):

$$\text{HS—CH}_2\text{—}\underset{\underset{\text{O}}{\|}}{\text{C}}\text{—COOH} \longrightarrow \text{CH}_3\text{—}\underset{\underset{\text{O}}{\|}}{\text{C}}\text{—COOH} + \text{S}$$

In the presence of reducing substances such as 2-mercaptoethanol, cysteine, or glutathione, the sulfur appears as hydrogen sulfide (1379):

$$2 \text{ RSH} + \text{S} \rightleftharpoons \text{R—S—S—R} + \text{H}_2\text{S}$$

The enzyme that catalyzes the desulfuration of β-mercaptopyruvate was subsequently shown to catalyze a number of additional reactions, which are discussed below (see p. 797).

The desulfhydration of cysteine can therefore be explained in terms of a deamination or transamination step followed by conversion of the resulting β-mercaptopyruvate to pyruvate and sulfur (or hydrogen sulfide). In the presence of excess cysteine, the sulfur appears as hydrogen sulfide; conversion of cysteine to cystine has been observed during the desulfhydrase reaction, which does not proceed to completion. In preparations of several bacteria, desulfhydration of cysteine appears to take place in two steps: (a) deamination, and (b) release of hydrogen sulfide (1377, 1382–1384), and it has been observed that α-keto acids (e.g., α-ketoglutarate) increase the formation of hydrogen sulfide in certain desulfhydrase systems (1204, 1385). These findings suggest the following reactions:

$$\text{Cysteine} + \alpha\text{-ketoglutaric acid} \rightarrow \beta\text{-mercaptopyruvic acid} + \text{glutamic acid} \quad (1)$$

$$\beta\text{-Mercaptopyruvic acid} \rightarrow \text{pyruvic acid} + \text{S} \quad (2)$$

$$2 \text{ Cysteine} + \text{S} \rightarrow \text{cystine} + \text{H}_2\text{S} \quad (3)$$

$$\text{Glutamic acid} + \text{pyruvic acid} \rightarrow \text{alanine} + \alpha\text{-ketoglutaric acid} \quad (4)$$

Sum: $3 \text{ Cysteine} \rightarrow \text{alanine} + \text{H}_2\text{S} + \text{cystine}$

If the following reaction:

$$\text{Glutamic acid} \xrightarrow{\text{DPN}} \text{NH}_3 + \alpha\text{-ketoglutaric acid} \quad (5)$$

is postulated in place of reaction (4), the over-all action would be:

$$3 \text{ Cysteine} \rightarrow NH_3 + \text{pyruvic acid} + H_2S + \text{cystine}$$

These formulations seem to explain the desulfhydration of cysteine observed with a number of crude enzyme preparations. However, other mechanisms of desulfhydration exist. The formation of hydrogen sulfide from cysteine by *Proteus vulgaris* was interpreted in terms of an enzymatic cleavage of cysteine ("cysteinase") to alanine and a sulfur-free radical (1373).

In early studies on cystathionase, Binkley (1133) noted the close association between this enzyme activity and cysteine desulfhydrase, and suggested that the same enzyme catalyzed both reactions. This suggestion was apparently not widely accepted, probably because relatively crude enzyme preparations were employed. Recently, several investigators have proposed again that the enzyme that catalyzes the cleavage of cystathionine to cysteine, α-ketobutyrate, and ammonia also catalyzes the desulfhydration of cysteine (1386–1389, 1134, 1143). Flavin (1143) found that a highly-purified cystathionase preparation from *Neurospora* catalyzed the cleavage of cystine to hydrogen sulfide, pyruvate, and ammonia. Evidence was obtained for the intermediate formation of thiocysteine. In short anaerobic incubations, the disappearance of 1 mole of cystine gave 1 mole each of pyruvate, ammonia, cysteine, and elemental sulfur. In the presence of a diaryl disulfide, 2 moles each of pyruvate, ammonia, elemental sulfur, and arylmercaptan were formed from each mole of cystine. In the presence of iodoacetate, the cystine consumed is replaced by an equal amount of dialkyldisulfides and there is liberation of one equivalent each of ammonia, pyruvate, and iodide:

$$\text{Cystine} + \text{iodoacetate} + H_2O \rightarrow$$
$$\text{pyruvate} + NH_3 + I^- + HOOCCH(NH_2)CH_2SSCH_2COOH + H^+$$

These and other observations suggest that the reaction involves elimination of an unstable alkyl hydrogen disulfide, i.e., thiocysteine. Reaction of thiocysteine with cysteine would yield cystine and hydrogen sulfide; this and other reactions catalyzed by cystathionase are illustrated in Scheme 13.

Cavallini and co-workers (1386–1388) reached similar conclusions about the mechanism of the reaction, and showed that 2-mercaptoethanol inhibits the reaction, presumably by preventing the formation of cystine, the actual substrate. Hypotaurine also inhibits by reacting with cystine to form the corresponding thiosulfonate and cysteine (see below, p. 809). It is noteworthy that neither 2-mercaptoethanol nor hypotaurine affects the activity of the enzyme toward cystathionine.

It seems probable that "cysteine desulfhydrase" reactions are also catalyzed by other enzymes. Desnuelle *et al.* (1390) in relatively early studies observed hydrogen sulfide formation from both the D- and L-isomers of cysteine by *Propionibacterium pentosaceum.* More recently

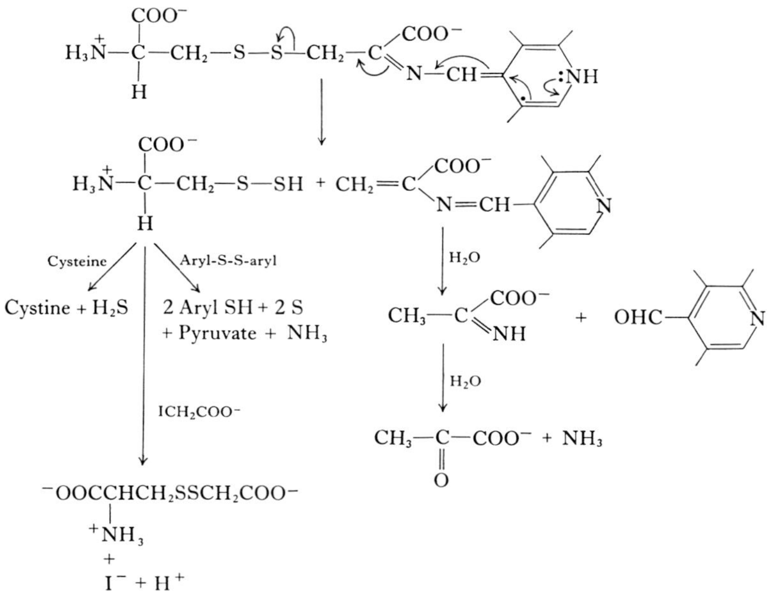

SCHEME 13

it was found that extracts of certain strains of *E. coli* catalyze desulf-hydration of D-cysteine much more rapidly than the L-isomer (1391). These studies were carried out with relatively crude systems and therefore are similar to many earlier studies cited above, but it is of interest that the D-isomer was attacked. Flavin (1143) reported that the highly purified *Neurospora* cystathionase attacks *meso*-cystine three times more rapidly than L-cystine, but the former substrate gives only one equivalent of pyruvate, suggesting that the D-configuration is preferred in the free end and that the L-amino acid moiety is bound to the enzyme. Stekol *et al.*

(1392) observed that the very low "cystine desulfurase" activity of mouse tumors could be increased considerably by addition of both reduced diphosphopyridine nucleotide and pyridoxal phosphate; this result was interpreted in terms of cystine reductase and cysteine desulfhydrase activities, but may also be explained by the coupled activities of β-mercaptopyruvate desulfurase and other enzymes as described above.

Chapeville and P. Fromageot (1393) found a pyridoxal phosphate-activated enzyme in the yolk of hens' eggs that catalyzes replacement of the sulfhydryl group of cysteine by sulfide, sulfite, or cysteine itself (in which case lanthionine is formed). When incubated with cysteine alone, the enzyme (cysteine lyase) catalyzes desulfhydration. A similar non-enzymatic reaction occurs in which pyridoxal or pyridoxal phosphate in the presence of certain metal ions catalyzes substitution of the sulfhydryl group of cysteine, the hydroxyl group of serine, or the phosphate ester group of phosphoserine by an —SH or —SO_3H group (1394).

Crystalline tryptophanase (see p. 879) and the B protein of tryptophan synthetase (see p. 848) also catalyze the deamination and desulfhydration of cysteine.

Desulfuration and Transsulfuration of β-Mercaptopyruvic Acid

The enzymatic desulfuration of β-mercaptopyruvate was first observed with preparations of rat liver, other rat tissues, and certain microorganisms (1379). A partially purified enzyme from rat liver catalyzes stoichio-metric conversion of approximately two thirds of the substrate to pyruvate and elemental sulfur; in the presence of 2-mercaptoethanol, a more rapid reaction that proceeds to completion occurs with the formation of stoichiometric quantities of pyruvate and hydrogen sulfide. As discussed above (see p. 794), this reaction appears to account in part for one type of "cysteine desulfhydration" reaction. Subsequent studies (1395–1401) showed that this same enzyme also catalyzes the transfer of sulfur from β-mercaptopyruvate to cyanide, sulfite, and cysteinesulfinate. Fanshier and Kun (1398) suggested the formation of an intermediate enzyme-persulfide, which transfers sulfur to an acceptor. In the absence of an acceptor, the unstable persulfide yields elemental sulfur. The several reactions known to be catalyzed by the enzyme are formulated below in terms of the hypothesis of persulfide formation. [See top of page 798.] The enzyme was purified from rat liver in the presence of 2-mercapto-ethanol; the protein obtained (molecular weight, 10,000) possesses one sulfhydryl group and one atom of copper per mole (1398).

$$\text{Enzyme—SH} + \text{HSCH}_2\overset{\underset{\|}{O}}{C}\text{COO}^- \rightarrow \text{enzyme—S—SH} + \text{CH}_3\overset{\underset{\|}{O}}{C}\text{COO}^-$$

$$\text{Enzyme—S—SH} \rightarrow \text{enzyme—SH} + \text{S}$$

$$\text{Enzyme—S—SH} + 2\text{RSH} \rightarrow \text{R—S—S—R} + \text{H}_2\text{S} + \text{enzyme—SH}$$

$$\text{Enzyme—S—SH} + \text{CN}^- \rightarrow \text{SCN}^- + \text{enzyme—SH}$$

$$\text{Enzyme—S—SH} + \text{SO}_3^{--} \rightarrow \text{SSO}_3^{--} + \text{enzyme—SH}$$

$$\text{Enzyme—S—SH} + {}^-\text{O}_2\text{SCH}_2\text{CH}\overset{+}{\text{N}}\text{H}_3\text{COO}^- \rightarrow$$

$$^-\text{SSO}_2\text{CH}_2\text{CH}\overset{+}{\text{N}}\text{H}_3\text{COO}^- + \text{enzyme—SH}$$

Another enzymatic reaction that leads to the formation of protein-bound sulfur was discovered by Maloof and associates (1402, 1403), who found that a particulate preparation from sheep thyroid catalyzed the desulfuration of thiourea and oxidized the resulting sulfur to sulfate. Similar preparations from liver and kidney were much less active. This observation may be of importance in understanding the effects of thiourea in producing goiter and inhibiting formation of thyroid hormone. Desulfuration of thiourea leads to formation of protein-bound sulfur, linked in a manner similar to that which occurs on treatment of the enzyme preparation with sulfite (which presumably yields *S*-sulfocysteine residues). The protein-bound sulfur is released as thiosulfate, thiocyanate, or hydrogen sulfide by addition of the appropriate reagent; in this respect, the phenomenon is analogous to that shown with β-mercaptopyruvate transsulfurase.

Alliinase

Alliin, which is present in onion and garlic oil (see p. 78), is converted by alliinase to allicin, pyruvate, and ammonia. Enzymes of this type have been obtained from garlic, onion, and other plant tissues (1404–1406). There is evidence that pyridoxal phosphate is the coenzyme (1407, 1408),

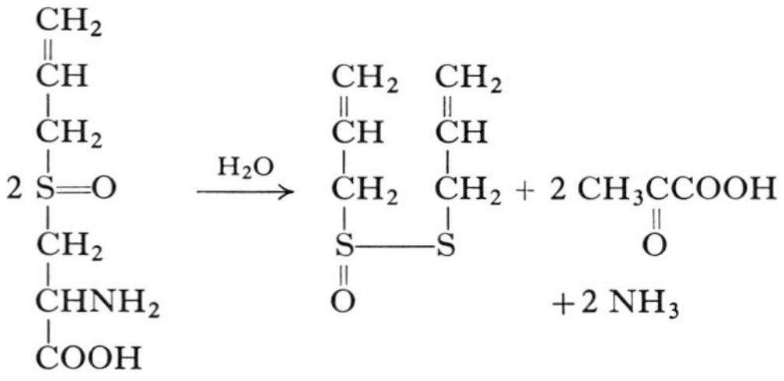

Alliin   Allicin

and the enzyme from onion has been shown to specifically require L-cysteine and sulfoxide moieties. However, other S-alkylcysteine sulfoxides such as the S-propyl and S-methyl derivatives are attacked by the enzyme.

Cysteine and Glutathione Reductases

Although oxidation of cysteine to cystine occurs readily nonenzymatically, it is known that this reaction as well as reduction of cystine to cysteine is catalyzed enzymatically. As indicated above, conversion of cysteine to cystine also takes place by reaction with elemental sulfur. The oxidation of cysteine to cystine by cytochrome c and cytochrome oxidase was observed by Keilin (1409) a number of years ago, and more recently a reaction involving diphosphopyridine nucleotide was observed with preparations of yeast and higher plants (1410, 1411):

$$\text{Cystine} + \text{DPNH} + \text{H}^+ \rightarrow 2\ \text{cysteine} + \text{DPN}^+$$

The enzyme involved is specific for cysteine and diphosphopyridine nucleotide; an analogous reaction involving glutathione (GSH) and triphosphopyridine nucleotide has been described (1412–1417):

$$\text{GSSG} + \text{TPNH} + \text{H}^+ \rightarrow 2\text{GSH} + \text{TPN}^+$$

A glutathione reductase has been purified approximately 25,000-fold from rat liver (1418), and the enzyme was also purified from germinating peas (1419). Glutathione reductase from plants and bacteria contains flavin adenine dinucleotide as the prosthetic group, but as yet there are no conclusive data about the presence of flavin in the rat liver enzyme. A detailed consideration of glutathione reductase is given by Black (1417), who has provided an interesting discussion of the function of disulfide bonds in physiological processes and subcellular structure.

Conversion of Cysteine to Cysteinesulfinic Acid, Taurine, and Related Compounds

About thirty years ago, Pirie suggested that cysteine is converted by oxidation to cysteinesulfinic acid, and that this compound is degraded to sulfite, which is oxidized to sulfate (1420). This suggestion significantly influenced later research on cysteine metabolism, and a pathway of oxidation from cysteine to cysteic acid was considered by early investigators (1322, 1421, 1422).

$$
\begin{array}{cccc}
\text{SH} & \text{SOH} & \text{SO}_2\text{H} & \text{SO}_3\text{H} \\
| & | & | & | \\
\text{CH}_2 & \xrightarrow{(1)} \quad \text{CH}_2 & \xrightarrow{(2)} \quad \text{CH}_2 & \xrightarrow{(3)} \quad \text{CH}_2 \\
| & | & | & | \\
\text{CHNH}_2 & \text{CHNH}_2 & \text{CHNH}_2 & \text{CHNH}_2 \\
| & | & | & | \\
\text{COOH} & \text{COOH} & \text{COOH} & \text{COOH} \\
\text{Cysteine} & \text{Cysteinesulfenic} & \text{Cysteinesulfinic} & \text{Cysteic acid} \\
 & \text{acid} & \text{acid} &
\end{array}
$$

Experimental evidence for the conversion of cysteine to cysteinesulfinic acid and of the latter compound and cysteine to cysteic acid has been obtained. The formation of cysteinesulfenic acid has not been observed; this compound would be expected to be unstable, and it has been postulated that its formation would be accompanied by rapid spontaneous dismutation yielding cysteinesulfinic acid and cysteine:

$$
2 \begin{bmatrix} \text{SOH} \\ | \\ \text{CH}_2 \\ | \\ \text{CHNH}_2 \\ | \\ \text{COOH} \end{bmatrix} \longrightarrow \begin{array}{c} \text{SH} \\ | \\ \text{CH}_2 \\ | \\ \text{CHNH}_2 \\ | \\ \text{COOH} \end{array} + \begin{array}{c} \text{SO}_2\text{H} \\ | \\ \text{CH}_2 \\ | \\ \text{CHNH}_2 \\ | \\ \text{COOH} \end{array}
$$

It is also possible that a compound at the oxidation level of cysteinesulfenic acid is formed as an enzyme-bound intermediate during the oxidation of cysteine.

Cysteinesulfinic acid was first synthesized by Schubert (1421a; see also, 1422), and was later found in nature (see p. 75). Although this compound is probably formed from cysteine, it is apparently not converted to a significant extent to cysteine in the rat, since it does not replace dietary cysteine in supporting growth (1423).

The conversion of cysteinesulfinic acid to alanine and sulfite was observed in early studies with rabbit liver preparations (1370, 1424, 1425). Subsequent work established that cysteinesulfinic acid transaminates with α-ketoglutarate (or oxaloacetate) to yield products that include sulfite and pyruvate. The expected product of transamination, β-sulfinylpyruvate, has not been isolated. Presumably this keto acid is extremely unstable and, if formed, would therefore break down spontaneously; however, the reaction might be enzyme-catalyzed and thereby provide a mechanism for incorporation of sulfite into cysteinesulfinate (1426, 1427). β-Sulfinylpyruvate or its Schiff base analog may break down directly on the surface of the enzyme without appearing as the free compound in solution. It has been concluded that the conversion of this keto acid to pyruvate and sulfite is catalyzed by manganous ions in a manner analogous to the decarboxylation of oxaloacetate (1428). These reactions can be represented as follows (1370, 1428–1434):

$$
\begin{array}{cccc}
\underset{\substack{\text{SO}_2\text{H}\\|\\\text{CH}_2\\|\\\text{CHNH}_2\\|\\\text{COOH}}}{} & + & \underset{\substack{\text{COOH}\\|\\\text{CH}_2\\|\\\text{CH}_2\\|\\\text{C}=\text{O}\\|\\\text{COOH}}}{} & \longrightarrow & \underset{\substack{\text{COOH}\\|\\\text{CH}_2\\|\\\text{CH}_2\\|\\\text{CHNH}_2\\|\\\text{COOH}}}{} & + & \left[\underset{\substack{\text{SO}_2\text{H}\\|\\\text{CH}_2\\|\\\text{C}=\text{O}\\|\\\text{COOH}}}{}\right]
\end{array}
$$

Cysteine- α-Keto-   Glutamic β-Sulfinyl-
sulfinic glutaric   acid pyruvic
acid acid   acid

$$
\left[\underset{\substack{\text{SO}_2\text{H}\\|\\\text{CH}_2\\|\\\text{C}=\text{O}\\|\\\text{COOH}}}{}\right] \longrightarrow \underset{\substack{\text{CH}_3\\|\\\text{C}=\text{O}\\|\\\text{COOH}}}{} + \underset{\substack{\text{SO}_2\\\downarrow\\\text{SO}_3^{--}}}{}
$$

The oxidation of sulfite to sulfate has received attention (1435–1439), and sulfite oxidase has been purified from mammalian liver (1437). Enzymatic activity is associated chiefly with the microsomal fraction of liver, heart, and kidney, and the purified enzyme is a hemoprotein whose absorption spectrum resembles that of cytochrome b_5. Oxygen, cytochrome c, and various dyes serve as electron acceptors from the reduced form of the enzyme. The interesting observation was made that several purified oxidative enzymes (e.g., xanthine oxidase) initiate a free radical chain reaction between sulfite and oxygen in the presence of substrate (1436, 1438).

Transamination between cysteinesulfinic acid and α-ketoglutarate (or oxaloacetate) is catalyzed by purified preparations of glutamate-aspartate transaminase, and it has been concluded (1428) that this enzyme is responsible for the conversion of cysteinesulfinic acid to sulfite (see, however, below). Transamination of cysteinesulfinic acid catalyzed by extracts of *E. coli* was found to yield hydrogen sulfide when reduced triphosphopyridine nucleotide was added, and the enzyme preparation used in these experiments was separated into two protein fractions which contained, respectively, transaminase and sulfite reductase activities (1440). Extracts of rat liver mitochondria catalyze the oxidation of cysteinesulfinic acid to pyruvate, sulfate, and ammonia in the presence of diphosphopyridine nucleotide (1428). Thus, there are at least two pathways for the conversion of cysteinesulfinic acid to pyruvate and sulfate, i.e., oxidative deamination and transamination.

Fromageot and his collaborators originally considered the possibility of a direct conversion of cysteinesulfinic acid to alanine and sulfite ("desulfination"), but discarded this hypothesis when they identified a cofactor required for the reaction as α-ketoglutarate (1432). Their subsequent studies and those of Singer and Kearney (1428) are consistent with the transamination mechanism described above in which pyruvate and sulfite are the primary products. The finding of alanine in earlier experiments can then logically be ascribed to transamination with amino acids present in the enzyme preparation, which undoubtedly contained transaminases as well as other enzymes. It may be observed, however, that a direct "desulfination" reaction would be analogous to the β-decarboxylation of aspartate. Aspartic acid β-decarboxylase has been obtained from several microorganisms, and it may also be present in mammalian tissues. This enzyme is markedly activated by α-keto-glutarate and other α-keto acids, but it has been conclusively demonstrated that the mechanism of decarboxylation does not involve transamination of aspartate to oxaloacetate (see p. 400). By analogy an enzyme catalyzing direct desulfination might also be activated by α-keto acids, and it cannot be concluded that acceleration of sulfite formation from cysteinesulfinic acid by α-keto acids is necessarily due to transamination at the substrate level. The argument for existence of direct desulfination is considerably strengthened by the finding that a highly purified preparation of aspartate β-decarboxylase from *Alcaligenes faecalis* catalyzes the conversion of cysteinesulfinic acid to alanine and sulfite. There is excellent evidence that the same enzyme catalyzes the following reactions (1441):

$$
\begin{array}{ccc}
\text{COOH} & & \\
| & & \\
\text{CH}_2 & & \text{CH}_3 \\
| & & | \\
\text{CHNH}_2 & \longrightarrow & \text{CHNH}_2 + \text{CO}_2 \\
| & & | \\
\text{COOH} & & \text{COOH}
\end{array}
$$

$$
\begin{array}{ccc}
\text{SO}_2\text{H} & & \\
| & & \\
\text{CH}_2 & & \text{CH}_3 \\
| & & | \\
\text{CHNH}_2 & \longrightarrow & \text{CHNH}_2 + \text{SO}_2 \\
| & & | \\
\text{COOH} & & \text{COOH}
\end{array}
$$

Both reactions are activated by α-keto acids and pyridoxal phosphate. The observation that incubation of rat liver preparations with pyridoxal phosphate, cysteinesulfinate, and C^{14}-pyruvate led to formation of unlabeled alanine and sulfate indicates a direct "desulfinase" reaction (1442). It is not yet known whether the liver enzyme also acts on aspartate.

It may be concluded that if β-sulfinylpyruvate is formed, it is probably not oxidized to β-sulfonylpyruvate, since the latter is not converted to pyruvate and sulfate by enzyme preparations that form sulfate and pyruvate from cysteinesulfinate. However, there is evidence for reversible transamination between sulfonylpyruvate (sulfopyruvate) and glutamate to yield cysteate and α-ketoglutarate (see p. 342).

It has been reported that extracts of certain strains of *Proteus* catalyze the reversible dehydrogenation of cysteinesulfinate to cysteate, and that this reaction requires a pyridine nucleotide coenzyme (1428):

$$
\begin{array}{ccc}
\begin{array}{l}
\text{SO}_2\text{H} \\
| \\
\text{CH}_2 \\
| \\
\text{CHNH}_2 \\
| \\
\text{COOH}
\end{array}
& + \tfrac{1}{2}\text{O}_2 \rightleftharpoons &
\begin{array}{l}
\text{SO}_3\text{H} \\
| \\
\text{CH}_2 \\
| \\
\text{CHNH}_2 \\
| \\
\text{COOH}
\end{array} \\[2ex]
\text{Cysteine-} & & \text{Cysteic} \\
\text{sulfinic} & & \text{acid} \\
\text{acid} & &
\end{array}
$$

There is evidence that one or more of the reactions involved in the degradation of cysteinesulfinic acid can proceed in the reverse direction. Thus, it has been reported that radioactive sulfate is incorporated into taurine in the chick embryo (1443, 1444). The experiments of Chapeville and P. Fromageot (1445, 1446) indicate that the mechanism of incorporation of sulfate involves reduction to sulfite and incorporation of the latter into the β-carbon atom of cysteine in a reaction coupled with the desulfhydration of cysteine, and which leads to formation of cysteic acid. Decarboxylation of cysteic acid yields taurine; the liver and other organs of the chick embryo exhibit significant cysteic acid decarboxylase activity (1447). Conversion of cysteinesulfinic acid to taurine has been observed in the dog (1448), and dog liver was shown to have cysteic acid decarboxylase activity (1449).

There is much evidence that hypotaurine (2-aminoethanesulfinic acid) is an important precursor of taurine. Thus, intravenous injection of cysteine to the rat gave rise to alanine, hypotaurine, and taurine in the liver (1450, 1451). Injection of cysteinesulfinic acid also increases liver alanine (1452). The enzymatic decarboxylation of cysteinesulfinic acid to hypotaurine by liver preparations was observed (1453), and hypotaurine was excreted in the urine of normal rats and of rats fed diets containing large amounts of cysteine (1454, 1455). Hypotaurine has been found in certain mollusks (1456), in rat brain (see p. 75), and undoubtedly occurs in other biological materials as well. The chemical synthesis of hypotaurine has been accomplished in several laboratories (1451, 1457–1459).

Both the decarboxylation of cysteic acid and the decarboxylation of cysteinesulfinic acid require pyridoxal phosphate (1460), and it has been found that rats deficient in vitamin B_6 excrete little or no taurine and hypotaurine (1454, 1461). The conversion of S^{35}-cysteine and S^{35}-cysteinesulfinic acid to labeled hypotaurine is catalyzed by extracts of rat liver (1462). Preliminary information indicates that hypotaurine is oxidized to taurine by a diphosphopyridine nucleotide-dependent enzyme (1462a). These reactions may be represented as follows:

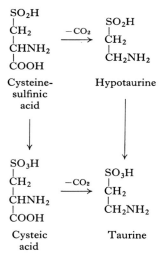

Although there is substantial evidence for the formation of taurine by the pathways described above, there are other mechanisms for taurine synthesis and there are data indicating significant species differences. For example, cysteic acid and cysteinesulfinic acid decarboxylase activities cannot be detected in human liver, although the brain exhibits some activity (1463). The decarboxylases are present in the liver and brain of the dog, rabbit, and rat, but are less active or not present in these tissues of the horse and cat (1460, 1463a). As discussed below, other tissues (e.g., heart) also catalyze taurine formation. The possibility that ingested taurine is utilized by the mammal for conjugation of bile acids and other purposes must also be considered.

An additional pathway to taurine, actually proposed a number of years ago (1420, 1421), postulates conversion of cysteine to cystine, followed by formation of cystine disulfoxide, which undergoes decarboxylation to taurine:

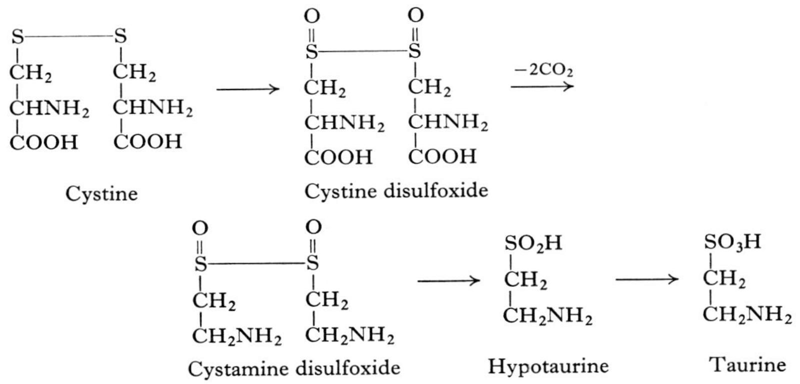

$$
\begin{array}{ccc}
\text{S}\!\!-\!\!\!-\!\!\text{S} & \text{S}\!\!-\!\!\!-\!\!\text{S} & \\
| \quad | & \overset{O}{\overset{\|}{S}}\!\!-\!\!\!-\!\!\overset{O}{\overset{\|}{S}} & \\
CH_2 \quad CH_2 & CH_2 \quad CH_2 & \xrightarrow{-2CO_2} \\
CHNH_2 \quad CHNH_2 & CHNH_2 \quad CHNH_2 & \\
COOH \quad COOH & COOH \quad COOH &
\end{array}
$$

Cystine   Cystine disulfoxide

$$
\begin{array}{cccc}
\overset{O}{\overset{\|}{S}}\!\!-\!\!\!-\!\!\overset{O}{\overset{\|}{S}} & \text{SO}_2\text{H} & \text{SO}_3\text{H} \\
CH_2 \quad CH_2 & \xrightarrow{\quad} & CH_2 & \xrightarrow{\quad} & CH_2 \\
CH_2NH_2 \quad CH_2NH_2 & & CH_2NH_2 & & CH_2NH_2
\end{array}
$$

Cystamine disulfoxide   Hypotaurine   Taurine

There is some evidence consistent with this sequence of reactions. Thus, cystine disulfoxide appears to be oxidatively decarboxylated by liver preparations, and it is readily converted to sulfate in animals (1322, 1464). Recent studies on the synthesis, structure, and chemical properties of cystine disulfoxide (1465, 1466) should pave the way for experimental test of this pathway which is still speculative. However, the possibility that the structure of chemically synthesized "cystine disulfoxide" (1422, 1467) is actually the isomeric thiosulfonate compound (1466), R—SO$_2$—S—R, must also be considered. Treatment of the synthetic product with cysteine yields cystine and cysteinesulfinic acid (1466, 1467), and reaction with hydrogen sulfide gives these products as well as alanine-thiosulfonic acid (1465). These reactions seem to be more consistent with the thiosulfonate than the disulfoxide structure, but more chemical and enzymatic work is needed.

A number of studies have been carried out on cystamine, the expected product of decarboxylation of cystine. Apparently the only known pathways for this type of decarboxylation are those associated with the biosynthesis of coenzyme A, i.e., the decarboxylation of pantothenyl-cysteine to pantetheine (1468–1470) or that of the corresponding 4'-phospho compound to give 4'-phosphopantetheine (1471).

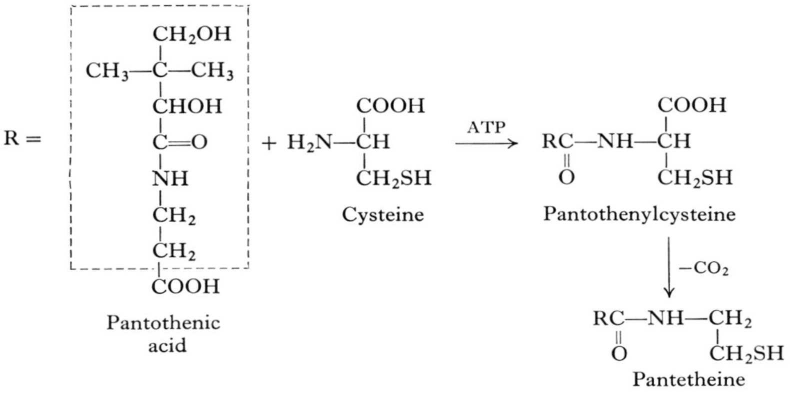

$$
R = \begin{Bmatrix}
CH_2OH \\
| \\
CH_3-C-CH_3 \\
| \\
CHOH \\
| \\
C=O \\
| \\
NH \\
| \\
CH_2 \\
| \\
CH_2 \\
| \\
COOH
\end{Bmatrix}
\quad +
\begin{matrix}
COOH \\
| \\
H_2N-CH \\
| \\
CH_2SH
\end{matrix}
\quad \xrightarrow{ATP} \quad
\begin{matrix}
COOH \\
| \\
RC-NH-CH \\
\| \qquad | \\
O \qquad CH_2SH
\end{matrix}
$$

Pantothenic acid   Cysteine   Pantothenylcysteine

$$\downarrow -CO_2$$

$$
\begin{matrix}
RC-NH-CH_2 \\
\| \qquad | \\
O \qquad CH_2SH
\end{matrix}
$$

Pantetheine

Cystamine might arise in the degradation of coenzyme A (1472), but alternative pathways of its formation (including direct decarboxylation of the parent amino acid) are possible. For example, transsulfuration between cysteine and aminoethanol would be expected to yield serine and 2-mercaptoethylamine (cysteamine):

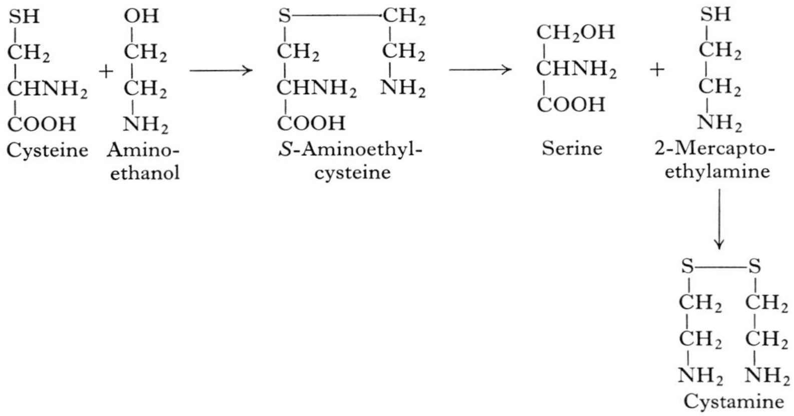

$$
\begin{matrix}
SH \\
| \\
CH_2 \\
| \\
CHNH_2 \\
| \\
COOH
\end{matrix}
+
\begin{matrix}
OH \\
| \\
CH_2 \\
| \\
CH_2 \\
| \\
NH_2
\end{matrix}
\longrightarrow
\begin{matrix}
S\!-\!\!-\!\!-\!\!CH_2 \\
| \qquad | \\
CH_2 \quad CH_2 \\
| \qquad | \\
CHNH_2 \ NH_2 \\
| \\
COOH
\end{matrix}
\longrightarrow
\begin{matrix}
CH_2OH \\
| \\
CHNH_2 \\
| \\
COOH
\end{matrix}
+
\begin{matrix}
SH \\
| \\
CH_2 \\
| \\
CH_2 \\
| \\
NH_2
\end{matrix}
$$

Cysteine   Amino-ethanol   S-Aminoethyl-cysteine   Serine   2-Mercapto-ethylamine

$$\downarrow$$

$$
\begin{matrix}
S\!-\!\!-\!\!-\!\!S \\
| \qquad | \\
CH_2 \quad CH_2 \\
| \qquad | \\
CH_2 \quad CH_2 \\
| \qquad | \\
NH_2 \quad NH_2
\end{matrix}
$$

Cystamine

In analogy with the formation of cystathionine, S-aminoethylcysteine would be formed and cleaved. Cavallini *et al.* (1473) found that rats injected with *S*-aminoethylcysteine excrete the corresponding α-*N*-acetyl derivative, *S*-aminoethylcysteine, and a conjugated form of cystamine; these observations provide some support for the proposed pathway. Other data indicate that cystamine is converted to taurine in several animals (1474, 1475), and hypotaurine could be an intermediate in this transformation.

Cystamine disulfoxide has been reported in the urine and liver of rats after injection of cysteine (1475), but this may have arisen as an artifact of isolation (1455). After injection of S^{35}-DL-cystine to rats, paper chromatographic study (with radioautography) of the urine and kidney revealed a large number of compounds, several of which were identified: taurine, hypotaurine, thiotaurine, thiazolidinecarboxylic acid, and *S*-sulfocysteine (1476). The finding of thiotaurine, thiazolidinecarboxylic acid, and *S*-sulfocysteine is consistent with the occurrence of metabolic reactions involving these compounds (see below). The large number of unidentified compounds suggests that only the surface of cystine metabolism has thus far been examined. Cavallini *et al.* (1477) examined the urinary excretion of sulfur-containing amino acids after oral administration to rats of the optical isomers of cysteine, cysteinesulfinic acid, and cysteic acid. L-Cysteic acid administration gave an increase in urinary taurine, and this result was not observed with D-cysteic acid. Both isomers of cysteine led to increased excretion of sulfate, cystine, and cysteic acid, but only L-cysteine gave increased excretion of taurine and hypotaurine. D-Cysteinesulfinic acid was excreted as such, although some oxidation to cysteic acid was observed; on the other hand, L-cysteinesulfinic acid administration led to increased excretion of taurine.

The metabolism of S^{35}-labeled cystamine and cysteamine was studied in mice as part of an investigation of the ability of certain thiol and disulfide compounds to protect against the effects of x-rays (1478). Evidence was obtained that most of the cystamine of the peripheral blood is bound to intra- and extracellular proteins and to other blood constituents by mixed disulfide linkages. Injection of S^{35}-hypotaurine into mice and rats led to rapid formation of labeled serum taurine and to extensive formation of urinary S^{35}-sulfate (1479). These observations are consistent with others described above on the oxidation of hypotaurine to taurine.

Information concerning the enzymatic conversion of cystamine to hypotaurine has come from the studies of Cavallini and his colleagues (1480–1487). They found that cystamine is oxidized by diamine oxidase preparations from various sources; cystaldimine (1,2-dehydrodithiomorpholine) was identified as the product, but further reaction occurred leading to protein-bound sulfur. Subsequently they observed that oxidation of cystamine by diamine oxidase in the presence of hypotaurine or cysteinesulfinic acid gives thiotaurine and alaninethiosulfonic acid.

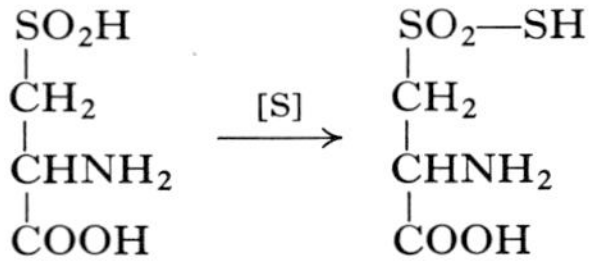

$$
\begin{array}{ccc}
SO_2H & & SO_2-SH \\
| & & | \\
CH_2 & \xrightarrow{\text{[S]}} & CH_2 \\
| & & | \\
CHNH_2 & & CHNH_2 \\
| & & | \\
COOH & & COOH \\
\text{Cysteine-} & & \text{Alanine-} \\
\text{sulfinic} & & \text{thiosulfonic} \\
\text{acid} & & \text{acid}
\end{array}
$$

A pig kidney enzyme preparation capable of converting cystamine to hypotaurine and thiotaurine converts thiocysteamine more rapidly to these products. This enzyme activity is widely distributed in animal tissues and it was partially purified from horse kidney. Study of this enzyme suggested that thiocysteamine is an enzymatically produced intermediate (formed from cysteamine and elemental sulfur), and that sulfide or sulfur acts catalytically in the formation of hypotaurine. By examining the enzymatic oxidation of cysteamine under various conditions, it was found that hypotaurine is the primary product. The formation of thiotaurine from hypotaurine occurs nonenzymatically in the presence of elemental sulfur (see Scheme 14). After injection of S^{35}-cystamine into rats, radioactive thiotaurine was found in the liver and kidney (1488); in addition, a number of unidentified labeled compounds were found on chromatograms. Thiotaurine was identified on chromatograms of the urine of rats fed L-cystine (1489). It was also found that incubation of cystathionase with cysteine and hypotaurine yields thiotaurine provided that oxygen is present. The mechanism of thiotaurine formation under these conditions involves oxidation of cysteine to cystine, which is cleaved by the enzyme to thiocysteine. Transsulfuration from the latter compound to hypotaurine yields thiotaurine (1490). Thiotaurine can be synthesized readily by transsulfuration between hypotaurine and elemental sulfur (1491, 1492). Injection of thiotaurine into rats leads to increased urinary excretion of thiosulfate (1493), and thiosulfate formation has also been observed upon incubation of rat liver preparations with thiotaurine in the presence of mercaptans (1494).

Taurine is known to be present in virtually all of the tissues of the mammal, and it is of interest that considerable amounts of taurine are present in the heart; in fact, more taurine is found in this tissue than in the liver. Injected taurine in animals is found in all of the organs and is concentrated most rapidly by the heart (1495). Taurine is also a normal

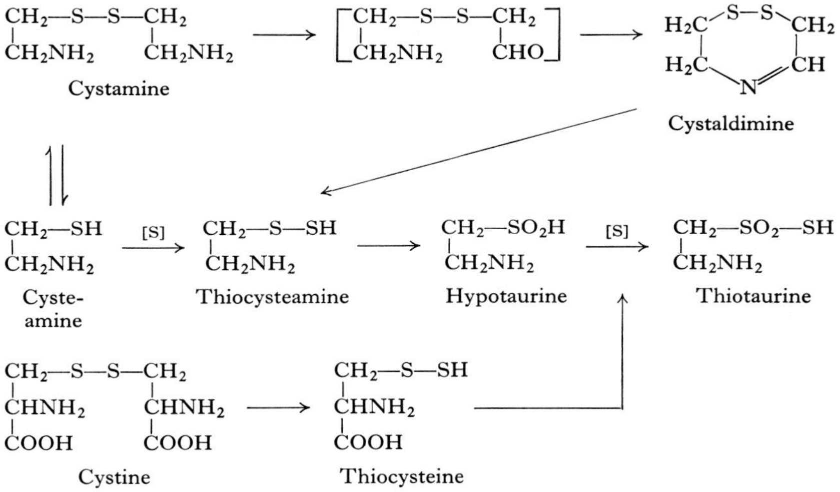

SCHEME 14

urinary excretion product (see p. 110); in man about 200 mg. are excreted per day (1496). The observed increase in excretion of urinary taurine after intraperitoneal administration of β-alanine, β-amino-isobutyric acid, and β-aminobutyric acid to the mouse suggests that these amino acids decrease the renal tubular reabsorption of taurine by a competitive transport mechanism (1497).

The axoplasm of the giant nerve fiber of the squid contains considerable amounts of taurine as well as isethionic acid (2-hydroxyethanesulfonic acid), the deamination product of taurine (1498). Isethionic acid, which is thought to have an effect on the irritability of nerves, is also present in heart muscle (1499), and the conversion of taurine to isethionic acid has

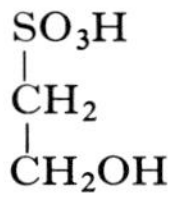

$$
\begin{array}{c}
SO_3H \\
| \\
CH_2 \\
| \\
CH_2OH
\end{array}
$$

Isethionic acid

been demonstrated in slices of dog heart (1500). It was also shown that incubation of S^{35}-cystine with heart slices leads to the formation of radioactive taurine, indicating that heart muscle contains the enzymes necessary for formation of taurine. The physiological function of isethionic acid may be related to the effect of its charge on cell membrane potential. Thus, conversion of taurine to isethionic acid transforms a zwitterion to a strong anion, which could function in the binding of potassium and other cations. Deamination of taurine to isethionic acid has also been demonstrated in *Aspergillus niger* (1501); this organism is able to grow on a medium containing taurine as the sole source of sulfur and under these conditions isethionic acid accumulates. The degradation of taurine to sulfate, ammonia, and carbon dioxide by a species of *Agrobacterium* has also been reported (1501a). The available data suggest that deamination precedes release of sulfate, but it is not certain whether isethionic acid is formed as an intermediate.

Taurine (as well as glycine) occurs in bile in conjugated form with cholic acid. The synthesis of taurocholic acid has been studied with guinea pig liver microsome preparations, which catalyze the following reactions (1502) (see p. 445):

Cholic acid + coenzyme A + ATP → cholyl-coenzyme A + AMP + pyrophosphate

Cholyl-coenzyme A + taurine → taurocholic acid + coenzyme A

Taurine occurs in certain invertebrates as taurocyamine and its *N*-phosphorylated derivative (1503, 1504), and hypotaurocyamine and the corresponding phosphagen have been found in marine worms (1506-1507a). Asterubin, an *N*-dimethyl derivative, has also been isolated (1505). Methylated taurine derivatives have been obtained from red algae (1508); certain of these might be precursors of choline sulfate.

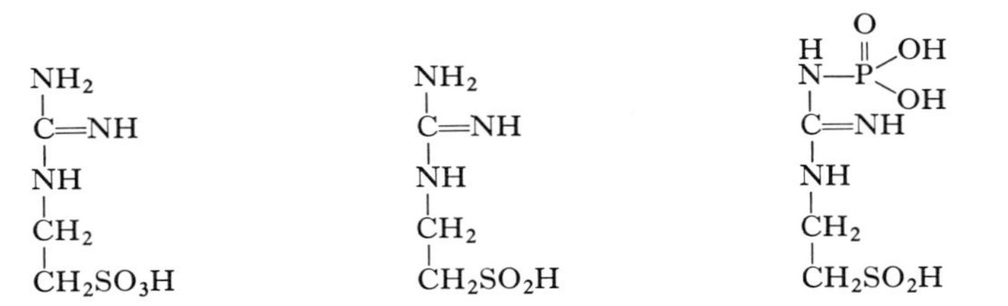

Taurocyamine	Hypotaurocyamine	Hypotaurocyamine phosphate

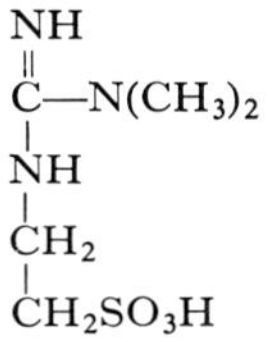

$$\begin{array}{c} NH \\ \parallel \\ C-N(CH_3)_2 \\ \mid \\ NH \\ \mid \\ CH_2 \\ \mid \\ CH_2SO_3H \end{array}$$

Asterubin

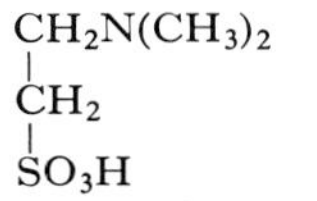

$$\begin{array}{c} CH_2N(CH_3)_2 \\ \mid \\ CH_2 \\ \mid \\ SO_3H \end{array}$$

N-Dimethyltaurine

$$\begin{array}{c} CH_2\overset{+}{N}(CH_3)_3 \\ \mid \\ CH_2 \\ \mid \\ OSO_3{}^- \end{array}$$

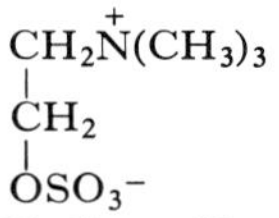

Choline sulfate

S-Sulfocysteine is one of several metabolic products found after injection of cystine into rats (1476). This amino acid has also been implicated in the biosynthesis of cysteine in microorganisms (see p. 792). The possibility that S-sulfoamino acid derivatives may be more widely distributed is suggested by the finding (see p. 119) of S-sulfoglutathione in the lens. Administration of S-sulfocysteine (as well as other sulfur-containing compounds) leads to increased urinary excretion of thiosulfate (1493). Nonenzymatic reaction of S-sulfocysteine with pyridoxal under alkaline conditions yields thiosulfate, ammonia, and pyruvate (1509, 1510). An analogous enzymatic reaction catalyzed by crude liver preparations has been observed by Sörbo (1511). Coletta *et al.* (1512, 1513) found that S-sulfocysteine participated in enzymatic transamination catalyzed by preparations of rat liver mitochondria with α-ketoglutarate (and oxaloacetate); the products include glutamate (or aspartate), pyruvate, and thiosulfate. It was also observed that the sulfite formed by transamination between α-ketoglutarate and cysteinesulfinic acid or that produced in the oxidative deamination of D-cysteinesulfinic acid reacts with cystine and cystamine to form S-sulfocysteine and S-sulfocysteamine, respectively. Although the formation of the S-sulfo compounds takes place nonenzymatically, such synthesis is evidently coupled effectively with enzymatic formation of sulfite.

Thiosulfate Utilization and Formation

The end products of sulfur metabolism in animals include sulfate and thiosulfate. The latter participates in a reaction which has received considerable attention:

$$\text{Thiosulfate} + \text{cyanide} \rightarrow \text{thiocyanate} + \text{sulfate}$$

The formation of thiocyanate by this reaction, which could function physiologically to detoxify cyanide, is catalyzed by the enzyme rhodanese, first observed by Lang (1514). The enzyme has been found in liver and other mammalian tissues (1514–1517). Sörbo (1516, 1518, 1519), who has made an extensive study of rhodanese, prepared the enzyme in crystalline form and showed that it catalyzes exchange between thiosulfate and sulfite:

$$S_2O_3^{--} + S^{35}O_3^{--} \rightleftharpoons S^{35}SO_3^{--} + SO_3^{--}$$

The ability of liver preparations to catalyze the formation of thiocyanate from cyanide and elemental sulfur (or β-mercaptopyruvate) may be ascribed to β-mercaptopyruvate transsulfurase (see above, p. 797). In contrast to the latter enzyme (1520), crystalline rhodanese does not utilize elemental sulfur. Crystalline rhodanese has also been obtained from beef kidney and liver (1521, 1522), and studies with S^{35} indicate a double displacement mechanism for rhodanese activity. The isolation of an enzyme-substrate intermediate containing 2 atoms of S^{35} per molecule of enzyme from $S^{35}SO_3^{--}$, but not from $SS^{35}O_3^{--}$, indicates that 2 substrate molecules each donate a single sulfur atom to the enzyme. The S^{35}-enzyme reacts with SO_3^{--} to form thiosulfate or with CN^- to give SCN^-. Assuming the formation of persulfide groups on the enzyme, the proposed mechanism can be written as follows:

$$\text{enzyme} \diagdown_{SH}^{SH} + 2S-SO_3^{--} \rightleftharpoons \text{enzyme} \diagdown_{S-SH}^{S-SH} + 2SO_3^{--}$$

$$\text{enzyme} \diagdown_{S-SH}^{S-SH} + 2CN^- \rightleftharpoons \text{enzyme} \diagdown_{SH}^{SH} + 2SCN^-$$

The formation of thiosulfate from sulfide has been examined by Baxter and his colleagues (1523), who studied this reaction with preparations of rat liver and kidney. It was established that the oxidation requires both heat-stable and heat-labile factors, and that it does not require peroxide. Evidence for the intermediate formation of a protein-bound thiosulfonate derivative was obtained. These investigators concluded that sulfide is first oxidized to sulfite, and postulated the following mechanism:

$$HS^- + 1\tfrac{1}{2}O_2 \rightarrow HSO_3^-$$
$$R-S-S-R + HSO_3^- \rightarrow RSH + R-S-SO_3^-$$
$$R-S-SO_3^- + HS^- \rightarrow S_2O_3^{--} + RSH$$

$$2RSH + \tfrac{1}{2}O_2 \rightarrow R-S-S-R + H_2O$$
$$\text{Sum: } 2HS^- + 2O_2 \rightarrow S_2O_3^{--} + H_2O$$

In other studies it was found that artificial iron-protein preparations and ferritin also catalyze oxidation of sulfide. The rate of thiosulfate formation is directly proportional to the concentration of ferritin; the observation that ferritin oxidizes sulfide to thiosulfate about 45 times more rapidly than does rat liver extract suggests that in mammals oxidation by ferritin may be of physiological importance. Other aspects of sulfide oxidation and metabolism have been recently reviewed (1524, 1525).

The presence of sulfate and thiosulfate in the urine of animals was observed many years ago, and there is substantial evidence for the oxidation of thiosulfate to sulfate in animals (for a review, see (1526)). Microorganisms can use thiosulfate as such (e.g., *Aspergillus nidulans*; see p. 792), or after conversion to sulfite for synthesis of cysteine. Studies on *Thiobacillus thioparus* with $S^{35}-SO_3^{--}$ and $S-S^{35}O_3^{--}$ showed that only the outer sulfur atom was incorporated into cysteine, and that the inner sulfur atom was converted to sulfate (1527). Although there is some evidence for incorporation of sulfate into cysteine in animals, it is not certain whether the utilization observed is due to the activity of the bacterial flora (1526). When the two singly S^{35}-labeled thiosulfates were injected into rats, 98% of the inner sulfur atom and 60% of the outer sulfur atom were excreted within one day, suggesting that there is some metabolism of the outer sulfur atom (1528). Recently, the outer sulfur atom of thiosulfate was reported to be incorporated into cysteine in the presence of rat liver mitochondria, cysteine, serine, oxygen, and pyridoxal phosphate (1529). The mechanism of incorporation is not yet clear, and the fact that the reaction proceeds with the D-isomers of cysteine and serine as well as the L-isomers is somewhat surprising; the possibility that a nonenzymatic reaction functions in incorporation must be considered.

Other Products of Cysteine Metabolism

The oxidation of cysteine in the presence of formaldehyde yields *N*-formylcysteine; thiazolidinecarboxylic acid, formed by condensation of cysteine and formaldehyde (1530, 1531), gives the same product (1532). L-Thiazolidinecarboxylic acid (or a mixture of L-cysteine and formaldehyde) is converted in good yield to *N*-formylcysteine by preparations of liver mitochondria. Although the primary product of the reaction is *N*-formylcysteine, this is readily oxidized to *N,N'*-diformylcystine. The evidence indicates that the reaction is catalyzed by a specific thiazolidine-carboxylate dehydrogenase.* Homocysteine condenses with formaldehyde in a similar reaction to yield 1,3-thiazane-4-carboxylic acid (1533). Incubation of L-thiazane carboxylate-2-C^{14} with liver homogenates is not associated with oxygen consumption, but the corresponding D-enantiomorph is rapidly oxidized by such preparations. It is of interest that although thiazolidine carboxylate can replace cystine in the diet, thiazine carboxylate does not serve in place of dietary cystine or homocystine for the rat. The observed *in vitro* oxidation of D-1,3-thiazane-4-carboxylate

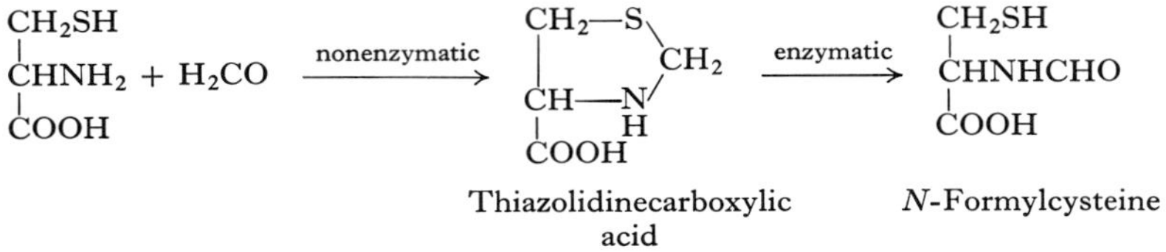

$$
\begin{array}{c}
CH_2SH \\
| \\
CHNH_2 + H_2CO \\
| \\
COOH
\end{array}
\xrightarrow{\text{nonenzymatic}}
\begin{array}{c}
CH_2{-}S \\
| \qquad CH_2 \\
CH{-}N \\
| \quad H \\
COOH
\end{array}
\xrightarrow{\text{enzymatic}}
\begin{array}{c}
CH_2SH \\
| \\
CHNHCHO \\
| \\
COOH
\end{array}
$$

Thiazolidinecarboxylic   N-Formylcysteine
acid

is due to D-amino acid oxidase, which catalyzes dehydrogenation to the expected product; partial conversion to the corresponding sulfoxide and sulfone occurs (1534). Related compounds have been isolated from plants (see p. 79). 1,3-Thiazane-4-carboxylic acid has been identified in *Aerobacter aerogenes* treated with formaldehyde (1535). Treatment of cystine with aqueous calcium hydroxide at room temperature leads to products that include 2-methylthiazolidine-2,4-dicarboxylic acid; the same product was obtained from lanthionine and similar treatment of djenkolic acid yields some thiazolidine-4-carboxylic acid (1536, 1537).

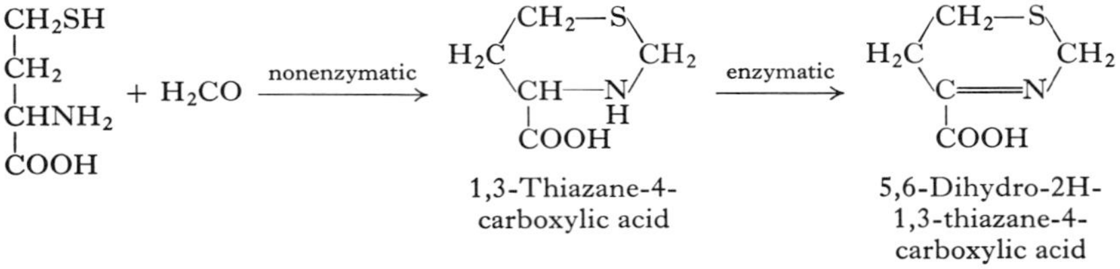

$$
\begin{array}{c}
CH_2SH \\
| \\
CH_2 \\
| \\
CHNH_2 \\
| \\
COOH
\end{array}
+ H_2CO
\xrightarrow{\text{nonenzymatic}}
\begin{array}{c}
CH_2{-}S \\
H_2C \qquad CH_2 \\
CH{-}N \\
| \quad H \\
COOH
\end{array}
\xrightarrow{\text{enzymatic}}
\begin{array}{c}
CH_2{-}S \\
H_2C \qquad CH_2 \\
C{=}N \\
| \\
COOH
\end{array}
$$

1,3-Thiazane-4-   5,6-Dihydro-2H-
carboxylic acid   1,3-thiazane-4-
                         carboxylic acid

Cysteine reacts with cyanide to yield a product which is probably 2-imino-4-thiazolidinecarboxylic acid (1538); rats given sodium cyanide by subcutaneous injection excrete this compound in the urine. Its formation may be responsible for the known protective effect of cysteine against cyanide (1539).

* However, the possibility that this reaction is catalyzed by proline oxidase (see p. 714) should be considered.

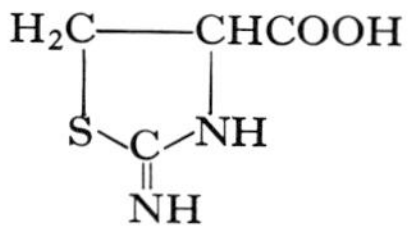

$$H_2C\text{-----}CHCOOH$$
$$S\diagdown C\diagup NH$$
$$\parallel$$
$$NH$$

2-Imino-4-thiazolidinecarboxylic acid

The possibility that S-phosphate derivatives of cysteine and other thio compounds (e.g., coenzyme A) are intermediates in various enzymatic reactions has been considered from time to time. Thus far, there seems to be no conclusive evidence for the phosphorylation of sulfur in this way, but observations have been made that suggest the occurrence of compounds of this type (1540–1543). Enzymatic hydrolysis of a compound thought to be cysteine S-phosphate by preparations of rat kidney (1544) and the hydrolysis of cysteamine S-phosphate to cysteamine and orthophosphate by an enzyme present in human red blood cells (1545) have been reported. Further investigation of this interesting class of compounds might be of much significance, especially in relation to the possible function of protein-S-phosphate linkages in certain enzymatic reactions.

Administration of certain halogenated aromatic hydrocarbons to animals leads to urinary excretion of these compounds in the form of acetylated cysteine derivatives known as mercapturic acids. The formation of such compounds was investigated many years ago and has been the subject of continued investigation (1546–1549). The process of mercapturic acid formation can involve substitution of a nuclear or aliphatic halogen atom, a nuclear hydrogen atom, or a nitro group. Certain aromatic compounds are converted to acid-labile precursors of mercapturic acids; for example, evidence has been found for the formation of N-acetyl-S-(2-hydroxy-1,2-dihydronaphthyl)-L-cysteine after administration of naphthalene (1550, 1551).

It is generally believed that acetylation of the S-substituted cysteine derivative is the final step in mercapturic acid formation. However, the origin of the cysteine portion of the molecule is not known with certainty and has been the subject of considerable investigation. It has been

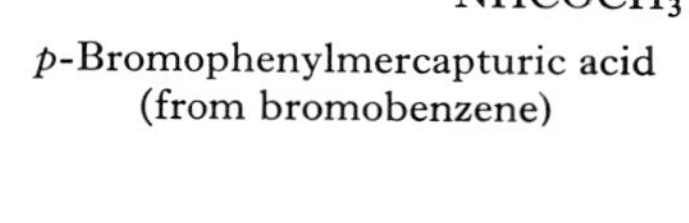

$$Br\text{---}\langle\bigcirc\rangle\text{---}S\text{---}CH_2CHCOOH$$
$$NHCOCH_3$$

p-Bromophenylmercapturic acid
(from bromobenzene)

Cl—⟨benzene ring⟩—S—CH₂CHCOOH
Cl' |
                        NHCOCH₃

$$Cl \text{—} \bigcirc \text{—} S\text{—}CH_2CHCOOH$$
$$NHCOCH_3$$

3,4-Dichlorophenylmercapturic acid
(from *o*-dichlorobenzene)

$$\bigcirc \text{—}CH_2SCH_2CHCOOH$$
$$NHCOCH_3$$

Benzylmercapturic acid
(from benzyl chloride)

suggested that protein cysteine is utilized (1552, 1553); although administration of cystine has been found to increase excretion of certain mercapturic acids, there is evidence that free cysteine is not an intermediate

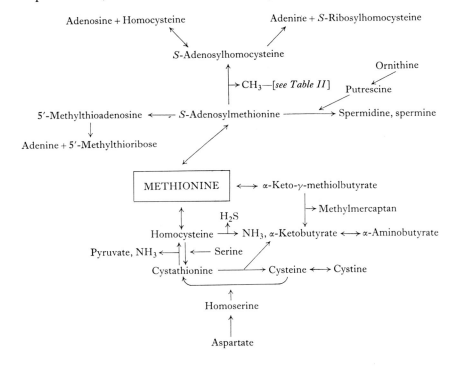

Summary scheme for the metabolism of methionine.

in mercapturic acid formation. Recently, an enzyme has been found in liver that catalyzes the formation of *S*-conjugates of glutathione from glutathione and various aromatic mercapturic acid precursors (1554–1556). An enzyme activity found in rat kidney cleaves the glycine and glutamyl moieties of such conjugates. Presumably acetylation occurs after these reactions. Sulfobromophthalein, a compound used in clinical work for evaluation of liver function, is conjugated with glutathione by a liver enzyme. This reaction involves loss of sulfhydryl groups and the release of 1 atom of bromide for each mole of conjugate formed (1557).

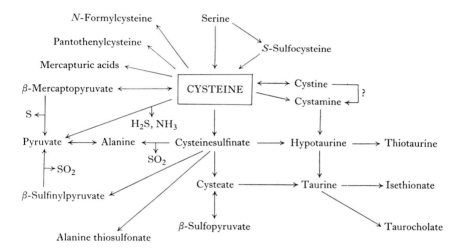

Summary scheme for the metabolism of cysteine.

Although the phenomenon of mercapturic acid formation has been known for many years, studies of the formation of these compounds at the enzymatic level have only recently been attempted and many details remain to be elucidated. Mercapturic acid formation, originally of interest in relation to studies on cystine metabolism, is also of significance in the understanding of the effects of various aromatic compounds on animal metabolism. The formation of mercapturic acid has been used to remove selenium from animals poisoned with this element; thus, administration of *p*-bromobenzene to selenized animals was followed by excretion of *p*-bromophenylmercapturic acid containing selenium (1558). A similar result was reported in the treatment of a human patient whose selenium dermatitis was apparently ameliorated by treatment with bromobenzene (1559).

M. Histidine

Biosynthesis

The biosynthesis of histidine takes place in microorganisms and plants, and the details of this pathway have been largely elucidated by studies on microorganisms in which chemical, microbiological, isotopic, and enzymatic approaches have been used. All animal species studied except man require dietary histidine for growth or maintenance of nitrogen equilibrium (see p. 203). There is evidence that nitrogen balance can be maintained in young adult men without inclusion of histidine in the diet. Although this suggests that histidine is synthesized by human tissues, studies on the biosynthesis of histidine do not seem to have been carried out in man; other explanations have been advanced for the apparent dispensability of dietary histidine (see p. 206). In the rat, the α-keto and α-hydroxy acid analogs of histidine, α-N-acetylhistidine, and D-histidine can replace L-histidine in supporting growth (1560–1564). D-Histidine and imidazolelactic acid appear to have some growth-promoting activity for the mouse provided that a small quantity of L-histidine is included in the diet (1564). This finding suggests that the dietary L-histidine is used for the synthesis of D-amino acid oxidase; however, it may also reflect the limited ability of the mouse to use D-amino acids, and the D-histidine in the diet might have spared the L-histidine requirement (see p. 221).

In relatively early studies it was found that the α-keto acid analog of histidine could be converted to histidine by certain bacteria provided that pyridoxal 5′-phosphate was present, and that *Lactobacillus arabinosus* exhibited a histidine requirement only in the absence of vitamin B_6 (1565). Although these observations suggested that imidazolepyruvate is a precursor of histidine, other data have shown that the α-keto acid is not on the main biosynthetic pathway. As indicated in the diagram below, it is now known that carbon atom 2 of the imidazole ring arises from formate, that nitrogen atom 1 comes from the amide nitrogen of glutamine, and that ribose is the precursor of the 5-carbon chain. [See top of page 819.]

Information about the formation of the carboxyl group of histidine, the last step in the biosynthesis of this amino acid, was obtained in studies by Vogel and associates, who isolated L-histidinol from a histidine-requiring

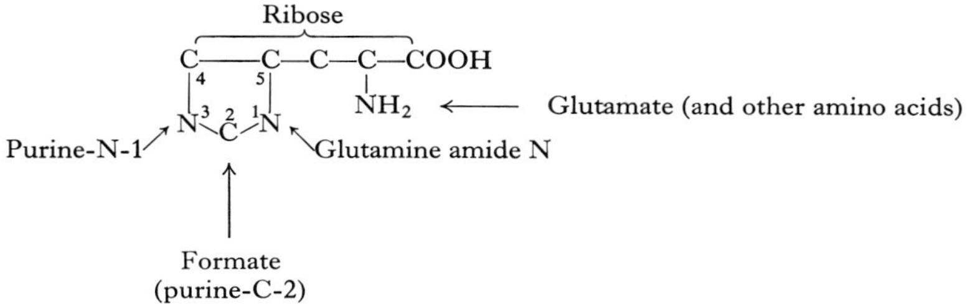

$$\underset{\text{Purine-N-1}}{\nearrow}\ \overset{\displaystyle\overbrace{}^{\text{Ribose}}}{\underset{\underset{\underset{\text{Formate}}{\uparrow}}{\underset{4}{\text{N}}\underset{\text{C}}{\overset{3\ \ 2\ \ 1}{\text{N}}}\text{N}}}{\text{C}\text{—C—C—C—COOH}}}$$

Ribose

C——C—C—C—COOH
|4   5|
| NH₂ ⟵——— Glutamate (and other amino acids)
³ ² ¹
N C N
Purine-N-1 ↗   Glutamine amide N

↑

Formate
(purine-C-2)

mutant of *Escherichia coli* (1566). Histidinol, accumulated by one mutant, stimulated the growth of another mutant blocked in histidine biosynthesis. Ames and Mitchell (1567–1570) isolated histidinol as well as imidazole-glycerol and imidazoleacetol from various histidine-requiring mutants of *Neurospora crassa*. They also isolated the corresponding phosphate esters of these compounds. Chemical and genetic considerations support the pathway shown in Scheme 15.

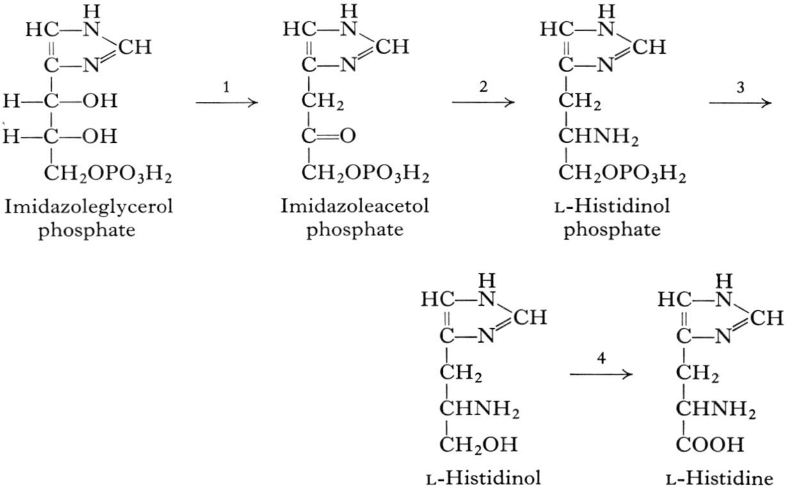

SCHEME 15

The phosphate esters do not support the growth of *N. crassa* mutants, presumably because they are not transported into the cell, nor do the unphosphorylated compounds promote growth. However, subsequent enzymatic investigations have provided substantial support for the proposed pathway. Adams (1571) demonstrated enzymatic conversion of histidinol to histidine using preparations obtained from several bacteria. The oxidation, which requires 2 moles of diphosphopyridine nucleotide, probably takes place in two steps with the intermediate formation of enzyme-bound L-histidinal. Synthetic L-histidinal was converted to L-histidine by enzyme preparations capable of catalyzing the conversion of L-histidinol to L-histidine, but the two enzymatic activities could not be physically separated. D-Histidinal was much less active than the L-isomer, and a time lag was observed in its utilization suggesting occurrence of racemization. The enzyme preparation catalyzes the reduction of L-histidinal to L-histidinol in the presence of reduced diphosphopyridine nucleotide, indicating that this step is reversible, but no evidence was obtained for the reversibility of the over-all reaction.

$$
\begin{array}{ccc}
\begin{array}{l}
\text{HC—N}\diagdown \\[-2pt]
\ \| \quad\ \ \diagup\text{CH} \\[-2pt]
\text{C—N} \\
\ | \\
\text{CH}_2 \\
\ | \\
\text{CHNH}_2 \\
\ | \\
\text{CH}_2\text{OH}
\end{array}
& + \text{DPN}^+ \rightleftharpoons &
\begin{array}{l}
\text{HC—N}\diagdown \\[-2pt]
\ \| \quad\ \ \diagup\text{CH} \\[-2pt]
\text{C—N} \\
\ | \\
\text{CH}_2 \\
\ | \\
\text{CHNH}_2 \\
\ | \\
\text{CHO}
\end{array}
& + \text{DPNH} + \text{H}^+ \\
\text{L-Histidinol} & & \text{L-Histidinal}
\end{array}
$$

$$
\begin{array}{ccc}
\begin{array}{l}
\text{HC—N}\diagdown \\[-2pt]
\ \| \quad\ \ \diagup\text{CH} \\[-2pt]
\text{C—N} \\
\ | \\
\text{CH}_2 \\
\ | \\
\text{CHNH}_2 \\
\ | \\
\text{CHO}
\end{array}
& + \text{DPN}^+ + \text{H}_2\text{O} \longrightarrow &
\begin{array}{l}
\text{HC—N}\diagdown \\[-2pt]
\ \| \quad\ \ \diagup\text{CH} \\[-2pt]
\text{C—N} \\
\ | \\
\text{CH}_2 \\
\ | \\
\text{CHNH}_2 \\
\ | \\
\text{COOH}
\end{array}
& + \text{DPNH} + \text{H}^+ \\
\text{L-Histidinal} & & \text{L-Histidine}
\end{array}
$$

Ames purified an enzyme from *N. crassa* that catalyzes the conversion of D-*erythro*-imidazoleglycerol phosphate to imidazoleacetol phosphate (1572), and showed that manganese ions and a thiol compound are required for activity. D-*erythro*-Imidazoleglycerol phosphate dehydrase activity was not present in a mutant that accumulated imidazoleglycerol phosphate, but it was found in the wild strain and in other histidine-requiring mutants. The conversion of imidazoleacetol phosphate to histidinol phosphate occurs by transamination, and a partially purified preparation of a *Neurospora* transaminase that catalyzes this reaction was obtained (1573). The specificity of this interesting transamination reaction is discussed elsewhere (see p. 361). *N. crassa* contains an L-histidinol phosphate phosphatase, which is specific for L-histidinol phosphate (1574). It does not act on the other phosphorylated intermediates in histidine biosynthesis and is not present in extracts of mutants that accumulate histidinol phosphate; on the other hand, mutants that accumulate histidinol contain the phosphatase but lack histidinol dehydrogenase. The available data indicate that the biosynthetic sequence described above takes place in *E. coli*, *N. crassa*, *Salmonella*, and in other microorganisms (1575, 1576).

Early consideration of the problem of the biosynthesis of the imidazole ring of histidine suggested that the imidazole rings of histidine and purines might be formed by a common mechanism (1577, 1578). Thus, the purine requirement of *Lactobacillus casei* is spared by histidine (1565), and it was known that formate was incorporated into carbon atom 2 of the imidazole ring of histidine and carbon atom 8 of the imidazole ring of purine (1579; see p. 630). However, subsequent investigation showed that carbon atom 2 of the imidazole ring of histidine does not arise from carbon atom 8 of guanine, but that it can come from carbon atom 2 of guanine in *L. casei* (1580). Additional work demonstrated clearly that nitrogen atom 3 and carbon atom 2 of the imidazole ring of histidine arise from nitrogen atom 1 and carbon atom 2, respectively, of the purine ring, and that the imidazole moiety of the purine ring is not a precursor of histidine (1581–1583).

Studies on cultures of *E. coli* showed that the amide nitrogen atom of glutamine is efficiently utilized for the synthesis of nitrogen atom 1 of the imidazole ring of histidine (1583, 1584), and it was shown that free ammonia, the amino groups of glutamate and aspartate, and the amide group of asparagine do not compete with glutamine as a source for this histidine nitrogen atom. In these experiments, adenine was found to be an efficient precursor of nitrogen atom 3 of the imidazole ring of histidine.

Elucidation of the enzymatic steps leading to biosynthesis of the imidazole ring of histidine began with the demonstration of the synthesis of D-*erythro*-imidazoleglycerol phosphate in cell-free preparations obtained from several bacteria (1585). In these experiments, bacterial extracts were incubated with ribose 5-phosphate, glutamine, and an adenosine triphosphate-generating system; the products included imidazoleglycerol phosphate and 5-amino-1-ribosyl-4-imidazole-carboxamide 5′-phosphate. It was shown that nitrogen atom 1 and carbon atom 2 of the purine ring of adenosine triphosphate are transferred to the

imidazole ring of imidazoleglycerol phosphate. In the absence of glutamine, an intermediate accumulated which was tentatively assigned the
structure shown below ("compound III"; Scheme 16). Subsequent
studies (1586) showed that enzyme preparations from S*almonella*
typhimurium catalyze the condensation of 5-phosphoribosyl-1-pyrophos-
phate and adenosine triphosphate to yield phosphoribosyl-adenosine
triphosphate and pyrophosphate. The reaction is reversible, and the
enzyme (phosphoribosyl-adenosine triphosphate pyrophosphorylase) is
not present in certain histidine-requiring mutants. Phosphoribosyl-
adenosine triphosphate pyrophosphorylase was obtained in partially
purified form from *S. typhimurium*, and the enzyme preparation was
found to catalyze exchange between phosphoribosyl pyrophosphate and
P^{32}-pyrophosphate as well as between phosphoribosyl-adenosine triphosphate and C^{14}-adenosine triphosphate (1587). These findings are
consistent with a mechanism involving two steps; the first of these is
formation of a phosphoribosyl-enzyme, which reacts in a second step
with adenosine triphosphate:

Enzyme + phosphoribosyl pyrophosphate $\rightleftharpoons$
$\qquad\qquad\qquad\qquad$ phosphoribosyl-enzyme + pyrophosphate

Phosphoribosyl-enzyme + ATP $\rightleftharpoons$ enzyme + phosphoribosyl-ATP

Phosphoribosyl-adenosine triphosphate is enzymatically converted to
phosphoribosyl-adenosine 5'-monophosphate, the intermediate ("compound III") whose accumulation was observed in earlier studies. The
conversion of phosphoribosyl-adenosine 5'-monophosphate to imidazoleglycerol phosphate takes place in isolated enzyme systems in the presence
of either glutamine or ammonium ions. It was reported that ammonium
ions were more effective than glutamine under certain conditions. In one
study, glutamine was reported to be inactive after glutaminase was
removed from the enzyme preparation. This result is surprising in view of
the data indicating that the amide nitrogen atom of glutamine rather than
that of ammonium ion, or the amino groups of glutamate and aspartate,
is the precursor of nitrogen atom 1 of the imidazole ring of histidine
(1583, 1584). It is conceivable that the "glutaminase" activity of such
enzyme preparations functions in the transfer of the amide nitrogen of
glutamine, or that the enzyme that normally uses glutamine is modified
in some way during isolation. Certain other amide nitrogen-transfer
reactions also occur with ammonia (see p. 624). The possibility that

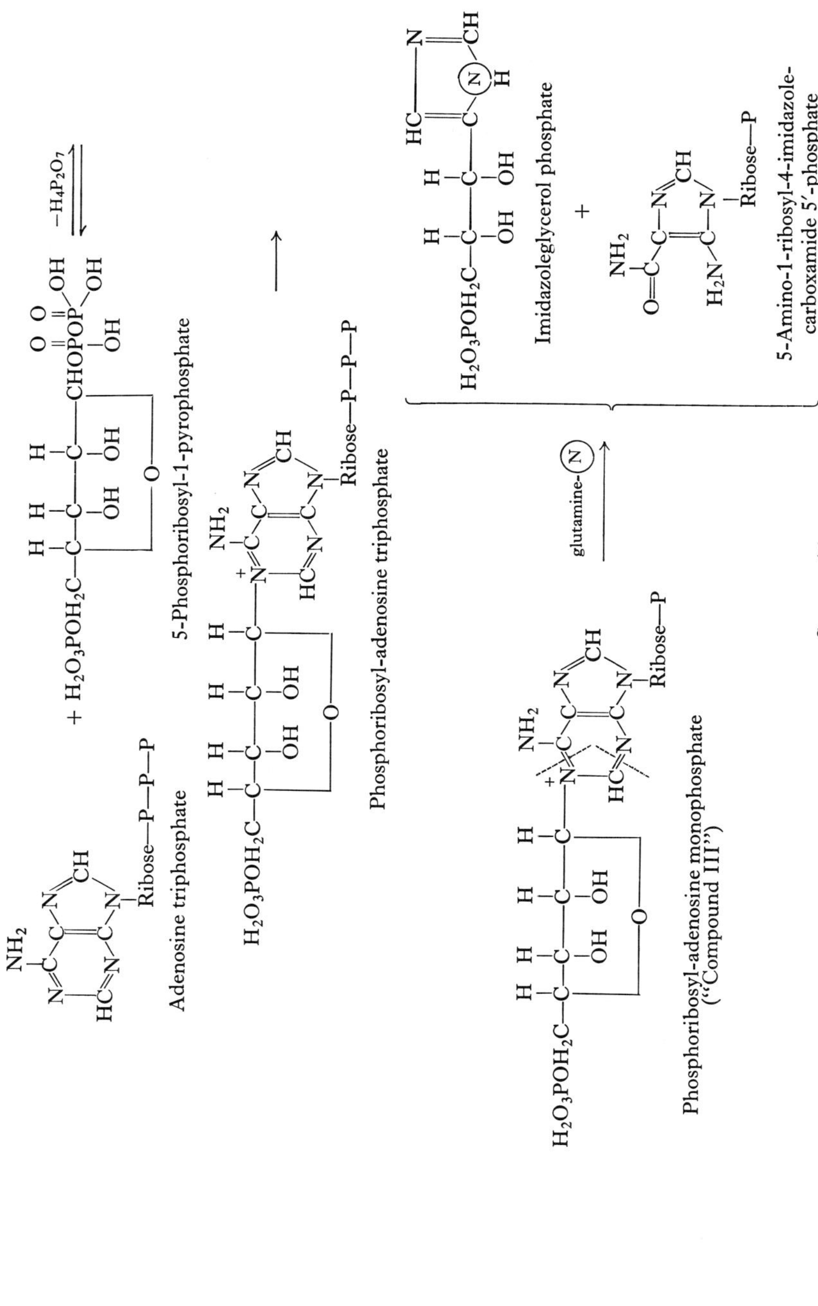

Adenosine triphosphate

+ H$_2$O$_3$POH$_2$C

5-Phosphoribosyl-1-pyrophosphate

$-$H$_4$P$_2$O$_7$

Phosphoribosyl-adenosine triphosphate

Phosphoribosyl-adenosine monophosphate
("Compound III")

glutamine-N

Imidazoleglycerol phosphate

+

5-Amino-1-ribosyl-4-imidazole-
carboxamide 5'-phosphate

Scheme 16

separate enzymes exist for the utilization of the amide group of glutamine and ammonia must also be considered. The pathway of imidazoleglycerol phosphate biosynthesis may be represented as shown in Scheme 16.

Although the mechanism of the conversion of phosphoribosyl-adenosine 5'-monophosphate to 5-amino-1-ribosyl-4-imidazolecarboxamide 5'-phosphate and imidazoleglycerol phosphate has not yet been studied in detail, elucidation of the over-all sequence provides insight into important relationships between purine metabolism and histidine biosynthesis (1588). Thus, 5-amino-1-ribosyl-4-imidazolecarboxamide 5'-phosphate is converted in turn to inosine 5'-monophosphate, adenylosuccinate, adenosine 5'-monophosphate, and adenosine triphosphate (see p. 632). Histidine controls this cycle by inhibiting phosphoribosyl-adenosine triphosphate pyrophosphorylase. In the presence of sufficient histidine to cause inhibition, the operation of the cycle is markedly reduced, and under these conditions, there is relatively little utilization of purine for histidine biosynthesis. Such a mechanism seems to explain the observation that histidine exerts a sparing action on the purine requirement of *L. casei* (1565). These relationships are also consistent with earlier findings on the inhibition of growth of *Torula* and *Lactobacillus arabinosus* by aminopterin (1589). Aminopterin was less toxic to *L. arabinosus* when histidine was present, and growth inhibition of *Torula* by aminopterin was reversed by histidine provided that adenine was also present.

Histidine is a feedback inhibitor of the enzymatic synthesis of "compound III" and a structural analog of histidine, 2-thiazolealanine, shares this property (1590, see p. 254). Histidine inhibits the first step in histidine biosynthesis, i.e., phosphoribosyl-adenosine triphosphate pyrophosphorylase; inhibition by histidine is specific and noncompetitive with both substrates. Treatment of the enzyme with mercuric ions under specific conditions gave a modified enzyme that was no longer inhibited by histidine, and restoration of feedback inhibition (histidine sensitivity) was achieved by treatment of the enzyme with 2-mercaptoethanol (1587). Histidine also represses the synthesis of four enzymes (imidazoleglycerol phosphate dehydrase, imidazoleacetol phosphate transaminase, histidinol phosphatase, and histidinol dehydrogenase) in its biosynthetic pathway, and the synthesis of these enzymes increases considerably and to the same extent when organisms are grown in media containing limited quantities of histidine (1591). This type of "coordinate repression" suggests that the genes responsible for the synthesis of these enzymes are controlled as a unit. This hypothesis is supported by the finding that the genes that control the synthesis of these enzymes in *Salmonella* are adjacent to each other on the genetic map (1592).

Degradative Metabolism

The metabolism of histidine involves decarboxylation to histamine, conversion to imidazolepyruvic acid and related compounds, incorporation into ergothioneine and dipeptides (e.g., carnosine), and degradation via the urocanic acid pathway. Metabolism by the last-mentioned route, which leads to products that include glutamate, is the major quantitative pathway of histidine degradation in animals, and in certain other organisms.

The Urocanic Acid Pathway. The degradation of histidine by mammalian liver was first studied by György and Röthler (1593) and by Edlbacher (1594, 1595). The reaction, originally thought to be catalyzed by a specific enzyme (histidase), results in cleavage of the imidazole ring, formation of ammonia, and disappearance of Van Slyke α-amino nitrogen. The early workers found that the major product of the reaction could be readily hydrolyzed to ammonia, glutamic acid, and formic acid (1596–1599).

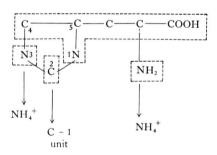

Glutamate

Fate of histidine carbon and nitrogen (urocanic acid pathway)

The occurrence of urocanic acid in the urine of a dog was reported by Jaffe in 1874, some years before histidine was recognized as a constituent of protein (1600). For a considerable time, urocanic acid was thought to be a relatively unimportant side product of histidine metabolism. A number of early reports of the occurrence or formation of urocanic acid apparently could not be confirmed by other investigators. Even Jaffe failed to repeat his own observation because the dog used in his original study ran away, and the other dogs available for Jaffe's subsequent investigations did not produce urinary urocanic acid.

However, in later work, urocanic acid was often found in the urine of animals after administration of histidine (1602–1609). The finding that certain bacteria could convert histidine to urocanic acid (1601, 1602) suggested that urocanic acid formation in intact animals might be due to reactions catalyzed by the bacterial flora, but subsequent studies by a number of investigators (1610–1619) demonstrated that liver fractions catalyze the conversion of histidine to urocanic acid, and in several experiments urocanic acid was converted to glutamic acid derivatives. Thus, Takeuchi (1612) obtained optically inactive isoglutamine, and Sera and Aihara (1611) and Oyamada (1614) isolated compounds which appeared to be formyl derivatives of isoglutamine. Although a pathway of degradation involving conversion of histidine to urocanic acid followed by metabolism of the latter compound to glutamate was indicated by several investigations (1610, 1611, 1614), experiments with specifically labeled histidine unequivocally demonstrated the urocanic acid pathway. Tabor and Hayaishi (1620) found that a cell-free extract of *Pseudomonas fluorescens*, grown on a histidine-containing medium, catalyzes the conversion of L-histidine to L-glutamic acid, formic acid, and 2 moles of ammonia. When this reaction was studied with L-histidine labeled with N^{15} in the α- or γ-nitrogen atoms, the α-amino nitrogen atom of histidine was liberated as ammonia and the γ-nitrogen atom appeared in the glutamic acid (1621). Studies with C^{14}-histidine demonstrated that the formate comes from the 2-position of the imidazole ring (1622).

The conversion of histidine to urocanic acid, which is consistent with many experiments (1610–1630), is catalyzed by an enzyme (found in liver and various microorganisms) which has been designated histidase, histidine deaminase, and desamino histidase (see p. 320). The finding that a purified preparation of histidase from *Pseudomonas* catalyzes incorporation of C^{14}-urocanic acid (but not $N^{15}H_3$) into histidine, suggests that the reaction involves formation of an amino-enzyme (1631). (See top of p. 827.) According to this mechanism there is an exchange of hydrogen ion between the β-carbon atom of histidine and the medium. Such an exchange was shown by carrying out the reaction in tritiated water, and it was demonstrated that the incorporated tritium was on the β-carbon atom. Furthermore, the ratio of the rates of the urocanic acid and tritium exchanges was essentially constant during purification of the enzyme.

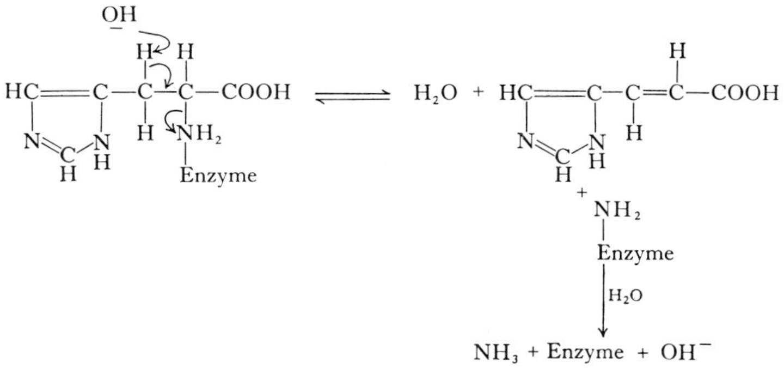

These observations offer strong support for an amino-enzyme; direct demonstration of this would clearly be of importance in order to establish the manner of attachment of the amino group to the enzyme.

The reaction catalyzed by histidase is analogous to those catalyzed by aspartase (see p. 608). β-methylaspartase (see p. 609), acrylyl coenzyme A aminase (see p. 601), and to the nonoxidative deamination of phenylalanine (see p. 922), tyrosine (see p. 922) dihydroxyphenylalanine (see p. 922), and ergothioneine (see p. 840). The over-all histidase reaction and the deamination of phenylalanine and tyrosine are irreversible, while the aspartase and β-methylaspartase reactions are reversible. The equilibrium for the amination of acrylyl coenzyme A lies markedly in the direction of β-alanyl-coenzyme A formation. Complete understanding of these reactions and of their markedly different equilibrium positions requires further study. The possibility that they all involve an amino-enzyme mechanism must be considered. The irreversibility of the formation of urocanic acid from histidine is in accord with the inability of urocanic acid to replace histidine in supporting the growth of rats (1564). Both the over-all histidase reaction and the incorporation of tritium from the medium are stimulated by 2-mercaptoethanol; other data suggest that histidase requires sulfhydryl groups (1631, 1628, 1632, 1633) and possibly also metal ions (1622, 1629, 1632, 1634). The purified histidase obtained from *Pseudomonas* is inhibited by both isomers of cysteine and ethylenediaminetetraacetic acid in competitive fashion; although these findings suggest the possibility that a metal is involved in the enzymatic reaction, definitive studies of the metal content of the enzyme are needed (1634). The reported evidence (1635) for a function of folic acid in the histidase reaction is discussed below (see p. 829).

The human inborn error of metabolism, histidinemia (see p. 1055), is associated with absence of histidase activity.

In addition to its role as an intermediate in the degradation of histidine, urocanic acid is a constituent of urocanylcholine (murexine), which occurs in *Murex trunculus* and other mollusks. Urocanylcholine has pharmacological effects similar to those of nicotine and curare (1636, 1637). Urocanic acid is present in sweat, and it has been suggested that this compound functions in protection against ultraviolet radiation (1638, 1639); see, however, page 1055.

$$\underset{\displaystyle \text{HC}}{\overset{\displaystyle \text{NH}\text{—}\text{CH}}{\diagdown}} \underset{\displaystyle \text{N—}}{} \text{—C—CH=CH—C—O—CH}_2\text{—CH}_2\overset{+}{\text{N}}(\text{CH}_3)_3$$

O   OH⁻

Urocanylcholine

The enzymatic degradation of urocanic acid has been studied by several investigators and products including formyl-DL-isoglutamine (1614, 1617), formyl-L-glutamine (1597), and α-formamido-L-glutamic acid (N-formimino-L-glutamic acid, L-α-formamidinoglutaric acid) (1599, 1632, 1640–1644) have been obtained. Studies on extracts of *Aerobacter aerogenes* that catalyze the quantitative conversion of urocanic acid to glutamic acid and formamide via the intermediate N-formiminoglutamic acid led to discovery of an intermediate that was identified as 4-imidazolone-5-propionic acid (1645). Evidence for the formation of the same compound was obtained in studies on beef liver urocanase (1646). The absorption spectrum, lability, and other properties of this compound are consistent with 4(5)-imidazolone-5(4)-propionic acid. Its properties are similar to those of 4(5)-imidazolone and 4(5)-imidazolone-5(4)-acetic acid, which have been prepared in solution by chemical synthesis (1647, 1648). Nonenzymatic hydrolysis of imidazolonepropionic acid yields formylisoglutamine, which can be racemic or of the L-configuration, depending on conditions of hydrolysis. Presumably rapid hydrolysis of L-imidazolonepropionic acid would yield L-formylisoglutamine, while formation of DL-formylisoglutamine suggests extensive enolization of imidazolonepropionic acid prior to hydrolysis. Although imidazolonepropionic acid is extremely labile, it can be purified by chromatography; it is stable in acid solution in the presence of air, and under anaerobic conditions it is stable at neutral values of pH (1649). Imidazolonepropionic acid undergoes nonenzymatic oxidation in the presence of ferricyanide and 2,6-dichlorophenolindophenol (1646, 1650); the product of oxidation yields α-ketoglutaric acid on acid hydrolysis, and has been shown to be 4-ketoglutaramic acid (1650a).

Urocanase has been partially purified from beef liver; the enzyme is inhibited by sulfhydryl reagents and such inhibition is partially reversed by glutathione. A preliminary report that the enzyme contains pyridoxal phosphate (1651) is interesting but additional data are needed.

Imidazolonepropionic acid is converted to N-formiminoglutamic acid by a hydrolase; these two compounds are key intermediates in the urocanic acid pathway, which is summarized in Scheme 17. Highly purified preparations of imidazolonepropionic acid hydrolase are not yet available, but its activity has been demonstrated in liver and bacterial preparations (1652, 1653). The product of this reaction is optically active, indicating that the corresponding optical isomer of imidazolonepro-pionic acid is formed by the action of urocanase on urocanic acid. The conversion of imidazolonepropionic acid to formimino-L-glutamic acid is analogous to the enzymatic cleavage of imidazolone to formimino-glycine and the cleavage of 4(5)-imidazolone-5(4)-acetic acid to formim-inoaspartic acid (1647, 1648). Imidazolonepropionic acid hydrolase has been purified 60-fold from the soluble supernatant fraction of rat liver homogenates. The purified enzyme does not contain urocanase activity demonstrating the separate identity of the enzymes that catalyze the conversion of urocanic acid to formimino-L-glutamic acid (1652).

Studies on folic acid-deficient rats showed that the rate of disappear-ance of histidine in preparations of liver was less than that observed in nondeficient controls (1635). Subsequent studies (1654) indicated that there is a reduction in liver urocanase (but not histidase) activity in folic acid deficiency. Enzymatic studies on the participation of folic acid in the metabolism of histidine (see below) do not offer an obvious explanation for this finding. At the present time there is no substantial evidence for a function of folic acid in the conversion of urocanic acid to imidazolone-propionic acid or formiminoglutamic acid; it has been suggested (1654) that accumulation of formiminoglutamic acid might inhibit urocanase activity. On the other hand an indication that folic acid derivatives function in the degradation of histidine arose from the finding that formimino-L-glutamic acid is excreted in the urine of folic acid-deficient animals (1626, 1642, 1644, 1655–1658). Subsequent investigations revealed that formiminoglutamic acid can serve as a formylating agent for tetrahydrofolic acid (1659–1661). Thus it was shown that preparations of

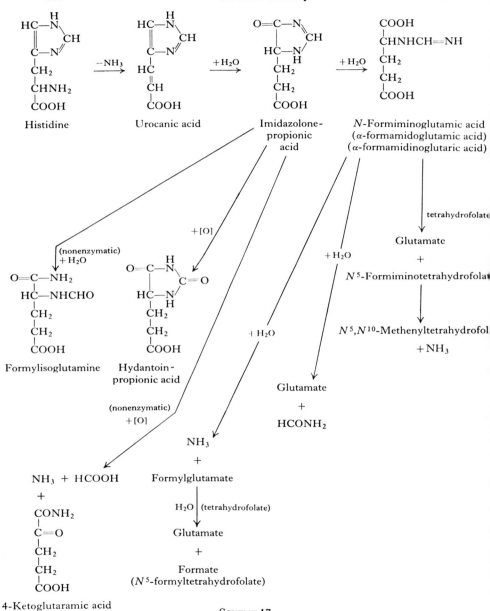

Histidine   Urocanic acid   Imidazolone-propionic acid   N-Formiminoglutamic acid (α-formamidoglutamic acid) (α-formamidinoglutaric acid)

Formylisoglutamine   Hydantoin-propionic acid

4-Ketoglutaramic acid

SCHEME 17

mammalian liver catalyze the formation of N^{10}-formyltetrahydrofolic acid, glutamic acid, and ammonia from formiminoglutamic acid and tetrahydrofolic acid. This reaction represents the sum of three separate enzymatically catalyzed reactions:

N-Formimino-L-glutamic acid + tetrahydrofolic acid $\rightleftharpoons$
$\qquad\qquad\qquad$ N^5-formiminotetrahydrofolic acid + L-glutamic acid

N^5-Formiminotetrahydrofolic acid $\rightarrow$
$\qquad\qquad\qquad$ N^5,N^{10}-methenyltetrahydrofolic acid + ammonia

N^5,N^{10}-Methenyltetrahydrofolic acid + H_2O $\rightleftharpoons$ N^{10}-formyltetrahydrofolic acid

The structures of the folic acid derivatives appear on page 651, and the metabolic relationships between these and other folic acid derivatives are indicated in the diagram on page 658. The enzyme that catalyzes the formation of N^5-formiminotetrahydrofolic acid was purified 700-fold from hog liver acetone powder, and a substantial purification of N^5-formiminotetrahydrofolate cyclodeaminase was obtained from the same source (1662). N^5,N^{10}-Methenyltetrahydrofolate cyclohydrolase was purified from rabbit liver acetone powder and evidence was obtained for the reversibility of the reaction catalyzed by this enzyme. Formiminoglutamic acid formiminotransferase does not act upon formiminoglycine, and the bacterial enzyme that catalyzes the formation of glycine, ammonia, and formate from formiminoglycine (1663) does not act upon formiminoglutamate. The conversion of N^5-formiminotetrahydrofolic acid to N^5,N^{10}-methenyltetrahydrofolic acid and ammonia is essentially irreversible, and accounts for the formation of the second molecule of ammonia from histidine. It is of interest that reduced pteroyltriglutamic acid and pteroylaspartic acid can substitute for tetrahydrofolic acid in the enzymatic conversion of formiminoglutamate to glutamate and ammonia (1661).

The metabolism of histidine in certain organisms such as *Clostridium tetanomorphum* and *Aerobacter aerogenes* leads to the accumulation of formamide (1664–1666). In these organisms, N-formimino-L-glutamic acid is hydrolyzed to glutamic acid and formamide (see chart, p. 830).

The degradation of histidine by *Pseudomonas fluorescens* involves hydrolysis of N-formimino-L-glutamic acid to N-formyl-L-glutamic acid and ammonia (1632, 1641, 1667–1669). Formyl-L-glutamic acid is hydrolyzed by an enzyme that is stimulated by ferrous ions.

An enzyme has been obtained from hog liver that catalyzes the transfer of the formyl group of N^5-formyltetrahydrofolate to glutamic acid to yield N-formylglutamic acid (1670); this enzyme preparation also utilizes formiminoglutamic acid with the production of N^{10}-formyltetrahydrofolate or N^5,N^{10}-methenyltetrahydrofolate, indicating that the preparation contains several activities. Although enzyme preparations have been obtained that utilize both formimino-L-glutamic acid and formyl-L-glutamic acid (1661), a purified preparation of formiminoglutamic acid formiminotransferase exhibited very low activity with formyl-L-glutamic acid (1662).

The observation that formiminoglutamic acid is excreted in the urine of rats fed low protein diets and deprived of either folic acid or vitamin B_{12} suggests that a major pathway for the metabolism of the formimino group is conversion to a methyl group by reactions involving both folic acid and vitamin B_{12} (1671). The addition of excess methionine to the diet in the absence of either folic acid or vitamin B_{12} significantly reduced urinary formiminoglutamic acid. When methionine was given to animals deprived of folic acid and vitamin B_{12}, there was increased excretion of $C^{14}O_2$ from L-histidine-2-C^{14}. Administration of homocysteine led to a decrease in the urinary excretion of formiminoglutamic acid, but had no effect on the formation of carbon dioxide from L-histidine-2-C^{14} (1672). The mechanism by which methionine decreases the formation of urinary formiminoglutamic acid and increases conversion of histidine-2-C^{14} to carbon dioxide requires additional study. Several explanations for these effects have been suggested (1672); these phenomena are probably associated with formation of N^5-methyltetrahydrofolate (see Section L).

Studies on the metabolism of L-histidine-C^{14} in the rat, man, and monkey revealed that hydantoin-5-propionic acid is a urinary excretion product derived from histidine (1673). Administered hydantoinpropionic acid was excreted unchanged. The formation of this product from imidazolonepropionic acid is catalyzed by preparations of guinea pig liver; the reaction is represented in the chart on page 830. The oxidation of imidazolonepropionic acid to hydantoinpropionic acid is also catalyzed by preparations of xanthine oxidase obtained from milk. A soluble fraction of guinea pig liver that catalyzes the formation of hydantoinpropionic acid exhibited no detectable xanthine oxidase activity, indicating that the liver enzyme is not identical with xanthine oxidase (1674).

An organism has been obtained from soil by enrichment culture that catalyzes the conversion of L-hydantoin-5-propionic acid to glutamate, ammonia, and carbon dioxide; carbamylglutamate is an intermediate in this transformation (1675):

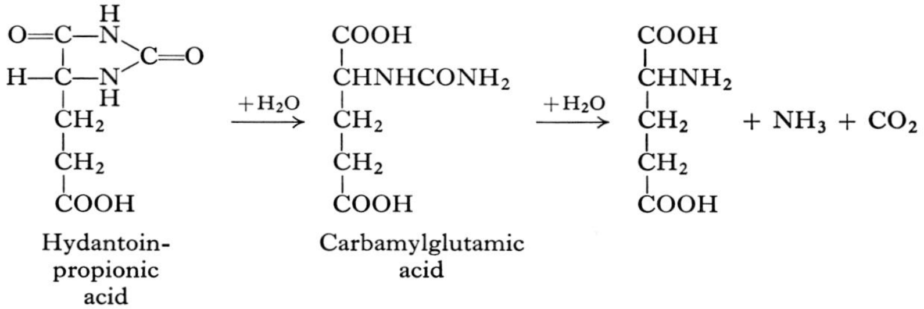

$$\underset{\text{Hydantoin-}\atop\text{propionic}\atop\text{acid}}{\begin{array}{c}\text{H}\\O=C-N\\\quad\diagdown C=O\\H-C-N\diagup\\\quad\;\;|\;\;H\\CH_2\\|\\CH_2\\|\\COOH\end{array}}\quad\xrightarrow{+H_2O}\quad\underset{\text{Carbamylglutamic}\atop\text{acid}}{\begin{array}{c}COOH\\|\\CHNHCONH_2\\|\\CH_2\\|\\CH_2\\|\\COOH\end{array}}\quad\xrightarrow{+H_2O}\quad\begin{array}{c}COOH\\|\\CHNH_2\\|\\CH_2\\|\\CH_2\\|\\COOH\end{array}\quad +\;NH_3\;+\;CO_2$$

Histamine. The decarboxylation of histidine to histamine (see p. 326) is catalyzed by histidine decarboxylase, which has been found in bacteria, plants, and animal tissues. Histamine exerts profound physiological and pharmacological effects in animals (1676). The histidine decarboxylase activity of the mast cells is extremely high; these cells contain large quantities of histamine, some of which occurs in a bound form, the nature of which has not yet been entirely clarified. The oxidation of histamine is catalyzed by histaminase (diamine oxidase; see p. 318), and the product of oxidation has been shown to be imidazoleacetaldehyde (1677). Oxidation of the latter compound to imidazoleacetic acid is catalyzed by xanthine oxidase and also by aldehyde dehydrogenase in the presence of diphosphopyridine nucleotide; the oxidation of histamine to imidazole-acetic acid has been demonstrated *in vivo* in several species (1678–1683).

Administration of labeled histamine or imidazoleacetic acid to rats leads to urinary excretion of imidazoleacetic acid ribonucleoside (1684–1686). Alivisatos and collaborators (1687–1690) observed that histamine

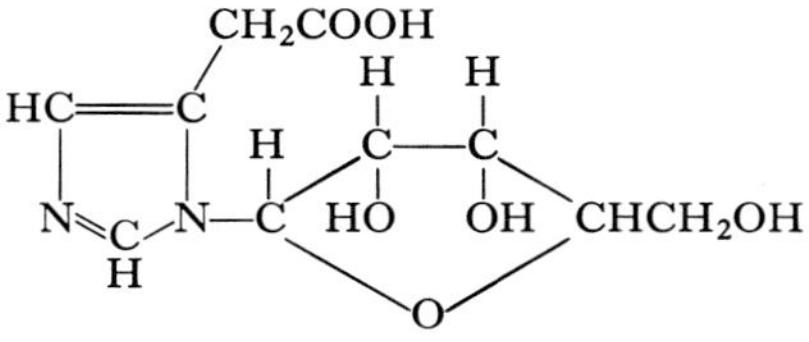

$$\begin{array}{c}CH_2COOH\\HC{=\!\!=}C\quad\;\;H\quad\;H\\|\qquad\quad H\;\;C-C\\N{\equiv}C-N-C\;\;HO\;\;OH\;\;CHCH_2OH\\\;\;\;\;|\qquad\qquad\qquad\diagdown\;\;\diagup\\\;\;\;\;H\qquad\qquad\qquad\quad O\end{array}$$

Imidazoleacetic acid ribonucleoside

reacts with diphosphopyridine nucleotide in the presence of purified beef spleen diphosphopyridine nucleotidase as follows:

Diphosphopyridine nucleotide + histamine →
Histamine dinucleotide + nicotinamide + H$^+$

A reaction of this type between diphosphopyridine nucleotide and imidazoleacetic acid, or oxidation of histamine dinucleotide to imidazoleacetic acid dinucleotide followed by cleavage of the latter (by pyrophosphatase and phosphatase), would yield imidazoleacetic acid ribonucleoside. However, administration of histamine dinucleotide to mice led to urinary excretion of histamine ribonucleoside (1691), and there is at present no evidence for oxidation of histamine ribonucleoside or ribonucleotide.

An enzyme has been purified from rabbit liver that catalyzes the formation of imidazoleacetic acid ribonucleotide according to the following reaction (1691a):

$$\text{Imidazoleacetic acid} + \text{5-phosphoribosyl-1-pyrophosphate} \xrightarrow{\text{ATP}} \text{imidazoleacetic acid ribonucleotide}$$

Treatment of the product with acid phosphatase gave imidazoleacetic acid ribonucleoside. It seems probable that these reactions are responsible for the formation of urinary imidazoleacetic acid ribonucleoside in rats (1684) and man (1691b).

An imidazoleacetic acid-adapted strain of *Pseudomonas* catalyzes the conversion of imidazoleacetic acid to formylaspartic acid, and studies carried out with a partially purified enzyme preparation showed that the reaction requires reduced diphosphopyridine nucleotide as well as oxygen (1692). Studies on the mechanism of the reaction indicate that oxidation of imidazoleacetic acid is accompanied by incorporation of one atom of oxygen from atmospheric oxygen into the carboxyl group of formylaspartic acid, and it was also shown that formiminoaspartate is an intermediate. The initial product is probably 4(5)-imidazolone-5(4)-acetic acid; synthetic 4(5)-imidazolone-5(4)-acetic acid is enzymatically hydrolyzed to formiminoaspartic acid (1648). Nonenzymatic degradation of imidazoloneacetic acid yields formylisoasparagine. Extracts of the adapted *Pseudomonas* also catalyze hydrolysis of formiminoaspartic acid to formylaspartic acid and ammonia, and hydrolysis of formylaspartic acid to formate and aspartate. These reactions are analogous to those involved in the degradation of formiminoglutamic acid by the same organism; the data suggest that different enzymes are involved in the hydrolysis of formylaspartate and formylglutamate. The studies with O^{18} indicate that the enzyme that catalyzes the conversion of imidazoleacetic acid to imidazoloneacetic acid is an oxygenase; the reactions involved in the conversion of imidazoleacetic acid to ammonia, formic acid, and aspartic acid may be represented as shown in Scheme 18 (1692–1695).

Another pathway of histamine metabolism is conversion to the N-acetyl derivative [4-(β-acetylaminoethyl)imidazole]. Crystalline acetylhistamine has been isolated from dog urine after oral administration of histamine (1696). An enzyme that catalyzes the acetylation of various amines including histamine by acetyl-coenzyme A was purified from pigeon liver (1697). Extracts of *Clostridium kluyveri* catalyze the synthesis of N-acetylimidazole from acetylphosphate and imidazole (1698), and a purified preparation of an enzyme from this organism catalyzes the formation of acetylimidazole from acetyl-coenzyme A (1699). The latter enzyme was not found in a number of animal tissues, and the bacterial enzyme does not catalyze acetylation of histidine, histamine, histidinol, and several other compounds.

A significant pathway of histamine metabolism in animals leads to the formation of methylhistamine [1-methyl-4-(β-aminoethyl)imidazole] (1700) (see p. 770). The enzyme imidazole-N-methyltransferase catalyzes transfer of the methyl group of S-adenosylmethionine to the nitrogen atom of the imidazole ring that is remote from the side chain (1220, 1221, 1701). It is of interest that tissues on which histamine acts physiologically exhibit relatively high N-methyltransferase activity, and that the transferase activity is highest in the guinea pig, which is most sensitive to histamine, and lowest in the rat, which is rather insensitive.

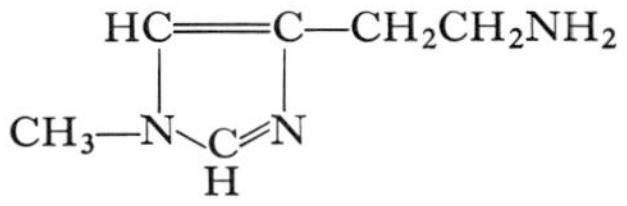

$$HC\!\!=\!\!\!=\!\!C\!-\!CH_2CH_2NH_2$$
$$CH_3\!-\!N\!\diagdown\!\!_{C\diagup\!\!^{\nwarrow}N}$$
$$H$$

1-Methyl-4-(β-aminoethyl)imidazole

$$HC\!\!=\!\!\!=\!\!C\!-\!CH_2CH_2NH_2$$
$$N\!\diagdown\!\!_{C\diagup}\!\!N\!-\!CH_3$$
$$H$$

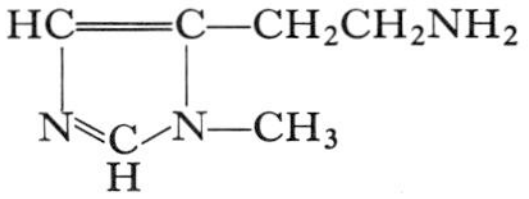

1-Methyl-5-(β-aminoethyl)imidazole

Injection of histamine into animals is followed by urinary excretion of methylhistamine and 1-methylimidazole-4-acetic acid (1700a).

Other Products of Histidine Metabolism. Histidine can be converted to imidazolepyruvic acid by transamination or oxidative deamination; subsequent oxidative decarboxylation of the α-keto acid would yield

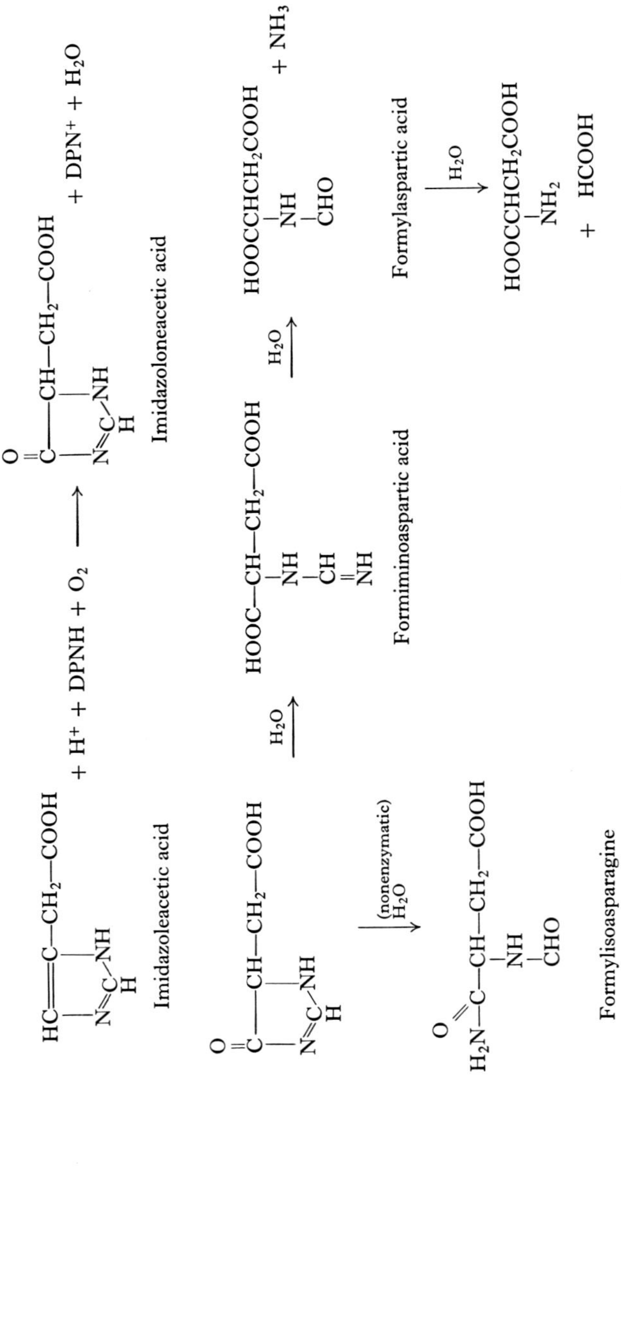

$$HC=\!\!=\!\!C-CH_2-COOH + H^+ + DPNH + O_2 \longrightarrow \underset{\substack{\|\\O}}{C}-CH-CH_2-COOH + DPN^+ + H_2O$$

Imidazoleacetic acid $\qquad\qquad\qquad\qquad$ Imidazoloneacetic acid

$$\xrightarrow{\;H_2O\;} HOOC-CH-CH_2-COOH$$

Formiminoaspartic acid

$$\xrightarrow{\;H_2O\;} HOOCCHCH_2COOH + NH_3$$

Formylaspartic acid

$$\xrightarrow{\;H_2O\;} HOOCCHCH_2COOH + HCOOH$$

$$\underset{\substack{\|\\O}}{C}-CH-CH_2-COOH \xrightarrow[\text{(nonenzymatic)}]{H_2O} H_2N=C-CH-CH_2-COOH$$

Imidazoleacetic acid $\qquad\qquad$ Formylisoasparagine

SCHEME 18

imidazoleacetic acid and possibly other products. Thus, Roche and associates (1702, 1703) found evidence for conversion of histidine to a number of imidazole compounds (e.g., imidazolepyruvic acid, imidazoleacetic acid, imidazolemethanol) in mussel hepatopancreas. The presence of imidazolepyruvic acid, imidazoleacetic acid, and imidazolelactic acid in the urine after administration of histidine to animals is consistent with the existence of an oxidative or transamination pathway. That such reactions can occur in higher animals is indicated by the ability of the α-keto acid analog of histidine to support the growth of rats on histidine-free diets (see p. 222). In some of the experiments in which urinary metabolites were determined, racemic histidine was employed and, since D-histidine is oxidized by D-amino acid oxidase (see p. 298), it appears that urinary imidazolepyruvic acid formation after administration of racemic histidine could be due to oxidation of D-histidine as well as to transamination of the L-isomer. Urinary imidazoleacetic acid may reflect oxidation of histamine or oxidative decarboxylation of imidazolepyruvate. The several studies of urinary metabolites derived from histidine (1704–1707) also indicate the presence of urocanic acid, imidazolepropionic acid, 1-N-methylhistidine, 3-N-methylhistidine, glutamic acid, formiminoglutamic acid, and hydantoinpropionic acid. Studies on the urinary excretion of imidazolepropionic acid in rats suggest that this compound arises from urocanic acid, probably by reduction, but definitive studies are required (1707). Imidazoleethanol has also been found in the urine of the rat and man (1707a).

Histidine is a constituent of carnosine, anserine, ophidine, and homocarnosine (see p. 118). These dipeptides, as well as a number of other dipeptides of histidine, are synthesized by a mechanism involving activation of β-alanine (see p. 454). The synthesis of anserine can take place from β-alanine and 1-methylhistidine (see p. 105) or by the methylation of carnosine by S-adenosylmethionine (1708) (see p. 770). Carnosine, anserine, and certain other dipeptides of this type are hydrolyzed by the peptidase carnosinase (1709). The function of carnosine, anserine, and related compounds is not yet known. However, a relationship between these dipeptides and the function of vitamin E has arisen from several investigations. Thus, low concentrations of carnosine and anserine have been found in the skeletal muscle of vitamin E-deficient rabbits (1710). Urinary excretion of 1-methylhistidine (presumably formed by enzymatic hydrolysis of anserine) is markedly increased in vitamin E deficiency in rabbits (1711). The incorporation of labeled histidine and methyl-labeled methionine into anserine is greatly reduced in vitamin E deficiency. These findings indicate that the muscular dystrophy due to vitamin E deficiency is associated with decreased synthesis of anserine (1712).

Carnosine and anserine may participate in reactions involving phosphorylation of imidazole nitrogen. There are at this time no data that support this suggestion; various proposals concerning the participation of the imidazole group in enzymatic reactions have been made, and a number of studies on the reactions of phosphorylated imidazoles [including N-1-phosphohistidine (1713)] have been reported (1713–1718). A rapidly labeled phosphate-containing fraction of bovine liver mitochondria was degraded to yield a phosphorylated derivative of histidine, probably N-3-phosphohistidine (1717). Boyer (1718) has recently reviewed the evidence that this compound is an intermediate in oxidative phosphorylation (see also references 1718a and 1718b).

Ergothioneine (see p. 82) was first isolated from ergot (1719) and is known to be present in the red blood cells and a variety of animal tissues (1720, 1721). However, animal ergothioneine arises from dietary ergothioneine; a very low dietary concentration of ergothioneine (1 part in 100,000) led to the accumulation of ergothioneine in rat red blood cells (1722, 1723). The ability of the rat to accumulate ergothioneine varies with age, sex, and other factors (1724). Crystalline ergothioneine has been isolated from *Neurospora crassa*, and ergothioneine has been found in a number of species of fungi. Several bacterial organisms, which cannot catalyze the synthesis of ergothioneine, possess the ability to incorporate this compound from the medium. Its synthesis has been studied in *Claviceps purpurea* (1725) and in *Neurospora* (1726). Studies on *N. crassa* indicated that ergothioneine is derived from histidine rather than thiolhistidine, and that cysteine is an effective precursor of the sulfur of ergothioneine. Experiments with methyl-labeled methionine indicated that the methyl groups of ergothioneine arise from the methyl of methionine (1727). Ergothioneine synthesized by *Neurospora* supplied with uniformly labeled N^{15}-histidine contained isotopic nitrogen in both the imidazole ring and the trimethylammonium group, indicating incorporation of the intact histidine molecule. In experiments with methionine labeled in the methyl group with C^{14} and deuterium, evidence was obtained indicating that all three methyl groups arose from methionine by transmethylation (1728). The discovery that hercynine is present in the mycelia of *N. crassa*, the observation that this compound is synthe-

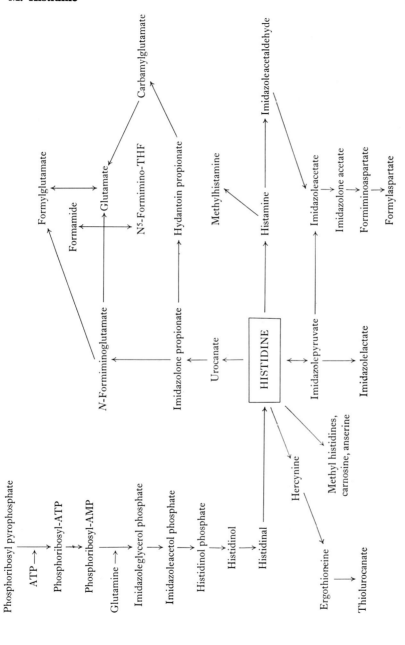

Summary scheme for the metabolism of histidine.

sized from histidine, and the demonstration that C^{14}-hercynine, doubly labeled in both the imidazole ring and the trimethylamine moiety, was converted to ergothioneine by *N. crassa* without loss of isotope, establish hercynine as an intermediate in ergothioneine biosynthesis. These observations support the following scheme for the synthesis of ergothioneine (1729; see also 1729a):

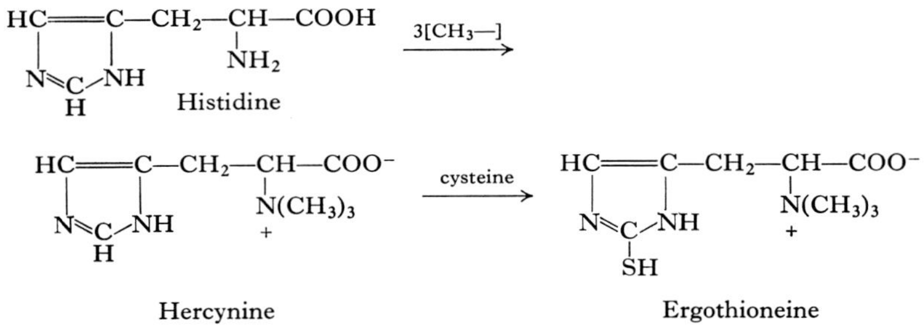

$$HC\!\!=\!\!C\!-\!CH_2\!-\!CH\!-\!COOH$$

with NH_2; ring $N\!\!\equiv\!\!C\!-\!NH$, H. Histidine $\xrightarrow{3[CH_3-]}$

$$HC\!\!=\!\!C\!-\!CH_2\!-\!CH\!-\!COO^-$$

with $\overset{+}{N}(CH_3)_3$; ring $N\!\!\equiv\!\!C\!-\!NH$, H.

Hercynine

$\xrightarrow{\text{cysteine}}$

$$HC\!\!=\!\!C\!-\!CH_2\!-\!CH\!-\!COO^-$$

with $\overset{+}{N}(CH_3)_3$; ring $N\!\!\equiv\!\!C\!-\!NH$, SH.

Ergothioneine

The degradation of ergothioneine has been studied in bacteria that can utilize ergothioneine as the sole source of carbon and energy (1730–1733). Thus, an adapted strain of *Alcaligenes faecalis* degrades ergothioneine to thiolurocanic acid and trimethylamine. Thiolurocanic acid is degraded more slowly and, under certain conditions, hydrogen sulfide, ammonia, and glutamic acid are formed. The reaction catalyzed by ergothionase is analogous to that catalyzed by histidase:

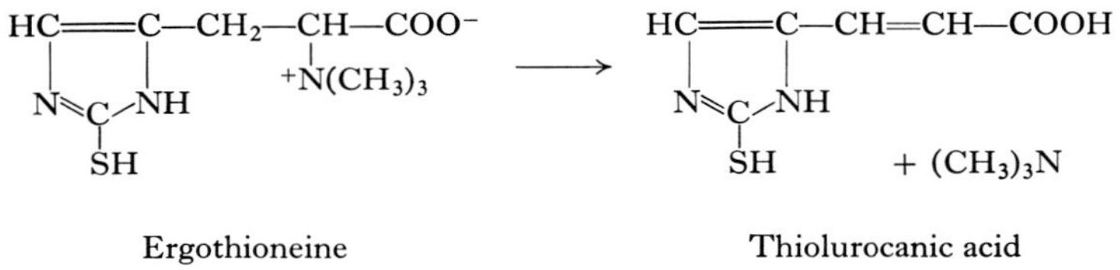

$$HC\!\!=\!\!C\!-\!CH_2\!-\!CH\!-\!COO^-$$

with $^+N(CH_3)_3$; ring $N\!\!\equiv\!\!C\!-\!NH$, SH.

Ergothioneine

$\longrightarrow$

$$HC\!\!=\!\!C\!-\!CH\!\!=\!\!CH\!-\!COOH$$

ring $N\!\!\equiv\!\!C\!-\!NH$, SH. $+ (CH_3)_3N$

Thiolurocanic acid

A highly active preparation of ergothionase was obtained from *E. coli* after growth on ergothioneine (1733). The enzyme, induced only by ergothioneine, is highly specific and exhibits no activity toward histidine; organisms grown on histidine do not form thiolurocanic acid from ergothioneine. The subsequent metabolism of thiolurocanic acid has not been investigated in detail, but the observation that its metabolism yields glutamate suggests a pathway analogous to that of urocanic acid.

Spinacin (found in shark liver and other animal sources) and zapotidin (of plant origin) are probably formed (in part) from histidine (1733a).

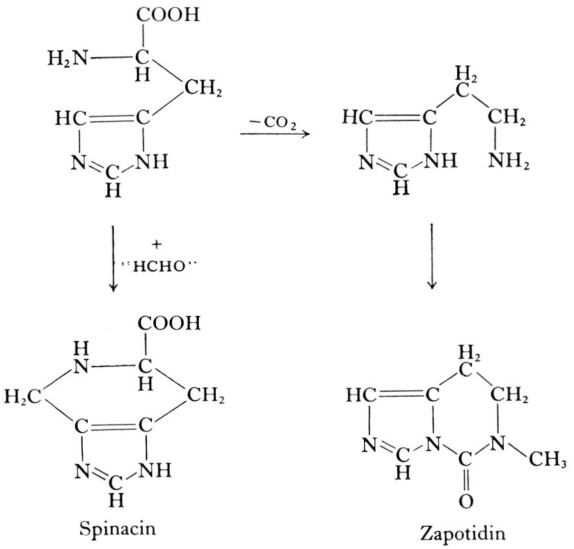

Spinacin

Zapotidin

N. Tryptophan

Biosynthesis

The early observation that indole and anthranilic acid could replace tryptophan in supporting the growth of several microorganisms suggested that these compounds are precursors of tryptophan (1734, 1735). Certain tryptophan-requiring mutants of *Neurospora crassa* and *Escherichia coli* accumulated indole and anthranilic acid (1736), and mutants were obtained that responded to indole but not to anthranilic acid. This suggested that anthranilic acid is converted to indole (1737, 1738), and other studies demonstrated that indole condenses with serine to yield tryptophan (1739–1741). When anthranilic acid containing C^{14} in the carboxyl group was given to a *Neurospora* mutant that required either anthranilic acid, indole, or tryptophan for growth, the tryptophan and nicotinic acid subsequently isolated from the mold contained no detectable isotope. In these experiments, much of the C^{14} was evolved as carbon dioxide during growth (1742). On the basis of experiments in which mutants of *Neurospora* were grown on media containing tryptophan, indole, or anthranilic acid containing N^{15}, it was concluded that the nitrogen atom of anthranilic acid (and of indole) is converted to the pyrrole nitrogen of tryptophan and niacin (1743). Studies on a tryptophan-requiring mutant of *E. coli* grown on media containing ribose-1-C^{14} indicated that carbon atom 2 of the pyrrole ring is derived exclusively from carbon atom 1 of ribose and that this carbon atom of ribose does not enter carbon 3 of the pyrrole ring (1744). It was also found that carbon atom 2 of the pyrrole ring arose from carbon atoms 1 and 2 of glucose, and that carbon atom 3 of the pyrrole ring comes from carbon atoms 2 and 3 of glucose. These data suggested that a ribose derivative is the donor of the two carbon atoms required for the conversion of anthranilic acid to indole. The observation that 5-phosphoribosyl-1-pyrophosphate functioned in the conversion of anthranilic acid to indole (1745) offered additional evidence for the contribution of ribose to the pyrrole ring.

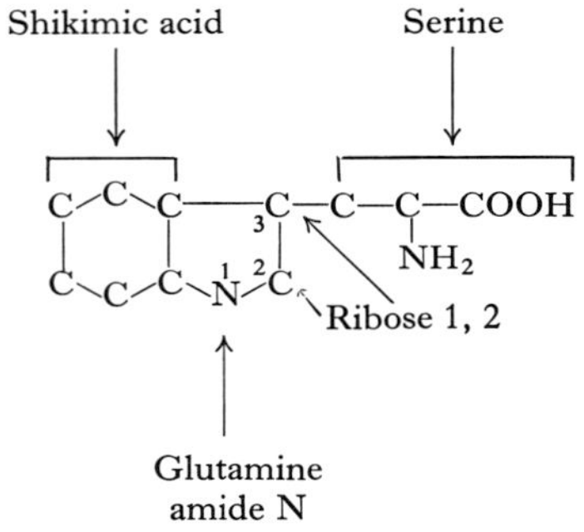

Anthranilic acid is formed from shikimic acid via 3-enolpyruvyl shikimate-5-phosphate (see p. 890) and a "branch-point compound" (chorismic acid) which can be converted to prephenic acid, anthranilic acid, or *p*-hydroxybenzoate (see p. 889). Earlier studies showed that the amide nitrogen atom of glutamine is the precursor of the amino group of anthranilic acid in *E. coli* (see p. 626). Cell-free extracts of a mutant of *E. coli* blocked between anthranilate and indole-3-glycerol phosphate converted shikimate to anthranilate in the presence of adenosine triphosphate and L-glutamine (1746), and shikimate-5-phosphate replaced shikimate and adenosine triphosphate. Such extracts were separated into two fractions, both of which were required for the synthesis of anthranilate. One of these catalyzed the disappearance of shikimate-5-phosphate; this fraction was shown to contain 3-enolpyruvyl shikimate-5-phosphate synthetase. The other fraction was needed for conversion of 3-enol-pyruvyl shikimate-5-phosphate into a new compound (chorismic acid), which gave anthranilate in the presence of L-glutamine, magnesium ions, diphosphopyridine nucleotide, and a system capable of reducing diphosphopyridine nucleotide (1747).

Studies with cell-free preparations of *E. coli* provided considerable insight into the reactions involved in the conversion of anthranilic acid to tryptophan (1745, 1748, 1749). Two fractions were obtained from extracts of a tryptophan-requiring mutant of *E. coli*; one catalyzed the formation of indole-3-glycerol phosphate from anthranilic acid and 5-phosphoribosyl-1-pyrophosphate, while the other catalyzed the reversible formation of indole and triose phosphate from indole-3-glycerol phosphate (1745, 1748). Mutants blocked at each of these steps were obtained, and accumulation of indole-3-glycerol by certain mutants was observed (1748, 1750). On the basis of these findings, Yanofsky (1745) postulated the formation of *N-o*-carboxyphenyl-D-ribosylamine-5′-phosphate from 5-phosphoribosyl-1-pyrophosphate and anthranilic acid; dehydration and rearrangement of the Amadori type would yield 1-(*o*-carboxy-phenylamino)-1-deoxyribulose-5′-phosphate (anthranilic deoxyribo-nucleotide). The latter compound could give indole-3-glycerol phosphate by removal of the hydroxyl group on carbon atom 2 of the deoxyribulose moiety and decarboxylation of the anthranilic acid carboxyl group. It is of interest that several anthranilic acid derivatives (e.g., 5-fluoroanthrani-late, 4-methylanthranilate) were utilized in the enzymatic reaction with phosphoribosyl pyrophosphate; in an earlier study conversion of 4-methylanthranilate to 6-methylindole was shown with cell suspensions (1751).

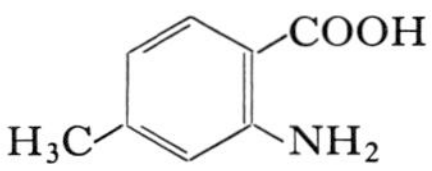

4-Methylanthranilic acid	6-Methylindole

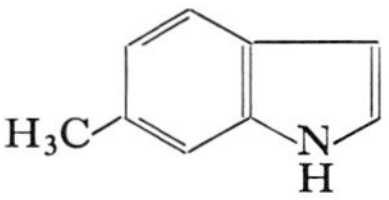

The important observation of Doy and Gibson (1752) that certain mutants of *A. aerogenes* and *E. coli* accumulate 1-(*o*-carboxyphenyl-amino)-deoxyribulose gave strong support to the postulated sequence of reactions. The structure of the isolated compound was demonstrated by synthesis. The deoxyribulose derivative, which was obtained from the culture media of mutants blocked between anthranilic acid and indole, presumably arose by dephosphorylation of the actual intermediate. The isolated compound supported the growth of mutants that could use anthranilic acid in place of tryptophan, indicating that the cell is capable of phosphorylating the nucleoside. Smith and Yanofsky (1753) found two types of *E. coli* and *S. typhimurium* mutants that were unable to convert anthranilate to indole-3-glycerol phosphate; a mixture of the extracts of both types could catalyze the conversion. Extracts of one type of tryptophan-requiring mutant catalyzed formation of a compound from anthranilic acid and 5-phosphoribosyl-1-pyrophosphate that could be converted to indole-3-glycerol phosphate by an extract of the other type, which did not catalyze formation of the intermediate. The intermediate contained radioactivity when carboxyl-labeled anthranilic acid was employed. Chemical synthesis of the presumed intermediate [1-(o-carboxyphenylamino)-1-deoxyribulose-5′-phosphate] from anthranilic acid and ribose 5-phosphate gave an impure product which served as substrate for enzymatic formation of indole-3-glycerol phosphate. Although difficulty has attended efforts to demonstrate accumulation or formation of N-o-carboxyphenyl-D-ribosylamine-5′-phosphate (a compound that would be expected to be very labile), indirect evidence for its enzymatic formation from anthranilic acid and 5-phosphoribosyl-1-pyrophosphate was obtained by Doy and collaborators (1754, 1755). Mutants blocked (*a*) between anthranilic acid and N-o-carboxyphenyl-D-ribosylamine-5′-phosphate and (*b*) between the latter compound and 1-(o-carboxyphenylamino)-1-deoxyriboluse-5′-phosphate were obtained. Extracts of mutants of type (*b*) but not of type (*a*) catalyzed conversion of anthranilate and phosphoribosyl pyrophosphate to an unstable product that promptly broke down to anthranilate. The biosynthesis of indole-3-glycerol phosphate may be represented as shown in Scheme 19.

According to Scheme 19, the enolic form of 1-(o-carboxyphenylamino)-1-deoxyribulose-5′-phosphate is the immediate precursor of the first compound that contains the pyrrole ring. It is not yet clear whether ring closure and decarboxylation occur stepwise or in a concerted reaction. Although the available data support the pathway as represented, unequivocal characterization of the intermediates has not yet been accomplished and a number of details require clarification. Mutants of yeast were reported to accumulate compounds which contain anthranilate and a hexose (1756, 1757), suggesting that an additional pathway of

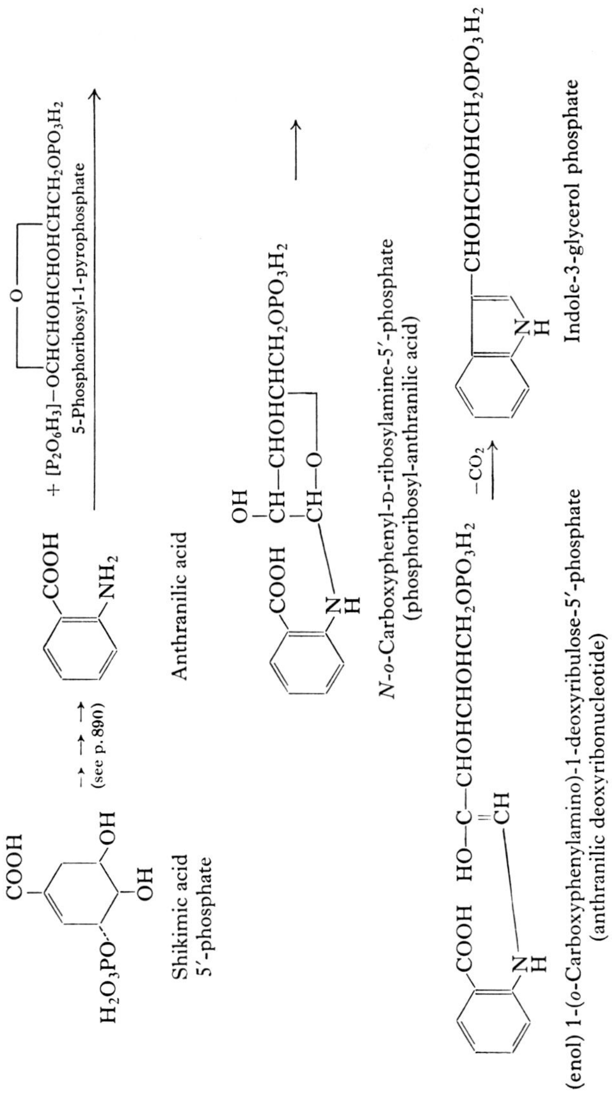

Shikimic acid 5′-phosphate

(see p. 890)

Anthranilic acid

+ $[P_2O_6H_3]$—$OCHCHOHCHOHCH_2OPO_3H_2$
5-Phosphoribosyl-1-pyrophosphate

N-o-Carboxyphenyl-D-ribosylamine-5′-phosphate
(phosphoribosyl-anthranilic acid)

(enol) 1-(o-Carboxyphenylamino)-1-deoxyribulose-5′-phosphate
(anthranilic deoxyribonucleotide)

Indole-3-glycerol phosphate

Scheme 19

indole-3-glycerol phosphate synthesis exists, or that anthranilate participates in reactions other than those indicated below; there is recent evidence in favor of the latter possibility (1757a).

The observation that indole-3-glycerol phosphate is enzymatically hydrolyzed to indole and triose phosphate by extracts of several microorganisms seemed to provide the final link in the biosynthetic sequence leading to tryptophan (1749). Thus, the formation of tryptophan from indole and serine catalyzed by "tryptophan synthetase" had been observed a number of years prior to elucidation of the pathway of indole synthesis (1739–1741). However, substantial evidence developed later that indole is not an intermediate in the normal biosynthesis of tryptophan and that indole-3-glycerol phosphate is the actual substrate. Studies on the enzymatic synthesis of tryptophan by extracts of N. crassa showed that the rate of hydrolysis of indole-3-glycerol phosphate is much lower than that of the synthesis of tryptophan from indole-3-glycerol phosphate and serine. Furthermore, no evidence could be obtained for the formation of free indole during the synthesis of tryptophan from indole-3-glycerol phosphate (1758, 1759). If the same enzyme catalyzes tryptophan synthesis from both indole and indole-3-glycerol phosphate, the experimental findings may be explained by postulating formation of an enzyme-indole intermediate from indole-3-glycerol phosphate, and that the same intermediate can be formed (more slowly) from free indole.

Studies on various mutants showed that certain of these lacked ability to convert indole-3-glycerol phosphate to indole, while others could not synthesize tryptophan from indole and serine (although they hydrolyze indole-3-glycerol phosphate and accumulate indole). Other mutants were unable to catalyze both the synthesis of tryptophan as well as the hydrolysis of indole-3-glycerol phosphate (1748, 1749, 1760). The situation was partly clarified by the observation that mutants that were unable to catalyze tryptophan synthesis from indole (but which retained the ability to form indole) contain protein (cross-reacting protein, CRM) that reacts with antibody to the enzyme that is lacking; thus, mutants unable to catalyze both tryptophan synthesis and hydrolysis of indole-3-glycerol phosphate lack CRM (1758–1761).

The tryptophan-synthesizing system of E. coli was separated by chromatography into two components, A and B (1759–1763). Although these exhibited little activity when tested separately, when A and B were mixed, all three reactions given below were catalyzed. [See top of p. 847.] Since component A catalyzes hydrolysis of indole-3-glycerol phosphate

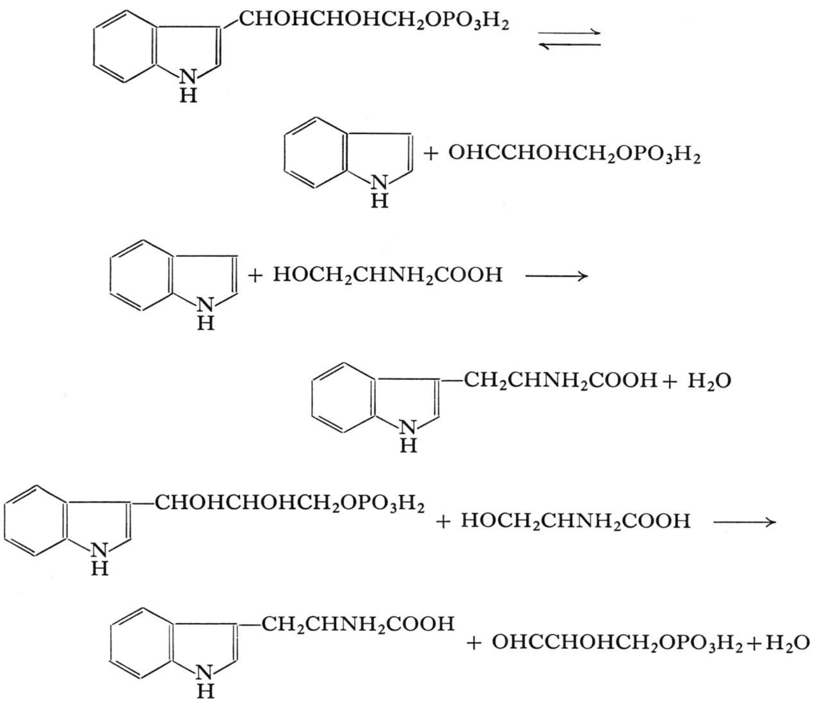

$$\text{(indole)}-CHOHCHOHCH_2OPO_3H_2 \rightleftharpoons$$

$$\text{(indole)} + OHCCHOHCH_2OPO_3H_2$$

$$\text{(indole)} + HOCH_2CHNH_2COOH \longrightarrow$$

$$\text{(indole)}-CH_2CHNH_2COOH + H_2O$$

$$\text{(indole)}-CHOHCHOHCH_2OPO_3H_2 + HOCH_2CHNH_2COOH \longrightarrow$$

$$\text{(indole)}-CH_2CHNH_2COOH + OHCCHOHCH_2OPO_3H_2 + H_2O$$

at a slow rate, this protein must have a binding site for indole-3-glycerol phosphate. Component B catalyzes the synthesis of tryptophan from indole and serine at a slow rate, and it has been concluded that this component combines with serine and pyridoxal phosphate. Enzymatic and immunological studies were employed to detect the presence of components A and B in various mutant organisms, and evidence was obtained that "tryptophan synthetase" mutants of *E. coli* lack either component A or component B, or contain altered forms of either of these. The A protein of *E. coli* was isolated in crystalline form and found to be homogenous on electrophoresis and ultracentrifugation. The protein (molecular weight, 29,000) does not contain tryptophan, and possesses three cysteinyl residues, one of which has a free sulfhydryl group (1764). Studies on the amino acid sequence of the amino terminal end of this molecule, which consists of a single peptide chain, have been carried out (1765).

Recent work suggests that in addition to indole-3-glycerol phosphate another indole-containing compound is formed when indole and glyceraldehyde-3-phosphate are incubated with *Neurospora crassa* tryptophan synthetase (1765a). Earlier work had failed to show stoichiometry between indole disappearance and indole-3-glycerol phosphate formation. The new compound was not formed when indole-3-glycerol phosphate was incubated with the enzyme. These findings suggest that the first reaction may not take place as written above. Other studies have shown that *E. coli* tryptophan synthetase catalyzes the deamination of serine and the desulfhydration of cysteine (588a). The *N. crassa* enzyme was reported not to deaminate serine (1765a).

The synthesis of tryptophan by microorganisms is not only catalyzed by the tryptophan synthetase complex described above, but can also be catalyzed by tryptophanase. Although the latter enzyme does not catalyze tryptophan synthesis from serine and indole-3-glycerol phosphate or hydrolysis of the latter compound, it can, under certain conditions, be of biosynthetic significance. Thus it is possible for a mutant lacking both A and B components of tryptophan synthetase to grow in media containing indole (see p. 879). Mechanisms for the pyridoxal phosphate-catalyzed synthesis of tryptophan have been proposed (see pp. 402 and 403).

Since anthranilic acid is also a degradation product of tryptophan, formed by the action of kynureninase (see p. 855), a cyclic relationship exists between the synthesis and degradation of tryptophan and the formation and utilization of anthranilic acid (1737, 1766). Evidence for such a cycle in *Neurospora* was obtained in experiments on the wild strain and mutants blocked (*a*) in the conversion of anthranilic acid to indole-3-glycerol phosphate, and (*b*) between shikimic acid and anthranilic acid. When these were grown in minimal medium containing tryptophan, growth of the mutant blocked at (*b*) and the wild strain was much greater than that of the mutant blocked at (*a*). This result is consistent with the inability of the poorly growing mutant (*a*) to utilize anthranilic acid formed by degradation of the tryptophan supplied; the other organisms can utilize anthranilate. When these organisms were grown on C^{14}-tryptophan labeled in the benzene ring, the specific activity of the protein tryptophan was about the same for each organism, showing that there is little tryptophan of endogenous origin. Similar studies with C^{14}-tryptophan labeled in the 2-position of the indole ring showed that the specific activity of the protein tryptophan of mutant

(a) was much higher than that obtained from the other organisms because in these operation of the cycle resulted in dilution of isotope. Mutant (a) accumulated C^{14}-anthranilic and formylanthranilic acids, which were derived exclusively from the C^{14}-tryptophan supplied in the medium; when the exogenous tryptophan was consumed, the specific radioactivity of the anthranilic acid decreased due to biosynthesis from shikimic acid. The latter result was also obtained in studies which showed that unlabeled shikimic acid diluted the isotope content of anthranilic acid accumulated by a mutant of *Neurospora* grown on C^{14}-sucrose (1767). The existence of the cycle makes it possible for tryptophan, the end product of a biosynthetic pathway, to be converted to an intermediate in its own biosynthesis. Accumulation of a compound by a mutant microorganism may therefore be the result of a more complex series of events than a straightforward block of a biosynthetic sequence.

Most of the studies on the biosynthesis of tryptophan have been carried out in microorganisms, and relatively little information is available about the biosynthetic pathway in plants. Infiltration of the intact seeds of the Bengal gram (*Cicer arietinum*) with indole and serine resulted in an increase in the tryptophan content of this legume. Tryptophan synthetase activity (indole plus serine) was demonstrated in extracts of the seeds; no tryptophan synthesis occurred in the absence of added pyridoxal 5'-phosphate. Although deoxypyridoxine phosphate inhibited tryptophan synthesis in the experiments with intact seeds, it is of interest that this compound did not inhibit the cell-free system even when preincubated with the enzyme preparation prior to addition of pyridoxal 5'-phosphate and substrates (1768).

Metabolism

General Considerations. The degradation of tryptophan in animals occurs mainly by two pathways. One involves oxidation of tryptophan to kynurenine, which is converted to 3-hydroxyanthranilic acid, nicotinic acid, and other compounds. Kynurenine is also converted to kynurenic acid and related products in several species. The other pathway involves oxidation of tryptophan to 5-hydroxytryptophan and decarboxylation of this amino acid to 5-hydroxytryptamine (serotonin). Other pathways also exist in animal tissues. In microorganisms, additional reactions occur including some that are similar to those catalyzed by animal tissues. In plants, a tryptophan metabolite of considerable interest and importance is the plant hormone, indoleacetic acid, which is also formed in animals.

In certain insects, tryptophan is converted to characteristic eye pigments. Tryptophan appears to be converted to a larger number of metabolites than any of the other amino acids. Some of these have attracted considerable attention because of their potential relationship to disease. It is of interest that one tryptophan metabolite, kynurenic acid, was discovered by Liebig (1769) many years before tryptophan itself was known. The discovery of new tryptophan metabolites has continued through the years and it is reasonably certain that the complete story of tryptophan metabolism has not yet been told.

Conversion to Kynurenine, Nicotinic Acid, and Related Compounds. Kynurenine was discovered in 1925 by Matsuoka and Yoshimatsu in the urine of rabbits fed large quantities of tryptophan (1770). Kynurenic acid, which had been isolated earlier (1769, 1771, 1772), is formed from kynurenine by ring closure, and kynurenine is also converted to 3-hydroxyanthranilic acid, xanthurenic acid, nicotinic acid, and a large number of other products. These metabolic transformations have been elucidated by nutritional and isotopic studies, experiments with mutant microorganisms, and enzymatic investigations.

The formation of kynurenine from tryptophan involves a cleavage of the pyrrole ring to yield formylkynurenine. The reaction is catalyzed by the enzyme tryptophan pyrrolase, whose activity was first recognized by Kotake and his collaborators (1773). The first definitive study of the enzymatic conversion of tryptophan to kynurenine was carried out by Knox and Mehler (1774), who obtained a soluble system from rat liver that catalyzed the following reactions:

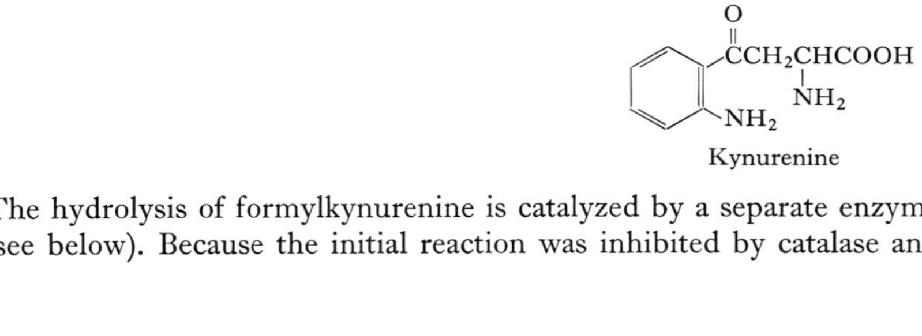

Tryptophan   Formylkynurenine

Kynurenine

The hydrolysis of formylkynurenine is catalyzed by a separate enzyme (see below). Because the initial reaction was inhibited by catalase and since this inhibition was reversed by hydrogen peroxide, the enzyme was originally considered to be a peroxidase (1775–1777). The reaction appeared to involve the formation of an intermediate (1778–1780); the possible intermediate formation of β-3-oxindolylalanine was considered, but excluded (1778, 1781, 1782). It is now known that the oxidation of

CH$_2$CHNH$_2$COOH

| β-3-Oxindolylalanine | α-Hydroxytryptophan |

tryptophan to formylkynurenine involves introduction of 2 atoms of oxygen. When the reaction was studied in separate experiments with O_2^{18} and H_2O^{18} with an enzyme preparation obtained from a tryptophan-adapted *Pseudomonas*, approximately 1 atom of atmospheric oxygen was incorporated into both kynurenine and formic acid (1783). These observations established that the enzyme is an oxygenase rather than a peroxidase. Investigation of the purified tryptophan pyrrolase of *Pseudomonas* (1784) indicated that its properties are extremely similar to those of the enzyme from liver that catalyzes the same reaction (1785). Although a requirement for peroxide was also observed with this enzyme preparation, catalytic rather than stoichiometric quantities of peroxide are needed, and it was shown that peroxide functions only initially in the reaction by reducing iron present in the enzyme from the ferric to the active ferrous form. Catalase does not inhibit the reaction after it has started. The enzyme is inhibited by cyanide and carbon monoxide; these observations, spectrophotometric studies, and other findings indicate that the enzyme is an iron-porphyrin protein. Rat liver apotryptophan pyrrolase was obtained in highly purified form (1786); this preparation was inactive unless reconstituted with hematin, whose presence resulted in the appearance of an absorption spectrum with maxima at 430, 530, and 560 mμ. Other studies have shown that the apoenzyme may be reconstituted with either heme or hematin; the latter exhibits greater tendency to associate with the enzyme than the former. Reduction of the hematin-enzyme yields the active heme-enzyme (1786a).

Administration of tryptophan to animals greatly increases the activity of hepatic tryptophan pyrrolase for a number of hours, after which it declines to normal levels. Adrenalectomy decreases the activity of rat liver, and cortisone treatment of adrenalectomized rats increases activity (1788–1792). These observations have attracted considerable attention and much work has been carried out on the activation and induction of tryptophan pyrrolase. Very little, if any, tryptophan pyrrolase is found in fetal liver, but activity appears soon after birth; tryptophan injection and administration of adrenocortical hormones do not produce an increase in the activity of fetal liver (1787). It has been suggested that tryptophan increases tryptophan pyrrolase activity by favoring the formation of the enzyme from apoenzyme and hematin (1793, 1794), but there is also substantial evidence that the enhanced enzymatic activity is due to *de novo* synthesis of enzyme. For example, the normal developmental increase in tryptophan pyrrolase as well as the adaptive increase in the adult is inhibited by puromycin, an inhibitor of protein synthesis (1795). Studies with 5-fluorouracil gave results parallel to those observed with puromycin and suggest that the synthesis of tryptophan pyrrolase from amino acids requires simultaneous synthesis of ribonucleic acid (1796). There is evidence that the induction of liver tryptophan pyrrolase by administration of substrate occurs by a mechanism different from that associated with injection of hydrocortisone. Thus, the effects of these agents are additive and injection of hydrocortisone does not produce increased concentrations of tryptophan in the liver. Tryptophan pyrrolase of perfused rabbit liver (1797) and rat liver slices (1798) is increased by tryptophan but not by hydrocortisone. It is notable that D-tryptophan, α-methyl-DL-tryptophan, and α-N-acetyl-L-tryptophan induce liver tryptophan pyrrolase in adrenalectomized rats; it is well known that enzyme activity in bacterial systems can be induced and repressed by metabolite analogs. Additivity of induction by tryptophan and insulin has also been observed (1799).

The hydrolysis of formylkynurenine is catalyzed by the enzyme kynurenine formylase (kynurenine formamidase) which has been found in liver and microorganisms (1774–1777, 1784, 1800).

Kynurenine is converted to nicotinic acid by a pathway which includes 3-hydroxykynurenine and 3-hydroxyanthranilic acid. That a mechanism exists for the conversion of tryptophan to nicotinic acid became evident from the studies of Krehl and associates in 1945 (1801), who found that rats given a diet deficient in nicotinic acid could grow if tryptophan was added to the diet. The conversion of tryptophan to nicotinic acid has subsequently been demonstrated by a variety of studies [see, for example (1737, 1742, 1802–1817)]. It is of interest that the beneficial effect of tryptophan on patients with pellagra was noted in 1921; W. F. Tanner, in a letter to his chief, Joseph Goldberger, dated August 5, 1921 (1818), stated: "The erythema has almost entirely disappeared. . . . The lesions on the feet are no longer acutely erythematous but appear of very normal color. . . . I might add that the improvement in this patient's skin condition has surpassed anything I have ever seen in a case of pellagra in an equal period of time." Goldberger's success in treating pellagra with tryptophan was reported in 1922 in a paper in which he concluded that "the primary etiological factor in pellagra is a specific defect in the amino acid supply" (1818).

A series of experiments with mutants of *Neurospora* (1737, 1742, 1806, 1807, 1809–1812, 1814, 1815) provided evidence that the conversion of tryptophan to nicotinic acid involved intermediate formation of kynurenine and 3-hydroxyanthranilic acid. Isotopic tracer studies by Heidelberger and associates (1819, 1820) revealed that carbon atom 3 of the indole ring of tryptophan becomes the carboxyl carbon atom of nicotinic acid in the rat. They also found that in the conversion of tryptophan to kynurenine in the rabbit, and of tryptophan to kynurenic acid in the dog, the β-carbon atom of tryptophan becomes the β-carbon atom of kynurenine and the C-3 atom of kynurenic acid. The tryptophan side chain does not appear in the nicotinic acid molecule (1819, 1821). The conversion of tryptophan to kynurenine, kynurenic acid, and xanthurenic acid in the rat and rabbit was also studied with N^{15}-ring-labeled tryptophan (1822). There was no conversion of tryptophan-ring nitrogen to hemin, nor was N^{15}-indole converted to tryptophan in the rat.

Evidence for the conversion of kynurenine to 3-hydroxykynurenine was obtained in relatively early studies [see, for example (1823, 1824)], and findings suggesting the participation of riboflavin were reported (1825–1827). Preparations of cat and rat liver mitochondria were found to catalyze the formation of 3-hydroxykynurenine from L-kynurenine in the presence of triphosphopyridine nucleotide (1828). The enzyme (L-kynurenine-3-hydroxylase) was subsequently obtained in soluble form from sonically disrupted rat liver mitochondria, and preparations were also obtained by treatment of the mitochondria with sodium cholate or digitonin. The enzyme catalyzes the conversion of L-kynurenine to 3-hydroxy-L-kynurenine and consumes 1 mole each of oxygen and reduced triphosphopyridine nucleotide per mole of substrate utilized. Experiments carried out in the presence of O^{18}-labeled water and oxygen demonstrated that the oxygen of the hydroxyl group of 3-hydroxykynurenine comes from atmospheric oxygen rather than from water, indicating that an oxygenase mechanism is involved (1829). The reaction catalyzed by L-kynurenine-3-hydroxylase may be represented as follows:

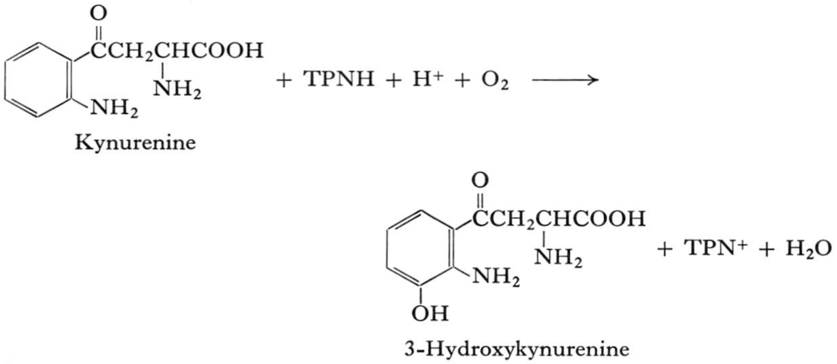

$$
\underset{\text{Kynurenine}}{\text{[structure]}} \quad + \text{ TPNH} + \text{H}^+ + \text{O}_2 \longrightarrow
$$

[structure]

O
‖
CCH₂CHCOOH (with NH₂ on the CH, NH₂ on ring) + TPN⁺ + H₂O

OH

3-Hydroxykynurenine

Preparations of kynurenine hydroxylase from liver mitochondria of riboflavin-deficient rats were 30 to 50% less active than similar preparations from pair-fed control animals. No significant activation of hydroxylase activity was observed when riboflavin monophosphate, flavin adenine dinucleotide, or a boiled liver extract were added to the enzyme preparations (1830).

3-Hydroxykynurenine has been reported to accumulate as an intermediate in the formation of insect eye pigment [(1831); see also p. 883]. It has been found in insect larvae (1832, 1833), plants (1834), and in human urine in certain diseases (1835) and after ingestion of tryptophan by normal individuals (1836). The phosphate derivative of hydroxyanthranilic acid was found in liver preparations (1837, 1838). α-N-Acetyl-3-hydroxykynurenine has been detected in *Neurospora* (1839), and this compound and α-N-acetylkynurenine have been found in the urine of vitamin B₆-deficient rats given large doses of tryptophan (1778). Kynurenine has been identified as the white-blue fluorescent substance in the wings of Papilionid butterflies (1840).

Kynurenine and 3-hydroxykynurenine are cleaved by kynureninase to alanine and anthranilic acid (or 3-hydroxyanthranilic acid). Kynureninase (1778, 1841–1848) is present in mammalian liver and kidney and in a number of microorganisms, but not in *E. coli*. The function of pyridoxal phosphate in kynureninase was indicated by the early studies of Braunstein *et al.* (1844), who found that the kynureninase activity of the livers of vitamin B₆-deficient animals was reduced and that addition of pyridoxal phosphate to the liver preparations restored enzymatic activity. The mechanism of the reaction has been considered by several workers (1849–1851), and Longenecker and Snell (1851) proposed that the Schiff base formed between kynurenine and pyridoxal phosphate-enzyme (I) is converted to the Schiff base of α-aminoacrylic acid (III). Intermediate (II) undergoes oxidation-reduction with (III) to yield anthranilic acid and the Schiff base of alanine (see Chapter IV, Section J).

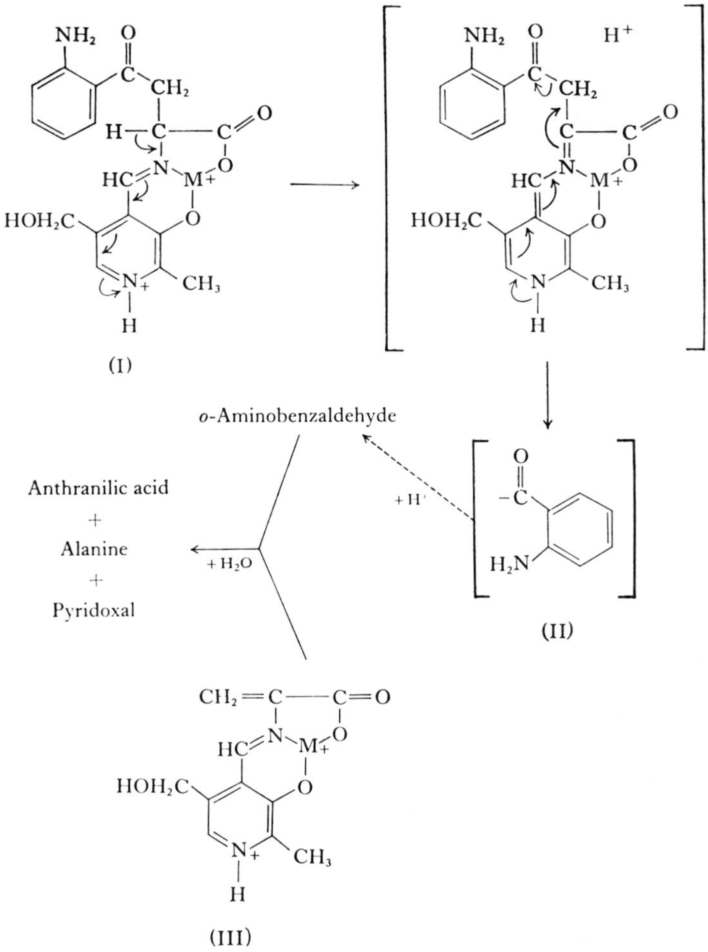

(I)

o-Aminobenzaldehyde

Anthranilic acid
+
Alanine
+
Pyridoxal

(II)

(III)

In addition to kynurenine and 3-hydroxykynurenine, kynureninase cleaves formylkynurenine to formylanthranilic acid and alanine (as well as 5-hydroxykynurenine to 5-hydroxyanthranilic acid) (1852, 1853). Formylanthranilic acid accumulates in *Neurospora* grown on media containing tryptophan (1766). Other data (1854) indicate that kynureninase of *Neurospora* exhibits much greater affinity for formylkynurenine than does formylkynurenine formylase. These considerations suggest that in *Neurospora* the conversion of tryptophan to anthranilic acid occurs primarily via the corresponding formyl derivatives. Both kynureninase and kynurenine 3-hydroxylase are inhibited by the kynurenine analog, nicotinylalanine (1855).

Evidence that 3-hydroxyanthranilic acid is an intermediate in the biosynthesis of nicotinic acid from tryptophan in *Neurospora* was reported in 1948 by Mitchell and Nyc (1856). 3-Hydroxyanthranilic acid can replace nicotinamide or tryptophan in supporting the growth of rats, but the dietary requirement for 3-hydroxyanthranilic acid is much higher than that of nicotinamide (1857–1859). Henderson (1860, 1861) showed that urinary excretion of quinolinic acid occurred in the rat following administration of tryptophan or 3-hydroxyanthranilic acid. Injection of tryptophan or 3-hydroxyanthranilic acid led to increased excretion of nicotinic acid, N^1-methylnicotinamide as well as quinolinic acid. A mutant of *Neurospora* was obtained that could utilize quinolinic acid as a source of nicotinic acid under certain conditions. Hankes and Henderson (1862) found that 3-hydroxyanthranilic acid labeled with C^{14} in the carboxyl group was converted to highly labeled N^1-methylnicotinamide and quinolinic acid in the rat. Other experiments showed that carbon atom 3 of the indole ring of tryptophan is the precursor of the carboxyl carbon of nicotinic acid (1820) and that the indole nitrogen atom of tryptophan is the precursor of the nitrogen atom of quinolinic acid (1863). In studies on *N. crassa* with N^{15}-label, evidence was obtained that the indole nitrogen atom of tryptophan is the precursor of the pyridine nitrogen atom of nicotinic acid (1864). These observations indicate that the conversion of 3-hydroxyanthranilic acid to nicotinic acid and quinolinic acid involves cleavage of the aromatic ring of 3-hydroxyanthranilic acid and a cyclization reaction in which the amino nitrogen atom of 3-hydroxyanthranilic acid is incorporated into the pyridine ring.

Studies on the conversion of 3-hydroxyanthranilic acid to quinolinic acid catalyzed by preparations of rat liver indicated accumulation of an intermediate compound which exhibited maximum absorbancy at 360 $m\mu$ (1865–1869). Enzyme activity was dependent upon the presence of oxygen and ferrous ions. Mehler (1869) found that the metabolism of 3-hydroxyanthranilic acid by liver preparations takes place in two steps; in the first of these, 2 atoms of oxygen are utilized to yield an intermediate compound that absorbs maximally at 360 $m\mu$. This compound is converted nonenzymatically to quinolinic acid, and enzymatically to picolinic acid. The N-methyl derivative of picolinic acid (homarine) has been found in certain marine forms [(1870); see p. 106]. Studies on the compound formed in the course of oxidation of 3-hydroxyanthranilic acid suggest that it contains amino and aldehyde groups; its properties are consistent with 2-acroleyl-3-aminofumaric acid. The nonoxidative decarboxylation of this compound to form picolinic acid involves loss of the original carboxyl group of 3-hydroxyanthranilic acid (1871); when labeled picolinic acid was administered to rats, it was excreted quantitatively as its glycine conjugate. The livers of alloxan-diabetic rats contain greater than normal amounts of picolinic acid carboxylase, and following insulin administration carboxylase activity tends to return towards normal values. The increase in picolinic acid carboxylase activity of the diabetic rat is associated with decreased excretion of N-methylnicotinamide (1872), and apparently requires cortisone or related adrenal hormones (1873). Liver preparations from the mouse, pig, and rat exhibit much less picolinic carboxylase activity than do similar preparations from beef and cat liver. Thus, cat liver extracts converted 3-hydroxyanthranilic acid chiefly to picolinic acid, while extracts of rat liver synthesized mainly quinolinic acid (1874).

The formation of 2-acroleyl-3-aminofumaric acid from 3-hydroxyanthranilic acid involves cleavage of the benzene ring at a bond adjacent to the phenolic hydroxyl group with incorporation of 2 atoms of atmospheric oxygen (1875, 1876). Thus, in the conversion of 3-hydroxyanthranilic acid to picolinic acid, in the presence of O_2^{18}, 1 atom of labeled oxygen is introduced into picolinic acid since the other atom of oxygen is lost as water during pyridine ring formation. The formation of picolinic acid, as stated above, involves loss of the original carboxyl group of 3-hydroxyanthranilic acid, and the 3-carbon atom of 3-hydroxyanthranilic acid (attached to the phenolic hydroxyl group) becomes the α-carboxyl group carbon atom of quinolinic acid (1877).

Purified preparations of liver 3-hydroxyanthranilic acid oxidase have been obtained (1878–1881). The enzyme requires sulfhydryl compounds and ferrous ions; it is not highly sensitive to chelating agents and there is evidence that ferrous iron functions in the binding and activation of oxygen (1880).

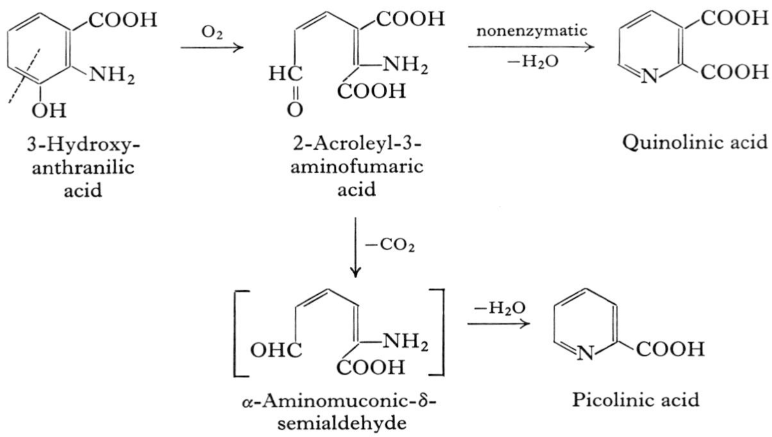

3-Hydroxy-   2-Acroleyl-3-   Quinolinic acid
anthranilic   aminofumaric
acid   acid

α-Aminomuconic-δ-   Picolinic acid
semialdehyde

A number of studies with labeled tryptophan show that a large fraction of the carbon of the benzene ring is converted via acetate to carbon dioxide in the intact rat (1882–1885). Although it has been reported that under certain experimental conditions rat liver homogenates oxidize tryptophan to carbon dioxide more rapidly than kynurenine (1886), studies *in vivo* provide substantial evidence that the complete oxidation of the benzene ring of tryptophan occurs by a pathway involving the intermediate formation of kynurenine and 3-hydroxyanthranilic acid (1887). Until relatively recently, little information was available concerning the metabolism of hydroxyanthranilic acid to products other than nicotinic acid, quinolinic acid, and picolinic acid. Gholson *et al.* (1888) recently showed that preparations of cat liver catalyze the oxidation of 3-hydroxyanthranilic acid to glutaric acid, and that γ-oxalocrotonic acid is an intermediate. Their enzyme preparation catalyzed the diphosphopyridine nucleotide-linked oxidation of α-hydroxymuconic-δ-semialdehyde to γ-oxalocrotonic acid, and when the latter compound was incubated with reduced pyridine nucleotide and the enzyme preparation, evidence for formation of α-ketoadipic acid was obtained. These observations are consistent with a pathway of oxidation involving the conversion of 2-acroleyl-3-aminofumaric acid by decarboxylation and deamination to α-hydroxymuconic semialdehyde followed by oxidation to γ-oxalocrotonic acid. The latter compound is reduced to α-ketoadipic acid, whose metabolism follows known pathways via glutaryl-coenzyme A to carbon dioxide and acetyl-coenzyme A; these reactions are identical to those which occur in the course of lysine metabolism (see p. 945). The observations of Gholson *et al.* would appear at last to clarify the major quantitative degradative pathway of tryptophan in animals.

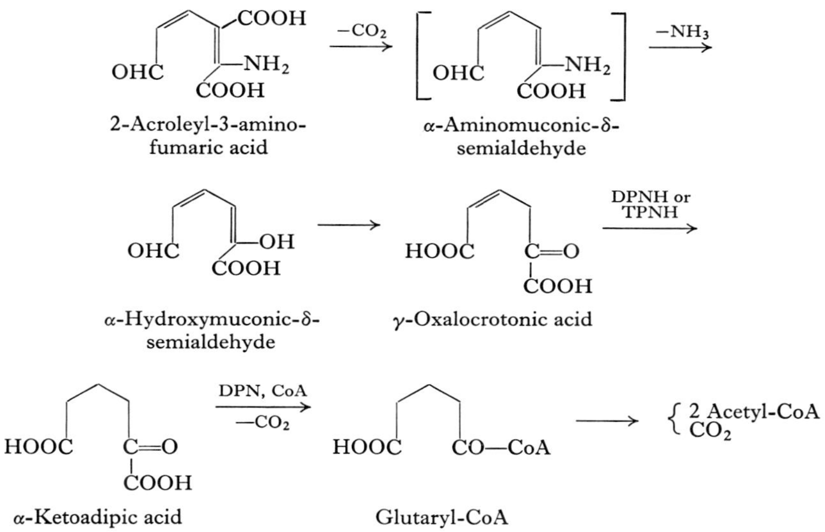

2-Acroleyl-3-amino-
fumaric acid

α-Aminomuconic-δ-
semialdehyde

α-Hydroxymuconic-δ-
semialdehyde

γ-Oxalocrotonic acid

α-Ketoadipic acid

Glutaryl-CoA

The mechanism of the conversion of 3-hydroxyanthranilic acid to nicotinic acid and its derivatives had also been a puzzle. There was, however, good evidence for the conversion of 3-hydroxyanthranilic acid to nicotinic acid, and the ability of quinolinic acid to replace niacin in supporting the growth of rats had been observed a number of years ago. Recently, Nishizuka and Hayaishi (1889) obtained evidence for the conversion of 3-hydroxyanthranilic acid to niacin ribonucleotide in the presence of 5-phosphoribosyl-1-pyrophosphate and a rat liver enzyme preparation. In these experiments, 3-hydroxykynurenine uniformly labeled in the benzene ring was incubated with adenosine triphosphate, 5-phosphoribosyl-1-pyrophosphate and the liver fraction; after incubation, carrier picolinic acid, quinolinic acid, niacin, diphosphopyridine nucleotide, deamidodiphosphopyridine nucleotide, and niacin ribonucleotide were added and the reaction mixture was chromatographed. Radioactivity was found in three major products: picolinic acid, niacin ribonucleotide and quinolinic acid. In similar studies with radioactive 2-acroleyl-3-aminofumaric acid (prepared enzymatically from 3-hydroxyanthranilic acid), radioactivity was found in deamidodiphosphopyridine nucleotide as well as niacin ribonucleotide. Niacin ribonucleotide formation was also demonstrated from C^{14}-quinolinic acid and 5-phosphoribosyl-1-pyrophosphate; the latter reaction was associated with carbon dioxide formation. These observations are consistent with the following pathway for the conversion of quinolinic acid to diphosphopyridine nucleotide:

Quinolinic acid

Quinolinic acid ribonucleotide

Niacin ribonucleotide

Deamidodiphosphopyridine nucleotide

ATP, glutamine (see p. 624)

Diphosphopyridine nucleotide

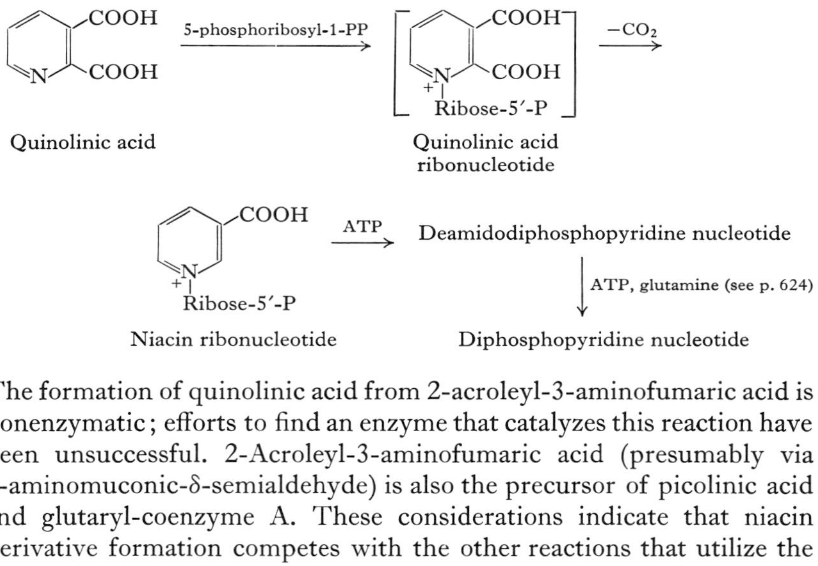

The formation of quinolinic acid from 2-acroleyl-3-aminofumaric acid is nonenzymatic; efforts to find an enzyme that catalyzes this reaction have been unsuccessful. 2-Acroleyl-3-aminofumaric acid (presumably via α-aminomuconic-δ-semialdehyde) is also the precursor of picolinic acid and glutaryl-coenzyme A. These considerations indicate that niacin derivative formation competes with the other reactions that utilize the precursor of quinolinic acid. Data in support of this conclusion were obtained by Mehler et al. (1872); as noted above, the increased picolinic acid decarboxylase activity in diabetic rats is accompanied by decreased N-methylnicotinamide excretion. The relatively low conversion of tryptophan to niacin in the cat as compared to the rat seems to be associated with reduced enzymatic activity capable of niacin ribonucleotide synthesis and high picolinic decarboxylase activity (1890).

The formation of niacin ribonucleotide from quinolinic acid and 5-phosphoribosyl-1-pyrophosphate catalyzed by quinolinate transphosphoribosylase does not lead to detectable quinolinate ribonucleotide. The latter may be an enzyme-bound intermediate, or perhaps condensation and decarboxylation occur in a single step (1891).

β-Alanine-2-C^{14} is converted to urinary quinolinic acid in the rat, mouse, and guinea pig (1892), and these observations indicate that animals as well as plants and certain microorganisms (see below, p. 863) possess a pathway for quinolinic acid synthesis that does not involve the well-established route from tryptophan.

Nicotinic acid is excreted unchanged in certain species, whereas in others it may be amidated, methylated, or excreted in conjugated form. Most carnivorous and omnivorous species excrete N-methylnicotinamide (1893, 1894); herbivorous animals excrete free or conjugated nicotinic acid (1895). Certain birds and reptiles conjugate ornithine with nicotinic acid to form nicotinuric acid (1896, 1897; see p. 441). N-Methylnicotinamide is oxidized to N-methyl-2-pyridone-5-carboxamide in man and a number of other animals (1898–1903).

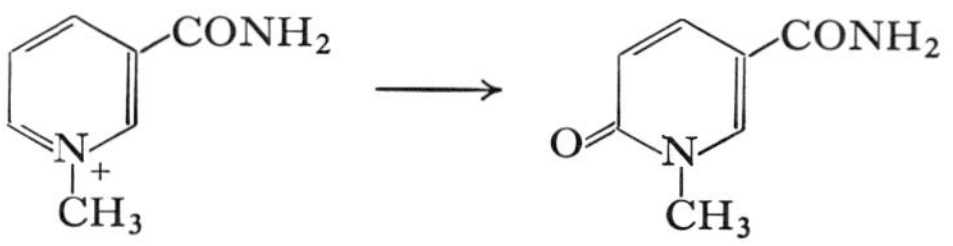

N-Methylnicotinamide   N-Methyl-2-pyridone-5-carboxamide

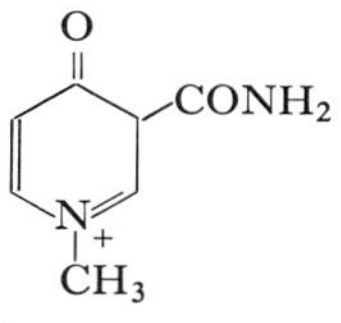

N-Methyl-4-pyridone-5-carboxamide

N-Methyl-2-pyridone-5-carboxylic acid and its glycine conjugate have also been found in normal human urine (1904). N-Methyl-4-pyridone-5-carboxamide has been found in the urine of the rat, monkey, and man (1905), and also in human plasma (1906).

It has been known for some time that trigonelline, the N-methyl derivative of nicotinic acid, is present in certain plants. The synthesis of trigonelline from nicotinic acid and S-adenosylmethionine has been demonstrated with extracts of pea seedlings (1907). This enzyme exhibits no activity with nicotinamide. Coffee beans contain considerable amounts of trigonelline, which is converted to nicotinic acid during roasting. Instant coffee powder has been reported to contain 18–40 mg. of nicotinic acid per 100 g. (1908).

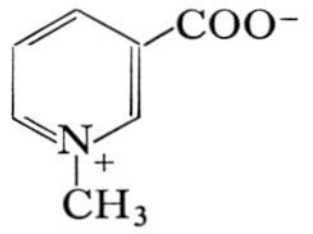

Trigonelline

The metabolism of trigonelline has been examined in *Torula cremoris* and in young pea plants. In the yeast, trigonelline is converted to nicotinic acid apparently by oxidative demethylation, and the nicotinic acid formed is utilized for the synthesis of diphosphopyridine nucleotide. Pea plants utilize trigonelline for diphosphopyridine nucleotide biosynthesis, but information concerning the mechanism of demethylation is still lacking. In the pea plant, considerable degradation of nicotinic acid occurs (1909). The degradative metabolism of nicotinic acid has been extensively investigated in *Pseudomonas fluorescens* (1910). There is evidence for a pathway involving hydroxylation at the 6-position followed by oxidative decarboxylation to 2,5-dihydroxypyridine, which is cleaved to maleamic and formic acids. Maleamic acid is deamidated to maleic acid which isomerizes to fumaric acid. These transformations may be represented as shown in Scheme 20.

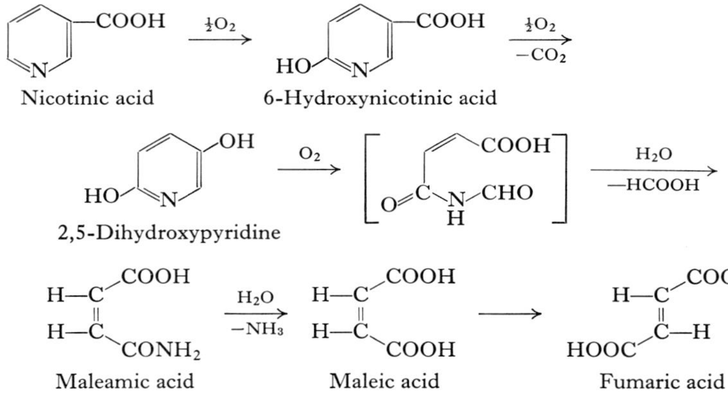

Nicotinic acid   6-Hydroxynicotinic acid

2,5-Dihydroxypyridine

Maleamic acid   Maleic acid   Fumaric acid

SCHEME 20

The pathway of nicotinic acid biosynthesis in certain microorganisms and plants differs from that described above. Thus, *E. coli* and *B. subtilis* lack kynureninase activity, and in experiments in which labeled indole or tryptophan was supplied to certain mutants of these organisms, relatively little label appeared in the nicotinic acid (1911, 1912). In earlier studies it had been found that neither kynurenine nor 3-hydroxyanthranilic acid could replace nicotinic acid as a growth factor for bacteria (1913). In addition, a strain of *Pseudomonas* adapted to grow on tryptophan was found to be unable to oxidize 3-hydroxyanthranilic acid (1914). Tryptophan is neither a precursor of nicotinic acid in corn nor of nicotine in the tobacco plant (1915). It should also be mentioned that the pyridine moieties of a number of alkaloids do not arise from tryptophan.

Ortega and Brown (1916) found that the synthesis of nicotinic acid by growing *E. coli* was increased by supplementation of the medium with alanine, aspartate, glutamate, pyruvate, or oxaloacetate. In studies with resting cell suspensions of *E. coli*, maximal synthesis of nicotinic acid was achieved in the presence of glycerol, a 4-carbon dicarboxylic acid, ribose, and adenine. The carbon chains of glycerol and succinic acid were efficiently incorporated into nicotinic acid, and evidence was obtained that the carboxyl group of nicotinic acid is derived from the carboxyl groups of succinic acid. The methylene carbon atoms of succinic acid served as precursors of the pyridine ring as did carbon atoms 1 and 3 of glycerol. The data suggest that the pyridine ring of nicotinic acid is synthesized from a 3-carbon compound related metabolically to glycerol, and a 4-carbon dicarboxylic acid. Studies on the incorporation of β-alanine, glycerol, and other compounds into the pyridine ring of nicotine suggest a similar but perhaps not identical pathway (1917), and experiments with tritium and C^{14}-labeled nicotinic acid carried out with tobacco root cultures have shown that nicotinic acid is the precursor of the pyridine ring of nicotine (1918, 1919). There is evidence that the pyridine moiety of anabasine also arises from nicotinic acid (see p. 948).

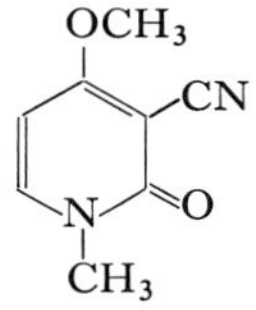

Ricinine

Ricinine, a toxic alkaloid produced by *Ricinus communis* L. (castor plant), is probably formed by a pathway involving utilization of nicotinamide. Thus, there is evidence that the cyano nitrogen atom of the alkaloid arises from the amide nitrogen atom of nicotinamide (1920). Methionine provides the methyl groups of ricinine (see p. 775), and it has been reported (1921) that labeling patterns found in ricinine formed from succinate-C^{14} and glycerol-C^{14} suggest condensation of a 3-carbon compound with a 4-carbon dicarboxylic acid to yield quinolinic acid, which could be decarboxylated to niacin and ultimately converted to ricinine. Evidence was obtained that quinolinic acid is converted to ricinine in castor seedlings without intermediate formation of free nicotinic acid. Extracts of seedlings catalyze a phosphoribosyl pyrophosphate-dependent decarboxylation of quinolinate, with concomitant nicotinic acid ribonucleotide formation. These observations suggest that the formation of niacin compounds from quinolinate takes place by the same pathway in plants and animals. In plants and certain microorganisms quinolinate synthesis does not involve tryptophan, while in animals tryptophan is the major precursor of quinolinate; another pathway may also exist in animals (1892) as noted above (see p. 861).

There is considerable species variation in the urinary products obtained after tryptophan administration. This is probably related to differences in the activities of the various enzymes that catalyze the degradation of tryptophan. Thus, the cat, which does not excrete detectable amounts of kynurenic and xanthurenic acids in the urine, has lower tryptophan pyrrolase activity than do other animals; the cat also possesses relatively low kynurenine transaminase (1922, 1923). As noted above (see p. 857), decreased niacin formation from tryptophan in cats has been correlated with enzymatic activities. Paper chromatographic study of urine voided by normal human subjects after ingestion of D-tryptophan revealed the presence of tryptophan, kynurenine, and traces of indolepyruvic acid and acetyltryptophan (1924). Since the D- and L-isomers of kynurenine exhibit significantly different R_F values (1925), it could be established that the kynurenine excreted after D-tryptophan administration is also of the D-configuration. Results by other investigators are consistent with these observations (1926, 1927). The formation of D-kynurenine from D-tryptophan is surprising in view of the reported optical specificity of the tryptophan pyrrolase reaction (1774). However, it is conceivable that human tryptophan pyrrolase acts to some extent on D-tryptophan, or that the conversion of D-tryptophan to D-kynurenine is catalyzed by enzymes present in the bacterial flora. *Penicillium viridicatum* converts D-tryptophan to D-kynurenine and other products (1928), and this reaction probably occurs in other species.

Other Reactions of Kynurenine and Derivatives. 3-Hydroxykynurenine is converted to 4,8-dihydroxyquinoline by mouse liver homogenates, probably by the following pathway (1929):

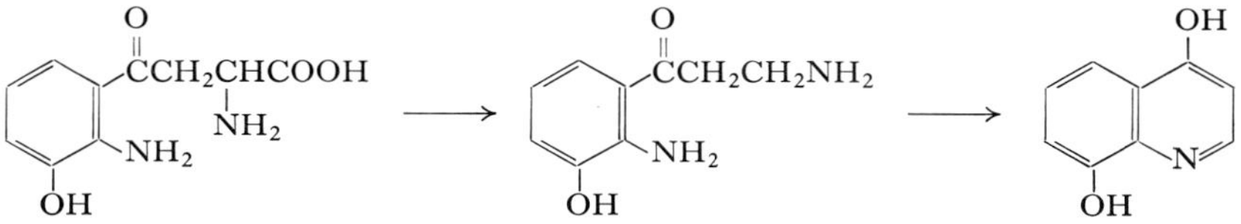

3-Hydroxykynuramine   4,8-Dihydroxy-
quinoline

This transformation involves decarboxylation of 3-hydroxykynurenine rather than of xanthurenic acid, which was inactive when added to this system. The first reaction is probably catalyzed by the aromatic amino acid decarboxylase (see p. 327), and the second reaction by monoamine oxidase followed by cyclization of the aminoaldehyde product (1929a, 1929b). 5-Hydroxykynurenine is the precursor of 5-hydroxykynuramine, whose formation is also catalyzed by mouse liver preparations (1929c).

Conversion of kynurenine to kynurenic acid takes place by transamination (see p. 367) or oxidative deamination (see p. 296). Kynurenine transaminase has been separated from kynureninase, which also requires pyridoxal phosphate. Kynurenine transaminase preparations have been obtained from animal tissues and from microorganisms (see p. 368). Transamination of kynurenine presumably yields *o*-aminobenzoyl-pyruvic acid, which spontaneously cyclizes to kynurenic acid. The formation of xanthurenic acid from 3-hydroxykynurenine could take place by a similar mechanism:

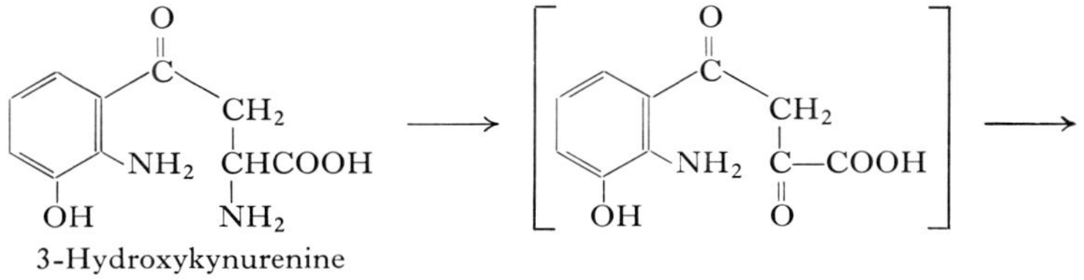

3-Hydroxykynurenine

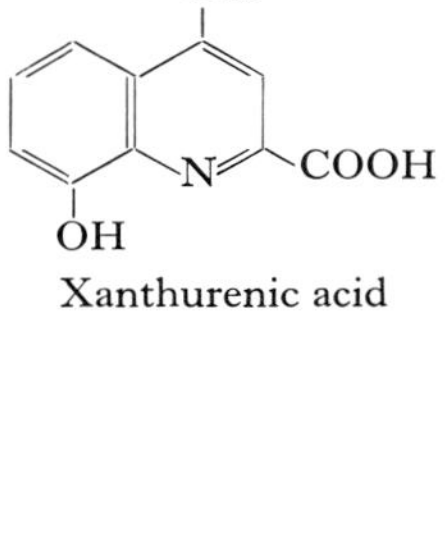

Xanthurenic acid

However, the free α-keto acids may not be formed in these reactions; the ketimine forms of the corresponding pyridoxal phosphate-Schiff bases could be the immediate precursors of kynurenic and xanthurenic acids:

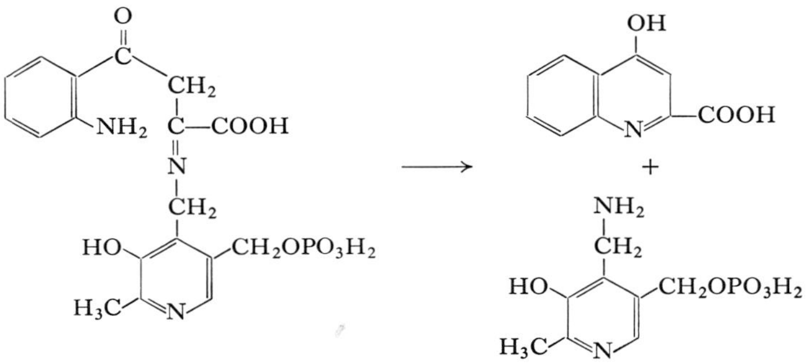

The conversion of kynurenine to β-(8-xanthurenyl)glucosiduronic acid by the rat and by rat kidney slices has been reported (1930). 3-Methoxy-anthranilic acid has been found in human urine (1931); this compound might be formed by the action of kynureninase on 3-methoxykynurenine, which could also be the precursor of the urinary 8-methoxykynurenic acid identified earlier (1932).

Kynurenic acid probably undergoes little if any metabolism in the mammal. Thus, when kynurenic acid-2- or 3-C^{14} was intraperitoneally administered to the rat, mouse, hamster, rabbit, guinea pig, cat, and dog, between 80 and 100% of the injected radioactivity was recovered in the urine during the first 24 hours. Little or no radioactivity appeared in the expired carbon dioxide or in the carcass. The urinary excretion of small amounts of quinaldic acid and quinaldylglycine was observed; although this may reflect the ability of animal tissues to metabolize kynurenic acid, the possibility that such results are due to the action of the bacterial flora cannot be excluded (1933).

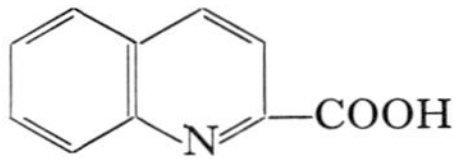

Quinaldic acid
(quinoline-2-carboxylic acid)

When quinaldic and kynurenic acids labeled in the carboxyl groups and xanthurenic acid-4-C^{14} were administered orally and by subcutaneous injection to rabbits, most of the administered radioactivity could be accounted for in the urine in the form of quinoline derivatives. More than two thirds of the orally administered kynurenic and xanthurenic acids were dehydroxylated to quinaldic and 8-hydroxyquinaldic acids, respectively. When these were administered by injection only 2 to 10% of the material given appeared in the urine as the corresponding dehydroxylated derivatives (1934). Earlier studies (1935–1937) described the conversion of xanthurenic acid to 8-hydroxyquinaldic acid, and of kynurenic acid to quinaldic acid by various animal species; quinaldylglycyltaurine is a urinary metabolite of quinaldic acid and kynurenic acid in the cat (1938).

Hayaishi and collaborators (1939–1941) have investigated the degradation of kynurenic acid by tryptophan-adapted cells of *Pseudomonas fluorescens*. L-Glutamic acid, D- and L-alanine, and acetic acid were among the main products of kynurenic acid degradation. It was found that the carbon chain of glutamic acid arose from the benzene moiety of kynurenic acid. Carbon atoms 6 and 9 of kynurenic acid were the precursors of carbon atoms 4 and 1 of glutamic acid, respectively, while carbon atoms 2 and 3 of kynurenic acid were distributed among carbon atoms 2, 3, 4, and 5 of glutamic acid. Carbon atom 2 of kynurenic acid was found in carbon atoms 2 and 3 of alanine and carbon atoms 1 and 2 of acetic acid. The carboxyl group of alanine and the α-carboxyl group of glutamic acid contained little radioactivity, and the carboxyl carbon of kynurenic acid was converted mainly to carbon dioxide. An enzyme preparation was obtained from *Pseudomonas* that catalyzes the conversion of kynurenic acid to a compound that exhibits the properties of 7,8-dihydrokynurenic acid-7,8-diol in the presence of reduced diphosphopyridine nucleotide (or triphosphopyridine nucleotide) and oxygen. This compound was dehydrogenated in the presence of diphosphopyridine nucleotide to 7,8-dihydroxykynurenic acid, which was isolated and definitely identified. Similar findings were reported by Behrman and Tanaka (1942). The postulated pathway for the enzymatic degradation of kynurenic acid by this organism is shown in Scheme 21.

Metabolism of Anthranilic Acid. Anthranilic acid, formed by the cleavage of kynurenine catalyzed by kynureninase, can be utilized for tryptophan biosynthesis as discussed above (p. 848), but in certain microorganisms anthranilic acid is metabolized by the so-called "aromatic pathway" (1943–1954) (see Scheme 22).

Cell-free preparations of several microorganisms including *Pseudomonas* have been obtained that catalyze the oxidation of anthranilic acid

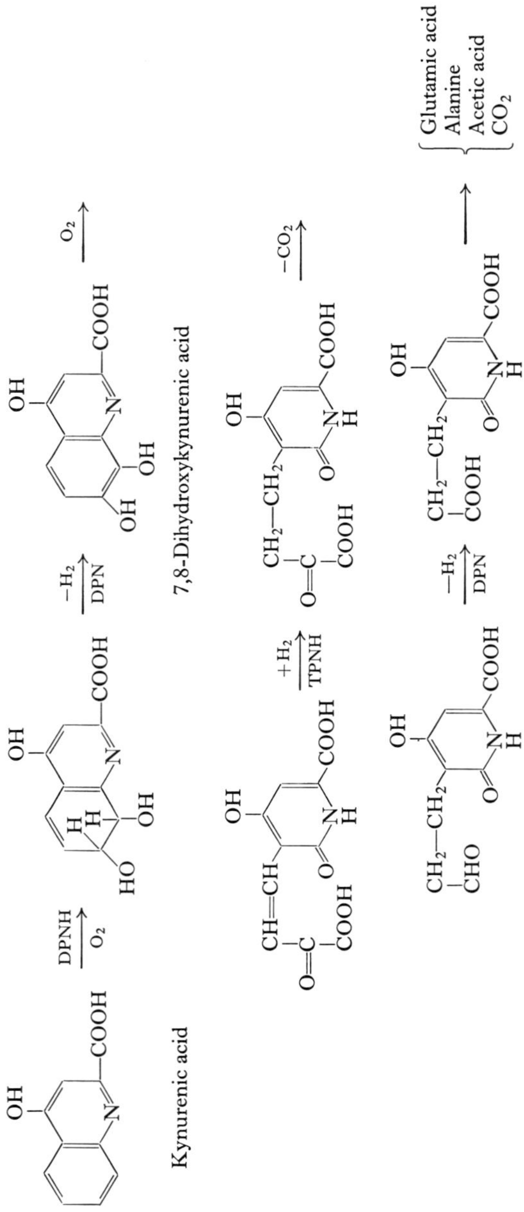
Kynurenic acid
DPNH
O2
−H2
DPN
7,8-Dihydroxykynurenic acid
O2
+H2
TPNH
−CO2
−H2
DPN
Glutamic acid
Alanine
Acetic acid
CO2

SCHEME 21

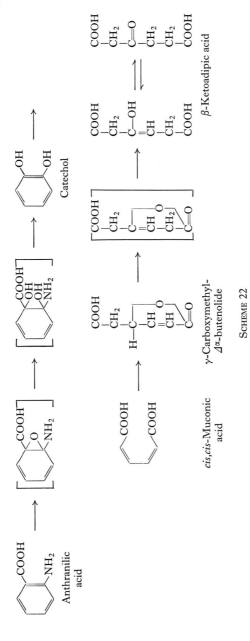

Anthranilic acid

cis,cis-Muconic acid

γ-Carboxymethyl-Δ^α-butenolide

Catechol

β-Ketoadipic acid

SCHEME 22

in the presence of reduced pyridine nucleotide. These preparations oxidize both anthranilic acid and benzoic acid, but there is evidence that different enzymes are involved (1955). Although the final product of oxidation of both substrates is β-ketoadipic acid, there is evidence that catechol is formed in the course of the reaction (1943). Enzymes that catalyze the conversion of catechol to *cis, cis*-muconic acid (pyrocatechase) have been purified from anthranilic acid-adapted cells of *Pseudomonas* and from *Brevibacterium fuscum* (1956). These catalyze the cleavage of catechol with the consumption of 1 mole of oxygen per mole of catechol cleaved. The enzyme has been obtained in homogeneous condition (molecular weight, about 80,000) and found to require ferrous ions. Studies with O^{18} have shown that the oxygen atoms added to catechol are derived from atmospheric oxygen (1957). The conversion of *cis,cis*-muconic acid to β-ketoadipic acid involves the participation of two enzymes (1951). These catalyze, respectively, conversion of *cis,cis*-muconic acid to γ-carboxymethyl-Δ^{α}-butenolide, and conversion of the latter compound to β-ketoadipic acid.

β-Ketoadipic acid is also formed by the oxidation of phenol, mandelic acid, and other compounds. β-Ketoadipic acid is converted to β-ketoadipyl-coenzyme A in the presence of succinyl-coenzyme A and a specific thiophorase (1958); this is followed by cleavage of β-ketoadipyl-coenzyme A in the presence of coenzyme A to yield succinyl-coenzyme A and acetyl-coenzyme A. The over-all reaction therefore requires catalytic amounts of succinyl-coenzyme A:

$$\beta\text{-Ketoadipic acid} + \text{succinyl-CoA} \rightleftharpoons \beta\text{-ketoadipyl-CoA} + \text{succinic acid}$$
$$\underline{\beta\text{-Ketoadipyl-CoA} + \text{CoA} \rightleftharpoons \text{succinyl-CoA} + \text{acetyl-CoA}}$$

Sum: $\beta\text{-Ketoadipic acid} + \text{CoA} \rightleftharpoons \text{succinic acid} + \text{acetyl-CoA}$

5-Hydroxytryptophan and Its Metabolites. An important pathway of tryptophan metabolism in animals is conversion to 5-hydroxytryptamine. Werle and Mennicken (1959) reported in 1937 that mammalian tissues could convert tryptophan to a pressor substance, which was thought to be tryptamine. Later investigations by Udenfriend and associates (1960, 1961) suggested that this substance may have been 5-hydroxytryptamine (but see p. 327), a compound identical with an invertebrate hormone described by Erspamer (1962) as enteramine, and a vasoconstrictor substance (serotonin) isolated from beef serum by Rapport and associates (1963–1965). That tryptophan was the precursor of 5-hydroxytryptamine was shown by experiments in which labeled tryptophan was fed to rabbits and toads, followed by isolation of labeled 5-hydroxytryptamine (1966). Administration of 5-hydroxytryptophan led to increased tissue 5-hydroxytryptamine in animals (1967). 5-Hydroxytryptamine is formed by the following reactions:

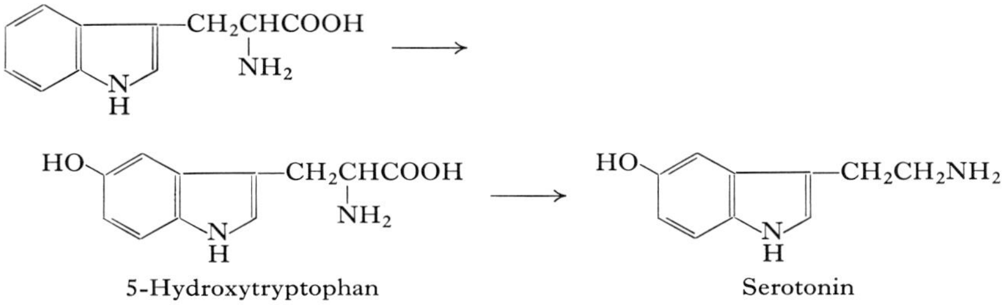

5-Hydroxytryptophan   Serotonin

The evidence clearly indicates that oxidation of the aromatic ring precedes decarboxylation rather than the reverse, because tryptamine is not formed under the same conditions nor does it serve as a precursor of 5-hydroxytryptamine. Conversion of tryptophan to 5-hydroxytryptophan in guinea pig and rat liver slices was shown by an isotopic trapping procedure, and administration of 5-hydroxytryptophan to dogs led to excretion of 5-hydroxytryptamine (1968). Conversion of L-tryptophan to 5-hydroxy-L-tryptophan has been demonstrated in studies with cell suspensions of *Chromobacterium violaceum* (1969); this organism does not possess a "kynurenine" pathway and can utilize 5-hydroxytryptophan for production of its characteristic pigment, violacein (1970). The hydroxylation of tryptophan to 5-hydroxytryptophan has been demonstrated with the supernatant fraction of rat liver (1971), and the data indicate that the hydroxylation of tryptophan can be catalyzed by the same enzyme that hydroxylates phenylalanine to form tyrosine (1972) (see p. 898). Hepatic phenylalanine hydroxylase preparations oxidize phenylalanine about 30 times more rapidly than tryptophan. There is evidence for the formation of 5-hydroxytryptamine (and also 5-hydroxytryptophan) in extrahepatic tissues; it is believed that phenylalanine hydroxylase is present mainly if not exclusively in the liver (see p. 1068). Thus, 5-hydroxytryptamine is formed in carcinoid tumors, which do not possess phenylalanine hydroxylase, and in neoplastic mouse mast cells grown in culture (1973). There is also evidence that indicates occurrence of tryptophan hydroxylation in intestinal mucosa presumably in the argentaffin cells (1974–1977). Hydroxylation of tryptophan to 5-hydroxytryptophan has been described in preparations of pigeon and rat brain (1977, 1978). Adrenalectomized rats exhibit essentially normal liver phenylalanine hydroxylase activity but markedly depressed tryptophan hydroxylase activity. The latter is restored by administration of cortisone (1979). Finally, it is of significance that patients with phenyl-ketonuria exhibit normal blood concentrations of 5-hydroxytryptamine and urinary 5-hydroxyindoleacetic acid when they are maintained on a diet low in phenylalanine (1980). There is often a decreased concentration of blood 5-hydroxytryptamine in untreated patients (probably due to inhibition of tryptophan hydroxylation by phenylalanine), but the formation of 5-hydroxytryptamine is not as markedly reduced as that of tyrosine from phenylalanine.

The enzyme responsible for the decarboxylation of 5-hydroxytrypto-phan has been found in several animal tissues (1961, 1981). As discussed elsewhere in this volume, there is evidence that this enzyme also decarboxylates 3,4-dihydroxyphenylalanine (see p. 327). The function of pyridoxal phosphate was demonstrated by enzymatic study and by experiments on vitamin B_6-deficient animals (1982, 1983). Although the hydroxylation and decarboxylation reactions are highly specific for the L-isomers of tryptophan and 5-hydroxytryptophan, respectively, when 5-hydroxy-D-tryptophan was infused into humans, a small amount of 5-hydroxyindoleacetic acid was formed (1984); this result was attributed to inversion of the D-isomer of tryptophan by the combined action of D-amino acid oxidase and L-specific transaminases (see p. 304).

Consideration of the physiological and pharmacological aspects of 5-hydroxytryptamine is beyond the scope of this treatise [see (1985) for a review of this area]. In addition to its effect on cerebral function, blood pressure, respiration, and smooth muscle activity, it is of interest that after intraperitoneal injection of 5-hydroxytryptamine into rats there was a significant increase in the phosphate uptake of the adrenal, pancreas, liver, and diaphragm, while uptake was decreased in the spleen and testis (1986). Certain aspects of the relationship of 5-hydroxytryptamine function to disease are considered elsewhere in this volume (see p. 1057).

5-Hydroxytryptophan is not a substrate for tryptophan pyrrolase nor is the amino acid utilized by tryptophan-adapted *Pseudomonas* (1853, 1987).

The conversion of 5-hydroxytryptamine to 5-hydroxyindoleacetic acid has been shown in dogs (1968). 5-Hydroxyindoleacetic acid is a normal constituent of human urine (1988, 1989), where it may exist in conjugated form with glycine (5-hydroxyindoleaceturic acid) (1990, 1991). Ingestion of bananas, which contain 5-hydroxytryptamine, leads to increased urinary 5-hydroxyindoleacetic acid (1992). The presence of 5-hydroxy-tryptamine in this food (and perhaps others) serves to complicate attempts to relate 5-hydroxyindoleacetic acid excretion and disease. There seems to be no obvious physiological effect of banana ingestion, although one may exist. The formation of 5-hydroxyindoleacetic acid is probably catalyzed by monoamine oxidase (see p. 314), whose action leads to the intermediate formation of 5-hydroxyindoleacetaldehyde (1966):

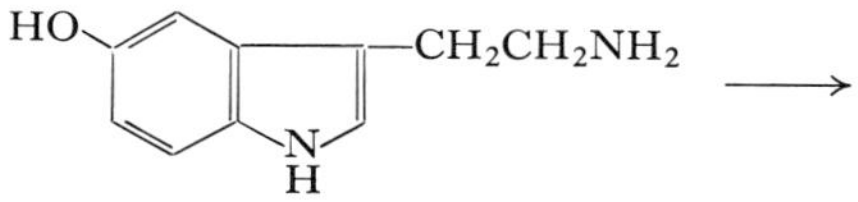

5-Hydroxytryptamine

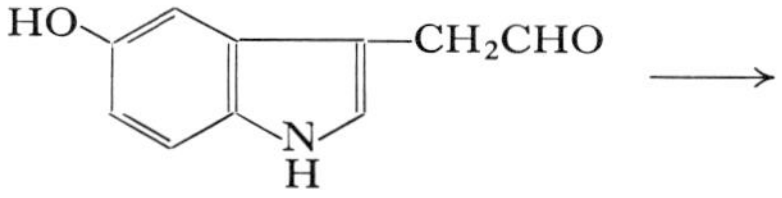

5-Hydroxyindoleacetaldehyde 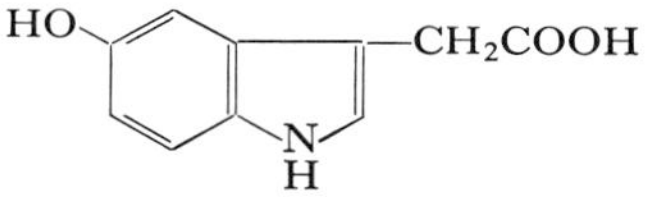   5-Hydroxyindoleacetic acid

A careful examination of the metabolism of C^{14}-5-hydroxytryptamine in rats and rabbits has been carried out by McIsaac and Page (1993). These workers found that 50 to 80% of administered 5-hydroxytryp-tamine was metabolized and eliminated in the urine within 24 hours. After administration of labeled 5-hydroxytryptamine considerable radioactivity was found in the platelet fraction of the plasma, and in the lung and brain. The urinary metabolites identified were 5-hydroxy-indoleacetic acid, 5-hydroxyindoleaceturic acid, N-acetyl-5-hydroxy-tryptamine, and 5-hydroxytryptamine glucuronide. In these studies, 35 to 83% of the injected material was oxidatively deaminated and 5 to 25% was acetylated; the other metabolites accounted for 5 to 10% of the dose given. It is of interest that rats excreted a mixture of 5-hydroxy-indoleacetic and 5-hydroxyindoleaceturic acids while rabbits excreted mainly the glycine conjugate. 5-Hydroxytryptophol and 5-hydroxy-tryptophol-O-glucuronide have also been identified as urinary meta-bolites of 5-hydroxytryptamine (1994).

Melatonin, a hormone found in bovine pineal glands which produces lightening of frog skin, has been shown to be N-acetyl-5-methoxytryptamine (1995). Subsequent study revealed the presence of an enzyme in pineal gland that catalyzes the O-methylation of N-acetyl-5-hydroxy-tryptamine to yield melatonin. The enzyme also catalyzed the O-methylation of several other hydroxyindoles but at a lower rate. The enzyme utilizes S-adenosylmethionine (see p. 766) (1996). It is of interest that the substrate for transmethylation, N-acetyl-5-hydroxy-tryptamine, had been found earlier as a urinary metabolite of 5-hydroxy-tryptamine. Administration of 5-methoxytryptamine led to excretion of 5-methoxyindoleacetic acid, and the products found in the urine after administration of melatonin included N-acetyl-6-hydroxy-5-methoxy-tryptamine, which was present as conjugates of sulfuric and glucuronic acids (1997). Some of these interrelationships are shown in Scheme 23. Toads (1998, 1999), invertebrates (2000), and certain plants (2001, 2002) contain N-dimethyl-5-hydroxytryptamine (bufotenin). In addition, a number of related 5-hydroxytryptamine derivatives have been isolated, e.g., bufotenidin (2003, 2004), dehydrobufotenin, and bufothionin (2005–2006a).

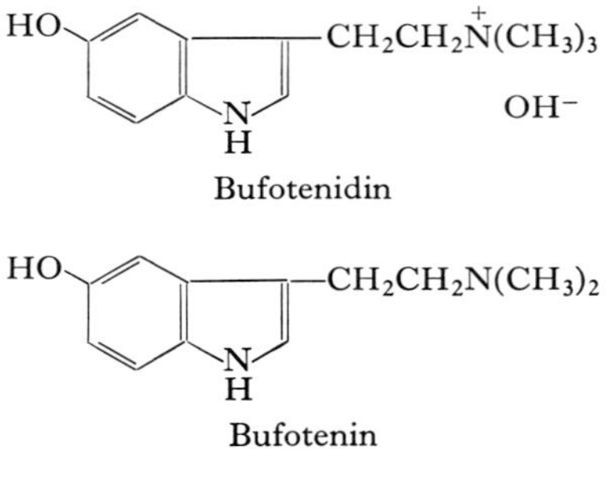

Bufotenidin

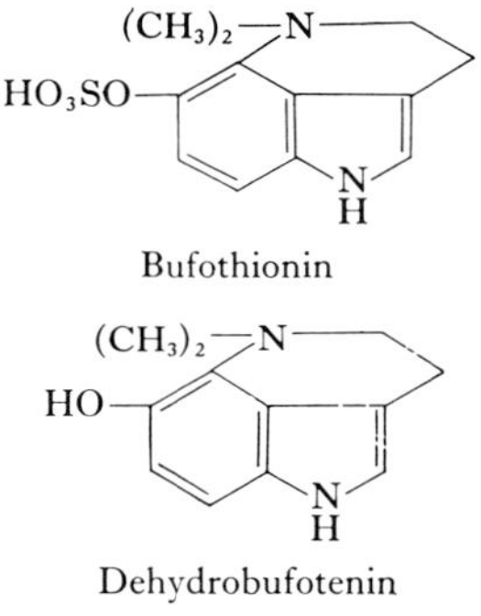

Bufothionin

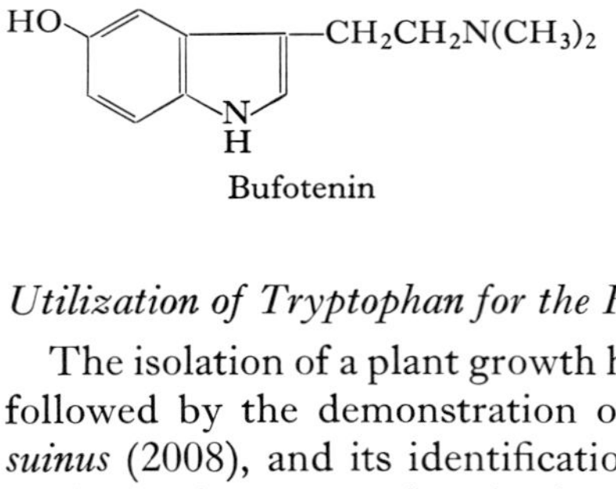

Bufotenin

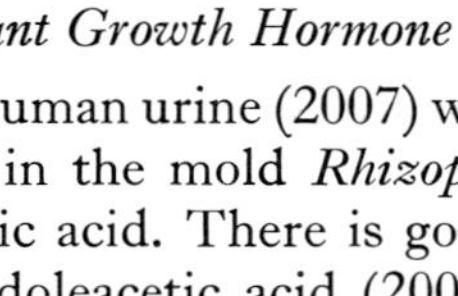

Dehydrobufotenin

Utilization of Tryptophan for the Formation of Plant Growth Hormone

The isolation of a plant growth hormone from human urine (2007) was followed by the demonstration of this material in the mold *Rhizopus suinus* (2008), and its identification as indoleacetic acid. There is good evidence that tryptophan is the precursor of indoleacetic acid (2008–2011), and several plausible pathways for the conversion of tryptophan to indoleacetic acid have been suggested. Thimann, who carried out some of the pioneer work in this area, has stated: "That at this stage we should still not know for certain whether indoleacetic acid normally comes from

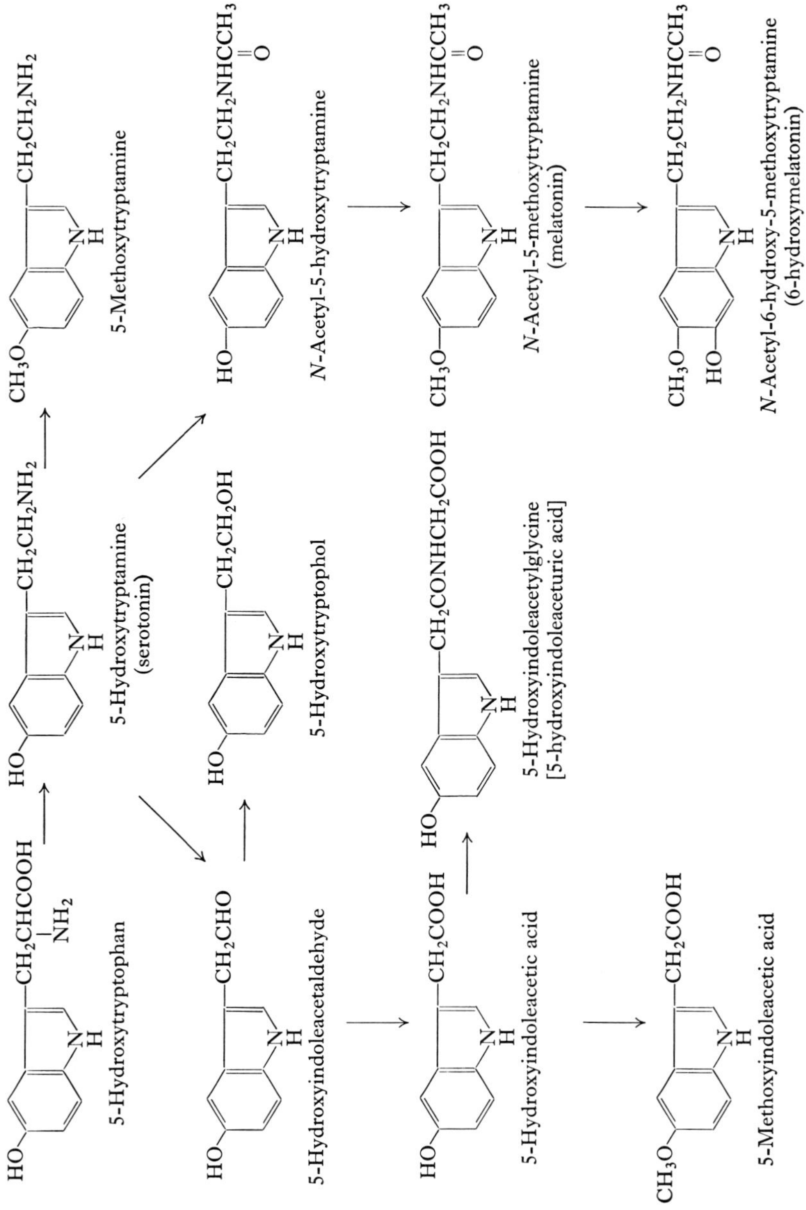

5-Methoxytryptamine

5-Hydroxytryptamine
(serotonin)

N-Acetyl-5-hydroxytryptamine

N-Acetyl-5-methoxytryptamine
(melatonin)

N-Acetyl-6-hydroxy-5-methoxytryptamine
(6-hydroxymelatonin)

5-Hydroxytryptophan

5-Hydroxytryptophol

5-Hydroxyindoleacetaldehyde

5-Hydroxyindoleacetylglycine
[5-hydroxyindoleaceturic acid]

5-Hydroxyindoleacetic acid

5-Methoxyindoleacetic acid

Scheme 23

tryptophan, tryptamine, indoleacetonitrile, or some other precursor, or is more directly synthesized, seems remarkable. Some evidence points in each direction, but none is conclusive" (2012). As indicated in Scheme 24, decarboxylation of tryptophan yields tryptamine, which in turn can be oxidized to indoleacetaldehyde. The latter product might arise by decarboxylation of indolepyruvic acid, which can be formed from tryptophan by oxidative deamination or transamination. Oxidation of indoleacetaldehyde yields indoleacetic acid. The natural occurrence of tryptamine (2013), indolepyruvic acid (2014), and indoleacetaldehyde (2015) has been reported. Tryptamine (2008, 2010, 2016) as well as indolepyruvic acid (2008, 2010) can lead to auxin formation in plants. In recent studies on the formation of indoleacetic acid from tryptophan by the crown gall-inducing organism *Agrobacterium tumefaciens*, conversion of tryptophan to indolepyruvic acid, indolelactic acid, tryptophol, and indoleacetic acid was observed (2017). Indolepyruvate undergoes spontaneous decomposition leading to the formation of several compounds, whose presence on paper chromatograms renders interpretation difficult. However, these studies support the belief that indoleacetic acid arises by a pathway involving indolepyruvic acid. Similar conclusions were drawn from studies in which conversion of tryptophan to indoleacetic acid by lyophilized tomato leaf preparations was inhibited by isonicotinic acid hydrazide (2018). Since the latter compound inhibited indoleacetic acid formation, and in contrast to iproniazid (see p. 316) does not inhibit monoamine oxidase, the data are consistent with the indolepyruvic acid pathway. The possibility that indoleacetonitrile is an intermediate in indoleacetic acid formation has also been suggested (2019). Indoleacetonitrile, a compound that exhibits potent auxin activity, has been found in cabbage (2020). The nitrile can be formed by enzymatic degradation at pH 3.5 of glucobrassicin (2021), a mustard oil glucoside found in cabbage, and perhaps by a mechanism involving oxidation of tryptamine. Its possible formation from indoleacetamide should also be considered. Incubation of various plant tissues with indoleacetic acid led to formation of indoleacetylaspartate and indoleacetamide (2022), but it is not clear as to whether these compounds were formed from the added indoleacetic acid or were products of endogenous synthesis. Indoleacetamide might be formed from tryptophan by an oxygenase-type mechanism similar to that observed with other amino acids (see p. 323). Hydrolysis of indoleacetonitrile or indoleacetamide would yield indoleacetic acid. The oxidative decarboxylation of indoleacetic acid to

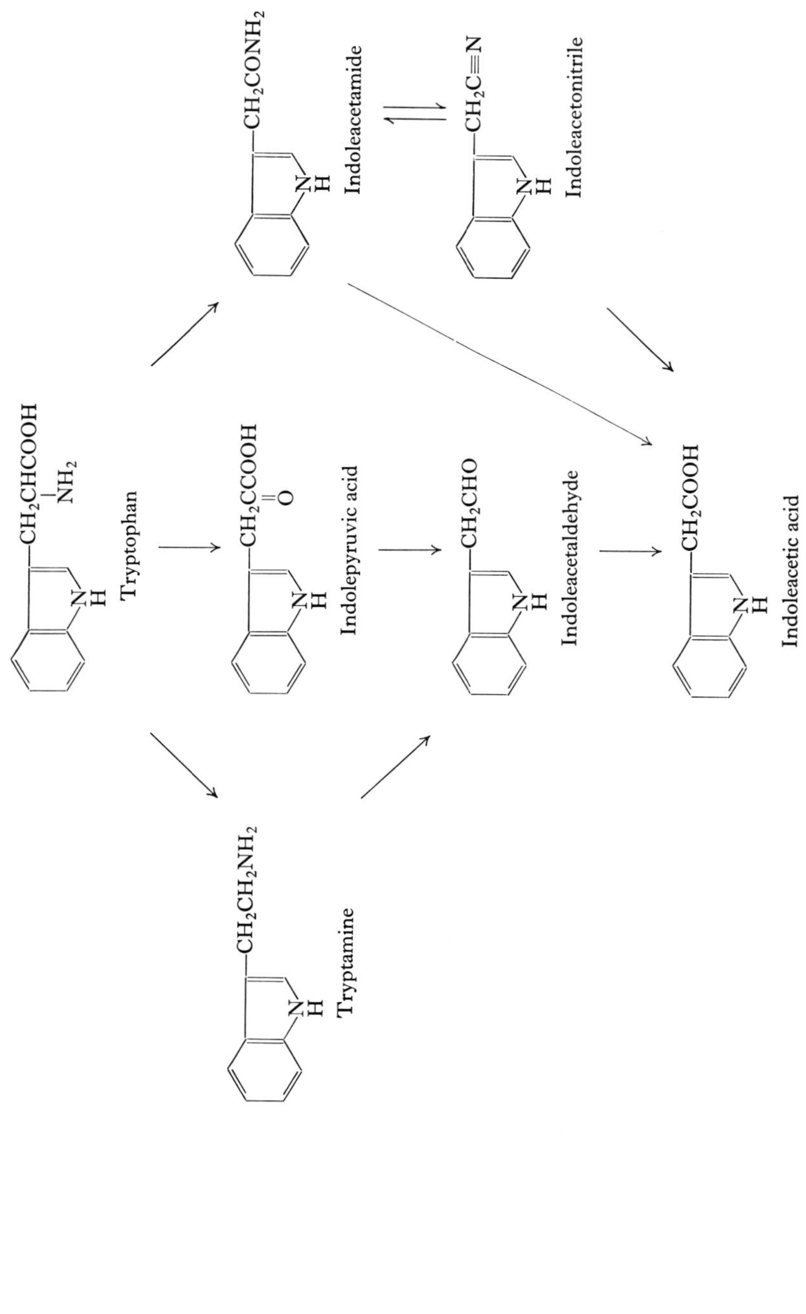

Tryptophan

CH₂CHCOOH
|
NH₂

Indoleacetamide

CH₂CONH₂

Indoleacetonitrile

CH₂C≡N

Indolepyruvic acid

CH₂CCOOH
‖
O

Indoleacetaldehyde

CH₂CHO

Indoleacetic acid

CH₂COOH

Tryptamine

CH₂CH₂NH₂

SCHEME 24

indole-3-aldehyde has been studied by several workers (2023–2025), and this compound is also formed nonenzymatically from indolepyruvic acid (2017). Current aspects of the physiological function of auxin in relation to other growth-influencing plant substances have recently been reviewed (2012). The mode of action of indoleacetic acid is not yet known. Recent studies have shown that incubation of indoleacetic acid with peroxidase yields a compound which forms a complex with ribonucleic acid isolated from pea shoots (2026). The nature of the product of peroxidase action and of the mechanism of its binding to nucleic acid are as yet unknown, as is the physiological significance of the ribonucleic acid compound itself.

Other Products of Tryptophan Metabolism. Degradation of tryptophan in certain bacteria takes place by the tryptophanase reaction, in which tryptophan is converted to indole, pyruvic acid, and ammonia:

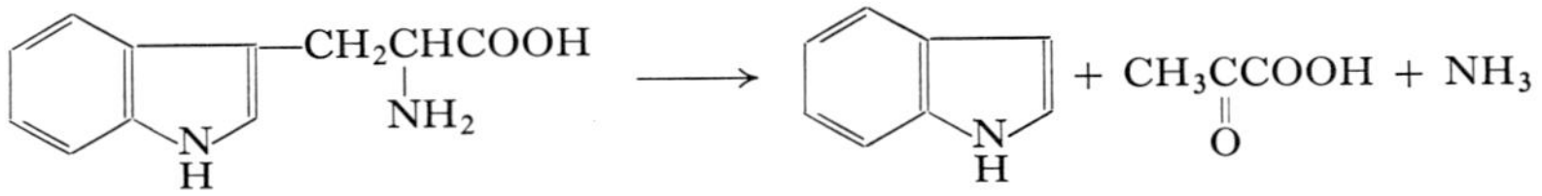

$$\text{(indole-CH}_2\text{CHCOOH, NH}_2) \longrightarrow \text{(indole)} + CH_3CCOOH + NH_3$$

This reaction, first observed by Hopkins and Cole (2027), has been studied in detail by others (2028, 2029). Wood and associates (2030) prepared the enzyme from *E. coli* and demonstrated that pyridoxal phosphate is the coenzyme. The reaction appears to require potassium or ammonium ions and perhaps iron (2031). Metzler and collaborators (2032) have suggested a mechanism involving cleavage of the side chain of a pyridoxal–tryptophan–metal complex:

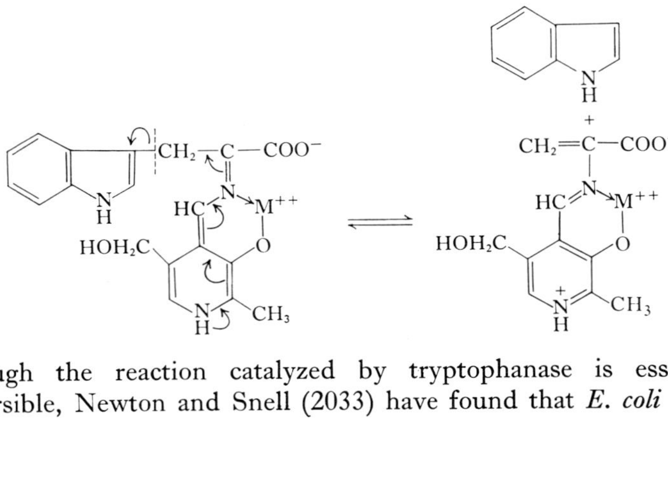

$$\rightleftharpoons$$

Although the reaction catalyzed by tryptophanase is essentially irreversible, Newton and Snell (2033) have found that *E. coli* tryptophanase can catalyze the synthesis of tryptophan from indole and serine. The enzyme activity, which is induced by growth in media containing high concentrations of tryptophan, is clearly distinct from tryptophan synthetase. Thus, the enzyme was obtained from mutants of *E. coli* that lack both A and B components of tryptophan synthetase (see p. 846), which is repressible by tryptophan. In addition, the inducible trypto-phanase does not catalyze hydrolysis of indole-3-glycerol phosphate or synthesis of tryptophan from indole-3-glycerol phosphate and serine. This enzyme can be of biosynthetic significance; thus, mutants lacking "true" tryptophan synthetase were able to grow in media supplemented with indole provided that the inocula were grown in media containing high concentrations of tryptophan. Such mutants inoculated from cultures grown on media containing little tryptophan grew in media containing indole and 5-methyltryptophan (which does not replace tryptophan for growth). This finding suggests that 5-methyltryptophan induces tryptophanase. More recent work (2033a) has led to the crystall-ization of *E. coli* tryptophanase; in addition to the reactions mentioned above, the crystalline enzyme catalyzes the desulfhydration of cysteine (see p. 793), the deamination of serine (see p. 668), the conversion of *S*-methylcysteine to pyruvate, methylmercaptan, and ammonia, and the synthesis of tryptophan from indole and cysteine (or *S*-methylcysteine).

Indigo, indirubin, indoxyl, and indican (2034–2036), which are found in human urine, are probably formed from indole (produced by the action of intestinal bacteria on tryptophan). Indole is converted to indoxyl by the liver microsomal hydroxylating system (2036a); con-jugation of indoxyl to yield indican may also take place in the liver.

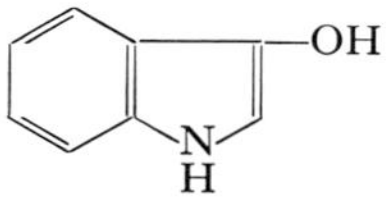

Indoxyl

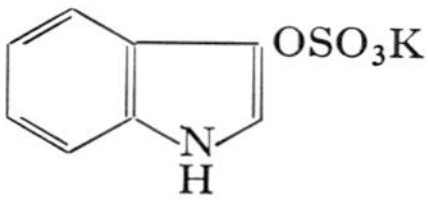

Indican

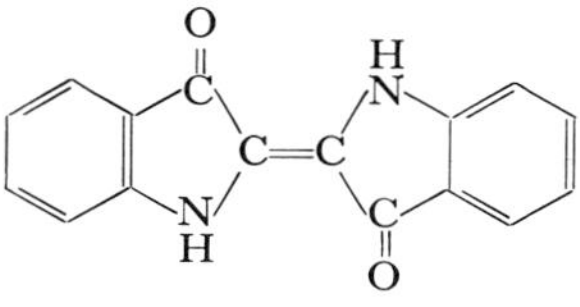

Indigo

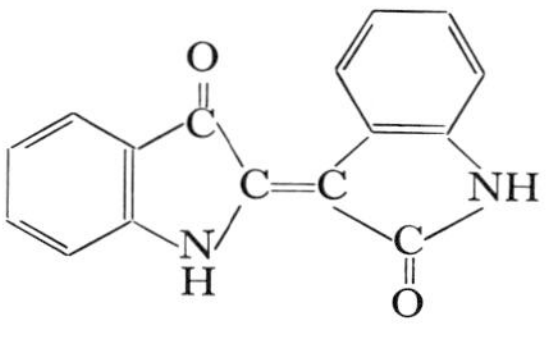

Indirubin

It has been suggested that certain bacteria may degrade indole by the following sequence (2037):

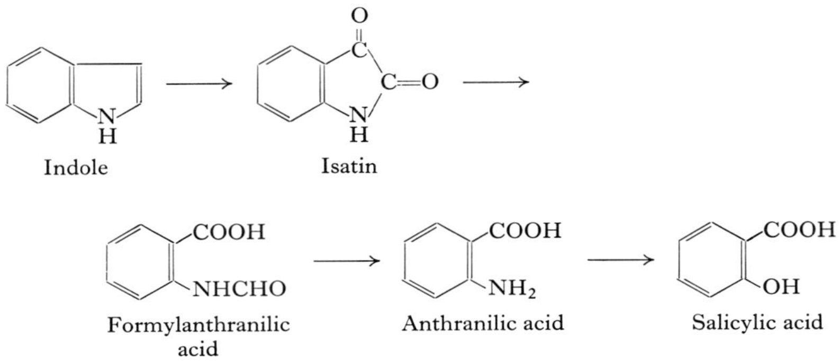

Indole   Isatin

Formylanthranilic   Anthranilic acid   Salicylic acid
acid

McMenamy *et al.* (2038) and McMenamy and Oncley (2039) have made the interesting observation that L-tryptophan is bound to human serum albumin predominantly at a single site in a highly stereospecific manner; thus, D-tryptophan was bound with one hundredth the affinity observed with L-tryptophan. On the basis of binding studies with modified albumins, these workers concluded that the N-terminal group of albumin is involved in the binding of L-tryptophan, and the data indicated that the indole ring is a strong point of attachment at the binding site. Other amino acids of human blood serum did not exhibit similar binding; as yet the physiological significance of this phenomenon is not evident.

As stated above, indoleacetic acid was found in early investigations in human urine (see p. 874). The excretion of indoleacetic acid is increased in patients with phenylketonuria (2040), and this compound is also excreted along with other tryptophan metabolites (e.g., indolylacetylglutamine) in patients with H disease (2041) (see p. 1056). Possible pathways for the conversion of tryptophan to indoleacetic acid include (*a*) transamination of tryptophan to indolepyruvic acid followed by decarboxylation of the α-keto acid to indoleacetic acid, and (*b*) decarboxylation of tryptophan to tryptamine followed by oxidative deamination. Evidence consistent with both pathways has been obtained; pathway (a) is probably the major one (2042). In retrospect, the early studies of Werle and Mennicken (1959) (see p. 870) may have reflected the formation of both tryptamine and 5-hydroxytryptamine from tryptophan. The possibility that indoleacetic acid is formed by hydrolysis of indoleacetamide, formed in turn by direct oxidation of the tryptophan side chain (see p. 323, above), must also be considered.

Administration of tryptophan-7α-C^{14} to patients with multiple myeloma led to excretion of labeled urinary o-aminophenol (2043), a finding that could be explained by decarboxylation of 3-hydroxy-anthranilic acid:

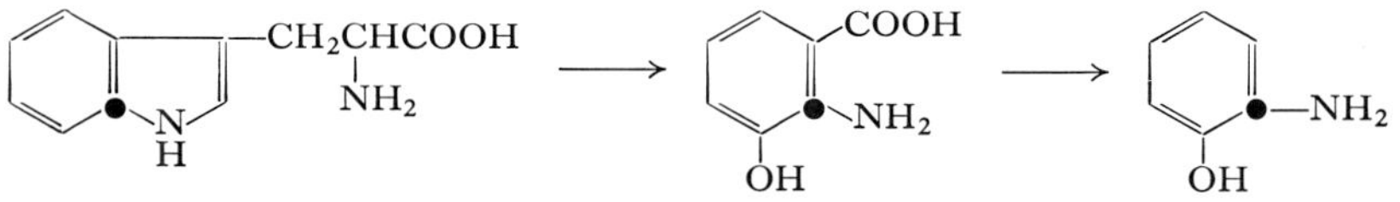

Tryptophan is utilized for biosynthesis of alkaloids of the harman group, and others including yohimbine, cinchonine, strychnine, serpentine, and reserpine (14, 787, 2044–2046).

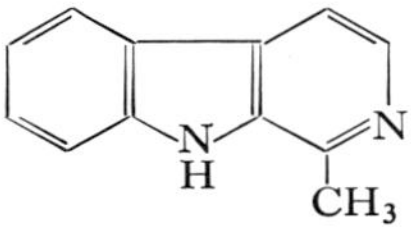

Harman

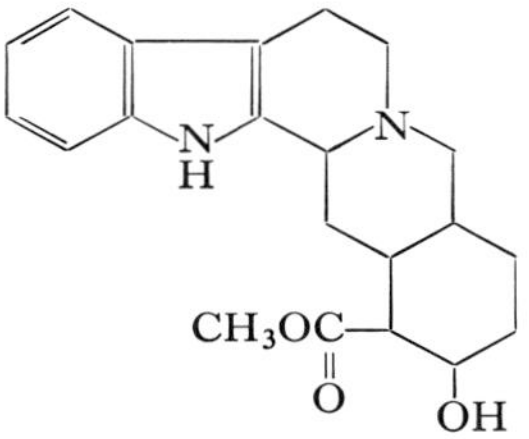

Yohimbine

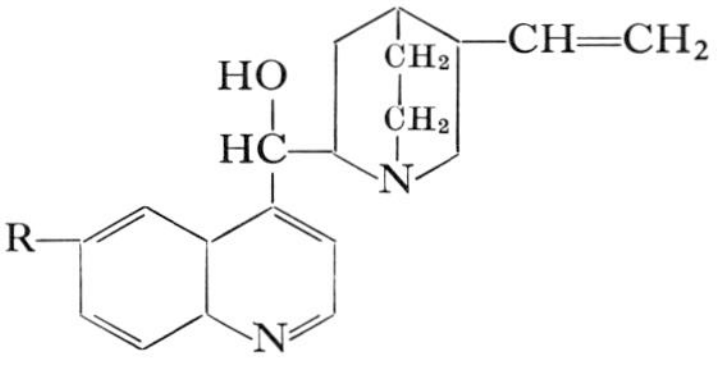

Cinchonine (R = H)
Quinine (R = OCH$_3$)

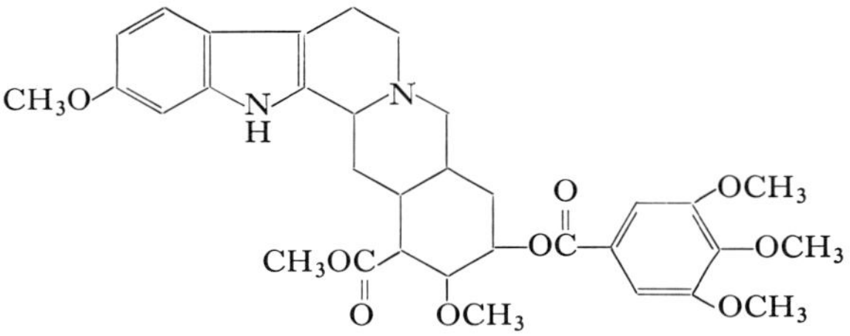

Reserpine

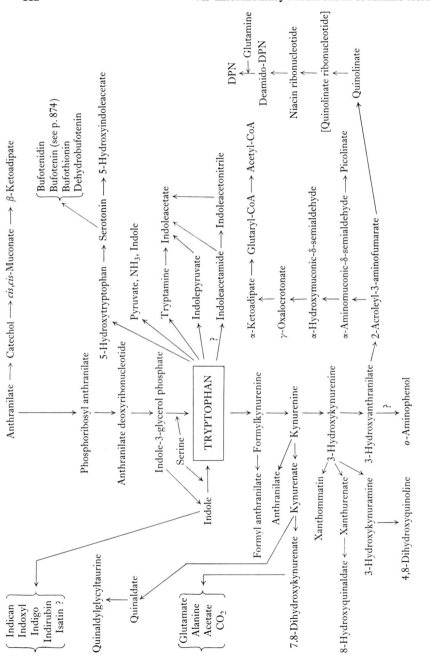

Summary scheme for the metabolism of tryptophan.

Tryptophan is also the precursor of psilocybine, a hallucinogenic compound present in fungi of the psilocybe group (2047). Studies on the biosynthesis of gramine in barley seedlings in which tryptophan-β-(H^3, C^{14}) was fed indicate that the methylene group of the tryptophan side chain remains intact during conversion of tryptophan to gramine (2048). A mechanism involving Schiff base formation between pyridoxal phosphate and tryptophan has been proposed to account for the conversion of tryptophan to 3-aminomethylindole (2049), and the formation of gramine from this compound takes place by stepwise methylation (2050, 2050a).

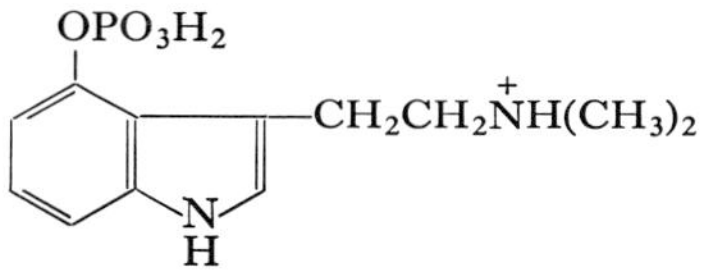

OPO$_3$H$_2$

$-CH_2CH_2\overset{+}{N}H(CH_3)_2$ $\qquad\qquad$ $-CH_2N(CH_3)_2$

N   N
H   H

Psilocybine 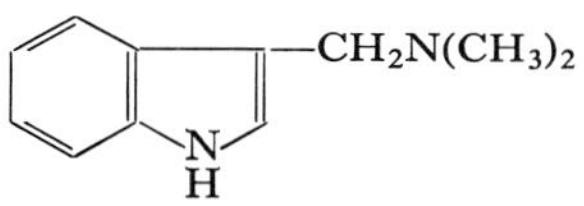 $\qquad\qquad\qquad\qquad\qquad$ Gramine

Tryptophan is a precursor of the ommochrome pigments which occur in the eye of insects and also in other species (2051–2056). The incorporation of tryptophan and kynurenine into xanthommatin (2057), ommatine, and rhodommatin has been demonstrated in studies on *Vanessa urticae* (small tortoise shell) larvae (2058). Tryptophan was also incorporated into xanthommatin of the eye of the blowfly, *Calliphora erythrocephala* (2059), and into the ommine of the eye of the silk moth, *Bombyx mori* (2060). An understanding of the enzymatic reactions that lead to the biosynthesis of these pigments is of interest in relation to genetic work on *Drosophila* and other insects in which eye color is used as a marker. The rapid conversion of 3-hydroxykynurenine to a pigment that exhibited the properties of xanthommatin by a rat liver preparation fortified with cytochrome c suggests that ommochrome pigments may occur in mammalian tissues (2061). Xanthommatin might be formed by condensation of 2 molecules of 3-hydroxykynurenine by a reaction involving oxidation and deamination. Rhodommatin is a glucosyl derivative of xanthommatin; a sulfate derivative is also known. Tyrosinase catalyzes the synthesis of xanthommatin and melanin from a mixture of 3-hydroxykynurenine and 3,4-dihydrophenylalanine. Since 3-hydroxykynurenine is not oxidized by tyrosinase, it appears that the quinone formed by oxidation of 3,4-dihydroxyphenylalanine (see p. 909) oxidizes 3-hydroxykynurenine to xanthommatin (2062).

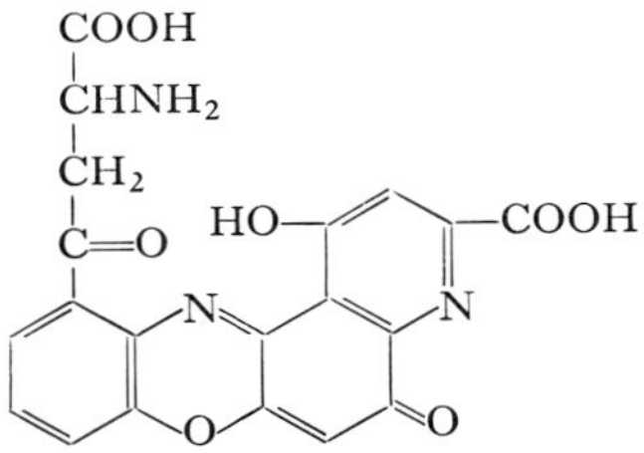

COOH
|
CHNH₂
|
CH₂
|
C=O   HO—⟨ring⟩—COOH

Xanthommatin

O. Phenylalanine and Tyrosine

Biosynthesis in Microorganisms

Studies on the biosynthesis of the aromatic amino acids in microorganisms began with the discovery of a series of mutants of *Escherichia coli, Neurospora crassa,* and *Aerobacter aerogenes* which required a mixture of four compounds for growth: phenylalanine, tyrosine, tryptophan, and *p*-aminobenzoic acid (2063). *p*-Hydroxybenzoic acid (2064) and a sixth factor were also required under certain conditions (2065). The pathway leading to the synthesis of the aromatic amino acids has been extensively investigated by Davis, Sprinson, and others (2066–2073). These investigations, which have led to considerable understanding of the intermediates and reactions involved in the biosynthesis of aromatic amino acids, represent an ingenious integration of information derived from the study of mutants and the application of enzymatic and isotopic labeling techniques. It is now known that four carbon atoms of the aromatic ring arise from D-erythrose-4-phosphate; the other two carbon atoms of the ring and the side chain come from phosphopyruvate.

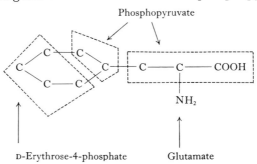

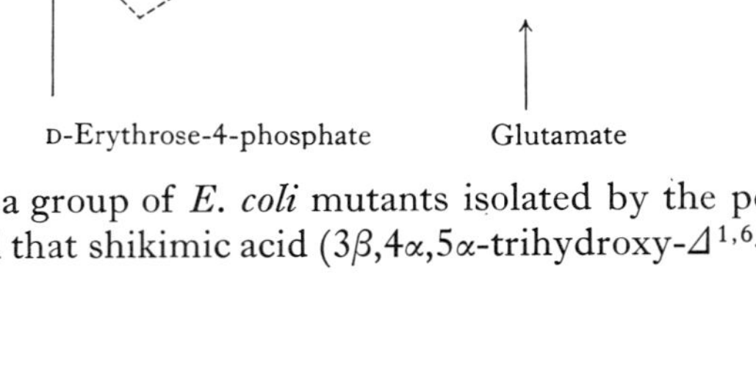

Phosphopyruvate

NH₂

D-Erythrose-4-phosphate   Glutamate

Studies on a group of *E. coli* mutants isolated by the penicillin technique showed that shikimic acid (3β,4α,5α-trihydroxy-$\Delta^{1,6}$-cyclohexene-

1-carboxylic acid) could substitute for the multiple requirement for growth of these organisms (2063). Shikimic acid had been known prior to these studies as a constituent of certain plants, and in fact the shikimic acid used in these investigations was isolated by H. O. L. Fischer from the Chinese star anise, *Illicium religiosum*. It was subsequently observed that certain mutants blocked in the biosynthesis of the aromatic amino acids accumulate shikimic acid, and that mutants blocked prior to shikimic acid accumulate 5-dehydroshikimic acid (2074). The previously unknown 5-dehydroquinic acid (5-keto-1,4α,3β-trihydroxycyclohexane-1-β-carboxylic acid) was isolated in crystalline form from the culture medium of a mutant of *E. coli*, and shown to be a precursor of 5-dehydroshikimic acid (2075, 2076). Quinic acid, previously known to be present in plants, could replace 5-dehydroquinic acid in supporting the growth of certain mutants of *A. aerogenes* (2075, 2077); however, quinic acid was not a growth factor for any of the *E. coli* mutants studied, nor was it accumulated by this organism, and an enzyme activity that interconverts quinic acid and 5-dehydroquinic acid (quinic dehydrogenase), although found in some organisms, was not present in others capable of catalyzing aromatic amino acid biosynthesis (2078, 2079).

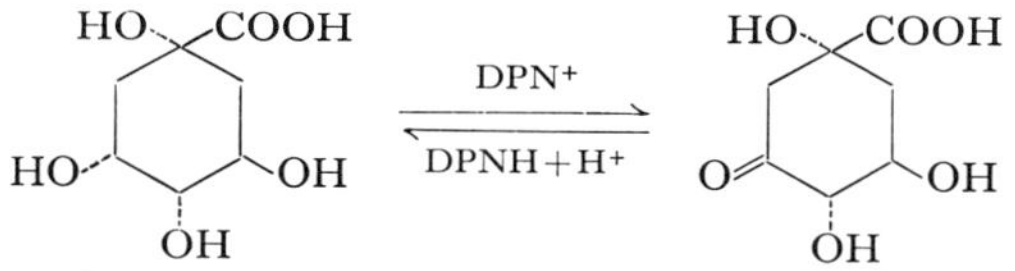

Quinic acid   5-Dehydroquinic acid

Quinic acid accumulates in large quantities in certain plants and can serve as a precursor of aromatic compounds via shikimic acid. In rose blooms the concentration of quinic acid increases until they are half-open, after which it decreases; conversion of quinate to shikimate has been observed in this plant (2080).

The enzyme that catalyzes the interconversion of 5-dehydroshikimic acid and shikimic acid (5-dehydroshikimic reductase) was obtained in moderately purified condition from *E. coli* and shown to catalyze the reaction given at the top of page 886 (2081).

Dehydroquinase, which catalyzes the interconversion of dehydroquinic and dehydroshikimic acids, was also partially purified and found to exhibit no apparent cofactor requirements (2078). These enzymes were found in all organisms examined that synthesize aromatic amino acids, and they were not present in the corresponding mutant organisms.

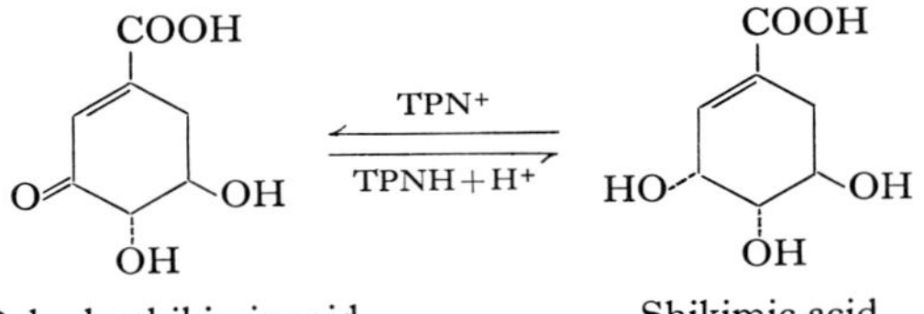

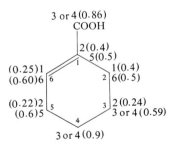

5-Dehydroshikimic acid   Shikimic acid

   The biosynthetic steps prior to 5-dehydroquinic acid were elucidated
by the isotopic investigations of Sprinson and collaborators (2073).
Earlier investigations on the incorporation of isotopic carbon from such
precursors as glucose, acetate, and pyruvate into the aromatic amino acids
suggested that the aromatic ring was synthesized from carbohydrate
precursors, and that the side chains of phenylalanine and tyrosine arose
from pyruvate or a similar compound (2082–2086). However, these
studies could not distinguish the precursors of the two sides of the
aromatic rings of phenylalanine and tyrosine because these are symmetrical. Sprinson *et al.* chose to investigate the biosynthesis of shikimic
acid in mutant microorganisms that accumulated this compound because
it could be chemically degraded in such a manner as to permit separate
determination of the radioactivity of each of its carbon atoms. In this
work, shikimic acid was isolated from bacterial cultures grown on glucose
labeled in various ways and on unlabeled glucose in the presence of
labeled bicarbonate, formate, acetate, or pyruvate. The last four compounds were not incorporated into shikimic acid. The diagram given
below summarizes the results of these experiments.

$$
\begin{array}{c}
3 \text{ or } 4\,(0.86) \\
\text{COOH}
\end{array}
$$

2(0.4)
5(0.5)

(0.25)1
(0.60)6

1(0.4)
6(0.5)

(0.22)2
(0.6)5

2(0.24)
3 or 4(0.59)

3 or 4(0.9)

Major contributions of glucose carbon atoms to shikimate (2073).

The numbers outside the parentheses indicate the position of the label in
glucose, and the numbers within parentheses give the fraction of that
carbon atom incorporated into the appropriate carbon atom of shikimic

acid (indicated on the diagram inside the ring). From these data it was concluded that the carboxyl group and carbon atoms 1 and 2 of shikimic are derived from a 3-carbon intermediate of glycolysis. This follows from the finding that carbon atom 2 of shikimic acid arises virtually entirely from carbon atoms 1 and 6 of glucose, that carbon atom 1 of shikimic acid is derived from carbon atoms 2 and 5 of glucose, and that the carboxyl group of shikimic acid comes from carbon atoms 3 and 4 of glucose. The contributions of carbon atoms 1 and 6 and those of carbon atoms 2 and 5 in these studies were about equal. The origin of the remaining carbon atoms of shikimic acid was also deduced from the observed labeling pattern, and it was concluded that this portion of the molecule arises from tetrose phosphate produced by the pentose phosphate pathway. The data also indicated that carbon atom 3 of the postulated 3-carbon intermediate is attached to carbon atom 1 of the tetrose. The finding that sonic extracts of a mutant blocked after dehydroshikimic acid could catalyze the formation of this compound from various carbohydrate precursors permitted further analysis of the pathway to shikimic acid (2087–2089). The attractive possibility that cyclization of the intact 7-carbon chain of sedoheptulose-1,7-diphosphate might lead to the formation of shikimic acid was considered and tested. Sedoheptulose-1,7-diphosphate was converted almost quantitatively to shikimic acid by extracts of an *E. coli* mutant (blocked after shikimic acid) in the presence of diphospho-pyridine nucleotide. Furthermore, it was found that carbon atoms 1, 2, and 3 of sedoheptulose-1,7-diphosphate were converted to the carboxyl group and carbon atoms 1 and 2 of shikimic acid; carbon atoms 4, 5, 6, and 7 of sedoheptulose gave rise to carbon atoms 3, 4, 5, and 6 of shikimic acid. However, a mechanism involving cyclization of sedoheptulose diphosphate, as illustrated below, had to be discarded when the data on

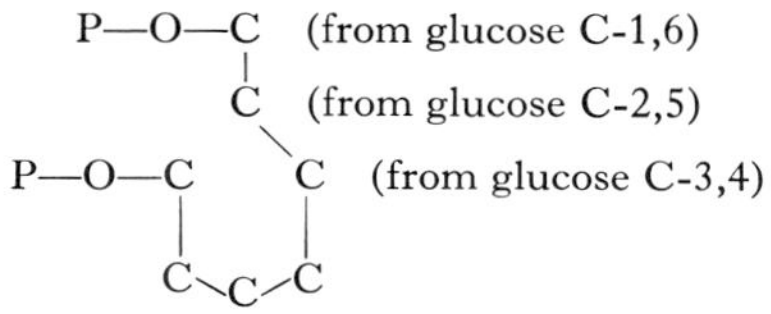

P—O—C   (from glucose C-1,6)
     C   (from glucose C-2,5)
P—O—C   C   (from glucose C-3,4)
    C—C—C

Sedoheptulose-1,7-diphosphate

COOH (from glucose C-3,4)
⟵ (from glucose C-2,5)
(from glucose C-1,6)

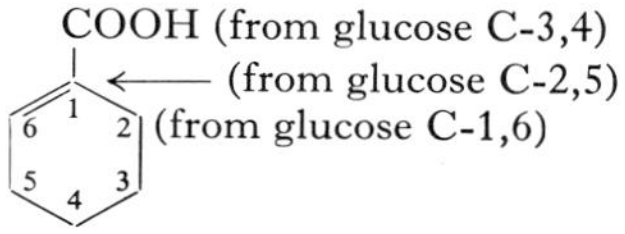

Shikimic acid

the synthesis of shikimic acid from glucose were considered. Thus, carbon atoms 1, 2, and 3 of sedoheptulose diphosphate are derived, respectively, from carbon atoms (1,6), (2,5), and (3,4), of glucose.

Therefore, if sedoheptulose diphosphate were an intermediate in the biosynthesis of shikimic acid from glucose, the carboxyl group of shikimic acid would have come from carbon atoms 1 and 6 of glucose, and carbon atom 2 of shikimic acid would have been derived from carbon atoms 3 and 4 of glucose; actually, as stated above, the reverse was found. These considerations indicate that the utilization of sedoheptulose-1,7-diphosphate for shikimic acid biosynthesis involves detachment of carbon atoms 1, 2, and 3 of sedoheptulose-1,7-diphosphate and inversion of this fragment prior to condensation with the 4-carbon unit. It thus appears that sedoheptulose diphosphate is cleaved by aldolase to D-erythrose-4-phosphate and triose phosphate. Enzymatic investigations demonstrated that the formation of shikimic acid involves condensation of phosphoenolpyruvate, derived from dihydroxyacetone phosphate, with D-erythrose-4-phosphate (2087, 2090). An enzyme was purified from *E. coli* that catalyzes this condensation to form 3-deoxy-D-*arabino*-heptulosonic acid-7-phosphate (2-keto-3-deoxy-D-*arabo*-heptonic acid-7-phosphate) and inorganic phosphate (2091):

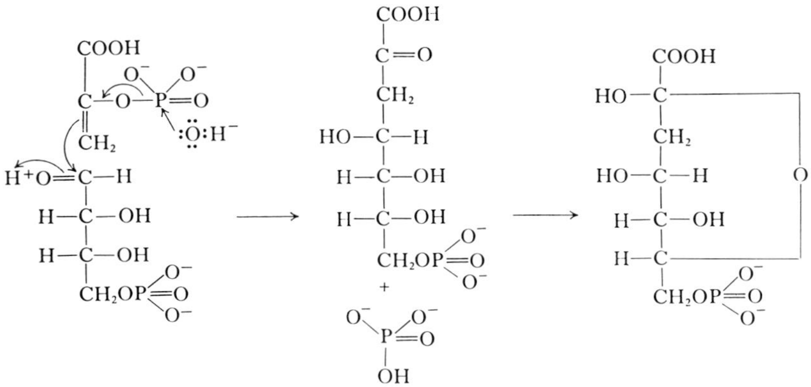

No cofactors are required for this reaction, which is not appreciably reversible. The product of the reaction catalyzed by 3-deoxy-D-*arabino*-heptulosonic acid-7-phosphate synthetase can be cleaved by a phosphatase to yield the corresponding heptonic acid (2092, 2093). The enzyme that catalyzes the transformation of 3-deoxy-D-*arabino*-heptulosonic acid-7-phosphate (2094) to dehydroquinic acid and orthophosphate was purified from *E. coli* and shown to require cobalt ions and diphosphopyridine nucleotide (2095). No evidence for intermediates could be obtained, and a hypothetical scheme (see structures in brackets in Scheme 25) was proposed to account for the dephosphorylation and cyclization steps, which seem to take place successively or simultaneously on the enzyme surface.

Certain mutant microorganisms blocked after shikimic acid accumulate shikimic acid-5-phosphate (2096, 2097) and another compound which was originally designated compound Z_1. Thus, enzyme preparations obtained from *E. coli* were found to catalyze a reaction between shikimic acid-5-phosphate and phosphoenolpyruvate to yield 3-enol-pyruvyl-shikimate-5-phosphate (2098). Dephosphorylation of this compound is inhibited by fluoride. The conversion of shikimic acid to shikimic acid-5-phosphate probably requires adenosine triphosphate, but this reaction does not seem to have been studied in detail at the enzymatic level. The pathway from phosphoenolpyruvate and D-erythrose-4-phosphate to 3-enol-pyruvylshikimate-5-phosphate may be represented as shown in Scheme 25.

Another intermediate, prephenic acid, was found to be accumulated by certain phenylalanine-requiring mutants (2099–2102); this very labile compound (2103) is readily converted on mild acidification to phenyl-pyruvic acid (2072, 2104). The observation that certain tyrosine-requiring mutants of *E. coli* also accumulate prephenic acid suggests that it is an intermediate in the biosynthesis of both phenylalanine and tyrosine (see Scheme 26).

Recent observations indicate that prephenic acid is formed from a precursor derived from 3-enol-pyruvylshikimate-5-phosphate (2105, 2106). The new intermediate (represented as compound X in Scheme 26), appears to be at the branching point in the biosynthesis of the aromatic amino acids; it can be converted to prephenic acid, anthranilic acid, and probably also to *p*-aminobenzoic and *p*-hydroxybenzoic acids. In these experiments, compound X was formed by incubating an extract of *A. aerogenes* with shikimic acid, diphosphopyridine nucleotide, adeno-sine triphosphate, magnesium chloride, and ribose 5-phosphate. The acidified reaction mixture was extracted with ether; after evaporation of the solvent, the extracted compound X was incubated with glutamine and a bacterial enzyme preparation. After incubation, evidence was obtained for the presence of anthranilic acid. Similar experiments indicate that compound X is converted in the presence of diphos-phopyridine nucleotide to a mixture of phenylpyruvic and *p*-hydroxy-

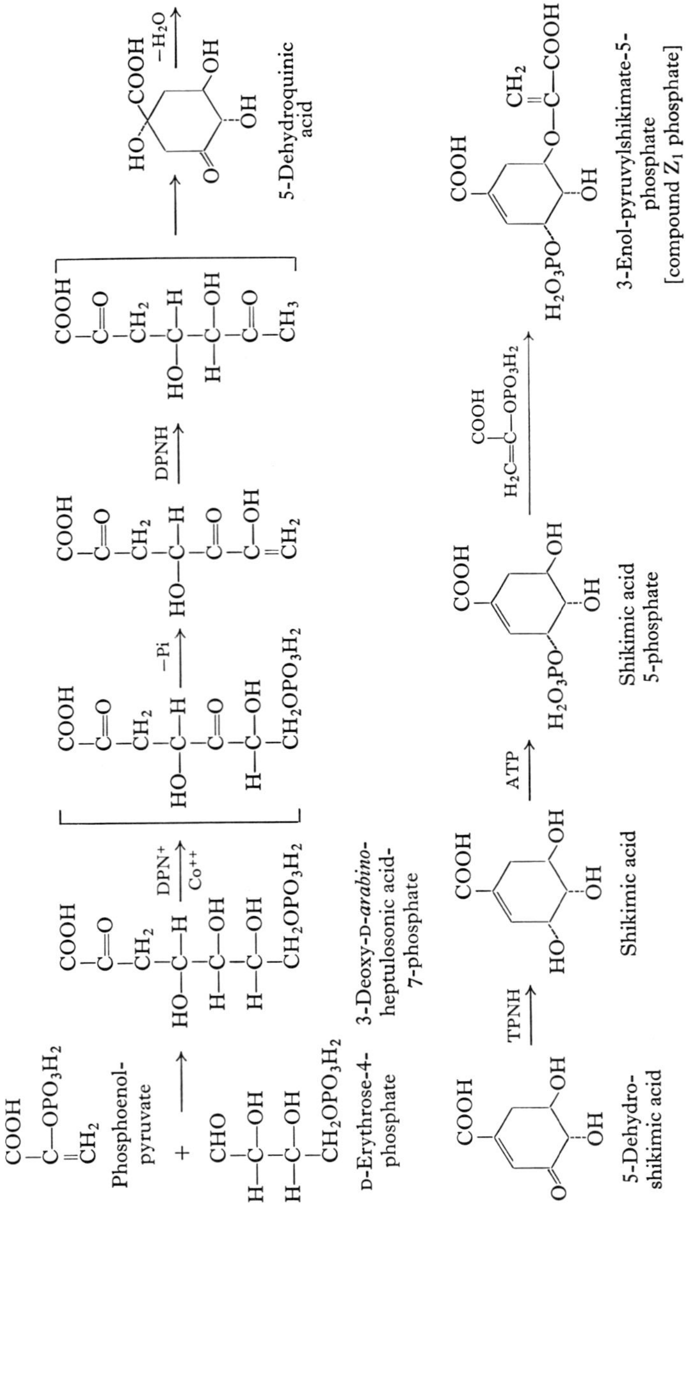

$$
\begin{array}{c}
\text{COOH} \\
|\\
\text{C}-\text{OPO}_3\text{H}_2 \\
\|\\
\text{CH}_2
\end{array}
\quad\text{Phosphoenol-}\atop\text{pyruvate}
$$

$$
+
$$

$$
\begin{array}{c}
\text{CHO} \\
|\\
\text{H}-\text{C}-\text{OH} \\
|\\
\text{H}-\text{C}-\text{OH} \\
|\\
\text{CH}_2\text{OPO}_3\text{H}_2
\end{array}
\quad\text{D-Erythrose-4-}\atop\text{phosphate}
$$

$$\xrightarrow[\text{Co}^{++}]{\text{DPN}^+}$$

$$
\begin{array}{c}
\text{COOH} \\
|\\
\text{C}=\text{O} \\
|\\
\text{CH}_2 \\
|\\
\text{HO}-\text{C}-\text{H} \\
|\\
\text{H}-\text{C}-\text{OH} \\
|\\
\text{H}-\text{C}-\text{OH} \\
|\\
\text{CH}_2\text{OPO}_3\text{H}_2
\end{array}
$$

3-Deoxy-D-*arabino*-heptulosonic acid-7-phosphate

$$\xrightarrow{-\text{Pi}}$$

$$
\left[
\begin{array}{c}
\text{COOH} \\
|\\
\text{C}=\text{O} \\
|\\
\text{CH}_2 \\
|\\
\text{HO}-\text{C}-\text{H} \\
|\\
\text{C}=\text{O} \\
|\\
\text{C}-\text{OH} \\
\|\\
\text{CH}_2
\end{array}
\right]
$$

$$\xrightarrow{\text{DPNH}}$$

$$
\begin{array}{c}
\text{COOH} \\
|\\
\text{C}=\text{O} \\
|\\
\text{CH}_2 \\
|\\
\text{HO}-\text{C}-\text{H} \\
|\\
\text{H}-\text{C}-\text{OH} \\
|\\
\text{C}=\text{O} \\
|\\
\text{CH}_3
\end{array}
$$

5-Dehydroquinic acid

$$\xrightarrow{-\text{H}_2\text{O}}$$

5-Dehydro-shikimic acid

$$\xrightarrow{\text{TPNH}}$$

Shikimic acid

$$\xrightarrow{\text{ATP}}$$

Shikimic acid 5-phosphate

$$\xrightarrow[\text{H}_2\text{C}=\text{C}-\text{OPO}_3\text{H}_2]{\text{COOH}}$$

3-Enol-pyruvylshikimate-5-phosphate
[compound Z_1 phosphate]

Scheme 25

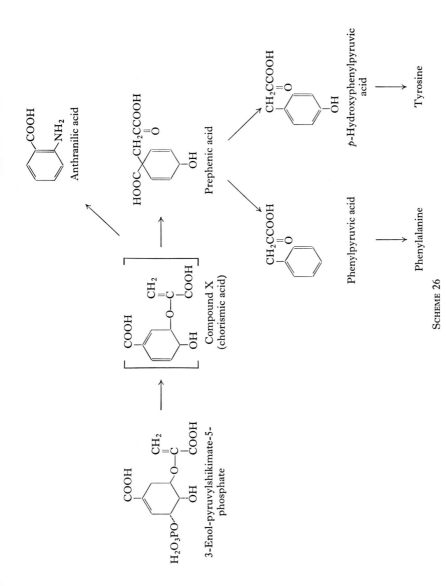

SCHEME 26

phenylpyruvic acids. Nonenzymatic formation of p-hydroxybenzoic acid was also observed. The structure of compound X and the mechanism of its formation from 3-enolpyruvylshikimate-5-phosphate, as well as its conversion to prephenic acid remain to be elucidated. The term chorismic acid (Greek, to branch) has been suggested for compound X (2106a, 2106b).

The conversion of prephenic acid to phenylpyruvic and p-hydroxy-phenylpyruvic acids has not yet been extensively investigated; mechanisms such as shown in Scheme 27 (2072) have been considered

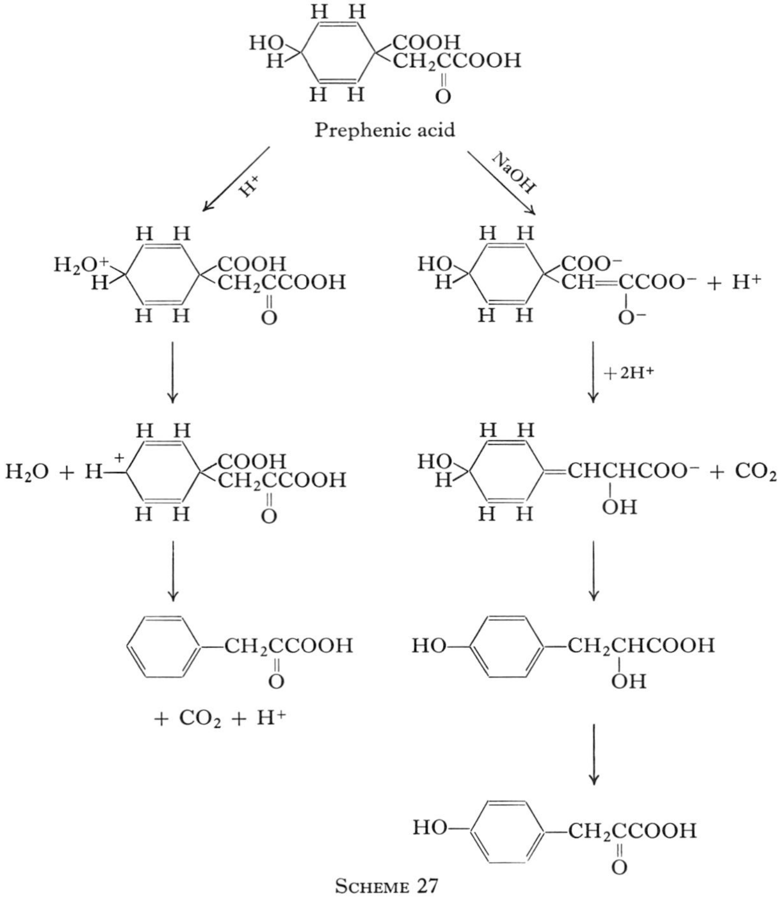

Prephenic acid

SCHEME 27

[see also (2103, 2107)]. According to Scheme 27, prephenic acid is a substrate for both pathways; it is conceivable that further studies will reveal intermediates (perhaps enzyme-bound) in these pathways. Extracts of a mutant of *E. coli* that was unable to catalyze the conversion of prephenic acid to phenylpyruvic acid were found to contain an enzymatic activity (prephenic dehydrogenase) capable of converting prephenic acid to *p*-hydroxyphenylpyruvic acid in the presence of diphosphopyridine nucleotide. The reaction involves dehydrogenation and decarboxylation; this enzymatic activity was not present in extracts of a tyrosine-requiring mutant (2107). The final steps in the biosynthesis of phenylalanine and tyrosine are transamination reactions (see p. 364).

The pathway described above also leads to the formation of other aromatic compounds. Thus, 5-dehydroshikimic acid is the precursor of protocatechuic acid, which is accumulated by a mutant of *Neurospora* (2108). Dehydroshikimic acid dehydrase was isolated from a wild strain of *Neurospora*, and evidence was obtained that conversion of 5-dehydroshikimic acid to protocatechuic acid takes place by a mechanism involving dehydration across carbon atoms 2 and 3 of the enol form of 5-dehydroshikimic acid with loss of the oxygen atom at carbon atom 3 (2109).

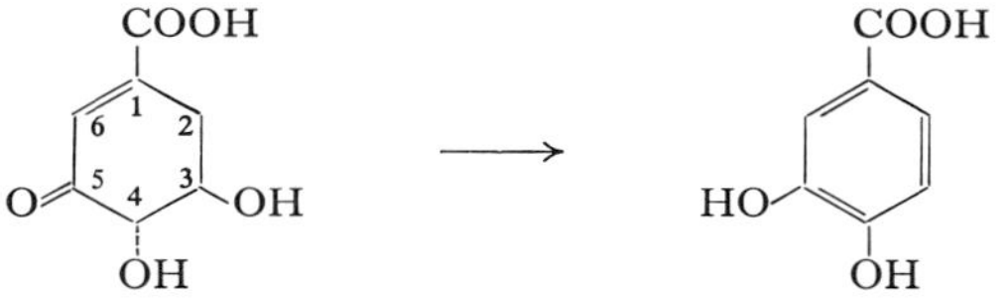

5-Dehydroshikimic acid   Protocatechuic acid

There is evidence that the pathway of aromatic amino acid biosynthesis is subject to end-product regulation similar to that observed in the biosynthesis of amino acids from aspartate. Two enzymes capable of catalyzing the synthesis of 3-deoxy-D-*arabino*-heptulosonic acid-7-phosphate have been separated from extracts of *E. coli* by ammonium sulfate fractionation. The activity of one of these is inhibited by L-phenylalanine and the other by L-tyrosine. Tyrosine represses synthesis of the tyrosine-sensitive synthetase and has no effect on the phenylalanine-sensitive enzyme. On the other hand, repression of the phenylalanine-sensitive synthetase was observed only in the presence of high concentrations of phenylalanine and under these conditions phenylalanine also repressed synthesis of the tyrosine-sensitive enzyme (2110).

Although the data suggest that these phenomena contribute to the regulation of phenylalanine and tyrosine biosynthesis, additional control mechanisms probably exist because the same pathway leads to the formation of tryptophan and other aromatic compounds. Evidence for a third synthetase that is repressible by L-tryptophan has been reported (2111). Tryptophan (as well as its 5-methyl derivative) can also affect the rate of its own biosynthesis by inhibiting the conversion of shikimic acid-5-phosphate to anthranilate (2112). Undoubtedly there are additional mechanisms for the control of aromatic amino acid biosynthesis.

Studies on the effects of antimetabolites (e.g., phenylserine) on the growth of *E. coli* suggested that phenylalanine might be converted to tyrosine in this organism (2113, 2114). Later work indicated that phenylserine inhibits the utilization of phenylalanine but not that of tyrosine (2115, 2116); it appears that the ability of exogenous tyrosine to reverse the toxicity of phenylserine may be due to a sparing effect of tyrosine on prephenic acid. Although it is conceivable that conversion of tyrosine to phenylalanine can occur by reversion to a common precursor, it seems unlikely that the aromatization reactions are reversible. On the other hand, certain microorganisms seem to exhibit phenylalanine hydroxylase activity (2118), and an adaptive organism has been obtained that contains substantial amounts of this enzyme (see p. 898). Thus, the "animal" pathway for tyrosine formation may be of biosynthetic significance in some bacteria. The possibility that α-phenylglycine is a precursor of phenylalanine has been considered (2117), but this does not seem to be supported by data.

Although aromatic amino acids cannot be synthesized *de novo* by higher animals, certain aromatization reactions have been demonstrated. Quinic acid can be converted to benzoic acid, and several other cyclic compounds are aromatized by preparation of liver and kidney (2119).

Metabolic Transformation in Animals

It has been known for many years that the metabolism of phenylalanine and tyrosine leads to formation of acetoacetic acid. The study of certain inborn errors of human metabolism (see Chapter VII) provided early clues to the intermediates in this pathway, and studies with isotopically labeled metabolites and with isolated enzyme preparations have clarified most of the reactions involved. The urinary excretion of homogentisic acid by alcaptonuric patients, the increase in homogentisic acid excretion in such patients after phenylalanine or tyrosine administration

(2120), and the formation of acetoacetate from homogentisic acid in liver perfusion systems (2121, 2122) indicated that homogentisic acid is an intermediate in phenylalanine metabolism. Other studies showed that intact normal animals oxidize homogentisic acid as well as phenylalanine and tyrosine to products that include acetoacetate. When very large quantities of phenylalanine and tyrosine were administered to animals, urinary excretion of homogentisic acid occurred (2123–2128).

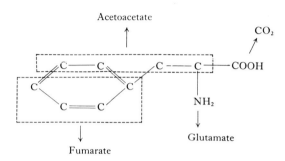

The conversion of phenylalanine to tyrosine, now known to be a quantitatively significant reaction in animals, was postulated as early as 1909 by Neubauer (2120). Embden and Baldes, in 1913, observed tyrosine formation from phenylalanine in liver perfusion experiments (2121). Administration of phenylalanine to a patient with tyrosinosis led to tyrosine excretion in the urine (2129). The sparing action of tyrosine on the dietary requirement for phenylalanine has been considered above (see p. 207). It has also been observed that ascorbic acid-deficient premature infants excrete tyrosine in response to phenylalanine administration (2130, 2131). All of these findings are consistent with conversion of phenylalanine to tyrosine. This reaction was unequivocally demonstrated in rats by isolation of deuterium-labeled tyrosine after similarly labeled phenylalanine had been given (2132). Studies with isotopic tyrosine indicate that the reverse reaction does not take place in animals (2133).

Evidence for the transformation of phenylalanine to a compound that appeared to be tyrosine was obtained in 1944 by Bernheim and Bernheim (2134) in studies with surviving liver slices.

The conversion of phenylalanine to tyrosine by slices and extracts of liver was demonstrated by Udenfriend and Cooper (2135), who found that liver preparations from the rat, guinea pig, rabbit, dog, human, and chicken exhibited phenylalanine hydroxylase activity, but no activity was found in lung, kidney, brain, and muscle of the rat. Hydroxylation required oxygen and diphosphopyridine nucleotide or triphosphopyridine nucleotide. The reaction was markedly inhibited by cyanide and azide, findings which led to the suggestion that the enzyme was a heavy metal oxidase. Addition of α,α'-dipyridyl inactivated the enzyme, and reactivation could be effected by dialysis and addition of ferrous ion (2136). Mitoma (2137) fractionated the rat liver phenylalanine-hydroxylase system into two protein components, one of which was very labile and present only in liver; the other was relatively stable and could be replaced by protein fractions obtained from other tissues. Considerable clarification of the mechanism of hydroxylation of phenylalanine has come from the studies of Kaufman (2138–2141). In his experiments, the two protein fractions necessary for hydroxylation of phenylalanine were further purified, and additional studies on the cofactors were carried out. Study of the stoichiometry of the reaction indicated that 1 molecule of oxygen is utilized and 1 molecule of reduced triphosphopyridine nucleotide is oxidized per molecule tyrosine formed. There is a lag period in the oxidation of phenylalanine which can be eliminated by preincubation of both protein fractions with triphosphopyridine nucleotide either in the presence or absence of oxygen. During purification of the enzyme, an unexpected loss of activity occurred, and it was found that activity could be restored by addition of a boiled extract prepared from rat liver. These findings led to the isolation of a cofactor that was required in addition to triphosphopyridine nucleotide for elimination of the lag period. Subsequent work showed that tetrahydrofolic acid can partially replace the natural cofactor, but that several tetrahydropteridines that lack a p-aminobenzoic acid residue are more active than tetrahydrofolate. The data indicate that the hydroxylation of phenylalanine is associated with oxidation of a tetrahydropteridine to an oxidized pteridine according to the following equation:

$$\text{Tetrahydropteridine} + \text{phenylalanine} + O_2 \rightarrow \text{tyrosine} + \text{oxidized pteridine} + H_2O$$

The intermediate oxidized pteridine is reduced to the original tetrahydropteridine in the presence of reduced triphosphopyridine nucleotide by the second enzyme fraction isolated (in Kaufman's experiments) from sheep liver. Evidence was obtained that the oxidation of tetrahydropteridines by molecular oxygen, hydrogen peroxide, 2,6-dichlorophenol-indophenol, and phenylalanine hydroxylase takes place by removal of hydrogen atoms from positions 7 and 8 of the pteridine ring to yield 5,6-dihydropteridine. It was subsequently found that sepia pteridine, a precursor of the red eye pigment of *Drosophila melanogaster*, is exceedingly active as a cofactor for phenylalanine hydroxylation; the K_m value for sepia pteridine for the hydroxylation reaction is $3\text{--}4 \times 10^{-6}$ M. This compound is about 25 times more active than tetrahydrofolate, and approximately as active as the compound isolated from rat liver (2140). The observation that the activity of both sepia pteridine and the purified rat liver cofactor in the phenylalanine hydroxylase system require dihydrofolic reductase gave further support to the belief that the natural cofactor is a dihydropteridine. However, in later work, it was found that biopterin (another pigment found in *Drosophila melanogaster*) after chemical reduction exhibited high activity (2141), and evidence was obtained that the primary oxidation product has a quinonoid rather than a 5,6-dihydro structure (2141a).

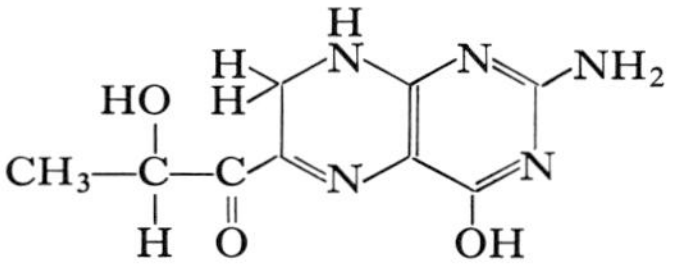

Sepia pteridine (2142)

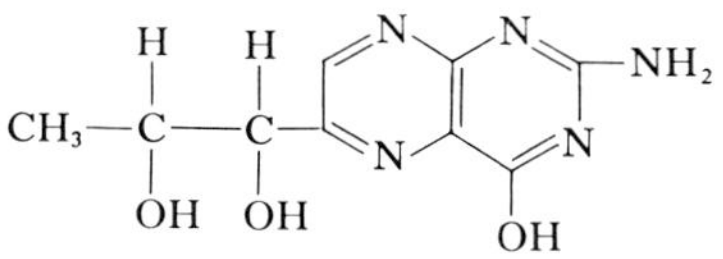

Biopterin

When amethopterin was administered to rats there was an increase in the blood concentration of phenylalanine, and the livers of rats treated with this compound exhibited only 25% of the phenylalanine hydroxylase activity of control animals. Aminopterin inhibits conversion of phenylalanine to tyrosine *in vitro*, but little inhibition occurs in the absence of reduced triphosphopyridine nucleotide, suggesting that the formation of tyrosine is less sensitive to aminopterin inhibition than the reduction of the oxidized pteridine to the tetrahydro form (2143).

Several phenylalanine hydroxylation systems (mammalian, bacterial, insect) have been shown in experiments with O^{18} to utilize atmospheric oxygen; thus, incorporation of O^{18} into the phenolic group of tyrosine was demonstrated indicating an oxygenase mechanism (2143a, 2143b).

Examination of a large number of aromatic compounds showed that only L-phenylalanine and 4-fluorophenylalanine were substrates for purified phenylalanine hydroxylase (2144). In addition, there is evidence (see below) that this enzyme oxidizes tryptophan to 5-hydroxytryptophan. The susceptibility of 4-fluorophenylalanine indicates that the fluorine atom can effectively replace hydrogen (see p. 232); the products of the reaction with 4-fluorophenylalanine, which is reported to proceed at about one sixth of the rate observed with phenylalanine, include L-tyrosine and fluoride ion.

Although there is evidence that tryptophan is hydroxylated by a specific enzyme (see p. 871), hepatic phenylalanine hydroxylase also catalyzes this reaction in the presence of relatively high concentrations of tryptophan. Glucocorticosteroid administration or feeding of L-tryptophan or L-phenylalanine to rats leads to an increase of both phenylalanine and tryptophan hydroxylation activities of the liver (2145). It was observed that both ascorbic acid and ferrous ions increase hepatic tryptophan hydroxylase activity *in vitro*, and that ethylenediaminetetraacetic acid decreased this activity, while these reagents do not affect phenylalanine hydroxylation. Phenylalanine hydroxylase activity is relatively low in newborn rats, but increases to a maximum in rats of about 50 to 60 days of age and then declines (2146).

Interest in phenylalanine hydroxylase has thus far been largely confined to preparations obtained from mammalian liver, but there is evidence that slices of beef adrenal medulla catalyze the hydroxylation of phenylalanine (2147); the latter activity could account for the small conversion of phenylalanine to tyrosine that has been observed in patients with phenylpyruvic oligophrenia (see p. 1067). Nutritional studies indicate that the conversion of phenylalanine to tyrosine also takes place in other animals (see p. 204); a report has appeared describing this reaction in the silkworm (2148). An inducible phenylalanine hydroxylase has been obtained from *Pseudomonas*. The enzyme is found when the organism is grown on media containing phenylalanine or tyrosine, but not asparagine. Data on the cofactors and mechanism are not yet available (2149). However, the existence of this enzyme and other studies on bacteria (see p. 894) suggest that some microorganisms use the "animal" pathway for tyrosine formation rather than (or in addition to) the prephenic acid pathway.

The conversion of phenylalanine to acetoacetate has been examined in investigations with isotopic carbon (2150–2155). In these elegant and conclusive studies, it was shown that (*a*) the α-carbon atom of phenylalanine becomes the carboxyl carbon atom of acetoacetate, (*b*) carbon atom 2 of the aromatic ring is a precursor of the carbonyl carbon atom of acetoacetate, and (*c*) carbon atom 1 or 3 of the ring is a precursor of the terminal carbon atom of acetoacetate. Other studies showed that the β-carbon atom of tyrosine becomes the α-carbon atom of acetoacetate (2151–2154). These findings indicate that there is a shift of the side chain during oxidation; such a shift was considered as early as 1901 (2156, 2157). One investigation showed that the degradation of tyrosine and phenylalanine resulted in the formation of two 4-carbon units, one of which was a ketone body, and the other malic acid or a similar compound (2155). These observations may be summarized and interpreted as shown in Scheme 28.

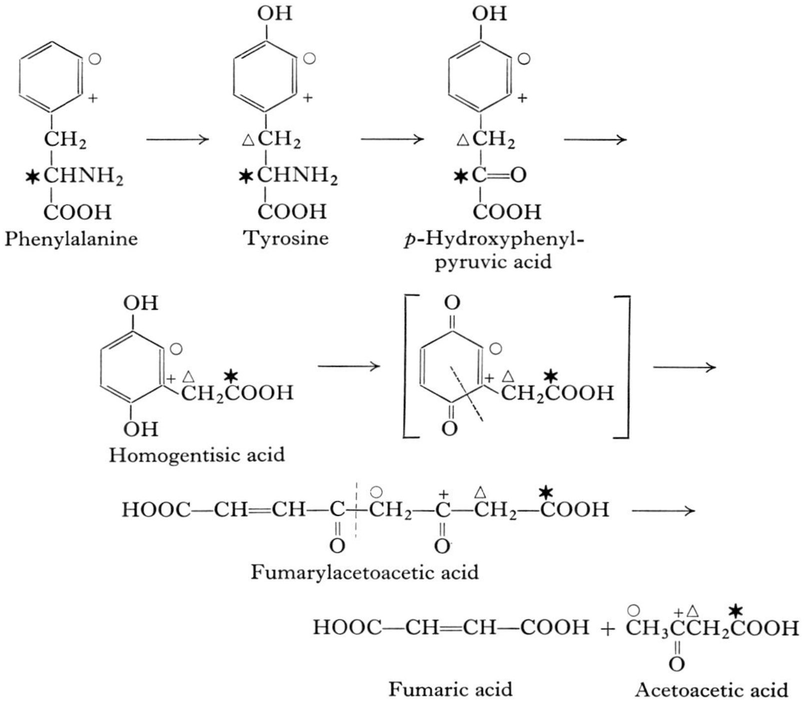

Phenylalanine

Tyrosine

p-Hydroxyphenyl-
pyruvic acid

Homogentisic acid

$$HOOC-CH=CH-C-CH_2-C-CH_2-COOH \longrightarrow$$

Fumarylacetoacetic acid

$$HOOC-CH=CH-COOH + CH_3CCH_2COOH$$

Fumaric acid   Acetoacetic acid

SCHEME 28

The sequence of reactions in Scheme 28 is supported by evidence derived from enzyme experiments, which revealed additional intermediates. The first step in the degradation of tyrosine is conversion to p-hydroxyphenylpyruvic acid by transamination, an obligatory step in tyrosine oxidation (2158–2160). It is of interest that the oxidation of tyrosine, studied earlier in liver brei preparations, was found not to be associated with the formation of ammonia. Furthermore, oxidation of both tyrosine and p-hydroxyphenylpyruvic acid to acetoacetate requires 4 atoms of oxygen. Partially purified preparations of glutamate-tyrosine transaminase have been obtained [(2161, 2162); see p. 363]; there is some uncertainty as to the specificity of this enzyme, but species differences may exist. It is possible that a single transaminase catalyzes reactions involving the aromatic amino acids. On the other hand, the purified glutamate-tyrosine transaminase isolated from rat liver (2162) exhibited no activity toward phenylalanine and tryptophan, and other studies (2163, 2164) led to the conclusion that separate glutamate-aromatic amino acid transaminases are present in rat liver. Glutamate-tyrosine transaminase is increased by injection of L-tyrosine, while administration of other amino acids does not produce this effect. Glutamate-tyrosine transaminase of the liver (but not of the kidney) is increased by administration of hydrocortisone, but phenylalanine-alanine transaminase is not increased by this hormone.

Although there is strong evidence that the metabolism of tyrosine proceeds via p-hydroxyphenylpyruvate, the possibility that 2,5-dihydroxyphenylalanine is a metabolite in mammals has been considered. 2,5-Dihydroxyphenylalanine is converted to homogentisic acid by alcaptonuric individuals (2165). A plausible pathway for this conversion is transamination to 2,5-dihydroxyphenylpyruvic acid followed by oxidative decarboxylation. However 2,5-dihydroxyphenylalanine was not oxidized by a system capable of oxidizing tyrosine, indicating that the free dihydroxy amino acid is not an obligatory intermediate in tyrosine oxidation (2159). The finding of 2,5-dihydroxyphenylpyruvic acid in the urine of patients with various collagen diseases (2166, 2167) has not been confirmed by studies in which a reliable procedure for the identification of this compound was employed (2168).

The conversion of p-hydroxyphenylpyruvic acid to homogentisic acid, catalyzed by p-hydroxyphenylpyruvic acid oxidase, involves the utilization of 1 mole of oxygen, hydroxylation of the aromatic ring, shift of the side chain, and the formation of carbon dioxide:

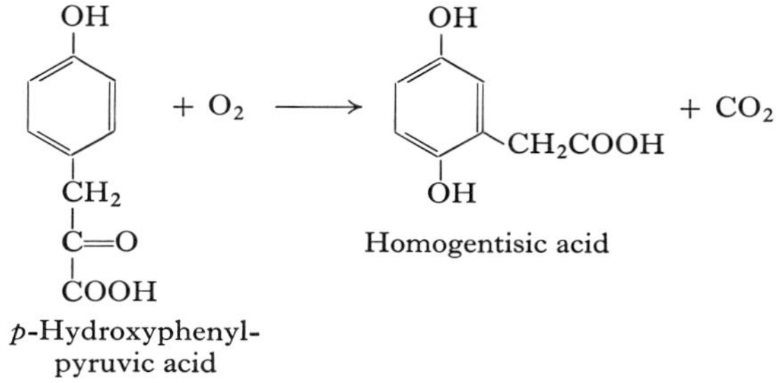

In an apparently analogous reaction, the oxidation of p-cresol to methyl-hydroquinone, a similar migration of the methyl group takes place and it has been postulated that the enzymatic formation of homogentisic acid occurs in a similar fashion (2169, 2170).

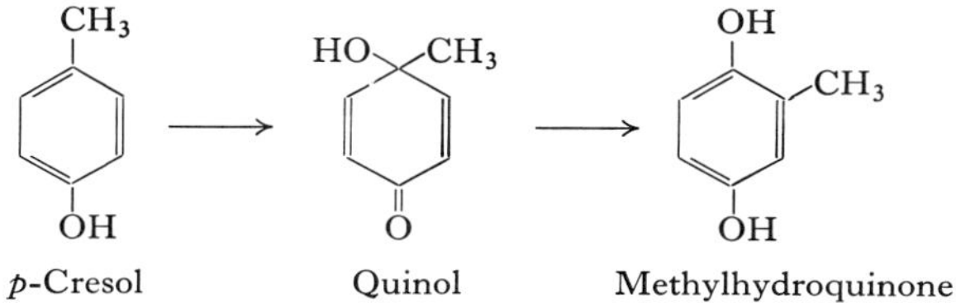

There is considerable evidence that ascorbic acid functions in the oxidation of p-hydroxyphenylpyruvate to homogentisate (2159, 2171–2177). A model nonenzymatic system consisting of ascorbic acid (or certain related compounds), ferrous ions, and oxygen promotes hydroxyl-ation of aromatic compounds (2178, 2179); hydroxylation, which is increased by ethylenediaminetetraacetate, was attributed to a product of ascorbic acid with hydrogen peroxide generated in the reaction mixture (see also (2180, 2181)). It has been observed that ascorbic acid-deficient animals fed large quantities of phenylalanine and tyrosine excrete p-hydroxyphenylpyruvate in the urine, and that excretion is reduced when ascorbic acid is administered (2124–2128). Similar observations have been made in human ascorbic acid deficiency (2182) and in premature infants (2130, 2131). Excretion of p-hydroxyphenylpyruvic acid as well as tyrosine was observed in the patient considered to have tyrosinosis (2129). Other observations suggest that folic acid functions in the oxida-tion of p-hydroxyphenylpyruvic acid; thus, folic acid prevented the urinary excretion of p-hydroxyphenylpyruvic acid produced by feeding tyrosine to scorbutic guinea pigs, but did not protect against scurvy (2183). Oxidation of tyrosine by liver preparations obtained from folic acid-deficient rats was activated by added folic acid (2184, 2185). However, other investigations of a similar nature have given contrary results; thus, folic acid did not affect excretion of p-hydroxyphenylpyruvic acid in scorbutic monkeys (2186, 2187), and *in vitro* addition of folic acid did not stimulate tyrosine oxidation catalyzed by rat liver homogenates (2159).

Although there is no evidence for free intermediates in the reaction catalyzed by p-hydroxyphenylpyruvate oxidase, it is conceivable that an enzyme-bound intermediate such as 2,5-dihydroxyphenylpyruvate might be formed. The report that 2,5-dihydroxyphenylpyruvate accumulates during oxidation of p-hydroxyphenylpyruvate (2174) has not been confirmed, and added 2,5-dihydroxyphenylpyruvate was found to be oxidized only slowly by p-hydroxyphenylpyruvate oxidase (2176). However, oxidation of 2,5-dihydroxyphenylpyruvate leads to the formation of homogentisic acid. The experimental results are consistent with formation of the enzyme-bound dihydroxy compound; failure of externally supplied 2,5-dihydroxyphenylpyruvate to be oxidized at the same rate as p-hydroxyphenylpyruvate might mean that the rate of formation of the enzyme-bound intermediate from the free dihydroxy α-keto acid is relatively slow.

Recent investigations in which p-hydroxyphenylpyruvate oxidase was purified and carefully studied have clarified certain aspects of the mechanism as well as earlier observations that suggested the participation of ascorbic acid and folic acid. These studies (2188–2191) showed that catalase, originally thought to be essential for the reaction, was required only under certain conditions, apparently to prevent inactivation of the enzyme. The enzyme is inhibited by excess substrate, and this can be prevented or reversed not only by ascorbic acid but also by isoascorbic acid, 2,6-dichlorophenolindophenol, coenzyme Q_{10}, and other compounds. The inhibition of p-hydroxyphenylpyruvic acid oxidase by excess substrate is such that the initial rate of reaction is unaffected, but inhibition appears after a lag period. Kinetic studies suggest formation of an inhibitor which accumulates during the course of the reaction. It has been postulated that the reducing agents act by protecting the enzyme, perhaps by maintaining an essential group of the enzyme in the reduced state. This type of inhibition (and protection against inhibition) can occur *in vivo*. Thus, administration of tyrosine to normal and scorbutic guinea pigs leads to excretion of p-hydroxyphenylpyruvate; this result is associated with decreased p-hydroxyphenylpyruvate oxidase. Administration of ascorbic acid, 2,6-dichlorophenolindophenol, and similar compounds prevents excretion of keto acid, as well as reduction of oxidase activity. Administration of tyrosine also increases the activity of liver glutamate-tyrosine transaminase, an effect that would tend to increase formation of p-hydroxyphenylpyruvic acid (2192, 2193). Injection of scorbutic guinea pigs with p-hydroxyphenylpyruvic acid produces markedly decreased liver p-hydroxyphenylpyruvic acid oxidase activity, and the enzyme can be reactivated *in vitro* by ascorbic acid or 2,6-dichlorophenolindophenol. It was also noted that scorbutic and normal guinea pigs exhibit approximately the same hepatic p-hydroxyphenyl-pyruvic acid oxidase activity (2194). The function of folic acid in this reaction appears to be similar to that of ascorbic acid and related com-pounds. Thus, administration of folic acid protects the liver p-hydroxy-phenylpyruvic acid oxidase of scorbutic guinea pigs from inhibition, and therefore prevents urinary excretion of p-hydroxyphenylpyruvate (2195). In summary, the available data indicate that neither ascorbic acid nor folic acid functions as a coenzyme in the formation of homogentisic acid; the exact nature of their action in preventing inhibition of the enzyme is not yet known.

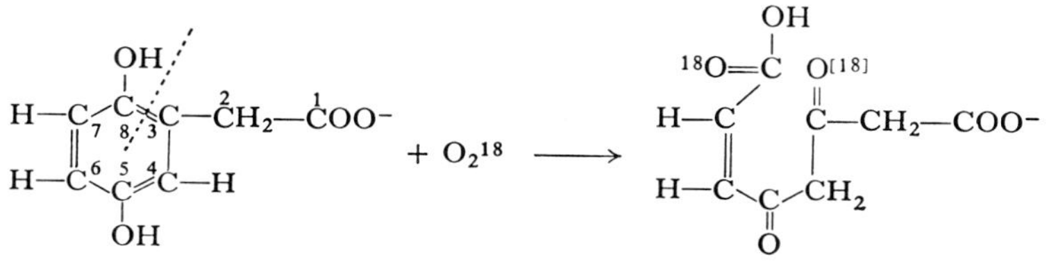

The oxidation of homogentisic acid has been studied in a number of *in vitro* systems (2196–2203). Homogentisic acid oxidase (homogentisi-case), which has been found in liver and kidney as well as in a strain of *Pseudomonas*, is markedly inhibited by α,α'-dipyridyl. A purified preparation from beef liver lost activity on dialysis and could be re-activated by addition of ferrous ions (2203). The observations that activity is increased by ascorbic acid and glutathione suggest that these agents act by maintaining ferrous ions and sulfhydryl groups, respectively. The reaction catalyzed by the enzyme involves the utilization of 1 mole of oxygen and the formation of maleylacetoacetate, which undergoes additional transformation as described below. When the oxidation of homogentisic acid was carried out in the presence of O_2^{18}, 1 atom of isotopic oxygen was found in the terminal carboxyl group of maleyl-acetoacetate; the carbonyl oxygen at position 3 was unlabeled. When the reaction was carried out in H_2O^{18}, both carbonyl oxygen atoms of the product contained isotopic oxygen. These observations are consistent with a mechanism involving incorporation of atmospheric oxygen into the 3-carbonyl oxygen atom and the terminal carboxyl group of maleyl-acetoacetate. Since isotopic oxygen was incorporated into both carbonyl oxygen atoms of maleylacetoacetate when the reaction was carried out in labeled water, it may be concluded that there is nonenzymatic exchange of the 3-carbonyl oxygen with oxygen of the medium (2204).

It has long been believed that the defect in congenital alcaptonuria is a lack of the enzyme responsible for oxidation of homogentisic acid, and relatively recent studies in which tissues of patients with alcaptonuria were examined have confirmed this hypothesis. Alcaptonuria is considered in Chapter VII.

The oxidation of homogentisic acid by horseradish peroxidase in the presence of sulfhydryl compounds leads to formation of thioether derivatives of homogentisic acid and sulfhydryl compounds (2205). The available data are consistent with the following postulated mechanism:

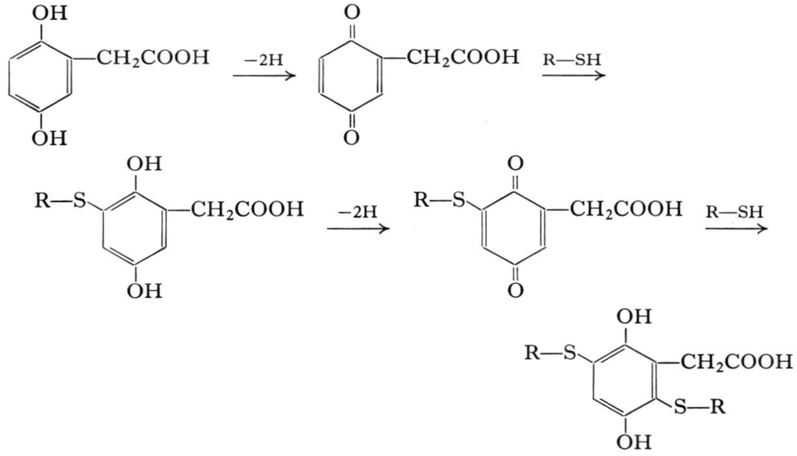

The products formed are similar to those obtained in the spontaneous reaction of sulfhydryl reagents with benzoquinoneacetic acid. Reactions of this type could lead to formation of the connective tissue pigment deposited in patients with ochronosis due to alcaptonuria or exposure to compounds such as phenol and resorcinol.

The conversion of homogentisic acid to fumarylacetoacetate was first demonstrated by Ravdin and Crandall (2196). Subsequent studies by Knox and Edwards (2202, 2207, 2208) showed that the initial product of cleavage was actually maleylacetoacetic acid, and that this compound was converted to the corresponding *trans*-isomer by an enzyme (maleyl-acetoacetate isomerase) that requires glutathione as a coenzyme. The recognition of maleylacetoacetate was facilitated by its spectro-photometric behavior. Maleylacetoacetate exhibits an absorbancy maximum at pH 13 at 326 mμ in contrast to fumarylacetoacetate which exhibits a maximum at 349 mμ under these conditions. Maleylaceto-acetate shows little absorbancy in strong acid, while fumarylacetoacetate exhibits high absorbancy at 315 mμ. Homogentisic acid oxidase has been used for the determination of homogentisic acid in human blood plasma and urine, by following the increase of the characteristic absorbancy of maleylacetoacetate (2206). In addition to glutathione, the isomerase is activated by γ-glutamylcysteine, cysteinylglycine, cysteine, and to some extent by other compounds. Glutathione also catalyzes *cis-trans*

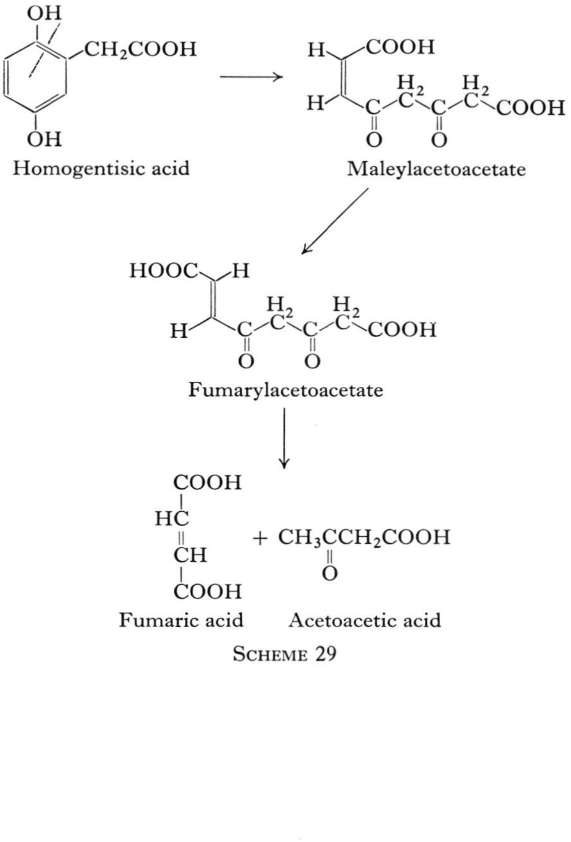

Homogentisic acid   Maleylacetoacetate

Fumarylacetoacetate

Fumaric acid   Acetoacetic acid

SCHEME 29

isomerization of maleylacetoacetate as well as other compounds in the absence of enzyme (2208).

The hydrolytic cleavage of fumarylacetoacetate to fumarate and acetoacetate is catalyzed by a soluble liver enzyme (2196). It is of interest that this enzyme was discovered several years prior to the discovery of its natural substrate; thus, an enzyme designated acylpyruvase had been obtained from liver and shown to hydrolyze α,γ-diketovaleric acid, a series of other α,γ-diketo acids (acylpyruvic acids) (2209), and β,δ-diketohexanoic acid (2210, 2211). The enzyme does not hydrolyze maleylacetoacetate. The oxidation of homogentisic acid and the subsequent enzymatic steps may be represented as shown in Scheme 29.

The oxidation of gentisic acid by bacteria proceeds by a pathway analogous to that of homogentisic acid in animal tissues (2212–2215). Thus, maleylpyruvic and fumarylpyruvic acids have been demonstrated as products of gentisic acid cleavage, and enzymes that catalyze isomerization of maleylpyruvate and hydrolysis of fumarylpyruvate have been isolated from a pseudomonad adapted to growth on gentisic acid. The isomerase of bacterial origin is considerably more active toward

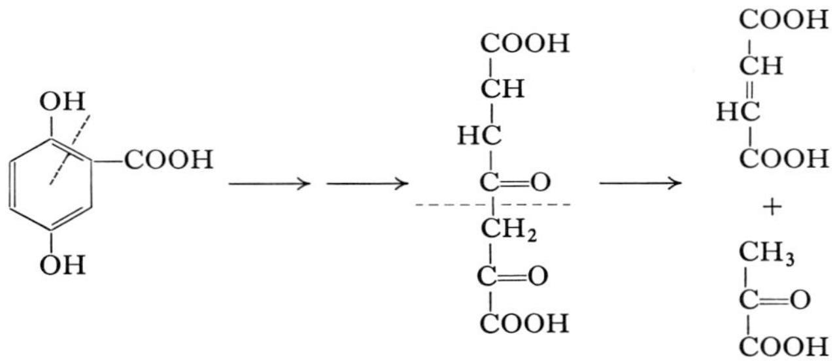

maleylpyruvate than maleylacetoacetate, and the bacterial acylpyruvase is much more active toward fumarylpyruvate than fumarylacetoacetate. On the other hand, the isomerase from rat liver acts upon maleylpyruvate and maleylacetoacetate at about equal rates; as expected from earlier studies (2209–2211), rat liver acylpyruvase cleaves both fumarylpyruvate and fumarylacetoacetate.

Gentisic acid, which has been found in the urine of patients with alcaptonuria and in scorbutic guinea pigs, is formed from homogentisic acid probably via 2,5-dihydroxyphenylglycolate, 2,5-dihydroxyphenylglyoxylate, and gentisic aldehyde (2211a).

An enzyme activity has been found in mammalian kidney and in several other animal tissues that catalyzes the keto-enol tautomerization of phenylpyruvate and other aromatic α-keto acids. The enzyme has been partially purified from hog kidney (2216). The reaction was followed by incubation of the α-keto acid with the enzyme in the presence of borate which reacts with the enol tautomer to yield an enol-borate complex exhibiting high characteristic ultraviolet absorbancy in the region of 300 mμ. Although phenylpyruvate and other α-keto acids of this type enolize spontaneously, the reaction proceeds more rapidly in the presence of enzyme (tautomerase). The enzyme has practical usefulness in the determination of these α-keto acids; its physiological significance is not yet clear.

In mammals, conversion of phenylalanine to tyrosine followed by subsequent metabolism as described above is a pathway of major quantitative significance. However, there is good evidence that phenylalanine is metabolized by a pathway in which transamination to phenylpyruvic acid is the initial step. Phenylacetyl-L-glutamine is a constituent of normal human urine (2217, 2218), and the excretion of this compound is greatly augmented by ingestion of phenylacetic acid (2219–2225). Virtually all of a 20-g. dose of phenylacetate is excreted in the form of phenylacetyl-L-glutamine. Administration of phenylacetate to all animals studied (including the dog, rat, rabbit, monkey, horse, sheep, and cat) leads to urinary excretion of phenylacetylglycine (phenylaceturic acid). Man and possibly also the chimpanzee excrete phenylacetyl-L-glutamine. The available data indicate the following reactions:

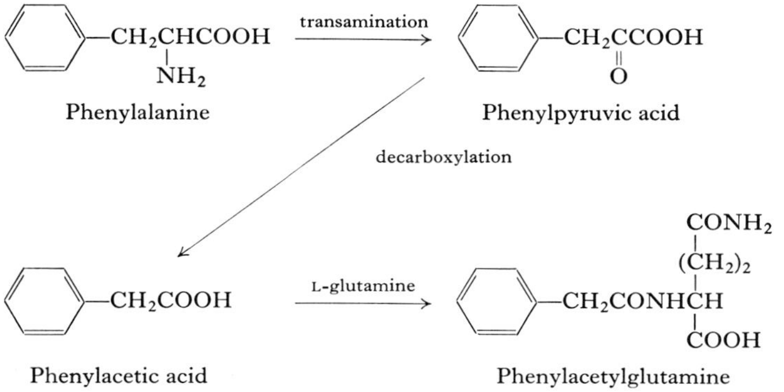

This pathway is exaggerated in patients with phenylpyruvic oligophrenia (Chapter VII). The conversion of labeled phenylalanine to phenylacetyl-L-glutamine has been demonstrated in experiments with human liver preparations (2226), and enzymatic studies have shown that phenyl-acetyl-coenzyme A and phenylacetyl adenylate are intermediates in the synthesis of phenylacetyl-L-glutamine from phenylacetic acid and glutamine (see p. 442).

Another pathway of phenylalanine metabolism is conversion to hippuric acid (benzoylglycine). Although the hippuric acid excreted by man and other mammals arises mainly from dietary benzoate (see p. 441), its presence in the urine of fasted humans (2218) and studies with labeled benzoic acid (2227) and labeled phenylalanine (2228–2231) indicate that some urinary hippuric acid is derived from phenylalanine. Additional evidence for this pathway comes from experiments in which labeled benzoic acid was fed to animals; the urinary hippuric acid subsequently isolated exhibited an appreciable decrease in specific activity, indicating dilution of endogenously synthesized benzoate. A possible pathway for the synthesis of hippuric acid from phenylalanine is conversion of phenylalanine to phenylpyruvate followed by oxidative cleavage to oxalate and benzaldehyde and oxidation of the latter to benzoate. Non-enzymatic cleavage of p-hydroxyphenylpyruvate and phenylpyruvate to the corresponding aldehydes and oxalate is well known [see Pitt (2232)]; this reaction takes place rapidly at values of pH greater than 8; cleavage might also be enzymatically catalyzed.

Phenylpyruvate is also the precursor of o-hydroxyphenylacetate, which is found in normal human urine and whose excretion is greatly increased in phenylketonuria (see p. 1069). Enzymatic activity capable of converting phenylpyruvate to o-hydroxyphenylacetate has been found in rat and guinea pig liver and kidney (2232a). The reaction requires atmospheric oxygen and a reducing substance (e.g., ascorbate). The enzyme activity was found to be irreversibly inhibited by substrate in a manner similar to that observed in studies on the oxidation of p-hydroxyphenylpyruvate. It is possible that the latter compound and phenylpyruvate are oxidized by the same enzyme.

Suspensions of a *Proteus* species have been reported to produce phenyl-acetaldehyde when shaken aerobically with glucose and phenylalanine (2233). Phenylacetaldehyde, which was identified as its 2,4-dinitro-phenylhydrazone, inhibited the oxidation of glucose. Although this compound might be formed by decarboxylation of phenylpyruvic acid in a manner analogous to the decarboxylation of α-keto acids by yeast decarboxylase, definitive enzymatic studies have not yet been carried out.

Epinephrine and Related Compounds

Gurin and Delluva (2234) showed that in the rat, deuterium- or tritium-labeled phenylalanine is converted to adrenal epinephrine. Their evidence indicated that oxidation of the ring occurs with the original side chain (except for the carboxyl group) intact. Subsequent studies (2235, 2236) showed that both labeled phenylalanine and tyrosine are precursors of epinephrine, that 3,4-dihydroxyphenylalanine (dopa), as well as tyrosine and phenylalanine, are precursors of epinephrine (adrenaline) and norepinephrine (noradrenaline, arterenol) in the rat, while tyramine and phenylethylamine are not. 3,4-Dihydroxyphenylethylamine (dopamine) was shown by an isotopic study to be a precursor of epinephrine in the intact rat (2237). The formation of epinephrine and norepinephrine from tyrosine, 3,4-dihydroxyphenylalanine, and 3,4-dihydroxyphenylethylamine was demonstrated in slices and homogenates of the adrenal (2238, 2239). Although the *erythro* (and to a lesser extent, the *threo*) diastereoisomer of 3,4-dihydroxyphenylserine is decarboxylated by kidney preparations to norepinephrine (2240), no evidence for the occurrence or formation of this compound in animals appears to have been reported, and it is not converted to norepinephrine in systems that catalyze the conversion of 3,4-dihydroxyphenylalanine to 3,4-dihydroxyphenylethylamine and norepinephrine (2241). The available information therefore indicates the pathway for the formation of norepinephrine and epinephrine given in Scheme 30.

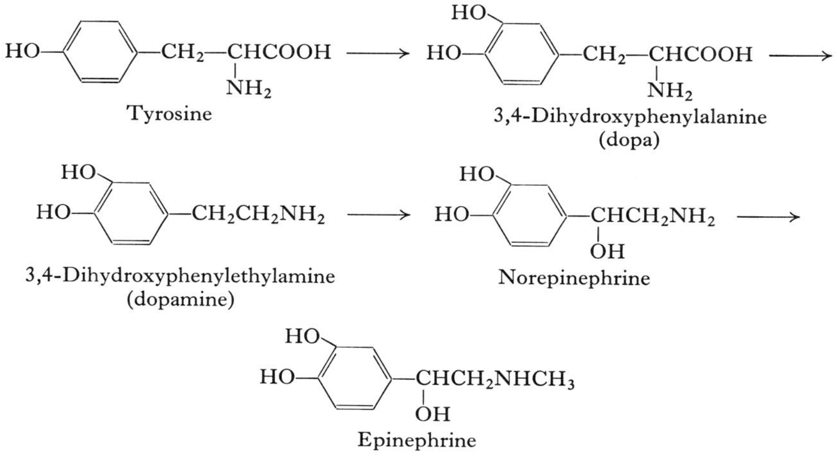

Tyrosine

3,4-Dihydroxyphenylalanine
(dopa)

3,4-Dihydroxyphenylethylamine
(dopamine)

Norepinephrine

Epinephrine
SCHEME 30

Although tyrosinase catalyzes the oxidation of tyrosine to 3,4-di-hydroxyphenylalanine in melanin-forming cells (see p. 919), this reaction in brain, adrenal medulla, and sympathetically innervated tissues is catalyzed by a specific hydroxylase. The enzyme has been obtained from adrenal medulla and brain; it requires a tetrahydropteridine cofactor and the mechanism may be analogous to the hydroxylation of phenylalanine to tyrosine (2241a).

The decarboxylation of 3,4-dihydroxyphenylalanine is catalyzed by preparations of many plant and animal tissues. The enzyme is present in kidney and adrenal, and as discussed elsewhere (see p. 327), there is evidence that the same enzyme decarboxylates 5-hydroxytryptophan. β-Hydroxylation of 3,4-dihydroxyphenylethylamine has been observed in several tissue preparations (2242, 2243), and an enzyme (dopamine-β-oxidase; dopamine-β-hydroxylase) that catalyzes this reaction was solubilized from bovine adrenal medulla particles and partially purified. Ascorbate, fumarate, and molecular oxygen are required for the reaction, which may be represented as follows (2244):

$$\text{3,4-Dihydroxyphenylethylamine} + \text{ascorbate} + O_2 \xrightarrow{\text{fumarate}}$$
$$\text{norepinephrine} + \text{dehydroascorbate} + H_2O$$

In addition to fumarate, certain other dicarboxylic acids (e.g., α-keto-glutarate, malate) stimulate the reaction. Adenosine triphosphate and glucose dehydrogenase or catalase also activate, and it appears that this effect is due to protection of the enzyme rather than to an action related to the mechanism of hydroxylation (2245). There is evidence that enzyme sulfhydryl groups are involved in the activity of the enzyme (2246). Studies with tritium- and carbon-labeled 3,4-dihydroxyphenylethylamine demonstrated that only one of the two hydrogen atoms on the β-carbon atom is removed in the hydroxylation reaction, and indicated that an α,β-dehydrogenation-hydration mechanism is not involved (2247, 2248). The specificity of the β-hydroxylase is low (2245, 2249, 2250); thus, it catalyzes hydroxylation of phenylethylamine to β-phenylaminoethanol, p-tyramine to norsynephrine, epinine to epinephrine, 3-methoxy-4-hydroxyphenylethylamine to 3-methoxynorepinephrine, amphetamine

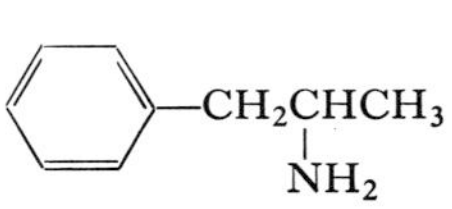

$$\text{⬡—CH}_2\text{CHCH}_3$$
$$\text{NH}_2$$

Amphetamine

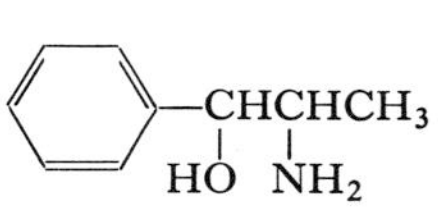

$$\text{⬡—CHCHCH}_3$$
$$\text{HO NH}_2$$

Norephedrine

to norephedrine, *p*-hydroxyamphetamine to *p*-hydroxynorephedrine, as well as other reactions of this type.

It is of interest that norepinephrine (as well as 5-hydroxytryptamine) is present in the banana plant and may also exist in other plant tissues (2251, 2252). Homogenates of various tissues of the banana plant catalyze the conversion of 3,4-dihydroxyphenylethylamine to norepinephrine in the presence of oxygen; cofactor requirements for the enzyme of the banana plant have not been demonstrated.

Evidence that the methyl group of methionine is incorporated into epinephrine of the adrenal gland was obtained in experiments on intact animals (see p. 774); *S*-adenosylmethionine is the methyl donor. An enzyme (phenylaminoethanol-*N*-methyltransferase) has been isolated from the adrenal medulla that catalyzes the *N*-methylation of a number of phenylaminoethanol derivatives including norepinephrine (1225, 2239); it was not active with phenylethylamine derivatives.

The physiological functions and metabolism of the catecholamines and related derivatives have been considered in recent reviews (2253, 2254). The major pathway of metabolism of circulating epinephrine and norepinephrine in man and other mammals involves inactivation by methylation of the 3-hydroxyl groups of these compounds to yield metanephrine and normetanephrine, respectively. In sympathetically innervated tissues monoamine oxidase attacks both the catecholamines and their *O*-methyl derivatives.

Epinephrine is oxidized *in vitro* by cytochrome oxidase, ferritin, and other iron-containing compounds to the corresponding *o*-quinone, which cyclizes to *N*-methylindolequinone (adrenochrome) (2255, 2256):

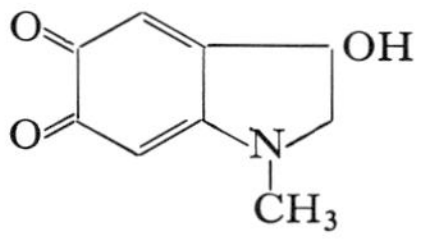

At the present time this transformation is not believed to be of major physiological significance, and there is no clear-cut evidence for its occurrence *in vivo*.

The administration of 3,4-dihydroxyphenylalanine to man and the rat leads to urinary excretion of homoprotocatechuic and homovanillic acids, and the latter compound has been identified as a normal constituent of human and rat urines (2257). Plausible pathways for the formation of these compounds are given here and in Scheme 31.

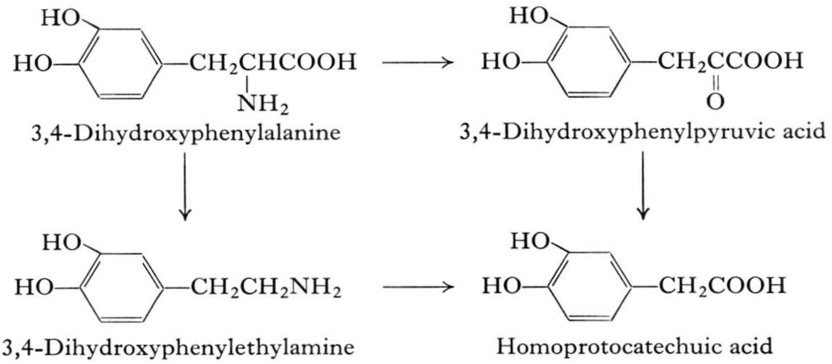

HO—⟨ ⟩—CH$_2$CHCOOH   ⟶   HO—⟨ ⟩—CH$_2$CCOOH

3,4-Dihydroxyphenylalanine   3,4-Dihydroxyphenylpyruvic acid

HO—⟨ ⟩—CH$_2$CH$_2$NH$_2$ ⟶   HO—⟨ ⟩—CH$_2$COOH

3,4-Dihydroxyphenylethylamine   Homoprotocatechuic acid

In rats, 3,4-dihydroxyphenylethylamine is oxidatively deaminated to homoprotocatechuic acid and methylated to 3-methoxytyramine (2258, 2259). Homovanillic acid could arise by oxidation of the latter compound or by methylation of homoprotocatechuic acid (see Scheme 31).

There is evidence for conversion of 3,4-dihydroxyphenylethylamine to 3-methoxy-4-hydroxyphenylethanol (2260), and to 2,4,5-trihydroxy-phenylethylamine (2261, 2270a) and its 5-O-methyl derivative (2262). 3-Methoxy-4-hydroxyphenylethanol might arise by reduction of the aldehyde formed in the oxidation of the corresponding amine, or by methylation of the alcohol formed in a similar manner from 3,4-dihydroxy-phenylethylamine. The conversion of 3,4-dihydroxyphenylethylamine to a dimethoxy derivative has been observed in liver homogenates, and urinary excretion of 3,4-dimethoxyphenylacetate was observed after administration of 3,4-dihydroxyphenylethylamine to patients with schizophrenia (control subjects were not studied) (2263).

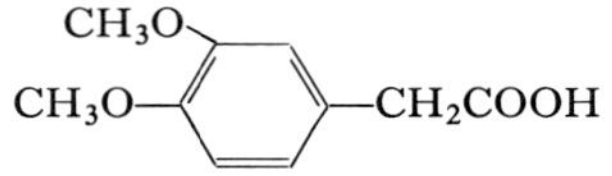

CH$_3$O—⟨ ⟩—CH$_2$COOH

3,4-Dimethoxyphenylacetic acid

N-Methyl-3,4-dihydroxyphenylethylamine (epinine) occurs in the parotid gland of the South American toad, *Bufo marinus* (2264). β-Hydroxylation of this compound yields epinephrine (2265). 3-Methoxy-4-hydroxymandelic acid is a major urinary metabolite of epinephrine and norepinephrine (2266). Other metabolites include 3,4-dihydroxy-mandelic acid, normetanephrine (2267), 3-methoxy-4-hydroxyphenyl-glycol (2268), N-acetylnormetanephrine (2269, 2270), and vanillic acid (2271). 3-O-Methylnormetanephrine and 3-O-methylepinephrine have

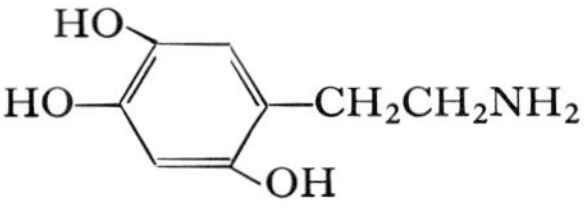

HO—, HO—〈 〉—$CH_2CH_2NH_2$, OH

2,4,5-Trihydroxyphenyl-
ethylamine

CH_3O—, HO—〈 〉—$CH_2CH_2NH_2$, OH

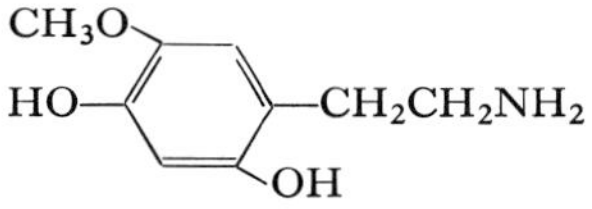

2,4-Dihydroxy-5-methoxy-
phenylethylamine

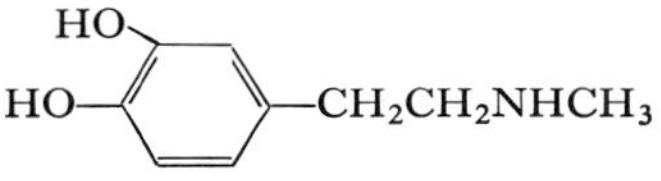

HO—, HO—〈 〉—$CH_2CH_2NHCH_3$

N-Methyl-3,4-dihydroxyphenylethylamine
(epinine)

been found as the corresponding glucosiduronic acids in rat urine and in rat adrenal after treatment with iproniazid. After administration of epinephrine, norepinephrine, and 3,4-dihydroxyphenylethylamine, the corresponding 3-*O*-methyl ether metabolites were identified in the urine

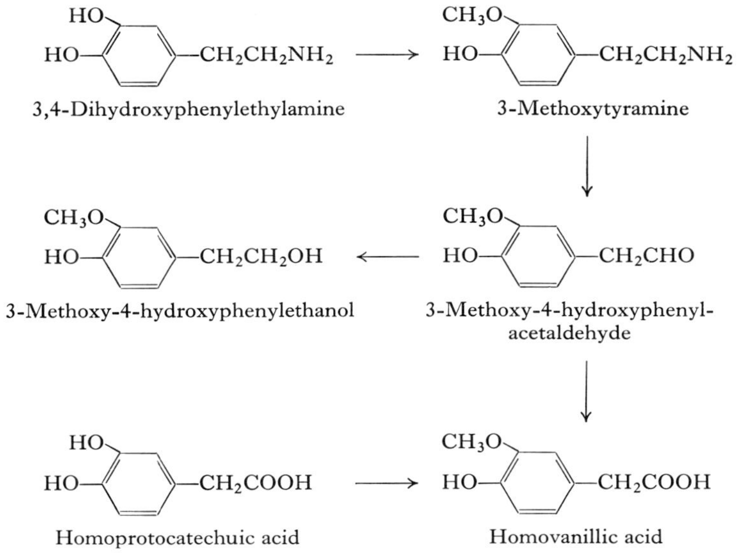

HO—, HO—〈 〉—$CH_2CH_2NH_2$ $\longrightarrow$ CH_3O—, HO—〈 〉—$CH_2CH_2NH_2$

3,4-Dihydroxyphenylethylamine   3-Methoxytyramine

CH_3O—, HO—〈 〉—CH_2CH_2OH $\longleftarrow$ CH_3O—, HO—〈 〉—CH_2CHO

3-Methoxy-4-hydroxyphenylethanol   3-Methoxy-4-hydroxyphenyl-
acetaldehyde

HO—, HO—〈 〉—CH_2COOH $\longrightarrow$ CH_3O—, HO—〈 〉—CH_2COOH

Homoprotocatechuic acid   Homovanillic acid

SCHEME 31

(2272). An enzyme (catechol-*O*-methyl transferase) that catalyzes the methylation of the 3-hydroxy group of epinephrine and other catechols has been found in the liver and other tissues of several mammalian species (2273; see p. 774).

The metabolism of norepinephrine and epinephrine leads to a large number of products which differ qualitatively and quantitatively in different species (see Scheme 32).

The metabolism of these compounds is undoubtedly even more complex than indicated above; attempts to estimate the magnitude of the various pathways have been reviewed recently (2274), and other aspects of the metabolism of synthetic sympathomimetic amines have also been discussed (2253, 2254).

p-Hydroxymandelamine (octopamine, norsynephrine, norsympathol, *p*-hydroxy-α-(aminomethyl)benzyl alcohol) occurs in extracts of the salivary glands of the octopus (2275). This compound has also been found in various tissues of the rabbit and in the urine of humans, rats, and rabbits treated with monoamine oxidase inhibitors (2276); it is present in much smaller amounts in the urine of untreated animals. In addition, *p*-hydroxymandelic acid (a probable product of octopamine metabolism) and synephrine (2277) have been found in human urine. A plausible pathway for the formation of synephrine is decarboxylation of tyrosine to tyramine followed by β-hydroxylation to norsynephrine (octopamine) and *N*-methylation.

HO—⟨ ⟩—CHCH$_2$NH$_2$
                          |
                         OH

p-Hydroxymandelamine
(octopamine; norsynephrine)

HO—⟨ ⟩—CHCOOH
                     |
                    OH

p-Hydroxymandelic acid

HO—⟨ ⟩—CHCH$_2$NHCH$_3$
                          |
                         OH

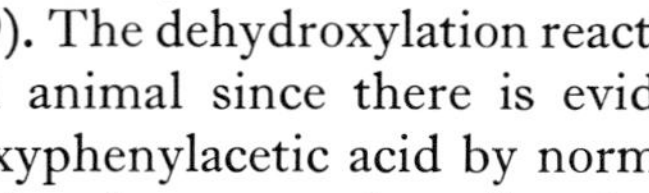

Synephrine

When guinea pigs are treated with tolbutamide [1-butyl-3-(*p*-tolylsulfonyl)urea], norepinephrine is converted to *m*-hydroxyphenyl-acetic acid (2278, 2279). The dehydroxylation reaction may occur to some extent in the normal animal since there is evidence for the urinary excretion of *m*-hydroxyphenylacetic acid by normal individuals (2280).

There is evidence for the conversion of various catecholamine and related compounds to the corresponding *N*-acetyl derivatives. Thus, *N*-acetyl-3,4-dihydroxyphenylethylamine and *N*-acetyl-3-methoxy-4-hydroxyphenylethylamine are found in the urine after administration of

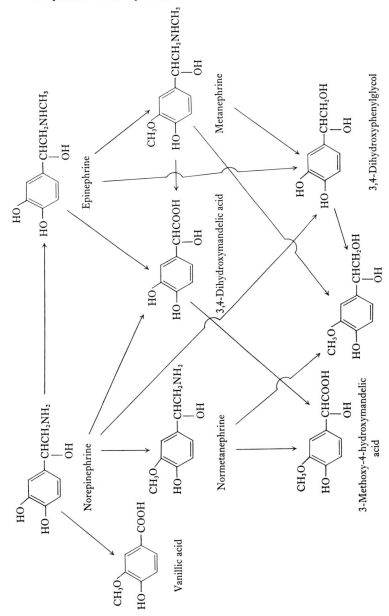

SCHEME 32. Some relationships among products of metabolism of norepinephrine and epinephrine.

3,4-dihydroxyphenylethylamine to rats (2281). *N*-Acetyl-3,4-dihydroxy-phenylethylamine has been found in insects, and there is evidence that its formation, which is hormonally controlled, is involved in cuticle development in the blowfly, *Calliphora erythrocephala*. Karlson and his colleagues (2282, 2283) obtained evidence for an enzyme (not identical with tyrosinase) that catalyzes the oxidation of tyrosine to 3,4-dihydroxy-phenylalanine; reduced triphosphopyridine nucleotide seems to be required for this reaction. Decarboxylation yields 3,4-dihydroxyphenyl-ethylamine, which is acetylated by a reaction involving acetyl-coenzyme A. A crystalline enzyme was obtained from *Calliphora* that oxidizes *N*-acetyl-3,4-dihydroxyphenylethylamine to a quinone, which is incorporated into the cuticle proteins. Ecdysone, a hormone of steroid type produced by the prothoracic glands, causes an increase in 3,4-dihydroxyphenylalanine decarboxylase activity and therefore promotes tyrosine metabolism via the *N*-acetyl-3,4-dihydroxyphenylethylamine pathway and decreases the amount of tyrosine metabolized by the transamination route. The biological effect of ecdysone, which is stimulation of puparium formation (darkening and hardening of the cuticle), seems to be explained in part by its action in increasing the synthesis of decarboxylase. The latter effect appears to be correlated with the formation by ecdysone of a swollen area ("puff") at a definite gene locus of a chromosome. Karlson has proposed a theory of ecdysone action based on its effect on messenger ribonucleic acid synthesis.

Thyroxine and Related Compounds

The thyroid gland contains 3-monoiodotyrosine, 3,5-diiodotyrosine, 3,3'-diiodothyronine, 3,3',5'-triiodothyronine, 3,5,3'-triiodothyronine, and thyroxine (3,5,3',5'-tetraiodothyronine) (see p. 82). Thyroxine and the other iodinated compounds are present in thyroglobulin, but also occur in the free state. There is ample evidence that administered isotopic iodide is converted to these compounds, but detailed knowledge of the mechanisms involved in the incorporation of iodide and in the synthesis of thyroxine and 3,3',5-triiodothyronine is still lacking. Two enzyme systems are known that catalyze the incorporation of iodide into mono-iodotyrosine in the thyroid gland. One of these, associated with the particulate fraction of thyroid homogenates, catalyzes the incorporation of iodide into protein-bound monoiodotyrosine; in experiments on this system very little diiodotyrosine and practically no thyroxine were formed (2284). The conversion of iodide to monoiodotyrosine is markedly accelerated by addition of 10^{-5} M flavin mononucleotide (2285). The other iodide incorporation system is soluble and leads to the formation of free monoiodotyrosine (2286–2289). The soluble system requires oxygen and is stimulated by cupric ion. Both the soluble and particulate systems also occur in the salivary glands of the rat, and the particulate system has been found in rat mammary tissue (2290, 2291). The finding that the soluble iodide-incorporating system requires hydrogen peroxide led to the suggestion that iodide reacts with hydrogen peroxide to yield "active iodine," and that in a second enzymatically catalyzed reaction, iodine is incorporated into tyrosine; these reactions have been formulated as follows (2292):

$$2I^- + H_2O_2 + 2H^+ \xrightarrow{\text{iodide peroxidase}} 2 \text{ "active iodine"} + 2H_2O$$

$$2 \text{ "Active iodine"} + \text{L-tyrosine} \xrightarrow{\text{tyrosine iodinase ?}} 2 \text{ monoiodotyrosine (or diiodotyrosine)}$$

Several other recent investigations have also dealt with the mechanism of tyrosine iodination (2293–2295). Hematin increases the iodinating activity of crude thyroid extracts, and when such extracts are chromatographed on an ion-exchange resin (Amberlite IRC-50), there is a marked reduction in activity, which can be completely restored by addition of hematin or methemoglobin. The findings suggest that the prosthetic group of thyroid iodide peroxidase is ferriprotoporphyrin IX (2295).

Free tyrosine as well as peptide and protein-bound tyrosine can be iodinated nonenzymatically, and certain iodinated preparations of this type exhibit activities similar to that of thyroxine. Biological iodination may involve both free and protein-bound amino acids, but definite information is still lacking. A plausible pathway for the formation of 3,3',5'-triiodothyronine is iodination of 3,3'-diiodothyronine, which might be formed by condensation of 2 molecules of monoiodotyrosine. The formation of 3,5,3'-triiodothyronine might take place by condensation of monoiodotyrosine with diiodotyrosine (2296); on the other hand, there is evidence that this compound is formed by deiodination of thyroxine (2297–2301). Thyroxine could arise by iodination of triiodothyronine or by condensation of 2 molecules of diiodotyrosine. The formation of thyroxine from diiodotyrosine has been the subject of considerable discussion (2169, 2302–2308), but the physiological mechanism is still not known. Shiba and Cahnmann (2309) made the interesting observation that oxidation of diiodotyrosine by rattlesnake venom L-amino acid oxidase in the presence of catalase at pH 6.7 leads to the formation of significant amounts of thyroxine. Earlier studies had shown the nonenzymatic formation of thyroxine from diiodotyrosine and its α-keto analog in the presence of an oxidizing agent (2310). Myeloperoxidase from dog uterine pus and a cell-free preparation of beef thyroid also catalyze thyroxine formation from diiodotyrosine (2311). It is conceivable that oxidation (or transamination) of diiodotyrosine functions in the physiologically significant mechanism of thyroxine biosynthesis. It is of interest in this connection that incubation of the α-keto acid analog of diiodotyrosine with thyroglobulin in the presence of oxygen led to formation of thyroxine residues (2311a). In other experiments rats treated with thiourea, which inhibits iodination, exhibited decreased incorporation of iodine into thyroid protein, but showed little or no reduction in the incorporation of tyrosine (2311b). On the other hand, treatment with puromycin inhibited incorporation of tyrosine but not that of iodine. The data suggest that iodination of preformed protein occurs.

Administration of monoiodotyrosine or diiodotyrosine to animals or incubation of these compounds with preparations of liver, kidney, submaxillary gland, or thyroid results in deiodination (2312–2314). Thyroid monoiodotyrosine deiodinase was found to be associated with the microsomes of this tissue and to require reduced triphosphopyridine nucleotide; a similar system was obtained from liver and kidney homogenates prepared in the presence of nicotinamide. The deiodination of diiodotyrosine takes place in an analogous manner and may be catalyzed by the same enzyme. No evidence for the participation of transamination in the process of deiodination was observed in experiments with thyroid, but evidence was obtained suggesting occurrence of transamination in liver and kidney preparations. It is of interest that one type of cretinism appears to be associated with the absence of monoiodotyrosine and diiodotyrosine deiodinase activities (2315). Thyroxine also undergoes deiodination when incubated with rat liver microsomes (2316–2318); in these experiments, evidence was obtained for the simultaneous removal of iodine from the 3′- and 5′-positions and cleavage of the diphenyl ether linkage to yield 3,5-diiodotyrosine. Other products not yet identified are also formed. The deiodination of thyroxine and 3,5,3′-triiodothyronine by preparations from rat brain, skeletal muscle, and other tissues has been reported to be stimulated by flavin mononucleotide, but recent work (2319) has shown that the deiodination of thyroxine by flavin mononucleotide in the presence of light takes place nonenzymatically, and that the rate of this reaction can be increased or decreased by addition of a variety of proteins. Thus, urease exhibited even more activity than a "thyroxine deiodinase" from muscle. These findings suggest the need for reevaluation and reinvestigation of earlier data.

Preparations of rat kidney mitochondria convert thyroxine and triiodothyronine to tetraiodothyroacetic acid and triiodothyroacetic acid, respectively; the enzymes that catalyze these reactions were solubilized by sonic disruption of the mitochondria and it was found that addition of diphosphopyridine nucleotide accelerated enzymatic activity (2320). Formation of the acetic acid analogs can probably be explained by transamination to the corresponding α-keto analogs followed by oxidative decarboxylation (2321, 2322). It is of interest that both the acetic acid analogs of thyroxine and triiodothyronine exhibit thyroid activity in the rat goiter-prevention assay.

The oxidation of 3,5-diiodotyrosine by peroxidase in the presence of hydrogen peroxide gives products that include 4-hydroxy-3,5-diiodophenylpyruvic acid, 4-hydroxy-3,5-diiodobenzaldehyde, and 3,5-diiodobenzoquinone (2323). This system also catalyzes the degradation of thyroxine, and the presence of peroxidase in the thyroid gland suggests that reactions of this type could be involved in the degradation of various iodine-containing amino acids.

Although much work has been done on the iodine-containing amino acids, especially in the decade that tollowed the discovery of 3,3′,5-triiodothyronine (2324, 2325), further experiments are needed to establish the physiologically significant enzymatic reactions. Several valuable reviews of this area have appeared (2326–2328).

Melanin

Tyrosine is a precursor of melanin; the investigations of Raper (2329, 2330), Mason (2331) and others (2332, 2333) have provided evidence for the pathway of melanin biosynthesis shown in Scheme 33.

Tyrosinase (polyphenol oxidase) has been known for many years as an enzyme that catalyzes oxidation of tyrosine, other monophenols, and such o-hydroxy phenols as 3,4-dihydroxyphenylalanine and catechol. The enzyme is very widely distributed and there is a substantial literature on this subject [see, for example (2334–2338)]. Tyrosinase catalyzes oxidation of tyrosine to 3,4-dihydroxyphenylalanine, which is used for the biosynthesis of catecholamines (see p. 910) and for formation of

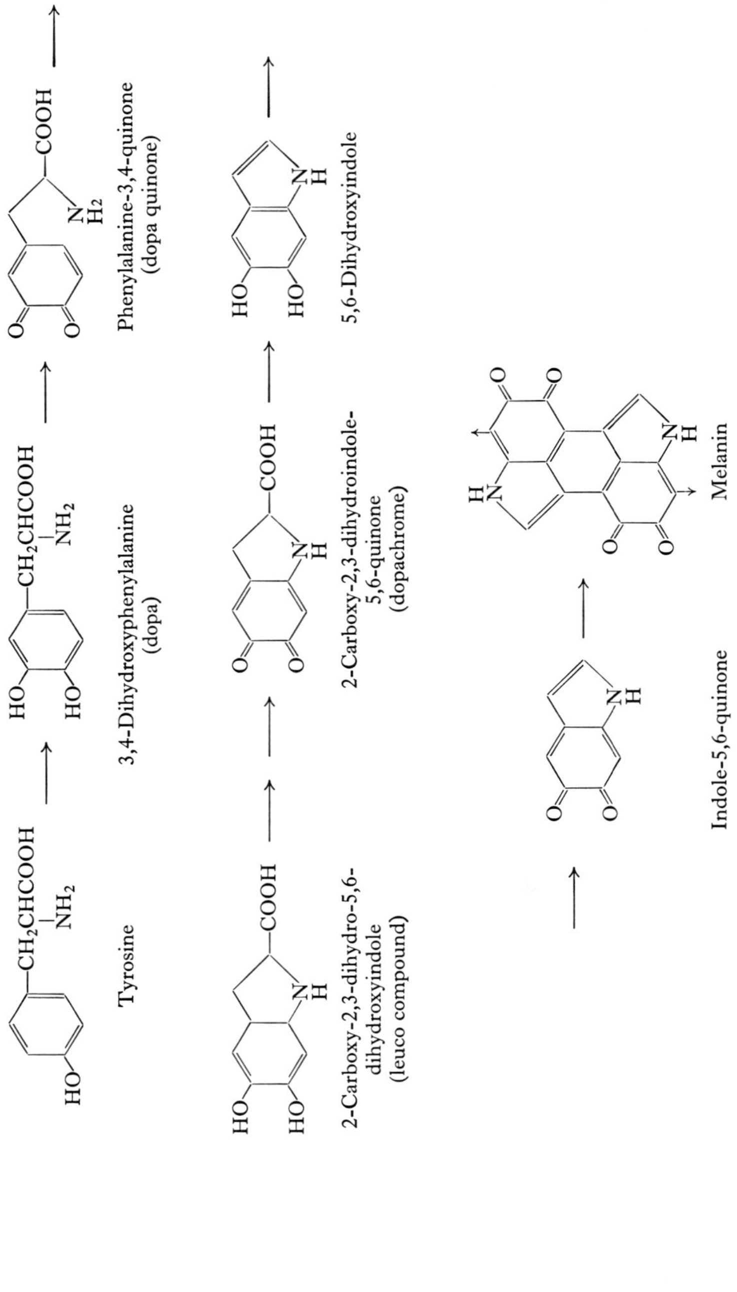

Tyrosine
3,4-Dihydroxyphenylalanine (dopa)
Phenylalanine-3,4-quinone (dopa quinone)
2-Carboxy-2,3-dihydro-5,6-dihydroxyindole (leuco compound)
2-Carboxy-2,3-dihydroindole-5,6-quinone (dopachrome)
5,6-Dihydroxyindole
Indole-5,6-quinone
Melanin

SCHEME 33

melanin. Many aspects of animal and plant tyrosinase activity and function are not yet understood. In insects, tyrosinase functions in the process of pupation, possibly in the process of cuticle hardening. The partial or complete absence of tyrosinase is responsible for albinism in animals and man (2339). Genetic studies on the biosynthesis of tyrosinase have been carried out in *Neurospora* (2340); the *Neurospora* enzyme has been crystallized (2341). Although the first product of the action of tyrosinase on L-tyrosine is 3,4-dihydroxy-L-phenylalanine (2342), there is evidence that the latter compound is not an obligatory free intermediate in the conversion of tyrosine to melanin catalyzed by mushroom tyrosinase (2343). The oxidation of tyrosine by this enzyme exhibits a lag period, which recent studies suggest is due to inhibition by a protein inhibitor (2344). This protein inhibits oxidation of 3,4-dihydroxy-L-phenylalanine, but does not cause a similar lag period when the latter compound is the substrate. Earlier work showed that 3,4-dihydroxyphenylalanine shortened the lag period in the oxidation of tyrosine by tyrosinase prepared from Harding-Passey mouse melanoma (2334). Tyrosinase contains copper, which is essential for the activity of the enzyme (2345). It is of interest that tyrosinase, in particular highly purified mushroom tyrosinase, catalyzes the oxidation of the tyrosyl groups of certain proteins (2346–2349).

Several mechanisms have been proposed for the polymerization of 5,6-dihydroxyindole (2332, 2350). Recent studies have shown that catechol-*O*-methyltransferase from rat liver catalyzes the methylation of 5,6-dihydroxyindole and 5,6-dihydroxydihydroindole, primarily at position 6. Hydroxyindole-*O*-methyltransferase, found only in the pineal gland, catalyzes methylation of 5,6-dihydroxyindole mainly at position 5, but does not methylate 5,6-dihydroxydihydroindole. It has been suggested that *O*-methylation is of physiological significance in regulating melanin formation (2351).

Other Reactions of Tyrosine and Phenylalanine

Early studies provided evidence that phenylalanine (2352) and tyrosine (2353) could be enzymatically deaminated to the corresponding acrylic acid derivatives, and very recently an enzyme has been purified from barley, *Hordeum vulgare*, that catalyzes the conversion of L-phenylalanine to *trans*-cinnamic acid and ammonia (2354). The reaction catalyzed by phenylalanine deaminase is thus similar to the aspartase reaction and to several others which have been discussed above (see p.

320). Like the histidase reaction, the deamination of phenylalanine is irreversible. A similar enzyme has been found in several plants that catalyzes the analogous irreversible deamination of L-tyrosine (2355). Studies on several plants have indicated that monocotyledons and dicotyledons can convert phenylalanine to lignin via cinnamic acid, but that only monocotyledons can convert L-tyrosine to lignin through p-coumaric acid. Both coumaric acid and cinnamic acid are precursors of lignin and these are synthesized in plants via the aromatic amino acids. Recent reviews have appeared on the biosynthesis of lignin (2356, 2357). Another deaminase has been isolated from the dandelion; this acts on 3,4-dihydroxyphenylalanine (2358).

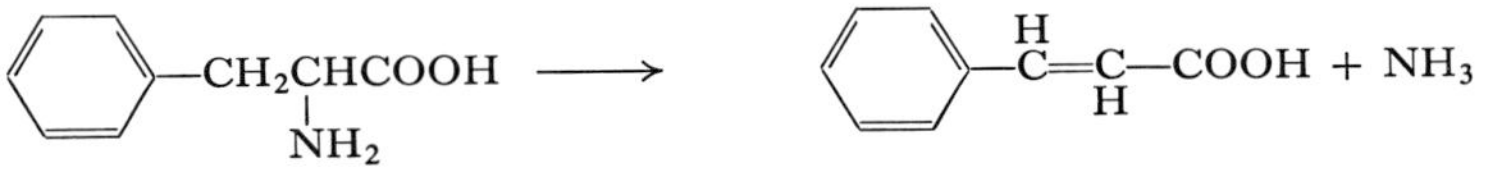

trans-Cinnamic acid

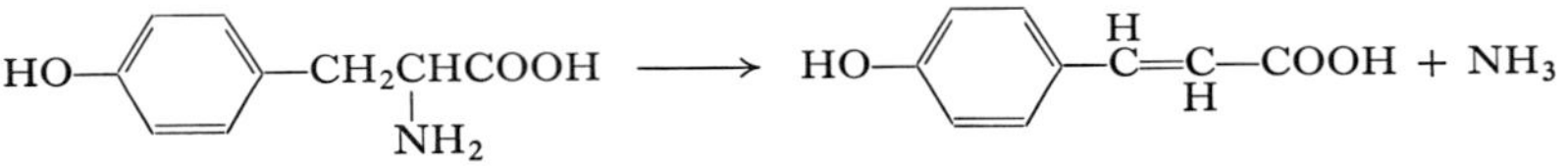

p-Coumaric acid

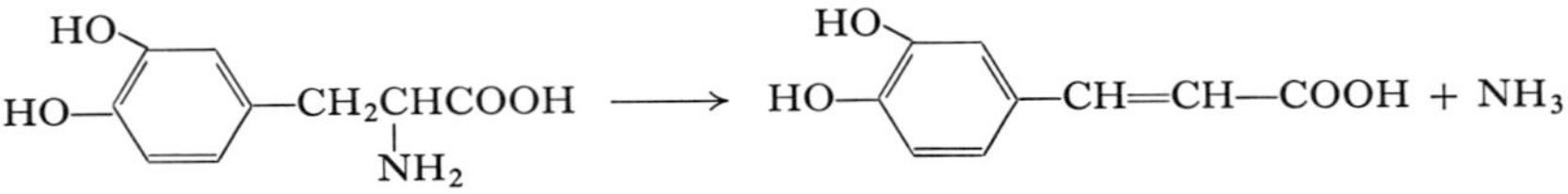

Tyrosine can undergo a number of degradative reactions in microorganisms; such products as phenol, p-cresol, p-hydroxybenzoic acid, p-hydroxyphenylethanol (tyrosol), etc., are formed (2359, 2360). Phenol is formed by a pyridoxal phosphate-dependent enzyme (β-tyrosinase) obtained from bacteria (2361):

$$\text{Tyrosine} \longrightarrow \text{phenol} + \text{pyruvate} + NH_3$$

Human urine contains a large variety of aromatic compounds (2362), some of which may be formed by enzymes present in the bacterial flora. The observation that o-hydroxyphenylacetic acid and m-hydroxyphenylacetic acid are present in the urine of patients with phenylketonuria in larger than normal amounts suggests that they arise from phenylalanine (see p. 1069).

Tyrosine is found in normal human urine as the *O*-sulfate derivative (2363), and it also occurs in this form in bovine fibrinogen (2364, 2365). Human fibrinogen does not contain tyrosine-*O*-sulfate, but both human and bovine fibrinogen contain serine phosphate residues (2366, 2367). Attempts to demonstrate the sulfurylation of free tyrosine in the presence of the hepatic sulfate-transferring enzyme and a source of adenosine-3'-phospho-5'-phosphosulfate were unsuccessful; only those tyrosine derivatives in which the carboxyl group was lacking or substituted and in which the amino group was unsubstituted were sulfurylated (2368). Tyrosine-*O*-sulfate may be formed via an N-terminal tyrosine peptide or possibly on an activated derivative such as tyrosyl-coenzyme A or tyrosyl adenylate. The identification (by paper chromatography) of tyrosine-*O*-sulfate in several marine animals (2369) suggests that these might be good sources of the enzyme (or enzymes) that catalyze the synthesis of this interesting amino acid derivative. When L-tyrosine-*O*-sulfate-S^{35} was injected into rats, the sulfate ester of *p*-hydroxyphenylpyruvic acid was found in the urine (2370); the latter compound is spontaneously converted to the corresponding benzaldehyde and phenylacetic acid derivatives. Injection of S^{35}-labeled fibrinopeptide B into rabbits was followed by the appearance of free L-tyrosine-*O*-sulfate and *p*-hydroxyphenylacetic acid sulfate in the urine (2371). In recent studies evidence was reported for the presence of tyrosine-*O*-phosphate as a prominent constituent of third instar larvae of *Drosophila melanogaster* (2371a).

L-Phenylalanine anhydride [*cis*-L(−)-3,6-dibenzyl-2,5-dioxopiperazine] has been isolated from the dried mycelium of a strain of *Penicillium nigricans* (2372). A similar compound, aspergillic acid, has also been obtained (see p. 754). The enzymatic formation of such diketopiperazine derivatives should be relatively easy to investigate and would be of interest.

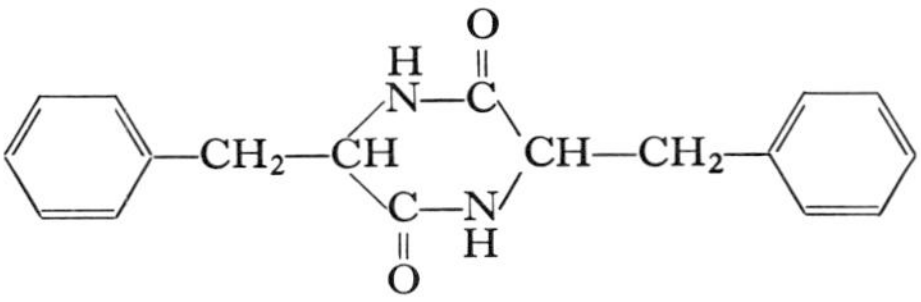

Phenylalanine anhydride

Phenylalanine and tyrosine are precursors of a large number of alkaloids (13, 14, 787); only a few examples are cited here.

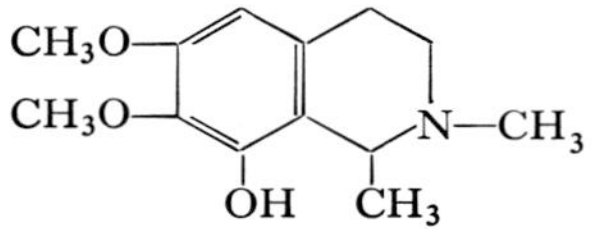

Pellotine

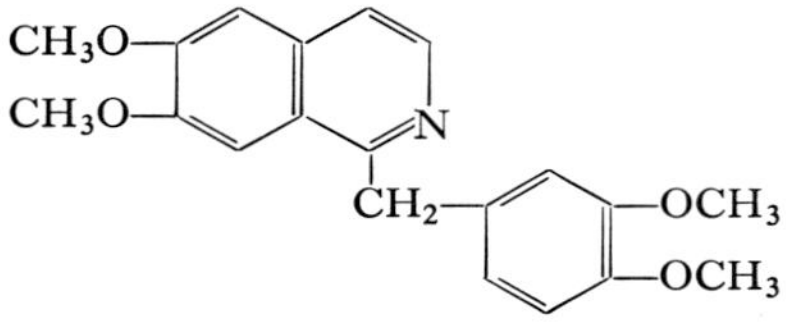

Papaverine

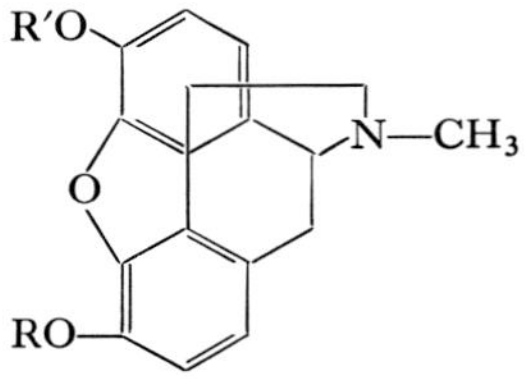

Morphine (R, R' = H)
Codeine (R' = H; R = CH₃)
Thebaine (R, R' = CH₃)
Oripavine (R' = CH₃; R = H)

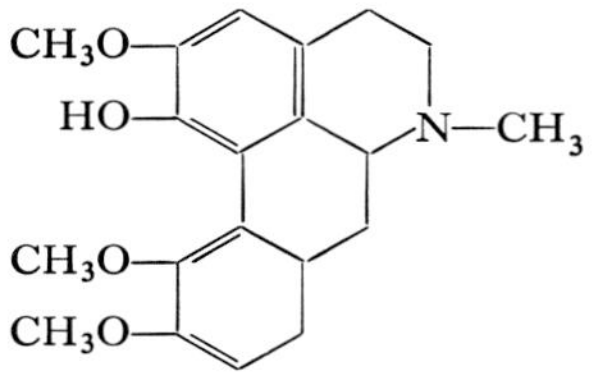

Isothebaine

Studies in which labeled tyrosine was fed to plants showed that this amino acid is incorporated into the alkaloids pellotine (2373), papaverine, morphine, codeine, and thebaine (787). It has been suggested that norlaudanosoline, formed by condensation of 3,4-dihydroxyphenyl-ethylamine and 3,4-dihydroxyphenylacetaldehyde, is a precursor of papaverine and of alkaloids possessing the morphine carbon skeleton. There is evidence that thebaine is converted to codeine and morphine by demethylation and that the N-methyl and O-methyl groups of these

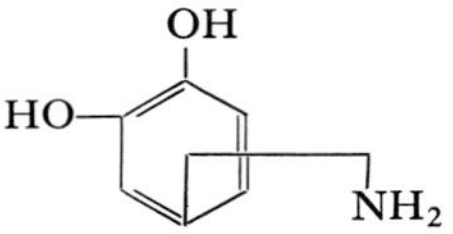

3,4-Dihydroxyphenyl-
ethylamine

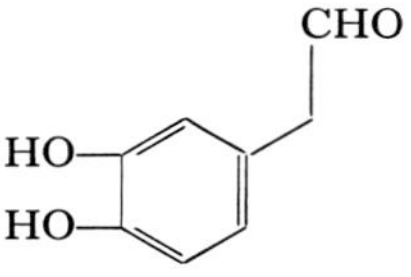

+

3,4-Dihydroxyphenyl-
acetaldehyde

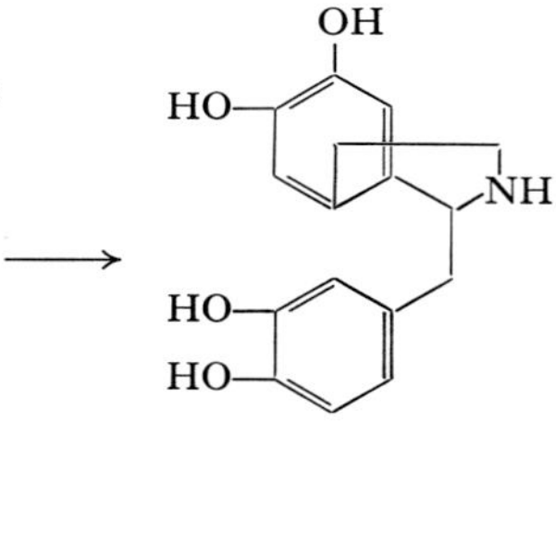

Norlaudanosoline

alkaloids arise from the methyl group of methionine. Studies in which labeled tyrosine was administered to seedlings of the oriental poppy showed that this amino acid is incorporated into thebaine, oripavine, and isothebaine. These studies also indicate that isothebaine can serve as a precursor of thebaine and oripavine (2374).

There is evidence that the tropic acid moiety of hyoscyamine and related alkaloids (see p. 704) arises from phenylalanine. Administration of DL-phenylalanine-3-C^{14} to *Datura stramonium* plants gave hyoscyamine and hyoscine in which all of the isotope was found in carbon atom 2 of the tropic acid portion of the molecule (2375). Similar studies with phenylalanine-2-C^{14} led to incorporation of isotope into the hydroxymethyl group of tropic acid (2376, 2377). Studies with L-phenylalanine-1-C^{14} indicate that the carboxyl group of phenylalanine is the precursor of the carboxyl group of tropic acid (2376). These data therefore suggest that tropic acid is formed from phenylalanine by a mechanism involving intramolecular rearrangement. On the other hand, a report has appeared describing the conversion of tryptophan-3-C^{14} in *Datura stramonium* to hyoscyamine tropic acid containing more than 99% of the radioactivity in the carboxyl group (2378); it would certainly be of interest if this plant possessed two biosynthetic pathways for tropic acid, but further studies are needed on the apparent conversion of tryptophan to tropic acid.

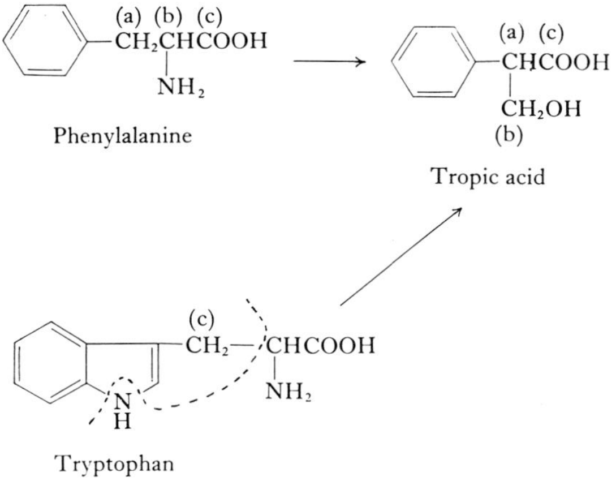

The conversion of labeled tyrosine and tyramine to hordenine has been demonstrated in barley (2379, 2380); this transformation takes place by

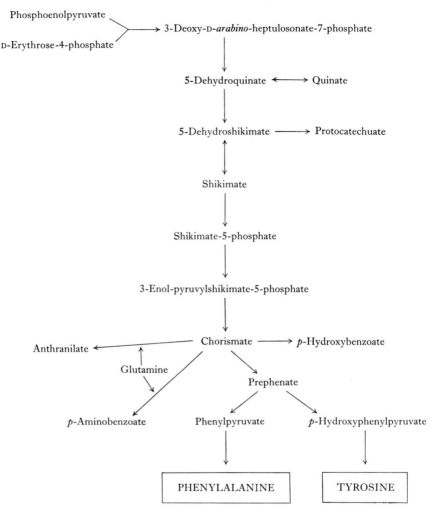

Summary scheme for the biosynthesis of phenylalanine and tyrosine.

stepwise methylation in which methionine and betaine can serve as methyl donors (2381–2385). There is also evidence that mescaline is formed from tyrosine (2386). Considerable attention has been given to the synthesis of colchicine; both phenylalanine (2387) and the methyl

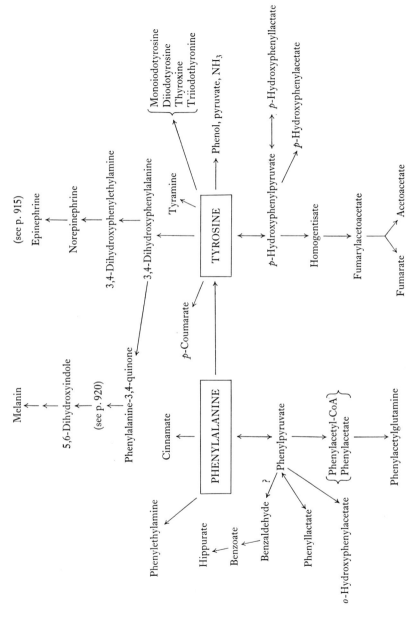

Summary scheme for the metabolism of phenylalanine and tyrosine.

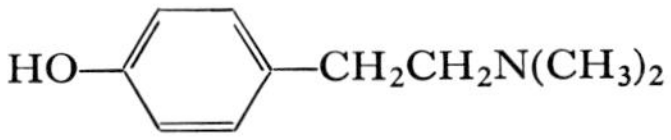

HO—⟨benzene ring⟩—$CH_2CH_2N(CH_3)_2$

Hordenine

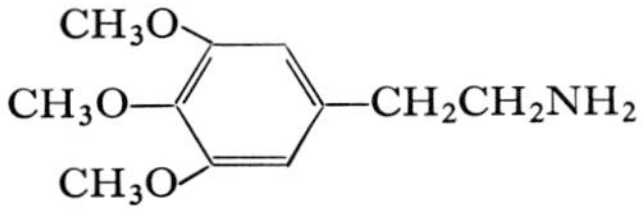

CH_3O, CH_3O—⟨benzene ring⟩—$CH_2CH_2NH_2$
CH_3O

Mescaline

group of methionine (2388) are incorporated into this alkaloid by *Colchicum byzantinum* corms. There is evidence that the benzoquinone

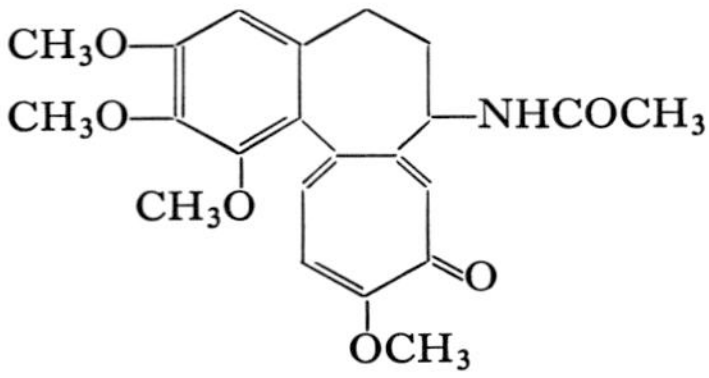

CH_3O—, CH_3O—⟨ring structure⟩—$NHCOCH_3$
CH_3O
—O
OCH_3

Colchicine

moiety of coenzyme Q arises from tyrosine, probably by a pathway not involving benzoate, although the latter compound can be incorporated into coenzyme Q (2389).

P. Lysine

Biosynthesis

Two distinct pathways are known that lead to the synthesis of lysine. In certain fungi and algae the carbon skeleton of lysine arises from acetate and α-ketoglutarate by a biosynthetic sequence that includes α-amino-adipic acid. The other pathway has been found in bacteria, higher plants, blue-green and green algae, and certain fungi; in these organisms, the lysine carbon chain is synthesized from pyruvate and aspartate and α,ε-diaminopimelic acid is a key intermediate. At the time of this writing, more is known about the diaminopimelic acid pathway, which will be considered first.

Diaminopimelic Pathway. The natural occurrence of α,ε-diamino-pimelic acid was first reported by Work (2390, 2391), who isolated this amino acid from hydrolyzates of *Corynebacterium diphtheriae*. The studies of Work and her collaborators and of others have shown that diamino-pimelic acid is present in many bacteria and certain other microorganisms including several species of blue-green algae (2392–2397). The amino acid isolated originally was shown to possess the *meso*-configuration, but subsequent investigations showed that the L-isomer also occurs; thus, the diaminopimelic acid accumulated by a mutant of *E. coli* was found to be a mixture of the L- and *meso*-forms (2398). Diaminopimelic acid is a constituent of the cell walls of many of the organisms that contain this amino acid, but it is not present in bacterial protein. Diaminopimelic acid was also found in a peptide in *Mycobacterium tuberculosis* (2399).

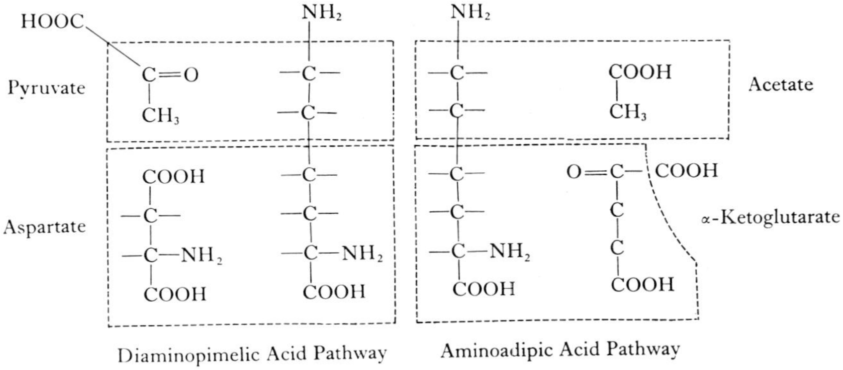

Diaminopimelic Acid Pathway   Aminoadipic Acid Pathway

LYSINE BIOSYNTHESIS

Structural considerations suggested that diaminopimelic acid might be a precursor of lysine and this possibility was supported by the finding of a specific diaminopimelic acid decarboxylase in *E. coli* (2400). Davis (2401) isolated a mutant of *E. coli* that exhibited an absolute growth requirement for diaminopimelic acid, and found that lysine exerted a sparing effect on the requirement for diaminopimelic acid. Certain lysine-requiring mutants of *E. coli* were found to accumulate diaminopimelic acid, and these did not exhibit diaminopimelic acid decarboxylase activity. These observations provided strong evidence for the participation of diamino-pimelic acid in lysine biosynthesis; the enzymatic steps involved in the conversion of diaminopimelic acid to lysine and in the biosynthesis of diaminopimelic acid are considered below.

Several approaches indicated that aspartate was a precursor of diamino-pimelic acid. Thus, isotopic competition studies showed that aspartate competes with glucose in providing four of the carbon atoms of diamino-pimelic acid and of lysine (2402). Extracts of mutants that accumulate diaminopimelic acid catalyze its synthesis, which is stimulated by addition of triphosphopyridine nucleotide, adenosine triphosphate, aspartate, succinate, and pyruvate (2403, 2404). Gilvarg made the significant observation that a mutant of *E. coli* that exhibited an absolute requirement for diaminopimelic acid accumulated a compound which he identified as *N*-succinyl-L-α,ε-diaminopimelic acid (2405, 2406). *N*-Succinyl diaminopimelate deacylase activity was found in extracts of organisms capable of synthesizing diaminopimelate, but was not present in a mutant that accumulated *N*-succinyl-L-α,ε-diaminopimelic acid. The enzyme was present in microorganisms capable of synthesizing lysine by the diaminopimelic acid pathway but was absent in others. The deacylase was partially purified and found to be activated by Co^{++} ions (2407). It is of interest that Co^{++} is a specific activator of *N*-acetylornithinase (see p. 710), and that it accelerates the enzymatic cleavage of glycylglycine (2408).

Further studies on the *E. coli* mutant that accumulates *N*-succinyl-L-α,ε-diaminopimelic acid revealed that this organism also accumulates *N*-succinyl-ε-keto-L-α-aminopimelic acid (2409). Transaminase activity capable of catalyzing reversible transamination between *N*-succinyldiaminopimelate and α-ketoglutarate was found in extracts of this mutant and also of the wild strain (2410). In view of the characteristically low specificity of many transaminases, the possibility that the accumulation of the α-keto acid represented a side reaction not directly involved in diaminopimelic acid biosynthesis had to be considered. However, it was demonstrated by partial purification of *N*-succinyldiaminopimelate-glutamate transaminase that this activity is not identical with transaminases previously shown to be present in *E. coli*; this observation supported the belief that *N*-succinyl-ε-keto-L-α-aminopimelic acid is on the direct pathway of diaminopimelic acid biosynthesis. It is of interest that, of the amino acids tested, only L-glutamate served as the amino donor, and that the transaminase exhibits no activity with *N*-succinyl-*meso*-diaminopimelic acid, L-diaminopimelic acid, L-lysine, or *meso*-diaminopimelic acid. Furthermore, the enzyme activity was shown to be distinct from that which catalyzes transamination of α-*N*-acetyl-L-ornithine (see p. 355).

Subsequent studies on the biosynthesis of *N*-succinyl-L-α,ε-diaminopimelic acid by a mutant of *E. coli* established that the four-carbon moiety of aspartate is the precursor of the portion of the molecule that becomes succinylated (2411). A very significant finding was the isolation of a mutant of *E. coli* that exhibited an absolute requirement for diaminopimelic acid, threonine, and methionine as well as a relative requirement

for lysine and isoleucine. This organism lacks aspartic acid β-semialde-
hyde dehydrogenase, the enzyme that catalyzes the formation of aspartic
acid β-semialdehyde from β-aspartyl phosphate (see p. 674). It is therefore evident that aspartic acid β-semialdehyde is the branching point in
the biosynthesis of several amino acids (see p. 678) (2412).

Evidence has been obtained for the biosynthesis of N-succinyl-ϵ-
keto-L-α-aminopimelic acid from aspartic acid β-semialdehyde and
pyruvate in the presence of triphosphopyridine nucleotide and succinyl-
coenzyme A. The data indicate a pathway involving condensation of
aspartic acid β-semialdehyde with pyruvate to yield 2,3-dihydrodipico-
linic acid, perhaps through an intermediate open-chain compound.
Reduction in the presence of reduced triphosphopyridine nucleotide
yields Δ^1-piperideine-2,6-dicarboxylic acid, which would be expected to
exist in equilibrium with the corresponding open-chain form. Succinyla-
tion of the latter yields N-succinyl-ϵ-keto-L-α-aminopimelic acid;
conversion of this compound to L-α,ϵ-diaminopimelic acid involves the
transamination and deacylation steps described above. The "branching
reaction," i.e., condensation of aspartic acid β-semialdehyde with
pyruvate, is inhibited by lysine (2413); this feedback effect thus affects
the first reaction in the sequence that leads only to lysine. These reactions
are summarized in Scheme 34.

The enzymatic steps in the conversion of L-α,ϵ-diaminopimelic acid
to L-lysine were discovered prior to elucidation of the pathway of
diaminopimelic acid biosynthesis. Diaminopimelic acid decarboxylase
is a constitutive enzyme in *E. coli* and this activity occurs in a variety of
microorganisms. The enzyme was partially purified and shown to
exhibit no activity toward the L-isomer of diaminopimelic acid or L-
lysine (2414, 2415). Its activity is inhibited by lysine (2416). There is
evidence that the enzyme requires pyridoxal 5'-phosphate. The high
specificity of the decarboxylase for the *meso*-form of α,ϵ-diaminopimelic
acid indicates clearly that this isomer is the immediate precursor of lysine.
Epimerization of L-α,ϵ-diaminopimelic acid to the *meso*-isomer is catalyzed by a specific epimerase which is present in *E. coli* and other microorganisms (2417: see p. 374).

The available data indicate that diaminopimelic acid is an obligatory
intermediate in the biosynthesis of lysine in *E. coli* and a number of other
microorganisms. An alternative pathway of lysine formation not involving diaminopimelic acid was suggested by studies in which a mutant
of *E. coli* partially blocked in lysine biosynthesis appeared to utilize

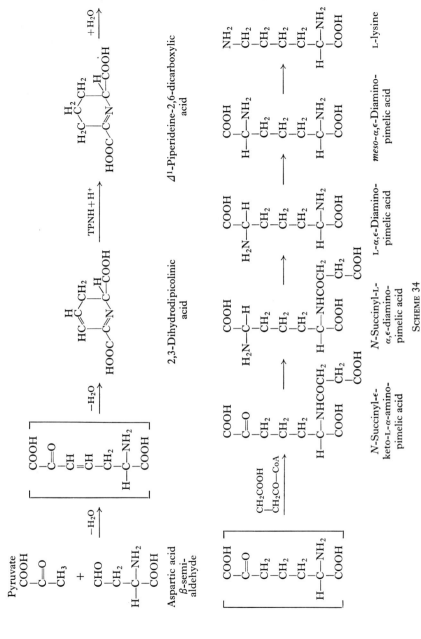

SCHEME 34

diaminopimelic acid effectively for cell-wall diaminopimelic acid but not for lysine synthesis (2418); although these findings require further examination, it appears unlikely that there is such an alternative pathway of lysine biosynthesis. The observation that certain mutants of *E. coli* require both diaminopimelic acid and lysine for optimal growth suggests that diaminopimelic acid is not transported rapidly into the cell. An interesting experiment indicating that the diaminopimelic acid pathway is the only one leading to lysine biosynthesis in *E. coli* was carried out by Rhuland and Hamilton (2419), who demonstrated that a mutant blocked in the biosynthesis of diaminopimelic acid could incorporate γ-methyl-diaminopimelic acid into its cell walls. This mutant did not grow when supplied with γ-methyldiaminopimelate, but required both the latter compound and lysine. The γ-methyl derivative of diaminopimelate therefore serves to replace diaminopimelate in cell-wall synthesis, but not in lysine biosynthesis.

The structural relationships between diaminopimelic acid (and the intermediates in its biosynthesis) and dipicolinic acid (see p. 86) suggest a similar biosynthetic pathway. In support of this possibility, there is evidence that aspartate and pyruvate (or closely related compounds) are precursors of dipicolinic acid (2420–2422). A plausible pathway would be condensation of aspartic acid β-semialdehyde and pyruvate to yield 2,3-dihydrodipicolinic acid, followed by oxidation of the latter compound (possibly by amino acid oxidase) to dipicolinic acid. An alternative pathway is suggested by the observation of nonenzymatic conversion of 2,6-diketopimelic acid (which might be formed from diaminopimelic acid or perhaps by another route) in the presence of ammonia to dipicolinic acid (2422a).

Studies on the occurrence of diaminopimelic acid in various microorganisms and experiments on the incorporation of labeled acetate and aspartate into lysine have provided data concerning the pathways of lysine biosynthesis in various microorganisms and plants. Thus, organisms using the diaminopimelic acid pathway incorporate aspartate carbon into protein lysine, aspartate, and threonine, while those using the α-aminoadipic acid pathway do not use aspartate carbon for the synthesis of protein lysine although aspartate and threonine become labeled. Vogel (2423) has surveyed the pathways of lysine biosynthesis in many bacteria, algae, and plants; a summary of his observations is given in Table III. Thus far, no evidence has been obtained for the occurrence of both pathways within the same organism. The protozoon, *Crithidia*

(*Strigomonas*) *oncopelti,* which is capable of growth on a medium lacking lysine, was found to utilize the diaminopimelic acid pathway (2424). This was surprising since apparently related organisms utilize the α-aminoadipic acid pathway. Earlier microscopic study had revealed the presence of bipolar bodies within the protozoon, and subsequent work showed that these are bacteria. When the protozoon was "cured" of its "disease" by treatment with penicillin, the intracellular inclusion bodies were no

Table III

BIOSYNTHESIS OF LYSINE (2425)

α,ε-Diaminopimelic acid pathway	α-Aminoadipic acid pathway
Bacteria	
Pseudomonads	
Eubacteria	
Actinomycetes	
Lower fungi	
Hyphochytriales	Chytrids
Saprolegniales	Blastocladiales
Leptomitales	Mucorales
Higher fungi	
	Ascomycetes
	Basidiomycetes
Green organisms	
Green algae	Euglenids
Ferns	
Flowering plants	

longer found. Other studies showed that the diaminopimelic decarboxylase activity present in the untreated protozoon is localized in the inclusion bodies. Presumably, the "cured" protozoon would not grow on a medium not containing lysine.

It is conceivable that in the course of evolution organisms that required diaminopimelic acid found it efficient to synthesize lysine also by this pathway; on the other hand, certain bacteria that do not use diaminopimelic acid for cell-wall formation synthesize lysine via diaminopimelic acid. The observations on *C. oncopelti* lead one to speculate as to whether bacterial deoxyribonucleic acid might be incorporated into and function in host cells.

Aminoadipic Acid Pathway. Studies on the biosynthesis of lysine in *Neurospora* began with the isolation of several different lysine-requiring mutants of this organism. One of these was able to use α-aminoadipic acid in place of lysine (2426). This and other *Neurospora* mutants did not grow on media supplemented with hydroxylysine, diaminopimelic acid, α-ketoadipic acid, and 6-piperidone-2-carboxylic acid. In experiments on a mutant that could grow on either lysine or α-aminoadipic acid, it was found that virtually all of the radioactivity of C^{14}-α-aminoadipic acid supplied in the medium was incorporated into lysine (2427). This result indicated that α-aminoadipic acid is a precursor of lysine in *Neurospora*, and, since no radioactivity was found in other amino acids, it can be concluded that appreciable degradation of α-aminoadipic acid to intermediates of the citric acid cycle did not occur. Certain lysine-requiring mutants of the yeast, *Ophiostoma multiannulatum*, grew when supplemented with DL-α-aminoadipic acid, L-α-aminoadipic acid, and α-ketoadipic acid; DL-α-aminoadipic acid was as effective as an equimolar quantity of L-α-aminoadipic acid (2428). A few *Neurospora* mutants grew when supplemented with α-amino-ε-hydroxycaproic acid (2429), and D-lysine supported the growth of lysine-requiring mutants of *Neurospora* blocked early in the biosynthetic sequence; mutants blocked just prior to lysine were unable to utilize D-lysine.

Isotopic tracer studies have provided clues to the steps leading to the formation of the six-carbon-atom chain in *Neurospora* and yeast (160, 2430–2433). The ε-carbon atom and the carboxyl carbon atom of lysine are entirely derived from the carboxyl group of acetate, while the remaining carbon atoms arise from the methyl carbon atom of acetate. The data obtained in such labeling experiments are consistent with a mechanism in which acetate condenses with α-ketoglutarate to yield homocitric acid, which by reactions analogous to those of the citric acid cycle, would yield homoisocitrate, oxaloglutarate, and α-ketoadipate (2432, 2433). This mechanism, which is also analogous to the steps involved in the biosynthesis of α-ketoisocaproic acid from α-ketoisovaleric acid (see p. 742), is illustrated in Scheme 35.

Studies with yeast extracts have shown conversion of acetate- and α-ketoglutarate-carbon to α-ketoadipate in the presence of coenzyme A, diphosphopyridine nucleotide, and adenosine triphosphate (2433a);

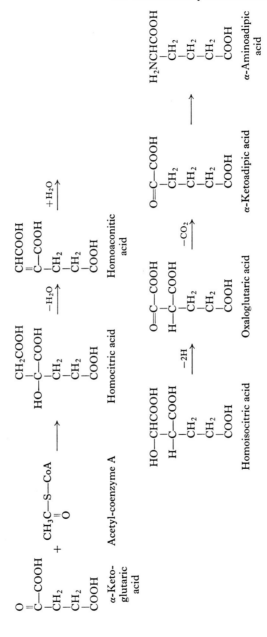

SCHEME 35

enzymatic formation of homocitrate (2433b) and its conversion to α-ketoadipate (2433c) have been demonstrated.

The formation of α-aminoadipic acid from α-ketoadipic acid takes place by transamination. Although the participation of α-aminoadipic acid as an intermediate in lysine biosynthesis is supported by considerable data, the steps in its conversion to lysine have not been fully clarified. The observation that α-amino-ε-hydroxycaproic acid could support the growth of certain lysine-requiring mutant microorganisms (2429) and the discovery of an enzyme in *Neurospora* that catalyzes the reversible oxidation of α-amino-ε-hydroxycaproic acid to α-aminoadipic acid-δ-semialdehyde (818, 819) suggest that utilization of the ε-hydroxy compound involves the conversion to the aldehyde; the latter compound might be oxidized to α-aminoadipic acid or serve as substrate for another reaction in the biosynthetic pathway. The enzyme that catalyzes the oxidation of α-amino-ε-hydroxycaproic acid also acts on α-amino-δ-hydroxyvaleric acid (see p. 708) and functions with either triphosphopyridine nucleotide or diphosphopyridine nucleotide.

Studies on the utilization of radioactive α-aminoadipic acid by yeast cells have indicated that this compound is efficiently utilized for the synthesis of lysine (2434–2436). α-Aminoadipic acid-δ-semialdehyde has often been suggested as an intermediate between α-aminoadipic acid and lysine, and there is evidence for the formation of the aldehyde in the conversion of lysine to aminoadipic acid in animal tissues (see p. 944). Conversion of α-aminoadipic acid to the corresponding δ-aldehyde might be expected to involve the intermediate formation of a carboxyl phosphate anhydride in analogy with the formation of aspartic acid β-semialdehyde from aspartate (see p. 675). Other possible intermediates include the analogous adenylate derivative or a thiol ester-containing intermediate such as one involving coenzyme A or perhaps an enzyme sulfhydryl group. An enzyme fraction obtained from yeast was found to catalyze the conversion of α-aminoadipic acid to the corresponding δ-aldehyde in the presence of adenosine triphosphate, reduced triphosphopyridine nucleotide, and magnesium ions. No evidence was obtained for the participation of coenzyme A or lipoic acid, and the reaction was markedly activated by glutathione (2437, 2438). This enzyme preparation also catalyzed an α-aminoadipic acid-dependent exchange of inorganic pyrophosphate into adenosine triphosphate. Adenosine monophosphate inhibited the reduction of α-aminoadipic acid to α-aminoadipic acid-δ-

semialdehyde catalyzed by this enzyme (2439). These data have led to the
suggestion that the reduction takes place in two steps, formation of
α-aminoadipyl-δ-adenylate, followed by reduction in the presence of
reduced triphosphopyridine nucleotide to the aldehyde. In other
investigations, formation of a compound with the properties of α-amino-
adipic acid-δ-semialdehyde (or its cyclized form) was observed when
resting yeast cells were incubated with α-aminoadipic acid in the presence
of o-aminobenzaldehyde. A similar compound was formed when a
crude cell-free yeast preparation was incubated with α-aminoadipic acid,
adenosine triphosphate, reduced pyridine nucleotide, and glutathione
(2436). The mechanism of the conversion of α-aminoadipic acid to
α-aminoadipic acid-δ-semialdehyde has not yet been unequivocally
settled, but the data suggest that the aldehyde is an intermediate in
lysine formation. A reasonable pathway for the formation of lysine from
α-aminoadipic acid-δ-semialdehyde would seem to be transamination or
reductive amination; however, this compound exists in solution predominantly in the cyclic configuration and thus far no convincing
evidence has been reported for its enzymatic transformation to lysine.
It has been suggested that α-N-acyl derivatives of α-aminoadipic acid
and α-aminoadipic acid-δ-semialdehyde are involved in lysine biosynthesis (in a manner similar to that shown for ornithine biosynthesis;
see p. 709), but no definitive experimental data are now available.
Another possible intermediate in lysine biosynthesis is α-keto-ϵ-amino-
caproic acid, but it is not clear as to how this compound could be formed
from α-aminoadipic acid. Possible mechanisms for formation of α-keto-
-ϵ-aminocaproic acid include direct conversion (in the cyclized form)
from Δ^1-piperideine-6-carboxylate, and oxidation of pipecolic acid,
which might be formed by reduction of Δ^1-piperideine-6-carboxylate.
Although oxidation of D-pipecolic acid by D-amino acid oxidase yields
Δ^1-piperideine-2-carboxylate, which is in equilibrium with α-keto-ϵ-
aminocaproate, an analogous reaction with L-pipecolic acid has not been
observed. Furthermore, interconversion of Δ^1-piperideine-2-carboxylate
and Δ^1-piperideine-6-carboxylate has not been observed and efforts to
demonstrate formation of lysine from α-keto-ϵ-aminocaproate by transamination have been unsuccessful.

A possible solution to the problem of the conversion of α-aminoadipic
acid-δ-semialdehyde to lysine has arisen from the discovery of saccharopine [ϵ-N-(L-glutaryl-2)-L-lysine] in yeast by Kjaer and Larsen
(see p. 104). Kuo et al. (2440) found that incubation of labeled α-amino-

adipic acid with yeast cells led to formation of labeled saccharopine; the biosynthesis of saccharopine can be visualized in terms of Schiff base formation between α-aminoadipic acid-δ-semialdehyde and glutamate followed by reduction. It has recently been reported that the formation of saccharopine requires reduced diphosphopyridine nucleotide, and that saccharopine is converted to α-ketoglutarate and lysine by a di-phosphopyridine nucleotide-linked dehydrogenase. Saccharopine de-hydrogenase is lacking in a mutant that accumulates saccharopine (2440a).

Certain mutants of *Aspergillus nidulans* blocked between α-aminoadipic acid and lysine accumulate L-pipecolic acid when grown in media containing growth-limiting concentrations of L-lysine (2441). Accumula-tion of pipecolic acid does not occur when these mutants are grown on optimal concentrations of lysine nor is pipecolic acid accumulation observed with other types of lysine-requiring mutants of this organism. When the mutants were grown on media containing o-aminobenzalde-hyde, accumulation of pipecolic acid was delayed and evidence was obtained for the formation of a precursor of pipecolic acid; on catalytic reduction, DL-pipecolic acid was obtained. These observations suggested that Δ^1-piperideine-2-carboxylic acid accumulated in the presence of o-aminobenzaldehyde since catalytic reduction of L-Δ^1-piperideine-6-carboxylic acid would yield L-pipecolic acid; however, the possibility that Δ^1-piperideine-6-carboxylic acid was formed and racemized was not unequivocally excluded. Studies with C^{14}- and N^{15}-labeled α-amino-adipic acid showed that the carbon chain and nitrogen atom of α-aminoadipic acid rather than those of lysine are the major precursors of pipecolic acid. Since pipecolic acid does not accumulate in the presence of high concentrations of L-lysine, the data suggest that such accumula-tion is related to a synthetic pathway; however, it is possible that pipe-colic acid is formed from an intermediate in lysine biosynthesis and is not on the direct biosynthetic pathway.

A lysine-requiring mutant of *Saccharomyces cerevisiae* has been reported to accumulate glutaric acid as well as α-aminoadipic acid (2442). At the present time there is little reason to believe that glutaric acid is an intermediate in lysine biosynthesis, and the most likely explanation for this finding is that the glutaric acid arises from the degradation of α-aminoadipic acid.

A tentative scheme for the α-aminoadipic acid-lysine pathway is given in Scheme 36.

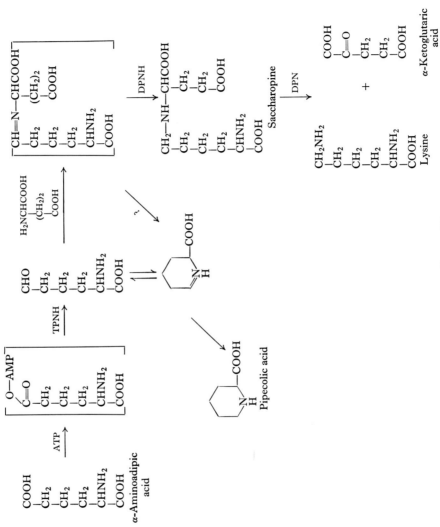

SCHEME 36

Degradation

Lysine is an essential dietary amino acid for mammals (see p. 204), and cannot be replaced by α-aminoadipic acid (2443), norleucine (2444), ε-hydroxycaproic acid (2445), ε-aminocaproic acid (2445), α-hydroxy-ε-aminocaproic acid (2445), pipecolic acid (2446), α-amino-ε-hydroxycaproic acid (2447), and homocitrulline (2446). A small growth response to homoarginine was obtained in the rat after a delay of several days (2448). This suggests that homoarginine is hydrolyzed to urea and lysine, or that conversion of homoarginine to lysine takes place by transamidination (see p. 642). In contrast to certain other amino acids, the growth-promoting effect of dietary L-lysine is not exhibited by D-lysine (2449, 2450) or by derivatives of L-lysine in which the α-amino group is substituted or replaced by a hydroxyl group. However, the ε-N-acetyl and ε-N-methyl derivatives of lysine can replace dietary lysine in supporting the growth of the rat (2451, 2452). Diacetyllysine does not replace lysine in the diet of growing rats (2453).

The observation that rat kidney slices catalyze the demethylation of ε-N-methyl-DL-lysine seems to explain the ability of this compound to replace lysine in the diet of the rat (2454). The failure of the rat to utilize α-N-acetyllysine in place of lysine suggests that the activity of kidney amino acid N-acylase (see p. 158) is insufficient to release appreciable amounts of the free amino acid from the acyl derivative; α-N-acetyl-L-lysine is not a very active substrate for this enzyme (514). On the other hand, when α-N-acetyl-DL-lysine containing N^{15} in the α-amino group and deuterium in the acetyl group was administered to rats, isotopic protein-lysine was formed (2455), indicating that some deacylation occurs. The ability of ε-N-acetyllysine to replace lysine in the diet is consistent with data showing that this compound can serve as a source of acetyl groups *in vivo* (2456). An enzyme has been found in rat kidney and other tissues that hydrolyzes ε-N-acetyl-L-lysine; ε-N-acetyl-L-lysine acylase is not identical with kidney α-N-acetyl amino acid acylase (2457). It is evident that the activity of this enzyme *in vivo* is not very great since ε-N-acetyllysine is only 30 to 50% as effective as lysine in supporting the growth of rats (2451, 2453). Enzyme activity capable of hydrolyzing α-N-acyllysine derivatives has been found in a number of microorganisms (2458, 2459), but the enzyme is not specific for α-N-acyllysine derivatives. An extensive survey of a large number of microorganisms for ε-lysine acylase has been carried out and this activity has been found in many bacteria, molds, and yeast (2460, 2461). The possibility that acyllysine derivatives are involved in biosynthesis was mentioned above, and the same speculation can be offered in relation to the degradation of lysine.

When lysine labeled with deuterium and N^{15} was administered to rats, it was incorporated into protein without appreciable change in the $D:N^{15}$ ratio (2455). Administration of N^{15}-ammonia or of N^{15}-amino acids to rats did not lead to incorporation of isotope into the α-amino group of lysine (661, 2462–2464). Only slight labilization of the α-hydrogen atom of lysine occurs in the intact rat. These observations indicate that lysine does not participate appreciably in reversible transamination or deamination reactions, but they do not exclude irreversible deamination or transamination, and indeed subsequent studies are consistent with a reaction of this type.

Lysine is "metabolically inert" in animals as compared to most of the other amino acids. α-Deamination or transamination of lysine would be expected to yield α-keto-ϵ-aminocaproic acid, which probably exists in solution predominantly in its cyclic form, Δ^1-piperideine-2-carboxylic acid (685). Thus far, efforts to demonstrate lysine formation from this α-keto acid enzymatically have not been successful, and although apparently neither Δ^1-piperideine-2-carboxylate nor Δ^1-piperideine-6-carboxylate has been tested as a dietary replacement for lysine in animals, these compounds do not support the growth of a number of lysine-requiring microorganisms (2465). There are several reports of transamination of lysine with α-keto acids in various animal tissue preparations, but in no instance was the reaction very great in extent, and the product of lysine transamination was not demonstrated. Both L- and D-isomers of lysine are attacked very slowly by the respective general amino acid oxidases (see p. 298). As discussed elsewhere (see pp. 346 and 306), both transamination and oxidative deamination of lysine and transamination of the α-keto acid analog of lysine have been observed when the ϵ-amino group is acylated.

Borsook and collaborators were the first to examine the degradation of lysine to glutaric acid in an *in vitro* mammalian system (2466–2468). Earlier studies in Borsook's laboratory had provided evidence that lysine nitrogen is used to some extent for the formation of citrulline and arginine; it was suspected that lysine might be converted to a-amino-adipic acid, whose amino group was utilized for citrulline formation. When guinea pig liver homogenates were incubated with ϵ-C^{14}-lysine, labeled α-aminoadipic acid could subsequently be isolated after addition of carrier and repeated crystallization. Other studies of this type indicated that α-aminoadipic acid is converted to α-ketoadipic acid, which in turn is converted to glutaric acid. A lysine-α-aminoadipic acid pathway is indicated also by the urinary excretion of the latter amino acid by guinea pigs after administration of L-lysine (2469). There is also a report describing the presence of α-ketoadipic acid in the urine of rats after feeding of lysine (2470).

The conclusions of Borsook and his colleagues that the metabolism of lysine leads to α-aminoadipic and glutaric acids was substantiated by later work which revealed other intermediates. Conversion of lysine to glutaric acid had been suggested as early as 1913 by Ringer and associates, who found that neither lysine nor glutaric acid forms glucose or aceto-acetate (2471). Using an isotope-trapping technique (metabolite-over-loading), Rothstein and Miller obtained evidence for formation of glutaric acid from lysine and from α-aminoadipic acid in the rat. Data suggesting conversion of glutaric acid to α-hydroxyglutaric and β-hydroxyglutaric acids were also obtained (2472, 2473). Although their findings indicated oxidation by rat liver mitochondria of glutaric acid to β-hydroxyglutaric acid (2473), studies on intact rats showed that the major route of glutarate metabolism is through acetate rather than α-ketoglutarate (2474). Additional experiments (2475) in which rats were given glutaric acid-3-C^{14} provided no evidence that the metabolism of glutarate proceeded through acetone dicarboxylic acid or β-hydroxyglutaric acid, but did indicate that glutarate is converted to acetate via acetoacetate. A plausible pathway for the metabolism of glutaric acid is therefore conversion to glutaryl-coenzyme A and oxidation of the latter followed by decarboxyla-tion and hydration to acetoacetyl-coenzyme A. It is of interest that similar reactions have been observed in extracts of *Pseudomonas* (2476).

The discovery of pipecolic acid in various plant tissues (2477–2481) was followed shortly by the demonstration of the conversion of lysine to pipecolic acid in higher plants (2482, 2483), *Neurospora* (2484), and the rat (2472). Evidence was obtained that pipecolic acid is an intermediate in the conversion of lysine to α-aminoadipic acid. Rothstein and Miller (2472) administered labeled L-lysine and unlabeled L-pipecolic acid to a rat and isolated labeled pipecolic acid of relatively high specific activity from the urine. They also made the important observation, in experiments in which α-N^{15}-lysine and ϵ-N^{15}-lysine were used, that the α-amino group rather than the ϵ-amino group of lysine was lost during conversion of lysine to pipecolic acid in the rat. Administration of C^{14}-labeled α-aminoadipic acid did not lead to the formation of radioactive pipecolic acid, but under the same conditions labeled lysine gave labeled urinary pipecolic acid. Conversion of C^{14}-pipecolic acid to labeled α-aminoadipic acid (and glutaric acid) has been shown in the intact rat and with rat liver mitochondria (2485). These findings, therefore, suggest the pathway shown in Scheme 37 for the degradation of lysine in the rat.

Not all of the individual steps in the scheme presented above have been demonstrated with isolated enzyme preparations. Thus, the first step, conversion of lysine to α-keto-ε-aminocaproic acid has not been shown with mammalian preparations. As noted above, studies on transamination of lysine have thus far failed to indicate that this reaction leads to α-keto-ε-aminocaproic acid. However, oxidative deamination of L-lysine has been observed with very high concentrations of snake venom L-amino acid oxidase (2465) and with an amino acid oxidase of turkey liver, which exhibits a high specificity for the basic amino acids (see p. 310). The formation of α-keto-ε-aminocaproic acid was shown with the latter enzyme. It is possible that a specific lysine oxidase exists in mammalian liver, but has thus far escaped detection. On the other hand, an attractive possibility is that acylation of the ε-amino group of lysine takes place prior to removal of the amino group. Although no studies have apparently been carried out on the ε-acylation of lysine by mammalian tissues, the hydrolysis of ε-acyl derivatives of lysine has been studied (2457). The latter activity is also present in a number of microorganisms (2486) and it has been found that this enzyme as well as that of mammalian tissues can catalyze the hydrolysis of α-keto-ε-N-acetylaminocaproic acid (2465, 2487).

Conversion of α-keto-ε-aminocaproic acid to the cyclic form Δ^1-piperideine-2-carboxylic acid occurs spontaneously (685). The reduction of Δ^1-piperideine-2-carboxylic acid to L-pipecolic acid is catalyzed by an enzyme present in rat liver, other mammalian tissues, as well as in microorganisms and plants (820, 2488). The enzyme functions with either reduced diphosphopyridine nucleotide or reduced triphosphopyridine nucleotide. The conversion of pipecolic acid to α-aminoadipic acid has been demonstrated with preparations of beef liver mitochondria in the presence of adenosine triphosphate and magnesium ions (2489). A similar reaction is catalyzed by *Pseudomonas* adapted to growth on pipecolic acid (2490) and evidence for the intermediate formation of Δ^1-piperideine-6-carboxylic acid has been obtained by trapping the com-

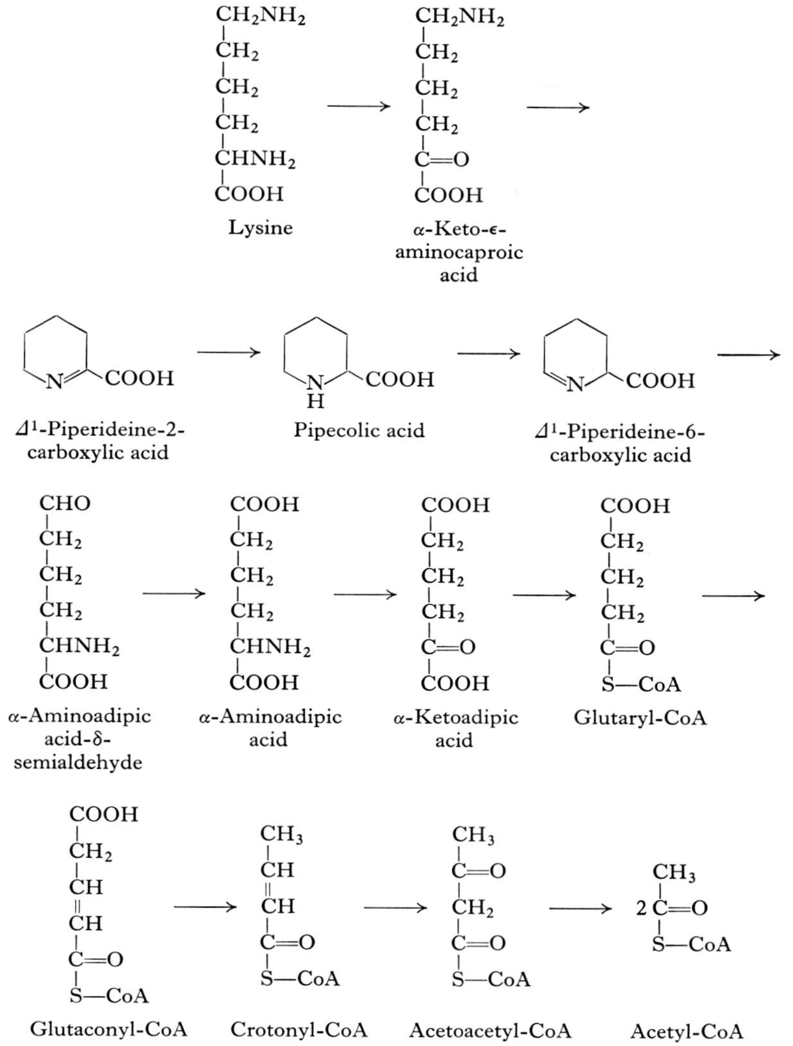

$$
\begin{array}{ccc}
\begin{array}{c} CH_2NH_2 \\ | \\ CH_2 \\ | \\ CH_2 \\ | \\ CH_2 \\ | \\ CHNH_2 \\ | \\ COOH \end{array}
&\longrightarrow&
\begin{array}{c} CH_2NH_2 \\ | \\ CH_2 \\ | \\ CH_2 \\ | \\ CH_2 \\ | \\ C{=}O \\ | \\ COOH \end{array}
\longrightarrow \\
\text{Lysine} & & \begin{array}{c}\alpha\text{-Keto-}\epsilon\text{-}\\ \text{aminocaproic}\\ \text{acid}\end{array}
\end{array}
$$

Δ^1-Piperideine-2-carboxylic acid $\longrightarrow$ Pipecolic acid $\longrightarrow$ Δ^1-Piperideine-6-carboxylic acid $\longrightarrow$

$$
\begin{array}{cccc}
\begin{array}{c} CHO \\ | \\ CH_2 \\ | \\ CH_2 \\ | \\ CH_2 \\ | \\ CHNH_2 \\ | \\ COOH \end{array}
&\longrightarrow&
\begin{array}{c} COOH \\ | \\ CH_2 \\ | \\ CH_2 \\ | \\ CH_2 \\ | \\ CHNH_2 \\ | \\ COOH \end{array}
&\longrightarrow
\begin{array}{c} COOH \\ | \\ CH_2 \\ | \\ CH_2 \\ | \\ CH_2 \\ | \\ C{=}O \\ | \\ COOH \end{array}
\longrightarrow
\begin{array}{c} COOH \\ | \\ CH_2 \\ | \\ CH_2 \\ | \\ CH_2 \\ | \\ C{=}O \\ | \\ S{-}CoA \end{array}
\longrightarrow
\end{array}
$$

| α-Aminoadipic acid-δ-semialdehyde | α-Aminoadipic acid | α-Ketoadipic acid | Glutaryl-CoA |

$$
\begin{array}{cccc}
\begin{array}{c} COOH \\ | \\ CH_2 \\ | \\ CH \\ \| \\ CH \\ | \\ C{=}O \\ | \\ S{-}CoA \end{array}
&\longrightarrow&
\begin{array}{c} CH_3 \\ | \\ CH \\ \| \\ CH \\ | \\ C{=}O \\ | \\ S{-}CoA \end{array}
&\longrightarrow
\begin{array}{c} CH_3 \\ | \\ C{=}O \\ | \\ CH_2 \\ | \\ C{=}O \\ | \\ S{-}CoA \end{array}
\longrightarrow
\begin{array}{c} CH_3 \\ 2\ C{=}O \\ | \\ S{-}CoA \end{array}
\end{array}
$$

| Glutaconyl-CoA | Crotonyl-CoA | Acetoacetyl-CoA | Acetyl-CoA |

SCHEME 37

pound in the presence of bisulfite (2491). *Pseudomonas* (2491), as well as mammalian kidney and liver preparations (2441), contains an enzyme that catalyzes the pyridine nucleotide-dependent oxidation of α-aminoadipic acid δ-semialdehyde to L-α-aminoadipic acid. The metabolism of α-aminoadipic acid proceeds by transamination to α-ketoadipic acid, and the conversion of the latter compound to glutaryl-coenzyme A probably occurs by an oxidative decarboxylation similar to that shown for other α-keto acids.

Evidence partially consistent with the scheme given above for the degradation of lysine to pipecolic acid and α-aminoadipic acid was obtained in studies on *Neurospora* by Schweet and associates (2484, 2492). These investigators reported data indicating conversion of lysine to Δ^1-piperideine-2-carboxylic acid and of the latter compound to pipecolic acid; evidence was also obtained for conversion of Δ^1-piperideine-2-carboxylic acid to lysine *in vivo*. The formation of α-hydroxy-ε-*N*-acetylaminocaproic acid was suggested by their data, but this product was not definitely identified.

The possibility that δ-aminovaleric acid is a metabolite of lysine was first suggested by Neuberger and Sanger (2454). This amino acid is known as a product of the nonenzymatic decarboxylation of the α-keto analog of lysine (685), and it might be formed enzymatically as the coenzyme A derivative in a reaction analogous to those involved in the degradation of the branched chain amino acids. Although δ-C^{14}-δ-aminovaleric acid is converted to glutaric acid in the rat (2493), the available data suggests that it is not a major metabolite of lysine. Transamination of δ-aminovaleric acid to glutaric acid semialdehyde has been described (2492–2495; see p. 356). Although δ-aminovaleric acid is the expected product of the oxidative deamination of lysine in the absence of catalase (see p. 296), an enzyme obtained from a pseudomonad catalyzes the conversion of lysine to δ-aminovaleric acid, carbon dioxide, and ammonia, by a mechanism of the oxygenase type (see p. 323).

Lysine occurs in yeast as ε-*N*-biotinyl-L-lysine (biocytin) (2496). An enzyme present in human blood hydrolyzes biocytin (2497) and biocytin is excreted in the urine in the form of biocytin sulfoxide (2498). Biotin is the prosthetic group of several carboxylases (see p. 745); biotin is linked to protein by a peptide bond between the carboxyl group of biotin and an ε-amino group of a protein lysine (see p. 446).

A surprisingly large number of investigations have been carried out with D-lysine in the mammal. Administration of D-lysine is followed by urinary excretion of most of the D-lysine given (2454, 2499). When D-lysine labeled with N^{15} and deuterium was fed to young rats, about half of the D-lysine was excreted unchanged in the urine, about 19% of the total N^{15} administered was present in urinary urea and ammonia, and 21% of the N^{15} was found in the amino acids of the tissue protein (2500). D-Lysine labeled with C^{14} in the ε-carbon atom was not converted to pipecolic acid in the rat, and the isotope was recovered in the urine and tissue nonprotein fractions (2501). The absence of evidence for appreciable metabolism of D-lysine in the mammal is not unexpected, but it is of interest that this D-amino acid is apparently metabolized to some extent under certain conditions. The bacterial flora may be responsible for some of the observed minimal metabolism of D-lysine, but there may be tissue enzymes capable of acting upon D-lysine as well. D-Amino acid oxidase exhibits very low activity toward lysine and it appears unlikely that this enzyme catalyzes significant *in vivo* oxidation of D-lysine.

Lysine is oxidized by pea seedling diamine oxidase to yield Δ^1-piperideine-6-carboxylic acid (α-aminoadipic acid-δ-semialdehyde) (2502). This compound is also formed by enzymatic oxidation of α-amino-ε-hydroxycaproic acid (818, 819), and has been chemically synthesized by ozonolysis of 2-amino-6-heptenoic acid (2441) and by oxidation of α-amino-ε-hydroxycaproic acid with chromic acid (2503).

A strain of *Clostridium* catalyzes the anaerobic degradation of D- and L-lysine according to the following equation:

$$\text{Lysine} + 2H_2O \rightarrow \text{butyrate} + \text{acetate} + 2NH_3$$

The reaction does not involve an overall oxidation or reduction and therefore is not a Stickland reaction (see p. 321). Studies with isotopically labeled lysine indicate that conversion to butyrate and acetate involves cleavage of a two-carbon fragment from either end of the molecule, leaving the corresponding four-carbon fragments of the lysine-carbon chain (2504, 2505). Recent studies on cell suspensions of another *Clostridium* indicate that this organism also degrades lysine in this manner, but soluble cell extracts cleave lysine so as to produce acetate only from the carboxyl end of the molecule. There is evidence that the reaction requires a cobamide coenzyme, a flavoprotein electron carrier, and that the enzyme contains a dimercaptan moiety (2506).

Other Reactions of Lysine

Lysine and cadaverine can serve as precursors of the piperidine ring of anabasine in *Nicotiana* plants (2507, 2508). When lysine-2-C^{14} was fed, all of the incorporated radioactivity was found in carbon atom 2 of the piperidine ring of anabasine. In studies with cadaverine-1,5-C^{14}, carbon atom 2 of the piperidine moiety of anabasine contained only half of the original radioactivity; this finding is analogous to observations on the formation of the pyrrolidine ring of nicotine (see p. 705). However, the data indicate that incorporation of lysine into anabasine proceeds asymmetrically. Another possible pathway of anabasine biosynthesis involves conversion of cadaverine to Δ^1-piperideine by diamine oxidase followed by spontaneous cyclization (787, 2509). Dimerization of Δ^1-piperideine has been observed, and the resulting tetrahydroanabasine can be oxidized by certain plant extracts to anabasine. However, evidence for the latter pathway is incomplete and other data suggest that the pyridine ring of anabasine arises from nicotinic acid (see p. 863).

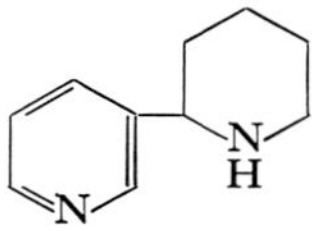

Anabasine

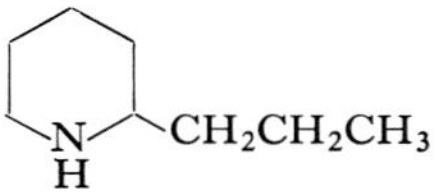

Coniine

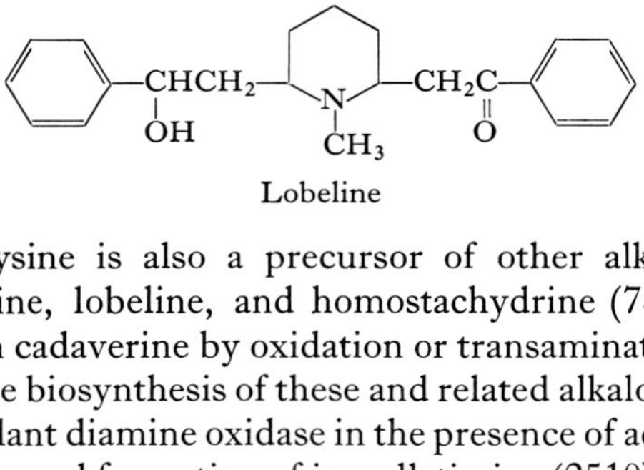

Lobeline

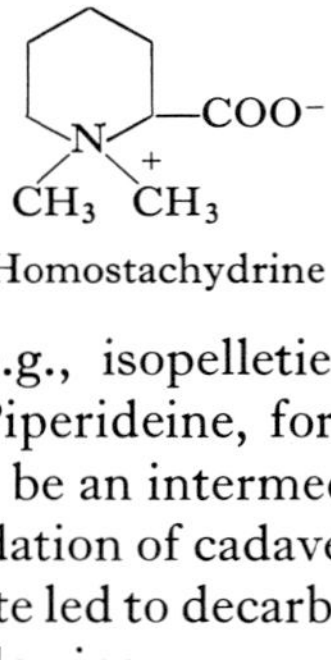

Homostachydrine

Lysine is also a precursor of other alkaloids, e.g., isopelletierine, coniine, lobeline, and homostachydrine (787). Δ^1-Piperideine, formed from cadaverine by oxidation or transamination, may be an intermediate in the biosynthesis of these and related alkaloids. Oxidation of cadaverine by plant diamine oxidase in the presence of acetoacetate led to decarboxylation and formation of isopelletierine (2510); the following sequence of events is plausible:

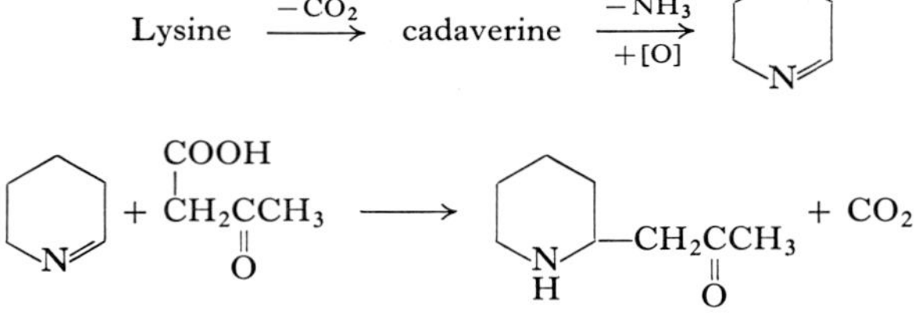

Lysine $\xrightarrow{-CO_2}$ cadaverine $\xrightarrow[+[O]]{-NH_3}$

Δ^1-Piperideine

Isopelletierine

Analogous studies were carried out with putrescine, and formation of norhygrine was observed (2510).

Hydroxylysine

Lysine is the precursor of collagen 5-hydroxylysine, which is probably formed by a mechanism similar to that involved in the conversion of proline to collagen hydroxyproline (see p. 716); however, neither conversion is as yet fully understood. When young rats were fed C^{14}-lysine for 3 weeks, the specific radioactivities of the skin collagen lysine and hydroxylysine were about the same (2511). This observation is consistent with the knowledge that hydroxylysine is not a dietary essential amino acid for animals. Several experiments indicate that free hydroxylysine is not a precursor of collagen hydroxylysine; thus, the presence of exogenous unlabeled hydroxylysine in the plasma of rats did not dilute labeled lysine during collagen hydroxylysine synthesis (2512). When radioactive

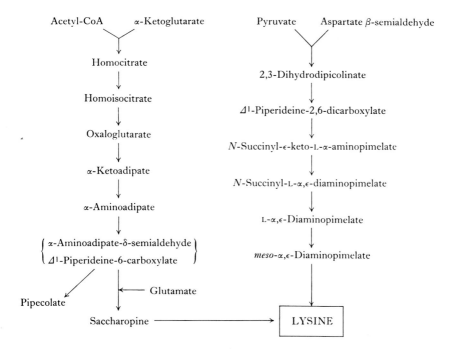

Summary scheme for the biosynthesis of lysine.

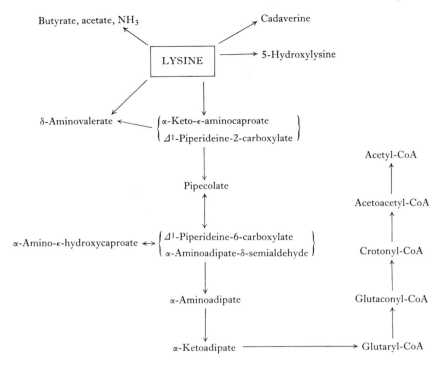

Summary scheme for the metabolism of lysine.

hydroxylysine was fed or injected into young rats, no significant incorporation of isotope occurred into the skin collagen (2513). When C^{14}-lysine was injected into young rats and the specific activities of the collagen lysine and hydroxylysine subsequently determined, it was found that these were equal to each other from 4 hours to 15 weeks after injection. The latter findings are consistent with the assumption that hydroxylation of lysine is completed during the process of incorporation into the collagen (2514). These and other observations (2515) are analogous to findings on the formation of collagen hydroxyproline (see p. 716). However, recent studies have demonstrated that the oxygen of water rather than atmospheric oxygen is incorporated into the oxygen of hydroxylysine during collagen formation (2516). These studies also showed that more tritium was incorporated from tritiated water into hydroxylysine than into lysine. The latter observations indicate that the mechanism of hydroxylation is different than that involved in the formation of hydroxyproline (see p. 721).

Studies with radioactive lysine and hydroxylysine have demonstrated that there is no interconversion between these in growing cultures of *Streptococcus faecalis*. However, it is significant that hydroxylysine markedly spares the lysine requirement of this organism; yet, no radioactive compounds other than hydroxylysine were found after growth on labeled hydroxylysine. The mechanism of the hydroxylysine-sparing effect is related to its ability to promote increased resistance to lysis. Cells grown in the presence of lysine undergo autolysis as lysine is depleted, while growth in the presence of hydroxylysine prevents lysis (2517). When cells of *S. faecalis* were suspended in media lacking lysine lysis promptly occurred, but addition of hydroxylysine led to an increase in turbidity, which was not affected by chloramphenicol. The findings suggest that hydroxylysine is incorporated into the cell wall in place of lysine, but this has not yet been demonstrated by isolation of the cell wall material and analysis (2518).

The degradation of hydroxylysine has not yet been extensively examined; however, incubation of labeled 5-hydroxylysine with homogenates of rat liver and kidney led to the formation of radioactive 5-hydroxypipecolic acid (2519). Hydroxy-L-lysine is oxidatively deaminated by turkey liver L-amino acid oxidase (2520), and both L-stereoisomers of hydroxylysine are attacked by lysine decarboxylase (see p. 334).

References

1. Cellular Regulatory Mechanisms, *Cold Spring Harbor Symp. Quant. Biol.* **26** (1961).
2. Freundlich, M., Burns, R. O., and Umbarger, H. E., *Proc. Natl. Acad. Sci. U.S.* **48**, 1804 (1962).
3. Armstrong, F. B., Gordon, M. L., and Wagner, R. P., *Proc. Natl. Acad. Sci. U.S.* **49**, 322 (1963).
4. Armstrong, F. B., and Wagner, R. P., *Proc. Natl. Acad. Sci. U.S.* **49**, 628 (1963).
5. Vogel, H. J., *in* "Control Mechanisms in Cellular Processes" (D. M. Bonner, ed.), p. 23. Ronald Press, New York, 1961.
6. Moyed, H. S., and Umbarger, H. E., *Physiol. Rev.* **42**, 444 (1962).
7. Stadtman, E. R., *Bacteriol. Rev.* **27**, 170 (1963).
8. Vogel, H. J., Bryson, V., and Lampen, J. O., (eds.), "Informational Macromolecules." Academic Press, New York, 1963.
9. Kinoshita, S., Udaka, S., and Shimono, M., *J. Gen. Appl. Microbiol. (Tokyo)* **3**, 193 (1957).

10. Kinoshita, S., *Adv. Appl. Microbiol.* **1**, 201 (1959).
11. Adelberg, E. A., *J. Bacteriol.* **76**, 326 (1958).
12. Robinson, R., *J. Chem. Soc.* **111**, 762 (1917).
13. Robinson, R., *J. Chem. Soc.* **111**, 876 (1917).
14. Robinson, R., "The Structural Relations of Natural Products." Oxford Univ. Press (Clarendon), London and New York, 1955.
15. Carnahan, J. E., and Castle, J. E., *Ann. Rev. Plant Physiol.* **14**, 125 (1963).
16. Yocum, C. S., *Ann. Rev. Plant Physiol.* **11**, 25 (1960).
17. Aleem, M. R. H., and Nason, A., *in* "Symposium on Marine Biology" (C. H. Oppenheimer, ed.), p. 392. Thomas, Springfield, Illinois, 1960.
18. McElroy, W. D., and Glass, B., eds., "Inorganic Nitrogen Metabolism." Johns Hopkins Press, Baltimore, Maryland, 1956.
19. Miller, S. L., *Science* **117**, 528 (1953); *J. Am. Chem. Soc.* **77**, 2351 (1955); *Federation Proc.* **15**, 316 (1956).
20. Miller, S. L., *Biochim. Biophys. Acta* **23**, 480 (1957).
21. Miller, S. L., and Urey, H. C., *Science* **130** 245 (1959).
22. Hasselstrom, T., Henry, M. C., and Murr, B., *Science* **125**, 350 (1957).
23. Oró, J., Kimball, A., Fritz, R., and Master, F., *Arch. Biochem. Biophys.* **85**, 115 (1959).
24. Fox, S. W., and Harada, K., *in* "Medical and Biological Problems of Space Flight" (G. H. Bourne, ed.), p. 261. Academic Press, New York, 1963.
25. Lowe, C. U., Rees, M. W., and Markham, R., *Nature* **199**, 219 (1963).
26. Ponnamperuma, C., Sagan, C., and Mariner, R., *Nature* **199**, 222 (1963).
27. Oparin, A. I., "The Origin of Life on Earth," 3rd ed. Academic Press, New York, 1957.
28. Calvin, M., *Adv. Biol. Med. Phys.* **8**, 315 (1962).
29. Ezra, H. C., and Cook, S. F., *Science* **126**, 80 (1957).
30. Heijkenskjold, F., and Mollerberg, H., *Nature* **181**, 334 (1958).
31. Abelson, P. H., *Carnegie Inst. Wash., Yearbook* **53**, 97 (1953–1954).
32. Sauberlich, H. E., and Baumann, C. A., *J. Biol. Chem.* **177**, 545 (1949).
33. Stadtman, E. R., *J. Am. Chem. Soc.* **77**, 5765 (1955).
34. Vagelos, P. R., Earl, J. M., and Stadtman, E. R., *J. Biol. Chem.* **234**, 490 (1959).
35. Fink, K., Henderson, R. B., and Fink, R. M., *Proc. Soc. Exptl. Biol. Med.* **78**, 135 (1951); *J. Biol. Chem.* **197**, 441 (1952).
36. Fink, K., McGaughey, C., Henderson, R. B., and Fink, R. M., *Federation Proc.* **15**, 251 (1956).
37. Fink, K., Cline, R. E., Henderson, R. B., and Fink, R. M., *J. Biol. Chem.* **221**, 425 (1956).
38. Fritzson, P., and Pihl, A., *J. Biol. Chem.* **226**, 229 (1957).
39. Canellakis, E. S., *J. Biol. Chem.* **221**, 315 (1956).
40. Wallach, D. P., and Grisolia, S., *J. Biol. Chem.* **226**, 277 (1957).
41. Caravaca, J., and Grisolia, S., *J. Biol. Chem.* **231**, 357 (1958).
42. Campbell, L. L., *J. Biol. Chem.* **235**, 2375 (1960).
43. Razin, S., Bachrach, U., and Gery, I., *Nature* **181**, 700 (1958).
44. Bachrach, U., Persky, S., and Razin, S., *Biochem. J.* **76**, 306 (1960).
45. Kupiecki, F. P., and Coon, M. J., *J. Biol. Chem.* **229**, 743 (1957).
46. Rendina, G., and Coon, M. J., *J. Biol. Chem.* **225**, 523 (1957).

47. Bush, M. T., Touster, O., and Brockman, J. E., *J. Biol. Chem.* **188**, 685 (1951).
48. Graff, J. and Hoberman, H. D., *J. Biol. Chem.* **186**, 369 (1950).
49. Sorvachev, K. F., *Biokhimiya* **18** (16), 696 (1953).
50. Pihl, A., and Fritzson, P., *J. Biol. Chem.* **215**, 345 (1955).
51. Hayaishi, O., Nishizuka, Y., Tatibana, M., Takeshita, M., and Kuno, S., *J. Biol. Chem.* **236**, 781 (1961).
52. Goldfine, H., and Stadtman, E. R., *J. Biol. Chem.* **235**, 2238 (1960).
53. Koser, S. A., Wright, M. H., and Dorfman, A., *Proc. Soc. Exptl. Biol. Med.* **51**, 204 (1942).
54. Stokes, J. L., Larsen, A., and Gunness, M., *J. Bacteriol.* **54**, 219 (1947).
55. Lardy, H. A., Potter, R. L., and Elvehjem, C. A., *J. Biol. Chem.* **169**, 451 (1947).
56. Shive, W., and Rogers, L. L., *J. Biol. Chem.* **169**, 453 (1947).
57. Lardy, H. A., Potter, R. L., and Burris, R. H., *J. Biol. Chem.* **179**, 721 (1949).
58. Broquist, H. P., and Snell, E. E., *J. Biol. Chem.* **188**, 431 (1951).
59. Moat, A. G., and Lichstein, H. C., *Arch. Biochem. Biophys.* **48**, 300 (1954).
60. Nakada, H. I., and Weinhouse, S., *J. Biol. Chem.* **187**, 663 (1950).
61. Ravel, J. M., Norton, S. J., Humphreys, J. S., and Shive, W., *J. Biol. Chem.* **237**, 2845 (1962).
62. von Fürth, O., and Friedmann, M., *Biochem. Z.* **26**, 435 (1910).
63. Clementi, A., *Arch. Intern. Physiol.* **19**, 369 (1922).
64. Steenholt, G., *Acta Physiol. Scand.* **8**, 342 (1944).
65. Greenstein, J. P., and Carter, C. E., *J. Natl. Cancer Inst.* **7**, 57 (1946).
66. Price, V. E., and Greenstein, J. P., *J. Natl. Cancer Inst.* **7**, 275 (1947).
67. Carter, C. E., and Greenstein, J. P., *J. Natl. Cancer Inst.* **7**, 433 (1947).
68. Errera, M., and Greenstein, J. P., *J. Natl. Cancer Inst.* **7**, 437 (1947).
69. Gonsalves, J. M., Price, V. E., and Greenstein, J. P., *J. Natl. Cancer Inst.* **7**, 281 (1947).
70. Errera, M. E., and Greenstein, J. P., *J. Natl. Cancer Inst.* **7**, 285 (1947).
71. Grover, C. E., and Chibnall, A. C., *Biochem. J.* **21**, 857 (1927).
72. Schmalfuss, K., and Mothes, K., *Biochem. Z.* **221**, 134 (1930).
73. Gorr, G., and Wagner, J., *Biochem. Z.* **254**, 1 (1932).
74. Grassmann, W., and Mayr, O., *Z. Physiol. Chem.* **214**, 185 (1933).
75. Utzino, S., and Imaizumi, M., *Z. Physiol. Chem.* **253**, 51 (1938).
76. Altenbern, R. A., *in* "Amino Acid Metabolism" (W. D. McElroy and B. Glass, eds.), p. 33. Johns Hopkins Press, Baltimore, Maryland, 1955.
77. Krebs, H. A., *Biochem. J.* **47**, 605 (1950).
78. Meister, A., *in* "Methods in Enzymology" (S. P. Colowick and N. O. Kaplan, eds.), Vol. 2, p. 383. Academic Press, New York, 1955.
79. Meister, A., Levintow, L., Greenfield, R. E., and Abendshein, P. A., *J. Biol. Chem.* **215**, 441 (1955).
80. Tower, D. B., Peters, E. L., and Curtis, W. C., *J. Biol. Chem.* **238**, 983 (1963).
81. Sansom, B. F., and Barry, J. M., *Biochem. J.* **68**, 487 (1958).
82. Kidd, J. G., *J. Exptl. Med.* **98**, 565, 583 (1953).
83. Herbut, P. A., Kraemer, W. H., *Am. J. Pathol.* **34**, 767 (1958).
84. Broome, J. B., *Nature* **191**, 1114 (1961).
85. Kapoor, M., and Waygood, E. R., *Biochem. Biophys. Res. Commun.* **9**, 7 (1962).
86. Harpaz, I., and Applebaum, S. W., *Nature* **192**, 780 (1961).

87. Quastel, J. H., and Woolf, B., *Biochem. J.* 20, 545 (1926).
88. Cook, R. P., and Woolf, B., *Biochem. J.* 22, 474 (1928).
89. Woolf, B., *Biochem. J.* 23, 472 (1929).
90. Virtanen, A. I., and Tarnanen, J., *Biochem. Z.* 250, 193 (1932).
91. Gale, E. F., *Biochem. J.* 32, 1583 (1938).
92. Williams, V. R., and McIntyre, R. T., *J. Biol. Chem.* 217, 467 (1955).
93. Ellfolk, N., *Acta Chem. Scand.* 7, 824,1155 (1953); 8, 151,443 (1954); 9, 771 (1955).
94. Ichihara, A. K., Kanagawa, H., and Uchida, M., *J. Biochem. (Tokyo)* 42, 439 (1955).
95. Depue, R. H., and Moat, A. G., *J. Bacteriol.* 82, 383 (1961).
96. Halpern, Y. S., and Umbarger, H. E., *J. Bacteriol.* 80, 285 (1960).
97. Krasna, A. I., *J. Biol. Chem.* 233, 1010 (1958).
98. Englard, S., *J. Biol. Chem.* 233, 1003 (1958).
99. Farrar, T. C., Gutowsky, H. S., Alberty, R. A., and Miller, W. G., *J. Am. Chem. Soc.* 79, 3978 (1957).
100. Emery, T. F., *Biochemistry* 2, 1041 (1963).
101. Barker, H. A., Smyth, R. D., Wilson, R. M., and Weissbach, H., *J. Biol. Chem.* 234, 320 (1959).
101a. Bright, H. J., and Silverman, R., *Biochim. Biophys. Acta* 81, 175 (1964).
101b. Bright, H. J., Ingraham, L. L., and Lundin, R. E., *Biochim. Biophys. Acta* 81, 576 (1964).
101c. Iodice, A. A., and Barker, H. A., *J. Biol. Chem.* 238, 2094 (1963).
102. Wachsman, J. T., *J. Biol. Chem.* 223, 19 (1956).
103. Barker, H. A., Smyth, R. D., Wawszkiewicz, E. J., Lee, M. N., and Wilson, R. M., *Arch. Biochem. Biophys.* 78, 468 (1958).
104. Bright, H. J., and Ingraham, L. L., *Biochim. Biophys. Acta* 44, 586 (1960).
105. Carter, C. E., and Cohen, L. H., *J. Am. Chem. Soc.* 77, 499 (1955).
106. Carter, C. E., *Federation Proc.* 15, 230 (1956).
107. Ballio, A., Barcellona, S., and Di Vittorio, V., *Arch. Biochem. Biophys.* 101, 311 (1963).
108. Carter, C. E., *J. Biol. Chem.* 223, 139 (1956).
109. Lieberman, I., *J. Am. Chem. Soc.*, 78, 251 (1956); *J. Biol. Chem.*, 223, 327 (1956).
110. Joklik, W. K., *Biochim. Biophys. Acta* 22, 211 (1956).
111. Ballio, A., and Serlupi-Crescenzi, G., *Nature* 179, 154 (1957).
112. Whitfeld, P. R., *Arch. Biochem. Biophys.* 65, 585 (1956).
113. Abelskov, J., *Biochim. Biophys. Acta* 32, 566 (1959).
114. Partridge, C. W. H., and Giles, N. H., *Arch. Biochem. Biophys.* 67, 237 (1957).
115. Weissmann, B., and Gutman, A. B., *J. Biol. Chem.* 229, 239 (1957).
116. Hampton, A., *J. Biol. Chem.* 237, 529 (1962).
117. Sallach, H. J., and Peterson, T. H., *J. Biol. Chem.* 223, 629 (1956).
118. Sallach, H. J., *J. Biol. Chem.* 229, 437 (1957).
119. Garcia-Hernandez, M., and Kun, E., *Biochim. Biophys. Acta* 24, 78 (1957).
120. Chow, C. T., and Vennesland, B., *J. Biol. Chem.* 233, 997 (1958).
121. Sallach, H. J., *J. Biol. Chem.* 234, 900 (1959).
122. Kornberg, H. L., and Morris, J. G., *Nature* 197, 456 (1963); *Biochim. Biophys. Acta* 56, 537; 65, 378 (1962).
123. Reichard, P., *Adv. Enzymol.* 21, 263 (1959).
124. Woods, L., Ravel, J. M., and Shive, W., *J. Biol. Chem.* 209, 559 (1954).

125. Lagerkvist, U., Reichard, P., and Ehrensvärd, G., *Acta Chem. Scand.* **5**, 1212 (1951).
126. Reichard, P., and Lagerkvist, U., *Acta Chem. Scand.* **7**, 1207 (1953).
127. Lieberman, I., and Kornberg, A., *J. Biol. Chem.* **207**, 911 (1954).
128. Lowenstein, J. M., and Cohen, P. P., *J. Biol. Chem.* **213**, 689 (1955); **220**, 57 (1956).
129. Jones, M. E., Spector, L., and Lipmann, F., *J. Am. Chem. Soc.* **77**, 819 (1955).
130. Reichard, P., *Acta Chem. Scand.* **8**, 795 (1954).
131. Lowenstein, J. M., and Cohen, P. P., *J. Biol. Chem.* **220**, 57 (1956).
132. Shepherdson, M., and Pardee, A. B., *J. Biol. Chem.* **235**, 3233 (1960).
133. Yates, R. A., and Pardee, A. B., *J. Biol. Chem.* **221**, 743, 757 (1956); **227**, 677 (1957).
134. Neumann, J., and Jones, M. E., *Nature* **195**, 709 (1962); see also *Arch. Biochem. Biophys.* **104**, 438 (1964).
135. Gerhart, J. C., and Pardee, A. B., *J. Biol. Chem.* **237**, 891 (1962).
136. Lieberman, I., and Kornberg, A., *J. Biol. Chem.* **212**, 909 (1955).
137. Lieberman, I., and Kornberg, A., *Biochim. Biophys. Acta* **12**, 223 (1953).
138. Cooper, C., Wu, R., and Wilson, D. W., *J. Biol. Chem.* **216**, 37 (1955).
139. Friedmann, H. C., and Vennesland, B., *J. Biol. Chem.* **233**, 1398 (1958).
140. Friedmann, H. C., and Vennesland, B., *J. Biol. Chem.*, **235**, 1526 (1960).
141. Graves, J. L., and Vennesland, B., *J. Biol. Chem.* **226**, 307 (1957).
142. Hurlbert, R. B., and Potter, V. R., *J. Biol. Chem.* **209**, 1 (1954).
143. Kornberg, A., Lieberman, I., and Simms, E. S., *J. Biol. Chem.* **215**, 389, 403 (1955).
144. Lieberman, I., Kornberg, A., and Simms, E. S., *J. Am. Chem. Soc.* **76**, 3608 (1954); *J. Biol. Chem.* **215**, 429 (1955).
145. Khorana, H. G., Fernandes, J. F., and Kornberg, A., *J. Biol. Chem.* **230**, 941 (1958).
146. Blair, D. G. R., Stone, J. E., and Potter, V. R., *J. Biol. Chem.* **235**, 2379 (1960).
147. Creasey, W. A., and Handschumacher, R. E., *J. Biol. Chem.* **236**, 2058 (1961).
148. Blair, D. G. R., and Potter, V. R., *J. Biol. Chem.* **236**, 2503 (1961).
149. Munch-Petersen, A., *Acta Chem. Scand.* **8**, 1102 (1954).
150. Berg, P., and Joklik, W. K., *J. Biol. Chem.* **210**, 657 (1954).
151. Strominger, J. L., Heppel, L. A., and Maxwell, E. S., *Arch. Biochem. Biophys.* **52**, 488 (1954).
152. Lieberman, I., *J. Am. Chem. Soc.* **77**, 2661 (1955); *J. Biol. Chem.* **222**, 757 (1956).
153. Lieberman, I., *J. Biol. Chem.* **222**, 765 (1956).
153a. Chakraborty, K. P., and Hurlbert, R. B., *Biochim. Biophys. Acta* **47**, 607 (1961).
154. Haslam, R. J., and Krebs, H. A., *Biochem. J.* **88**, 566 (1963).
155. Fairley, J. L., *J. Biol. Chem.* **210**, 347 (1954).
156. Hermann, R. L., and Fairley, J. L., *J. Biol. Chem.* **227**, 1109 (1957).
157. Tallan, H. H., *J. Biol. Chem.* **224**, 41 (1957).
158. Cutinelli, C., Ehrensvärd, G., Reio, L., Saluste, E., and Stjernholm, R., *Acta Chem. Scand.* **5**, 353 (1951).
159. Wang, C. H., Christensen, B. E., and Cheldelin, V. H., *J. Biol. Chem.* **201**, 683 (1953).
160. Ehrensvärd, G., Reio, L., Saluste, E., and Stjernholm, R., *J. Biol. Chem.* **189**, 93 (1951).

161. Cutinelli, C., Ehrensvärd, G., Reio, L., Saluste, E., and Stjernholm, R., *Arkiv. Kemi* **3**, 315 (1951).

162. Tager, J. M., and Slater, E. C., *Biochim. Biophys. Acta* **77**, 227 (1963).

163. Tomlinson, N., *J. Biol. Chem.* **209**, 597, 605 (1954).

164. Sekizawa, Y., Maragoudakis, M. E., Kerwar, S. S., Flikke, M., Baich, A., King, T. E., and Cheldelin, V. H., *Biochem. Biophys. Res. Commun.* **9**, 361 (1962).

165. Barker, H. A., Weissbach, H., and Smyth, R. D., *Proc. Natl. Acad. Sci. U.S.* **44**, 1093 (1958).

166. Weissbach, H., Toohey, J. I, and Barker, H. A., *Proc. Natl. Acad. Sci. U.S.* **45**, 521 (1959).

167. Lenhert, P. G., and Hodgkin, D. C., *Nature* **192**, 937 (1961).

168. Barker, H. A., Smyth, R. D., Weissbach, H., Munch-Peterson, A., Toohey, J. I., Ladd, J. N., Volcani, B. E., and Wilson, R. M. *J. Biol. Chem.* **235**, 181 (1960).

169. Barker, H. A., Smyth, R. D., Weissbach, H., Toohey, J. I., Ladd, J. N., and Volcani, B. E., *J. Biol. Chem.* **235**, 480 (1960).

170. Munch-Petersen, A., and Barker, H. A., *J. Biol. Chem.* **230**, 649 (1958).

171. Wilson, W. E., and Koeppe, R. E., *J. Biol. Chem.* **234**, 1186 (1959).

172. Wilson, W. E., and Koeppe, R. E., *J. Biol. Chem.* **236**, 365 (1961).

173. Ratner, S., *J. Biol. Chem.* **152**, 559 (1944).

174. Hillmann, G., Hillmann-Elies, A., and Methfessel, F., *Nature* **174**, 403 (1954); *Z. Naturforsch.* **9**, 660 (1954).

175. Meister, A., and Bukenberger, M. W., *Nature* **194**, 557 (1962).

176. Meister, A., Bukenberger, M. W., and Strassburger, M., *Biochem. Z.* **338**, 217 (1963).

177. Krebs, H. A., and Bellamy, D., *Biochem. J.* **75**, 523 (1960).

178. Cohen, M. M., Simon, G. R., Berry, J. F., and Chain, E. B., *Biochem. J.* **84**, 43P (1962).

179. Berl, S., Takagaki, G., Clarke, D. D., and Waelsch, H., *J. Biol. Chem.* **237**, 2562 (1962).

180. Racker, E., *J. Biol. Chem.* **190**, 685 (1951).

181. Strittmatter, P., and Ball, E. G., *J. Biol. Chem.* **213**, 445 (1955).

182. Krimsky, I., and Racker, E., *J. Biol. Chem.* **198**, 721, 731 (1952).

183. Lipke, H., and Kearns, C. W., *J. Biol. Chem.* **234**, 2129 (1959).

184. Perham, R. N., and Harris, J. I., *J. Mol. Biol.* **7**, 316 (1963).

185. Loomis, W. F., *Ann. N. Y. Acad. Sci.* **62**, 211 (1955).

186. Cliffe, E. E., and Waley, S. G., *Nature* **182**, 804 (1958).

187. Fodor, P. J., Miller, A., Neidle, A., and Waelsch, H., *J. Biol. Chem.* **203**, 991 (1953).

188. Knox, W. E., *in* "The Enzymes" (P. D. Boyer, H. Lardy, and K. Myrbäck, eds.), Vol. 2, p. 253. Academic Press, New York, 1960.

189. McIlwain, H., Fildes, P., Gladstone, G. P., and Knight, B. C. J. G., *Biochem. J.* **33**, 223 (1939).

190. McIlwain, H., *Biochem. J.* **33**, 1942 (1939).

191. Ayengar, P., and Roberts, E., *J. Biol. Chem.* **197**, 453 (1952).

192. Ayengar, P., and Roberts, E., *Growth* **17**, 201 (1953).

193. Ayengar, P., Roberts, E., and Ramasarma, G. B., *J. Biol. Chem.* **193**, 781 (1951).

194. Hac, L. R., Snell, E. E., and Williams, R. J., *J. Biol. Chem.* **159**, 273 (1945).

195. Hood, D. W., and Lyman, C. M., *J. Biol. Chem.* **185**, 39 (1950).

196. Lyman, C. M., Kuiken, K. A., Blotter, L., and Hale, F., *J. Biol. Chem.* **157**, 395 (1945).
197. Mueller, J. H., and Miller, P. A., *J. Biol. Chem.* **181**, 39 (1949).
198. Peeler, H. T., Daniel, L. J., Norris, L. C., and Heuser, G. F., *J. Biol. Chem.* **177**, 905 (1949).
199. Rickes, E. L., Koch, P. J., and Wood, T. R., *J. Biol. Chem.* **178**, 103 (1949).
200. Stokes, J. L., Koditschek, L. K., Rickes, E. L., and Wood, T. R., *J. Biol. Chem.* **178**, 93 (1949).
201. Woolley, D. W., *J. Biol. Chem.* **172**, 71 (1948).
202. Camien, M. N., and Dunn, M. S., *J. Biol. Chem.* **217**, 125 (1955).
203. Meister, A., *in* "The Enzymes" (P. D. Boyer, H. Lardy, and K. Myrbäck, eds.), Vol. 6, p. 443. Academic Press, New York, 1962.
204. Lang, S., *Hofmeister's Beitr.* **5**, 321 (1904).
205. Krebs, H. A., *Biochem. J.* **29**, 1951 (1935).
206. Greenstein, J. P., *Adv. Enzymol.* **8**, 117 (1949).
207. Errera, M., *J. Biol. Chem.* **178**, 483 (1949).
208. Errera, M., and Greenstein, J. P., *J. Biol. Chem.* **178**, 495 (1949).
209. Greenstein, J. P., and Carter, C. E., *J. Biol. Chem.* **165**, 741 (1946).
210. Greenstein, J. P., and Price, V. E., *J. Biol. Chem.* **178**, 695 (1949).
211. Shepherd, J. A., and Kalnitzsky, G., *J. Biol. Chem.* **192**, 1 (1951).
212. Otey, M. C., Birnbaum, S. M., and Greenstein, J. P., *Arch. Biochem. Biophys.* **49**, 245 (1954).
213. Klingman, J. D., and Handler, P., *J. Biol. Chem.* **232**, 369 (1958).
214. Blumson, N. L., *Biochem. J.* **65**, 138 (1957).
215. Williams, W. J., and Manson, L. A., *J. Biol. Chem.* **232**, 229 (1958).
216. Sayre, F. W., and Roberts, E., *J. Biol. Chem.* **233**, 1128 (1958).
217. Roberts, E., *in* "The Enzymes" (P. D. Boyer, H. Lardy, and K. Myrbäck, eds.), Vol. 4, p. 285. Academic Press, New York, 1960.
218. Gilbert, J. B., Price, V. E., and Greenstein, J. P., *J. Biol. Chem.* **180**, 209 (1949).
219. Meister, A., *J. Biol. Chem.* **210**, 17 (1954).
220. Meister, A., Levintow, L., Greenfield, R. E., and Abendschein, P. A., *J. Biol. Chem.* **215**, 441 (1955).
221. Davies, R. M. A., and Yudkin, J., *Biochem. J.* **52**, 407 (1952).
222. Rector, F. C., Seldin, D. W., and Copenhaver, J. H., *J. Clin. Invest.* **34**, 20 (1955).
223. Goldstein, L., Richterich-van Baerle, R., and Dearborn, E. H., *Proc. Soc. Exptl. Biol. Med.* **93**, 284 (1956).
224. Goldstein, L., and Kensler, C. J., *J. Biol. Chem.* **235**, 1086 (1960).
225. Geddes, W. F., and Hunter, A., *J. Biol. Chem.* **77**, 197 (1928).
226. Zittle, C. A., *in* "The Enzymes" (J. B. Sumner and K. Myrbäck, eds.), Vol. 1, Pt. 2, p. 922. Academic Press, New York, 1951.
227. Hughes, D. E., *Biochem. J.* **45**, 325 (1949).
228. Hughes, D. E., *Intern. Congr. Biochem., 1st Congr. Cambridge, Engl., 1949, Abstr. Communs.* p. 324 (1949).
229. Hughes, D. E., *Biochem. J.* **46**, 231 (1950).
230. Hughes, D. E., and Williamson, D. H., *Biochem. J.* **51**, 45 (1952).
231. Meister, A., *in* "Methods in Enzymology" (S. P. Colowick and N. O. Kaplan, eds.), Vol. 2, p. 380. Academic Press, New York, 1955.

232. Krebs, H. A., *Biochem. J.* **43**, 51 (1948).
233. Ehrenfeld, E., Marble, S. J., and Meister, A., *J. Biol. Chem.* **238**, 3711 (1963).
234. Waelsch, H., *in* "Phosphorus Metabolism" (W. D. McElroy and B. Glass, eds.), Vol. II, p. 109. Johns Hopkins Press, Baltimore, Maryland, 1952.
235. Waelsch, H., *Adv. Enzymol.* **13**, 237 (1952).
236. Meister, A., *in* "The Enzymes" (P. D. Boyer, H. Lardy, and K. Myrbäck, eds.), Vol. 6., p. 247. Academic Press, New York, 1962.
237. Preiss, J., and Handler, P., *J. Biol. Chem.* **225**, 759 (1957).
238. Preiss, J., and Handler, P., *J. Am. Chem. Soc.* **79**, 1514, 4246 (1957).
239. Preiss, J., and Handler, P., *J. Biol. Chem.* **233**, 488 (1958).
240. Preiss, J., and Handler, P., *J. Biol. Chem.* **233**, 111, 493 (1958).
241. Imsande, J., and Handler, P., *J. Biol. Chem.* **236**, 525 (1961).
242. Lagerkvist, U., *Acta Chem. Scand.* **9**, 1028 (1955).
243. Lagerkvist, U., *Acta Chem. Scand.* **11**, 1077 (1957).
244. Lagerkvist, U., *J. Biol. Chem.* **233**, 138, 143 (1958).
245. Abrams, R., and Bentley, M., *J. Am. Chem. Soc.* **77**, 4179 (1955).
246. Abrams, R., and Bentley, M., *Arch. Biochem. Biophys.* **56**, 184; **58**, 109 (1955).
247. Abrams, R., and Bentley, M., *Arch. Biochem. Biophys.* **79**, 91 (1959).
248. Moyed, H. S., and Magasanik, B., *J. Biol. Chem.* **226**, 351 (1957).
249. Becker, C. E., and Day, H. G., *J. Biol. Chem.* **201**, 795 (1953).
250. Rieder, S. V., and Buchanan, J. M., *J. Biol. Chem.* **232**, 951 (1958).
251. Roseman, S., Moses, F. E., Ludowieg, J., and Dorfman, A., *J. Biol. Chem.* **203**, 213 (1953).
252. Lowther, D. A., and Rogers, H. J., *Biochem. J.* **62**, 304 (1956).
253. Leloir, L. F., and Cardini, C. E., *Biochim. Biophys. Acta* **12**, 15 (1953).
254. Lowther, D. A., and Rogers, H. J., *Biochem. J.* **62**, 304 (1956).
255. Pogell, B. M., and Gryder, R. M., *J. Biol. Chem.* **228**, 701 (1957); **235**, 558 (1960).
256. Ghosh, S., Blumenthal, H. J., Davidson, E., and Roseman, S., *J. Biol. Chem.* **235**, 1265 (1960).
257. Otani, T. T., and Meister, A., *J. Biol. Chem.* **224**, 137 (1957).
258. Cohen, L. A., and Witkop, B., *J. Am. Chem. Soc.* **77**, 6595 (1955).
259. Levintow, L., Eagle, H., and Piez, K. A., *J. Biol. Chem.* **227**, 929 (1957).
260. Salzman, N. P., Eagle, H., and Sebring, E. D., *J. Biol. Chem.* **230**, 1001 (1958).
261. Kammen, H. O., and Hurlbert, R. B., *Biochim. Biophys. Acta* **30**, 195 (1958).
262. Hurlbert, R. B., and Kammen, H. O., *J. Biol. Chem.* **235**, 443 (1960).
263. Srinivasan, P. R., *J. Am. Chem. Soc.* **81**, 1772 (1959).
264. Weiss, B., and Srinivasan, P. R., *Proc. Natl. Acad. Sci. U.S.* **45**, 1491 (1959).
265. Srinivasan, P. R., and Weiss, B., *Biochim. Biophys. Acta* **51**, 597 (1961).
266. Levintow, L., *Science* **126**, 611 (1957).
267. Mardashev, S. R., and Lestrovaya, N. N., *Doklady Akad Nauk SSSR* **78**, 547 (1951).
268. Hsu, T.-S., *Biokhimya* **24**, 528 (1959).
269. McIlwain, H., Roper, J. A., and Hughes, D. E., *Biochem. J.* **42**, 492 (1948).
270. Lerner, E. M., and Mueller, J. H., *J. Biol. Chem.* **181**, 43 (1949).
271. Keynan, A., Strecker, H. J., and Waelsch, H., *J. Biol. Chem.* **211**, 883 (1954).
272. Rogers, L. L., Pelton, R. B., and Williams, R. J., *J. Biol. Chem.* **214**, 503 (1955); **220**, 321 (1956).

273. Steward, F. C., and Street, H. E., *Ann. Rev. Biochem.* **16**, 471 (1947).
274. Street, H. E., *Adv. Enzymol.* **9**, 391 (1949).
275. Steward, F. C., and Thompson, J. F., *Ann. Rev. Plant. Physiol.* **1**, 233 (1950).
276. Steward, F. C., and Thompson, J. F., *in* "The Proteins" (H. Neurath and K. Bailey, eds.), Vol. 2, Pt. A., p. 513. Academic Press, New York, 1954.
277. Archibald, R. M., *Chem. Rev.* **37**, 161 (1945).
278. Vickery, H. B., Pucher, G. W., Wakeman, A. J., and Leavenworth, C. S., *Conn. Agr. Expt. Sta. Bull.* **399**, 757 (1937).
279. Wood, J. G., *Ann. Rev. Biochem.* **14**, 665 (1945).
280. Archibald, R. M., *Euclides (Madrid)* **7**, 251 (1947).
281. Clarke, D. D., Neidle, A., Sarkar, N. K., and Waelsch, H., *Arch. Biochem. Biophys.* **71**, 277 (1957).
282. Neidle, A., Mycek, M. J., Clarke, D. D., and Waelsch, H., *Arch. Biochem. Biophys.* **77**, 227 (1958).
283. Clarke, D. D., Mycek, M. J., and Waelsch, H., *Arch. Biochem. Biophys.* **79**, 338 (1959).
284. Mycek, M. J., Clarke, D. D., Neidle, A., and Waelsch, H., *Arch. Biochem. Biophys.* **84**, 528 (1959).
285. Mycek, M. J., and Waelsch, H., *J. Biol. Chem.* **235**, 3513 (1960).
286. Dixon, R. O. D., and Fowden, L., *Ann. Botany (London)* **25**, 513 (1961).
287. Pietruszko, R., and Fowden, L., *Ann. Botany (London)* **25**, 491 (1961).
287a. Bessman, S. P., and Fishbein, W. N., *Nature* **200**, 1207 (1963).
288. Wilson, W. E., Hill, R. J., and Koeppe, R. E., *J. Biol. Chem.* **234**, 347 (1959).
289. Sisken, B., Sano, K., and Roberts, E., *J. Biol. Chem.* **236**, 503 (1961).
290. Elliott, K. A. C., *Rev. Can. Biol.* **17**, 367 (1958).
291. Elliott, K. A. C., and Jasper, H. H., *Physiol. Rev.* **39**, 383 (1959).
292. Curtis, D. R., and Watkins, J. C., *J. Neurochem.* **6**, 117 (1960).
293. Gaddum, J. H., *Nature* **197**, 741 (1963).
294. Seo, S., *Med. J. Osaka Univ.* **7**, 833 (1957).
295. Hardman, J. K., and Stadtman, T. C., *J. Bacteriol.* **85**, 1326 (1963).
295a. Hardman, J. K., and Stadtman, T. C., *J. Biol. Chem.* **238**, 2081, 2088 (1963).
296. Tesar, C., and Rittenberg, D., *J. Biol. Chem.* **170**, 35 (1947).
297. Bloch, K., *J. Biol. Chem.* **165**, 477 (1946).
298. Edson, N. L., *Australian J. Sci.* **9**, 102 (1946).
299. Edson, N. L., Krebs, H. A., and Model, A., *Biochem. J.* **30**, 1380 (1936).
300. Örström, A., Örström, M., and Krebs, H. A., *Biochem. J.* **33**, 990 (1939).
301. Buchanan, J. M., Sonne, J. C., and Delluva, A. M., *J. Biol. Chem.* **173**, 81 (1948).
302. Shemin, D., and Rittenberg, D., *J. Biol. Chem.* **167**, 875 (1947).
303. Sonne, J. C., Buchanan, J. M., and Delluva, A. M., *J. Biol. Chem.* **173**, 69 (1948).
304. Sonne, J. C., Lin, I., and Buchanan, J. M., *J. Am. Chem. Soc.* **75**, 1516 (1953).
305. Schulman, M. P., Sonne, J. C., and Buchanan, J. M., *J. Biol. Chem.* **196**, 499 (1952).
306. Greenberg, G. R., *J. Biol. Chem.* **190**, 611 (1951).
307. Levenberg, B., Hartman, S. C., and Buchanan, J. M., *J. Biol. Chem.* **220**, 379 (1956).
308. Stetten, M. R., and Fox, C. L., Jr., *J. Biol. Chem.* **161**, 333 (1945).

309. Shive, W., Ackermann, W. W., Gordon, M., Getzendaner, M. E., and Eakin, R. E., *J. Am. Chem. Soc.* **69**, 725 (1947).
310. Greenberg, G. R., *J. Am. Chem. Soc.* **74**, 6307 (1952).
311. Greenberg, G. R., and Spilman, E. L., *J. Biol. Chem.* **219**, 411 (1956).
312. Goldthwait, D. A., Peabody, R. A., and Greenberg, G. R., *J. Am. Chem. Soc.* **76**, 5258 (1954); *J. Biol. Chem.* **221**, 569 (1956).
313. Hartman, S. C., Levenberg, B., and Buchanan, J. M., *J. Am. Chem. Soc.* **77**, 501 (1955).
314. Peabody, R. A., Goldthwait, D. A., and Greenberg, G. R., *J. Biol. Chem.* **221**, 1071 (1956).
315. Hartman, S. C., Levenberg, B., and Buchanan, J. M., *J. Biol. Chem.* **221**, 1057 (1956).
316. Buchanan, J. M., and Hartman, S. C., *Adv. Enzymol.* **21**, 199 (1959).
317. Magasanik, B., *in* " The Bacteria " (I. C. Gunsalus and R. Y. Stanier, eds.), Vol. 3, p. 295. Academic Press, New York, 1962.
318. Goldthwait, D. A., Greenberg, G. R., and Peabody, R. A., *Biochim. Biophys. Acta* **18**, 148 (1955).
319. Goldthwait, D. A., *J. Biol. Chem.* **222**, 1051 (1956).
320. Hartman, S. C., and Buchanan, J. M., *J. Biol. Chem.* **233**, 451, 456 (1958).
321. Nierlich, D. P., Ph.D. Dissertation, Harvard Univ. (1962).
322. Nierlich, D. P., and Magasanik, B., *J. Biol. Chem.* **236**, PC 32 (1961).
323. Warren, L., and Buchanan, J. M., *J. Biol. Chem.* **229**, 613 (1957).
324. Hartman, S. C., and Buchanan, J. M., *J. Biol. Chem.* **234**, 1812 (1959).
325. Levenberg, B., and Buchanan, J. M., *J. Biol. Chem.* **224**, 1005, 1019 (1957).
326. Melnick, I., and Buchanan, J. M., *J. Biol. Chem.* **225**, 157 (1957).
327. Levenberg, B., Melnick, I., and Buchanan, J. M., *J. Biol. Chem.* **225**, 163 (1957).
328. French, T. C., Dawid, I. G., and Buchanan, J. M., *J. Biol. Chem.* **238**, 2186 (1963).
329. Lukens, L. N., and Buchanan, J. M., *J. Am. Chem. Soc.* **79**, 1511 (1957).
330. Lukens, L. N., and Buchanan, J. M., *J. Biol. Chem.* **234**, 1791, 1799 (1959).
331. Miller, R. W., and Buchanan, J. M., *J. Biol. Chem.* **237**, 485 (1962).
332. Miller, R. W., Lukens, L. N., and Buchanan, J. M., *J. Biol. Chem.* **234**, 1806 (1959).
333. Gots, J. S., and Gollub, E. G., *Proc. Natl. Acad. Sci. U.S.* **43**, 826 (1957).
334. Greenberg, G. R., Jaenicke, L., and Silverman, M., *Biochim. Biophys. Acta* **17**, 589 (1955).
335. Flaks, J. G., Erwin, M. J., and Buchanan, J. M., *J. Biol. Chem.* **229**, 603 (1957).
336. Warren, L., Flaks, J. G., and Buchanan, J. M., *J. Biol. Chem.* **229**, 627 (1957).
337. Roepke, R. R., Libby, R. L., and Small, M. H., *J. Bacteriol.* **48**, 401 (1944).
338. Tatum, E. L., *Federation Proc.* **8**, 511 (1949).
339. Abelson, P. H., *J. Biol. Chem.* **206**, 335 (1954).
340. Davis, B. D., *Adv. Enzymol.* **16**, 247 (1955).
341. Meinhart, J. O., and Simmonds, S., *J. Biol. Chem.* **213**, 329 (1955); **216**, 51 (1955).
342. Simmonds, S., and Miller, D. A., *J. Bacteriol.* **74**, 775 (1957).
343. Wright, B. E., *Arch. Biochem.* **31**, 332 (1951).
344. Muramatsu, M., and Shimura, K., *J. Biochem.* (*Tokyo*) **52**, 297 (1962).
345. Campbell, J. J. R., Smith, R. A., and Eagles, B. A., *Biochim Biophys. Acta* **11**, 594 (1953).
346. Olson, J. A., *Nature* **174**, 695 (1954).

347. Kornberg, H. L., and Krebs, H. A., *Nature* **179**, 988 (1957).
348. Smith, R. A., and Gunsalus, I. C., *J. Am. Chem. Soc.* **76**, 5002 (1954).
349. Wong, D. T. O., and Ajl, S. J., *Nature* **176**, 970 (1955).
350. Weissbach, A., and Horecker, B. L., *in* "Amino Acid Metabolism" (W. D. McElroy and B. Glass, eds.), p. 741. Johns Hopkins Press, Baltimore, Maryland, 1955.
351. Racker, E., *Adv. Enzymol.* **15**, 141 (1954).
352. Horecker, B. L., Gibbs, M., Klenow, H., and Smyrniotis, P. Z., *J. Biol. Chem.* **207**, 393 (1954).
353. Calvin, M., *Harvey Lectures Ser.* **46**, 218 (1952).
354. Schou, L., Benson, A. A., Bassham, V. A., and Calvin, M., *Physiol. Plantarum* **3**, 487 (1950).
355. Kearney, P. C., and Tolbert, N. E., *Arch. Biochem. Biophys.* **98**, 164 (1962).
356. Rabson, R., Tolbert, N. E., and Kearney, P. C., *Arch. Biochem. Biophys.* **98**, 154 (1962).
357. Weinhouse, S., *in* "Amino Acid Metabolism" (W. D. McElroy and B. Glass, eds.), p. 637. Johns Hopkins Press, Baltimore, Maryland, 1955.
358. Weissbach, A., and Sprinson, D. B., *J. Biol. Chem.* **203**, 1023 (1953).
359. Rabinowitz, J. C., and Pricer, W. E., Jr., *J. Biol. Chem.* **222**, 537 (1956).
360. Rabinowitz, J. C., *in* "The Enzymes" (P. D. Boyer, H. Lardy and K. Myrbäck, eds.), Vol. 2, p. 185. Academic Press, New York, 1960.
361. Weinhouse, S., and Friedmann, B., *J. Biol. Chem.* **191**, 707 (1951).
362. Nakada, H. I., and Weinhouse, S., *Arch. Biochem. Biophys.* **4**, 257 (1953).
363. Weinhouse, S., and Friedmann, B., *J. Biol. Chem.* **197**, 733 (1952).
364. Ratner, S., Nocito, V., and Green, D. E., *J. Biol. Chem.* **152**, 119 (1944).
365. Millerd, A., Morton, R. K., and Wells, J. R. E., *Biochem. J.* **88**, 276, 281 (1963).
366. Nakada, H. I., and Sund, L. P., *J. Biol. Chem.* **233**, 8 (1958).
367. Mathews, M. B., and Vennesland, B., *J. Biol. Chem.* **186**, 667 (1950).
368. Richert, D. A., Amberg, R., and Wilson, M., *J. Biol. Chem.* **237**, 99 (1962).
369. Sagers, R. D., and Gunsalus, I. C., *J. Bacteriol.* **81**, 541 (1961).
370. Barker, H. A., Volcani, B. E., and Cardon, B. P., *J. Biol. Chem.* **173**, 803 (1948).
371. Kornberg, H. L., *Ann. Rev. Microbiol.* **13**, 49 (1959).
372. Dagley, S., Trudgill, P. W., and Callely, A. G., *Biochem. J.* **81**, 623 (1961).
373. Tsuiki, S., and Kikuchi, G., *Biochim. Biophys. Acta* **64**, 514 (1962).
374. Bachrach, U., *Biochem. J.* **66**, 559 (1957).
375. Kornberg, H. L., and Gotto, A. M., *Biochem. J.* **78**, 69 (1961).
375a. Valentine, R. C., Drucker, H., and Wolfe, R. S., *J. Bacteriol.* **87**, 241 (1964).
376. Borsook, H., and Dubnoff, J. W., *J. Biol. Chem.* **138**, 389 (1941); *Science* **91**, 551 (1940).
377. Bloch, K., and Schoenheimer, R., *J. Biol. Chem.* **138**, 167 (1941).
378. Ratner, S., *in* "The Enzymes" (P. D. Boyer, H. Lardy, and K. Myrbäck, eds.), Vol. 6, p. 267. Academic Press, New York, 1962.
379. Fuld, M., *Federation Proc.* **13**, 215 (1954).
380. Horner, W. H., Siegel, I., and Bruton, J., *J. Biol. Chem.* **220**, 861 (1956).
381. Walker, J. B., *J. Biol. Chem.* **221**, 771 (1956).
382. Walker, J. B., *Proc. Soc. Exptl. Biol. Med.* **98**, 7 (1958).
383. Walker, J. B., *Biochim. Biophys. Acta* **73**, 241 (1963).

384. Walker, J. B., *J. Biol. Chem.* **235**, 2357 (1960).
385. Horner, W. H., *J. Biol. Chem.* **234**, 2386 (1959).
386. Walker, J. M., *J. Biol. Chem.* **236**, 493 (1961).
387. Fitch, C. D., Hsu, C., and Dinning, J. S., *J. Biol. Chem.* **235**, 2362 (1960); **236**, 490 (1961).
388. Walker, M. S., and Walker, J. B., *J. Biol. Chem.* **237**, 473 (1962).
389. Walker, J. B., *Proc. Soc. Exptl. Biol. Med.* **112**, 245 (1963).
390. Walker, J. B., and Gipson, W. T., *Biochim. Biophys. Acta* **67**, 156 (1963).
391. Irreverre, F., and Evans, R. L., *J. Biol. Chem.* **234**, 1438 (1959).
392. Pisano, J. J., Abraham, D., and Udenfriend, S., *Arch. Biochem. Biophys.* **100**, 323 (1963).
393. Walker, J. B., *J. Biol. Chem.* **231**, 1 (1958).
394. Nakatsu, S., *J. Biochem. (Tokyo)* **43**, 675 (1956).
395. Gerber, G. B., Koszalka, T. R., Gerber, G., and Altman, K. I., *Nature* **196**, 286 (1962).
396. Benedict, J. D., Kalinsky, H. J., Scarrone, L. A., Wertheim, R., and Stetten, D., Jr., *J. Clin. Invest.* **34**, 141 (1955).
397. Borsook, H., and Dubnoff, J. W., *J. Biol. Chem.* **168**, 493 (1947).
398. Van Pilsum, J. F., and Hiller, B., *Arch. Biochem. Biophys.* **85**, 483 (1959).
399. Almquist, H. J., Mecchi, E., Stokstad, E. L. R., and Manning, P. D. V., *J. Biol. Chem.* **134**, 465 (1940).
400. Shemin, D., and Rittenberg, D., *J. Biol. Chem.* **159**, 567 (1945); **166**, 621 (1946).
401. Altman, K. I., Casarett, G. W., Masters, R. E., Noonan, T. R., and Salomon, K., *J. Biol. Chem.* **176**, 319 (1948).
402. Radin, N. S., Rittenberg, D., and Shemin, D., *J. Biol. Chem.* **184**, 745 (1950).
403. Wittenberg, J., and Shemin, D., *J. Biol. Chem.* **178**, 47 (1949); **185**, 103 (1950).
404. Muir, H. M., and Neuberger, A., *Biochem. J.* **45**, 163 (1949); **47**, 97 (1950).
405. Shemin, D., and Wittenberg, J., *J. Biol. Chem.* **192**, 315 (1951).
406. Shemin, D., and Kumin, S., *J. Biol. Chem.* **198**, 827 (1952).
407. Shemin, D., and Russell, C. S., *J. Am. Chem. Soc.* **75**, 4873 (1953).
408. Shemin, D., Abramsky, T., and Russell, C. S., *J. Am. Chem. Soc.* **76**, 1204 (1954).
409. Shemin, D., *in* "Amino Acid Metabolism" (W. D. McElroy and B. Glass, eds.), p. 727. Johns Hopkins Press, Baltimore, Maryland, 1955.
410. Shemin, D., Russell, C. S., and Abramsky, T., *J. Biol. Chem.* **215**, 613 (1955).
411. Nemeth, A. M., Russell, C. S., and Shemin, D., *J. Biol. Chem.* **229**, 415 (1957).
412. Bagdasarian, M., *Nature* **181**, 1399 (1958).
413. Gibson, K. D., Neuberger, A., and Tait, G. H., *Biochem. J.*, **83**, 539 (1962).
414. Neuberger, A., and Scott, J. J., *Nature* **172**, 1093 (1953).
415. Wynn, R. W., and Corwin, A. H., *J. Org. Chem.* **15**, 203 (1950).
416. Dresel, E. I. B., and Falk, J. E., *Nature* **172**, 1185 (1953).
417. Schiffmann, E., and Shemin, D., *J. Biol. Chem.* **225**, 623 (1957).
418. Falk, J. E., Dresel, E. I. B., and Rimington, C., *Nature* **172**, 292 (1953).
419. Cookson, G. H., and Rimington, C., *Nature*, **171**, 875 (1953).
420. Kennard, O., *Nature* **171**, 876 (1953).
421. Westall, R. G., *Nature* **170**, 614 (1953).
422. Granick, S., and Mauzerall, D., *in* "Metabolic Pathways" (D. M. Greenberg, ed.), Vol. 2, p. 526. Academic Press, New York, 1961.

423. Shemin, D., Corcoran, J. W., and Miller, I., *Science* **124**, 272 (1956).
424. Corcoran, J. W., and Shemin, D., *Biochim. Biophys. Acta* **25**, 661 (1957).
425. Schwartz, S., Ikeda, K., Miller, I. M., and Watson, C. J., *Science* **129**, 40 (1959).
426. Brown, E. G., *Biochem. J.* **70**, 313 (1958).
427. Gibson, K. D., Laver, W. G., and Neuberger, A., *Biochem. J.* **70**, 71 (1958).
428. Laver, W. G., Neuberger, A., and Udenfriend, S., *Biochem. J.* **70**, 4 (1958).
429. Kikuchi, G., Kumar, A., Talmage, P., and Shemin, D., *J. Biol. Chem.* **233**, 1214 (1958).
430. Kikuchi, G., Shemin, D., and Bachmann, B. J., *Biochim. Biophys. Acta* **28**, 219 (1958).
431. Schulman, M. P., and Richert, D. A., *J. Biol. Chem.* **226**, 181 (1957).
432. Gibson, K. D., Matthew, M., Neuberger, A., and Tait, G. H., *Nature* **192**, 204 (1961).
433. Burnham, B. F., and Lascelles, J., *Biochem. J.* **87**, 462 (1963).
434. Urata, G., and Granick, S., *Biochim. Biophys. Res. Commun.* **4**, 96 (1961).
435. Neuberger, A., and Tait, G. H., *Biochem. J.* **84**, 317 (1962).
436. Mauzerall, B., and Granick, S., *J. Biol. Chem.* **219**, 435 (1956).
437. Urata, G., and Granick, S., *J. Biol. Chem.* **238**, 811 (1963).
438. Granick, S., and Urata, G., *Federation Proc.* **21**, 156 (1962).
439. Granick, S., *J. Biol. Chem.* **232**, 1101 (1958).
440. Granick, S., and Mauzerall, D., *J. Biol. Chem.* **232**, 1119 (1958).
441. Mauzerall, D., and Granick, S., *J. Biol. Chem.* **232**, 1141 (1958).
442. Bogorad, L., *J. Biol. Chem.* **233**, 501, 510, 516 (1958).
443. Bogorad, L., *Federation Proc.* **21**, 400 (1962).
444. Sano, S., and Granick, S., *J. Biol. Chem.* **236**, 1173 (1961).
445. Shemin, D., *J. Biol. Chem.* **162**, 297 (1946).
446. Goldsworthy, P. D., Winnick, T., and Greenberg, D. M., *J. Biol. Chem.* **180**, 341 (1949).
447. Winnick, T., Moring-Claesson, I., and Greenberg, D. M., *J. Biol. Chem.* **175**, 127 (1948).
448. Siekevitz, P., and Greenberg, D. M., *J. Biol. Chem.* **180**, 845 (1949).
449. Sakami, W., *J. Biol. Chem.* **176**, 995 (1948).
450. Elwyn, D., and Sprinson, D. B., *J. Biol. Chem.* **184**, 475 (1950).
451. Levine, M., and Tarver, H., *J. Biol. Chem.* **184**, 427 (1950).
452. Lascelles, J., and Woods, D. D., *Nature* **166**, 649 (1950).
453. Sakami, W., *in* "Amino Acid Metabolism" (W. D. McElroy and B. Glass, eds.), p. 658. Johns Hopkins Press, Baltimore, Maryland, 1955.
454. Deodhar, S., and Sakami, W., *Federation Proc.* **12**, 195 (1953).
455. Arnstein, H. R. V., *Adv. Protein Chem.* **9**, 2 (1954).
456. Mitoma, C., and Greenberg, D. M., *J. Biol. Chem.* **196**, 599 (1952).
457. Sprinson, D. B., *in* "Amino Acid Metabolism" (W. D. McElroy and B. Glass, eds.), p. 608. Johns Hopkins Press, Baltimore, Maryland, 1955.
458. Mackenzie, C. G., *in* "Amino Acid Metabolism" (W. D. McElroy and B. Glass, eds.), p. 684. Johns Hopkins Press, Baltimore, Maryland, 1955.
459. Handler, P., Bernheim, M. L. C., and Klein, J. R., *J. Biol. Chem.* **138**, 211 (1941).
460. Elwyn, D., Weissbach, A., and Sprinson, D. B., *J. Am. Chem. Soc.* **73**, 5509 (1951).
461. Arnstein, H. R. V., and Neuberger, A., *Biochem. J.* **55**, 259, 271 (1953).

462. Lowy, B. A., Brown, G. B., and Rachele, J. R., *J. Biol. Chem.* **220**, 325 (1956).

463. Welch, A. D., and Nichol, C. H., *Ann. Rev. Biochem.* **21**, 633 (1952).

464. Plaut, G. W. E., Betheil, J. J., and Lardy, H. A., *J. Biol. Chem.* **184**, 795 (1950).

465. Braunstein, A. E., and Vilenkina, G. Y., *Doklady Akad. Nauk SSSR* **80**, 639 (1951).

466. Vilenkina, G. Y., *Doklady Akad. Nauk SSSR* **84**, 559 (1952).

467. Totter, J. R., Kelley, R., Day, P. L., and Edwards, R. R., *J. Biol. Chem.* **186**, 145 (1950).

468. Weinhouse, S., and Friedmann, B., *J. Biol. Chem.* **210**, 423 (1954).

469. Lascelles, J., Cross, M. J., and Woods, D. D., *J. Gen. Microbiol.* **10**, 267 (1954).

470. Holland, B. R., and Meinke, W. W., *J. Biol. Chem.* **178**, 7 (1949).

471. Wolf, D. E., Anderson, R. C., Kaczka, E. A., Harris, S. A., Arth, G. E., Southwick, P. L., Mozingo, R., and Folkers, K., *J. Am. Chem. Soc.* **69**, 2753 (1947).

472. Shive, W., Bardos, T. J., Bond, T. J., Rogers, L. L., *J. Am. Chem. Soc.* **72**, 2817 (1950).

473. Brockman, J. A., Jr., Roth, B., Broquist, H. P., Hultquist, M. E., Smith, J. M., Jr., Fahrenbach, M. J., Cosulich, D. B., Parker, R. P., Stokstad, E. L. R., and Jukes, T. H., *J. Am. Chem. Soc.* **72**, 4325 (1950).

474. Welch, A. D., and Heinle, R. W., *Pharmacol. Rev.* **3**, 345 (1951).

475. May, M., Bardos, T. J., Barger, F. L., Lansford, M., Ravel, J. M., Sutherland, G. L., and Shive, W., *J. Am. Chem. Soc.* **73**, 3067 (1951).

476. Pohland, A., Flynn, E. H., Jones, R. G., and Shive, W., *J. Am. Chem. Soc.* **73**, 3247 (1951).

477. Roth, B., Hultquist, M. E., Fahrenbach, M. J., Cosulich, D. B., Broquist, H. P., Brockman, J. A., Jr., Smith, J. M., Jr., Parker, R. P., Stokstad, E. L. R., and Jukes, T. H., *J. Am. Chem. Soc.* **74**, 3247 (1952).

478. Sauberlich, H. E., *J. Biol. Chem.* **195**, 337 (1952).

479. Cosulich, D. B., Roth, B., Smith, J. M., Jr., Hultquist, M. E., and Parker, R. P. *J. Am. Chem. Soc.* **74**, 3252 (1952).

480. Cosulich, D. B., Smith, J. M., Jr., and Broquist, H. P., *J. Am. Chem. Soc.* **74**, 4215 (1952).

481. Keresztesy, J. C., and Silverman, M., *J. Am. Chem. Soc.* **73**, 5510 (1951); **75**, 1512 (1953).

482. Kisliuk, R. L., and Sakami, W., *J. Am. Chem. Soc.* **76**, 1456 (1954).

483. Kisliuk, R. L., and Sakami, W., *J. Biol. Chem.* **214**, 47 (1955).

484. Blakley, R. L., *Biochem. J.* **58**, 448 (1954).

485. Lascelles, J., and Woods, D. D., *Biochem. J.* **58**, 486 (1954).

486. Zakrzewski, S. F., *J. Biol. Chem.* **235**, 1776, 1780 (1960).

487. Brown, G. M., *J. Biol. Chem.* **237**, 536 (1962).

488. Brown, G. M., and Reynolds, J. J., *Ann. Rev. Biochem.* **32**, 419 (1963).

489. Wahba, A. J., and Friedkin, M., *J. Biol. Chem.* **236**, PC11 (1961).

490. Friedkin, M., *Ann. Rev. Biochem.* **32**, 185 (1963).

491. O'Dell, B. L., Vandenbelt, J. M., Bloom, E. S., and Pfeiffner, J. J., *J. Am. Chem. Soc.* **69**, 250 (1947).

492. Futterman, S., *J. Biol. Chem.* **228**, 1031 (1957).

493. Blakley, R. L., *Nature* **188**, 231 (1960).

494. Huennekens, F. M., *Biochemistry* **2**, 151 (1963).

495. Smith, K., Scrimgeour, K. G., and Huennekens, F. M., *Biochem. Biophys. Res. Commun.* **11**, 388 (1963).

496. Pastore, E. J., Friedkin, M., and Jardetsky, O., *J. Am. Chem. Soc.* **85**, 3058 (1963); see also 496a.

496a. Hillcoat, B. L., and Blakley, R. L., *Biochem. Biophys. Res. Commun.* **15**, 303 (1964).

497. Mathews, C. K., and Huennekens, F. M., *J. Biol. Chem.* **235**, 3304 (1960).

498. Wright, B. E., *Biochim. Biophys. Acta* **16**, 165 (1955).

499. Wright, B. E., and Stadtman, T. C., *J. Biol. Chem.* **219**, 863 (1956).

500. Alexander, N., and Greenberg, D. M., *J. Biol. Chem.* **214**, 821 (1955).

501. Alexander, N., and Greenberg, D. M., *J. Biol. Chem.* **220**, 775 (1956).

502. Huennekens, F. M., Hatefi, Y., and Kay, L. D., *J. Biol. Chem.* **224**, 435 (1957).

503. Hatefi, Y., Osborn, M. J., Kay, L.D., and Huennekens, F. M., *J. Biol. Chem.* **227**, 637 (1957).

504. Blakley, R. L., *Biochem. J.* **61**, 315 (1955); **65**, 342 (1957).

505. Schirch, L. G., and Mason, M., *J. Biol. Chem.* **237**, 2578 (1962); **238**, 1032 (1963).

506. Huennekens, F. M., and Osborn, M. J., *Adv. Enzymol.* **21**, 369 (1959).

507. Kisliuk, R. L., *J. Biol. Chem.* **227**, 805 (1957).

508. Osborn, M. J., Talbert, P. T., and Huennekens, F. M., *J. Am. Chem. Soc.* **82**, 4921 (1960).

509. Osborn, M. J., Vercamer, E. N., Talbert, P. T., and Huennekens, F. M., *J. Am. Chem. Soc.* **79**, 6565 (1957).

510. Wright, B. E., *Biochim. Biophys. Acta* **16**, 165; *J. Am. Chem. Soc.* **77**, 3930 (1955); *J. Biol. Chem.* **219**, 873 (1956).

511. Wright, B. E., Anderson, M. L., and Herman, E. C., *J. Biol. Chem.* **230**, 271 (1958).

512. Wilson, E. M., and Snell, E. E., *J. Biol. Chem.* **237**, 3171, 3180 (1962).

513. Longenecker, J. B., Ikawa, M., and Snell, E. E., *J. Biol. Chem.* **226**, 663 (1957).

514. Greenstein, J. P., and Winitz, M., "Chemistry of the Amino Acids," Wiley, New York, 1961.

515. Flaks, J. G., and Cohen, S. S., *J. Biol. Chem.* **234**, 1501 (1959).

516. Wahba, A. J., and Friedkin, M., *J. Biol. Chem.* **237**, 3794 (1962).

517. Weissbach, A., Elwyn, D., and Sprinson, D. B., *J. Am. Chem. Soc.* **72**, 3316 (1950).

518. Arnstein, H. R. V., *Biochem. J.* **48**, 27 (1951).

519. Elwyn, D., and Sprinson, D. B., *J. Am. Chem. Soc.* **72**, 3317 (1950); *J. Biol. Chem.* **207**, 459, 467 (1954).

520. Kay, L. D., Osborn, M. J., Hatefi, Y., and Huennekens, F. M. *J. Biol. Chem.* **235**, 195 (1960).

521. Osborn, M. J., and Huennekens, F. M., *Biochim. Biophys. Acta* **26**, 646 (1957).

522. Tabor, H., and Wyngarden, L., *J. Biol. Chem.* **234**, 1830 (1959).

523. Whiteley, H. R., and Huennekens, F. M., *J. Biol. Chem.* **237**, 1290 (1962).

524. Rabinowitz, J. C., and Pricer, W. E., Jr., *J. Biol. Chem.* **237**, 2898 (1962).

525. Himes, R. H., and Rabinowitz, J. C., *J. Biol. Chem.* **237**, 2903, 2915 (1962).

526. Bertino, J. R., Simmons, B., and Donohue, D. M., *J. Biol. Chem.* **237**, 1314 (1962).

527. Greenberg, G. R., Jaenicke, L., and Silverman, M., *Biochim. Biophys. Acta* **17**, 589 (1955).

528. Whiteley, H. R., Osborn, M. J., and Huennekens, F. M., *J. Am. Chem. Soc.* **80**, 757 (1958).

529. Nakagawa, H., Suzuki, F., and Takeda, Y., *J. Biochem.* (*Tokyo*) **49**, 191 (1961).

529a. Sly, W. S., and Stadtman, E. R., *J. Biol. Chem.* **238**, 2639 (1963).

530. Silverman, M., Keresztesy, J. C., Koval, G. J., and Gardiner, R. C., *J. Biol. Chem.* **226**, 83 (1957).

531. Byers, E. H., Jr., and Bond, T. J., *Nature* **187**, 416 (1960).

531a. Matkovics, B., Filvig, Gy., and Göndös, Gy., *Biochim. Biophys. Acta* **86**, 180 (1964).

532. Sallach, H. J., *Symp. Amino Acid Metab.* p. 782. Johns Hopkins Press, 1955.

533. Nyc, J. F., and Zabin, I., *J. Biol. Chem.* **215**, 35 (1955).

534. Sallach, H. J., *J. Biol. Chem.* **223**, 1101 (1956).

535. Hedrick, J. L., and Sallach, H. J., *Biochim. Biophys. Acta* **41**, 531 (1960).

536. Koeppe, R. E., Minthorn, M. L., Jr., and Hill, R. J., *Arch. Biochem. Biophys.* **68**, 355 (1957).

537. Ichihara, A., and Greenberg, D. M., *J. Biol. Chem.* **224**, 331; **225**, 949 (1957).

538. Schramm, M., *J. Biol. Chem.* **233**, 1169 (1958).

539. Neuhaus, F. C., and Byrne, W. L., *J. Biol. Chem.* **234**, 109, 113 (1959); **235**, 2019 (1960).

540. Nemer, M. J., Wise, E. M., Jr., Washington, F. M., and Elwyn, D., *J. Biol. Chem.* **235**, 2063 (1960).

541. Nemer, M. J., and Elwyn, D., *J. Am. Chem. Soc.* **79**, 6564 (1957).

542. Borkenhagen, L. F., and Kennedy, E. P., *Biochim. Biophys. Acta* **28**, 222 (1958); *J. Biol. Chem.* **234**, 849 (1959).

543. Lamprecht, W., Heinz, F., and Diamantstein, T., *Z. Physiol. Chem.* **328**, 204 (1962).

544. Hanford, J., and Davies, D. D., *Nature* **182**, 532 (1958).

545. Willis, J. E., and Sallach, H. J., *Biochim. Biophys. Acta* **62**, 443; *J. Biol. Chem.* **237**, 910 (1962).

546. Umbarger, H. E., and Umbarger, M. A., *Biochim. Biophys. Acta* **62**, 193 (1962).

547. Umbarger, H. E., Umbarger, A., and Siu, P. M. L., *J. Bacteriol.* **85**, 1431 (1963).

548. Horner, W. H., and Mackenzie, C. G., *J. Biol. Chem.* **187**, 15 (1950).

549. Mackenzie, C. G., *J. Biol. Chem.* **186**, 351 (1950).

550. Jukes, T. H., *Ann. Rev. Biochem.* **16**, 193 (1947).

551. du Vigneaud, V., "Trail of Research in Sulfur Chemistry and Metabolism and Related Fields." Cornell Univ. Press, Ithaca, New York, 1952.

552. Delwiche, C. C., and Bregoff, H. M., *J. Biol. Chem.* **233**, 430 (1958).

553. Bremer, J., and Greenberg, D. M., *Biochim. Biophys. Acta* **35**, 287 (1959).

554. Wolf, B., and Nyc, J. F., *J. Biol. Chem.* **234**, 1068 (1959).

555. Stetten, D., Jr., *J. Biol. Chem.* **144**, 501 (1942).

556. Elwyn, D., Weissbach, A., Henry, S. S., and Sprinson, D. B. *J. Biol. Chem.* **213**, 281 (1955).

557. Nemer, M. J., and Elwyn, D., *J. Biol. Chem.* **235**, 2070 (1960).

558. Bremer, J., Figard, P. H., and Greenberg, D. M., *Biochim. Biophys. Acta* **43**, 477 (1960).

559. Wilson, J. D., Gibson, K. D., and Udenfriend, S., *J. Biol. Chem.* **235**, 3539 (1960).

560. Borkenhagen, L. F., Kennedy, E. P., and Fielding, L., *J. Biol. Chem.* **236**, PC28 (1961).
561. Nord, F. F., *Biochem. Z.* **95**, 281 (1919).
562. Pilgeram, L. O., Hamilton, R. E., and Greenberg, D. M., *J. Biol. Chem.* **227**, 107 (1957).
563. Bremer, J., and Greenberg, D. M., *Biochim. Biophys. Acta* **37**, 173 (1960); **46**, 205 (1961).
564. Wilson, J. D., Gibson, K. D., and Udenfriend, S., *J. Biol. Chem.* **235**, 3213 (1960).
565. Gibson, K. D., Wilson, J. D., and Udenfriend, S., *J. Biol. Chem.* **236**, 673 (1961).
566. Kennedy, E. P., and Weiss, S. B., *J. Biol. Chem.* **222**, 193 (1956).
567. Kanfer, J., and Kennedy, E. P., *J. Biol. Chem.* **237**, PC270 (1962).
568. Hübscher, G., Dils, R. R., and Pover, W. F. R., *Biochim. Biophys. Acta* **36**, 518 (1959); **57**, 555 (1962).
569. Handler, P., Bernheim, M. L. C., and Klein, J. R., *J. Biol. Chem.* **138**, 211 (1941).
570. Mackenzie, C. G., and Frisell, W. R., *J. Biol. Chem.* **232**, 417 (1958).
571. Mackenzie, C. G., and Abeles, R. H., *J. Biol. Chem.* **222**, 145 (1956).
572. Hoskins, D. D., and Mackenzie, C. G., *J. Biol. Chem.* **236**, 177 (1961).
573. Frisell, W. R., and Mackenzie, C. G., *J. Biol. Chem.* **237**, 94 (1962).
574. Frisell, W. R., Cronin, J, R., and Mackenzie, C. G., *J. Biol. Chem.* **237**, 2975 (1962).
575. Beinert, H., and Frisell, W. R., *J. Biol. Chem.* **237**, 2988 (1962).
576. Klain, G., and Johnson, B. C., *J. Biol. Chem.* **237**, 123 (1962).
577. Nadkarni, G. V., Friedmann, B., and Weinhouse, S., *J. Biol. Chem.* **235**, 420 (1960).
578. Minthorn, M. L., Jr., Mourkides, G. A., and Koeppe, R. E., *J. Biol. Chem.* **234**, 3205 (1959).
579. Elwyn, D., Ashmore, J., Cahill, G. F., Jr., Zottu, S., Welch, W., and Hastings, A. B., *J. Biol. Chem.* **226**, 735 (1957).
580. Chargaff, E., and Sprinson, D. B., *J. Biol. Chem.* **151**, 273 (1943).
581. Yanofsky, C., and Reissig, J. L., *J. Biol. Chem.* **202**, 567 (1953).
582. Metzler, D. E., and Snell, E. E., *J. Biol. Chem.* **198**, 353 (1952).
583. Metzler, D. E., and Snell, E. E., *J. Biol. Chem.* **198**, 363 (1952).
584. Wood, W. A., and Gunsalus, I. C., *J. Biol. Chem.* **181**, 171 (1949).
585. Szentirmai, A., and Horvath, I., *Acta Microbiol. Acad. Sci. Hung.* **9**, 23 (1962).
586. Gregerman, R. I., and Christensen, H. N., *J. Biol. Chem.* **220**, 765 (1956).
587. Sayre, F. W., and Greenberg, D. M., *J. Biol. Chem.* **220**, 787 (1956).
588. Selim, A. S. M., and Greenberg, D. M., *J. Biol. Chem.* **234**, 1474 (1959).
588a. Crawford, I. P., and Ito, J., *Proc. Natl. Acad. Sci. U.S.* **51**, 390 (1964).
589. Lien, O. G., Jr., and Greenberg, D. M., *J. Biol. Chem.* **195**, 637 (1952).
590. Dickens, F., and Williamson, D. H., *Biochem. J.* **68**, 74 (1958).
591. Hedrick, J.L., and Sallach, H. J., *J. Biol. Chem.* **236**, 1867, 1872 (1961). *Arch. Biochem. Biophys.* **105**, 261 (1964).
592. Dickens, F., and Williamson, D. H., *Biochem. J.* **72**, 496 (1959).
593. Fukunaga, K., *J. Biochem.* (*Tokyo*) **47**, 741 (1960).
594. Kuratomi, K., and Fukunaga, K., *Biochim. Biophys. Acta* **37**, 376 (1960).
595. Brady, R. O., Formica, J. B., and Koval, G. J., *J. Biol. Chem.* **233**, 26, 1072 (1958).
596. Sprinson, D. B., and Coulon, A., *J. Biol. Chem.* **207**, 585 (1954).

597. Zabin, I., and Mead, J. F., *J. Biol. Chem.* **211**, 87 (1954).
597a. Weiss, B., *J. Biol. Chem.* **238**, 1953 (1963).
598. Fujino, Y., and Zabin, I., *J. Biol. Chem.* **237**, 2069 (1962).
599. Roberts, E., and Lowe, I. P., *J. Biol. Chem.* **211**, 1 (1954).
599a. Peterson, D. W., Lilyblade, A. L., and Lyon, J., *Proc. Soc. Exptl. Biol. Med.* **113**, 798 (1963).
600. Ennor, A. H., Rosenberg, H., Rossiter, R. J., Beatty, I. M., and Gaffney, T., *Biochem. J.* **75**, 179 (1960).
601. Rosenberg, H., and Ennor, A. H., *Biochem. J.* **73**, 521 (1959); **79**, 424 (1961).
602. Thoai, N. V., and Robin, Y., *Biochim. Biophys. Acta* **14**, 76 (1954).
603. Beatty, I. M., Magrath, D. I., and Ennor, A. H., *Nature* **183**, 591 (1959); *J. Am. Chem. Soc.* **82**, 4983 (1960).
604. Beatty, I. M., Ennor, A. H., Rosenberg, H., and Magrath, D., *J. Biol. Chem.* **236**, 1028 (1961).
605. Rossiter, R. J., Gaffney, T., Rosenberg, H., and Ennor, A. H., *Nature* **185**, 383 (1960); *Biochem. J.* **76**, 603 (1960).
606. Pant, R., *Biochem. J.* **73**, 30 (1959).
607. Rosenberg, H., Rossiter, R. J., Gaffney, T., and Ennor, A. H., *Biochim. Biophys. Acta* **37**, 385 (1960).
607a. Gaffney, T. J., Rosenberg, H., and Ennor, A. H., *Biochem. J.* **90**, 170 (1964).
608. Tudball, N., *Biochem. J.* **85**, 456 (1962).
609. Dodgson, K. S., Lloyd, A. G., and Tudball, N., *Biochem. J.* **79**, 111 (1961).
610. Teas, H. J., Horowitz, N. H., and Fling, M., *J. Biol. Chem.* **172**, 651 (1948).
611. Fling, M., and Horowitz, N. H., *J. Biol. Chem.* **190**, 277 (1951).
612. Abelson, P. H., Bolton, E. T., and Aldous, E., *J. Biol. Chem.* **198**, 173 (1952).
613. Cohen, G. N., Nisman, B., Hirsch, M. L., Wiesendanger, S. B., *Compt. Rend. Acad. Sci.* **238**, 1746 (1954).
614. Cohen, G. N., and Hirsch, M. L., *J. Bacteriol.* **67**, 182 (1954).
615. Nisman, B., Cohen, G. N., Wiesendanger, S. B., and Hirsch, M. L., *Compt. Rend. Acad. Sci.* **238**, 1342 (1954).
616. Black, S., and Gray, N. M., *J. Am. Chem. Soc.* **75**, 2271 (1953).
617. Black, S., and Wright, N. G., *J. Am. Chem. Soc.* **75**, 5766 (1953); *J. Biol. Chem.* **213**, 27, 39, 51 (1955).
618. Cohen, G. N., Nisman, B. *et al.* quoted by Black, S., and Wright, N. G., *in* "Amino Acid Metabolism" (W. D. McElroy and B. Glass, eds.), p. 591. Johns Hopkins Press, Baltimore, Maryland, 1955.
619. Moustafa, E., and Petersen, G. B., *Biochim. Biophys. Acta* **58**, 364 (1962).
620. Gibson, K. D., Neuberger, A., and Tait, G. H., *Biochem. J.* **84**, 483 (1962).
621. Watanabe, Y., and Shimura, K., *J. Biochem. (Tokyo)* **42**, 181 (1955).
622. Neuberger, A., and Tait, G. H., *J. Chem. Soc.*, p. 3963 (1962).
623. Watanabe, Y., and Shimura, K., *J. Biochem. (Tokyo)* **43**, 283 (1956); **44**, 229 (1957); **47**, 266 (1960).
624. Flavin, M., and Slaughter, C., *J. Biol. Chem.* **235**, 1103, 1112 (1960).
625. Flavin, M., and Kono, T., *J. Biol. Chem.* **235**, 1109 (1960).
626. Sasaoka, K., *Mem. Res. Inst. Food Sci. Kyoto Univ.* **14**, 42 (1958); **19**, 38 (1959); **21**, 12; **22**, 12 (1960).
627. Bilinski, E., and McConnell, W. B., *Can. J. Biochem. Physiol.* **35**, 365 (1957).

628. Hift, H., and Mahler, H. R., *J. Biol. Chem.* **198**, 901 (1952).

629. Meister, A., *Ann. Rev. Biochem.* **25**, 29 (1956).

630. Ravel, J. M., Woods, L., Felsing, B., and Shive, W., *J. Biol. Chem.* **206**, 391; **209**, 559 (1954).

631. Stadtman, E. R., Cohen, G. N., LeBras, G., and De Robichon-Szulmajster, H., *J. Biol. Chem.* **236**, 2033 (1961).

632. De Robichon-Szulmajster, H., and Corrivaux, D., *Biochim. Biophys. Acta* **73**, 248 (1963).

633. Freundlich, M., *Biochem. Biophys. Res. Commun.* **10**, 277 (1963).

634. Nara, T., Samejima, H., Fujita, C., Ito, M., Nakayama, K., and Kinoshita, S., *Agr. Biol. Chem. (Tokyo)* **25**, 532 (1961).

635. Karassevitch, Y., and De Robichon-Szulmajster, H., *Biochim. Biophys. Acta* **73**, 414 (1963).

636. Wormser, E. H., and Pardee, A. B., *Arch. Biochem. Biophys.* **78**, 416 (1958).

637. Elliott, D. F., and Neuberger, A., *Biochem. J.* **46**, 207 (1950).

638. Meltzer, H. L., and Sprinson, D. B., *J. Biol. Chem.* **197**, 461 (1952).

639. Lien, O. G., Jr., and Greenberg, D. M., *J. Biol. Chem.* **200**, 367 (1953).

640. Nishimura, J. S., and Greenberg, D. M., *J. Biol. Chem.* **236**, 2684 (1961).

641. Davis, L., and Metzler, D. E., *J. Biol. Chem.* **237**, 1883 (1962).

642. Goldstein, L., Knox, W. E., and Behrman, E. J., *J. Biol. Chem.* **237**, 2855 (1962).

643. Sayre, F. W., Jensen, D., and Greenberg, D. M., *J. Biol. Chem.* **219**, 111 (1956).

644. Pitot, H. C., and Peraino, C., *J. Biol. Chem.* **238**, PC 1910 (1963).

645. Szentirmai, A., and Horvath, I., *Acta Microbiol. Acad. Sci. Hung.* **9**, 31 (1962).

646. Tokushige, M., Whiteley, H. R., and Hayaishi, O., *Biochem. Biophys. Res. Commun.* **13**, 380 (1963).

646a. Hayaishi, O., Gefter, M., and Weissbach, H., *J. Biol. Chem.* **238**, 2040 (1963).

647. Braunstein, A. E., and Vilenkina, G. Y., *Doklady Akad. Nauk SSSR* **66**, 243 (1949).

648. Chao, F. C., Delwiche, C. C., and Greenberg, D. M., *Biochim. Biophys. Acta* **10**, 103 (1953).

649. Gilbert, J. B., *J. Am. Chem. Soc.* **79**, 2242 (1957).

650. Lin, S-C. C., and Greenberg, D. M., *J. Gen. Physiol.* **38**, 181 (1954).

651. Metzler, D. E., Longenecker, J. B., and Snell, E. E., *J. Am. Chem. Soc.* **75**, 2786 (1953); **76**, 639 (1954).

652. Karesek, M. A., and Greenberg, D. M., *J. Biol. Chem.* **227**, 191 (1957).

653. Gilbert, J. B., *J. Am. Chem. Soc.* **76**, 4183 (1954).

654. Bruns, F. H., and Fiedler, L., *Biochem. Z.*, **330**, 324 (1958); *Nature* **181**, 1533 (1958).

655. Knoop, F., *Z. Physiol. Chem.* **89**, 151 (1914).

656. Elliott, W. H., *Biochim. Biophys. Acta* **29**, 446 (1958); *Nature* **183**, 1051 (1959); *Biochem. J.* **74**, 90,479 (1960).

657. Neuberger, A., and Tait, G. H., *Biochim. Biophys. Acta* **41**, 164 (1960); *Biochem. J.* **84**, 317 (1962).

658. Krasna, A. I., Rosenblum, C., and Sprinson, D. B., *J. Biol. Chem.* **225**, 745 (1957)

659. Krebs, H. A., and Henseleit, K., *Z. Physiol. Chem.* **210**, 33 (1932).

660. Schoenheimer, R., "The Dynamic State of Body Constituents." Harvard Univ. Press, Cambridge, Massachusetts, 1942.

661. Foster, G. L., Schoenheimer, R., and Rittenberg, D., *J. Biol. Chem.* **127**, 319 (1939).
662. Clutton, R. F., Schoenheimer, R., and Rittenberg, D., *J. Biol. Chem.* **132**, 227 (1940).
663. Srb, A. M., and Horowitz, N. H., *J. Biol. Chem.* **154**, 129 (1944).
664. Volcani, B. E., and Snell, E. E., *J. Biol. Chem.* **174**, 893 (1948).
665. Bonner, D. M., *Am. J. Botany* **33**, 788 (1946).
666. Hogg, J. F., and Elliott, A. M., *J. Biol. Chem.* **192**, 13 (1951).
667. Wu, C., and Hogg, J. F., *J. Biol. Chem.* **198**, 753 (1952).
668. Campbell, J. W., and Bishop, S. N., *Biochim. Biophys. Acta* **7**, 149 (1963).
669. Coleman, R. G., *Nature* **181**, 776 (1958).
670. Baker, J. E., and Thompson, J. F., *Plant Physiol.* **37**, 618 (1962).
671. Kossel, A., and Dakin, H. D., *Z. Physiol. Chem.* **41**, 321; **42**, 181 (1904).
672. Baldwin, E., *Biochem. J.* **29**, 252 (1934).
673. Fuchs, B., *Z. Physiol Chem.* **114**, 101 (1931).
674. Folley, S. J., and Greenbaum, A. L., *Biochem. J.* **40**, 46 (1945).
675. Edlbacher, S., Becker, M., and Segesser, A. V., *Z. Physiol. Chem.* **255**, 53 (1938).
676. Stock, C. H., Perkins, M. E., and Hellerman, L., *J. Biol. Chem.* **125**, 753 (1938).
677. Hellerman, L., and Perkins, M. E., *J. Biol. Chem.* **112**, 175 (1935).
678. Edlbacher, S., and Baur, H., *Z. Physiol. Chem.* **254**, 275 (1938).
679. Anderson, A. B., *Biochem. J.* **39**, 139 (1945).
680. Akasi, S., *J. Biochem. (Tokyo)*, **26**, 129 (1937).
681. Felix, K., Müller, H., and Dirr, K., *Z. Physiol. Chem.* **178**, 192 (1928).
682. Hunter, A., *Biochem. J.* **32**, 826 (1938).
683. Richards, M. M., and Hellerman, L., *J. Biol. Chem.* **134**, 237 (1940).
684. Damodaran, M., and Narayanan, K. G. A., *Biochem. J.* **34**, 1449 (1940).
685. Meister, A., *J. Biol. Chem.* **206**, 577 (1954).
686. Thomas, K., *Z. Physiol. Chem.* **88**, 465 (1913).
687. Thomas, K., Kapfhammer, J., and Flaschenträger, B., *Z. Physiol. Chem.* **124**, 75 (1922).
688. Meyerhof, O., and Lohmann, K., *Biochem. Z.* **196**, 22 (1928).
689. Bach, S. J., and Killip, J. D., *Biochim. Biophys. Acta.* **29**, 273 (1958); *Biochem. J.* **89**, 263 (1963).
690. Grassman, W., Hörmann, H., and Janowsky, O., *Z. Physiol. Chem.* **312**, 273 (1958).
691. Greenberg, D. M., Bagot, A. E., and Roholt, O. A., Jr., *Arch. Biochem. Biophys.* **62**, 446 (1956).
692. Greenberg, D. M., *in* "The Enzymes" (P. D. Boyer, H. Lardy, and K. Myrbäck, eds.), Vol. 4, p. 257. Academic Press, New York, 1960.
693. Borsook, H., and Dubnoff, J. W., *J. Biol. Chem.* **141**, 717 (1941).
694. Krebs, H. A., *Biochem. J.* **36**, 758 (1942).
695. Ratner, S., and Pappas, A., *J. Biol. Chem.* **179**, 1183, 1199 (1949).
696. Ratner, S., and Petrack, B., *J. Biol. Chem.* **191**, 693 (1951); **200**, 161, 175 (1953).
697. Ratner, S., Petrack, B., and Rochovansky, O., *J. Biol. Chem.* **204**, 95 (1953).
698. Ratner, S., Anslow, W. P., Jr., and Petrack, B., *J. Biol. Chem.* **204**, 115 (1953).
699. Ratner, S., *Adv. Enzymol.* **15**, 319 (1954).
700. Ratner, S., *in* "The Enzymes" (P. D. Boyer, H. Lardy, and K. Myrbäck, eds.), Vol. 6, p. 495. Academic Press, New York, 1962.

701. Davison, D. C., and Elliott, W. H., *Nature* **169**, 313 (1952).
702. Walker, J. B., *Proc. Natl. Acad. Sci. U.S.* **38**, 561 (1952); *J. Biol Chem.* **204**, 139 (1953).
703. Westall, R. G., *Biochem. J.* **77**, 135 (1960).
704. Petrack, B., and Ratner, S., *J. Biol. Chem.* **233**, 1494 (1958).
705. Schuegraf, A., Ratner, S., and Warner, R. C., *J. Biol. Chem.* **235**, 3597 (1960).
706. Rochovansky, O., and Ratner, S., *J. Biol. Chem.* **236**, 2254 (1961).
707. Borsook, H., and Dubnoff, J. W., *J. Biol. Chem.* **169**, 461 (1947).
708. Cohen, P. P., and Hayano, M., *J. Biol. Chem.* **166**, 239,251 (1946); **170**, 687 (1947); **172**, 405 (1948).
709. Cohen, P. P., and Grisolia, S., *J. Biol. Chem.* **174**, 389 (1948); **182**, 747 (1950).
710. Grisolia, S., Koritz, S. B., and Cohen, P. P., *J. Biol. Chem.* **191**, 181 (1951).
711. Grisolia, S., and Cohen, P. P., *J. Biol. Chem.* **191**, 189 (1951).
712. Grisolia, S., Burris, R. H., and Cohen, P. P., *J. Biol. Chem.* **191**, 203 (1951).
713. Grisolia, S., and Cohen, P. P., *J. Biol. Chem.* **198**, 561 (1952); **204**, 753 (1953).
714. Grisolia, S., and Marshall, R. O., *Biochim. Biophys. Acta* **14**, 446 (1954).
715. Hall, L. M., and Cohen, P. P., *J. Biol. Chem.* **229**, 345 (1957).
716. Korzenovsky, M., and Werkman, C. H., *Arch. Biochem. Biophys.* **46**, 174 (1953).
717. Slade, H. D., Doughty, C. C., and Slamp, W. C., *Arch. Biochem. Biophys.* **48**, 338 (1954).
718. Oginsky, E. L., and Gehrig, R. F., *J. Biol. Chem.* **204**, 721 (1953).
719. Jones, M. E., and Lipmann, F., *Proc. Natl. Acad. Sci. U.S.* **46**, 1194 (1960).
720. Cohen, P. P., *in* "The Enzymes" (P. D. Boyer, H. Lardy, and K. Myrbäck, eds.), Vol. 6, p. 477. Academic Press, New York, 1962.
721. Reuter, G., *Z. Naturforsch.* **14b**, 475 (1959).
722. Brown, G. W., Jr., Brown, W. R., and Cohen, P. P., *J. Biol. Chem.* **234**, 1769, 1775 (1959).
723. Metzenberg, R. L., Marshall, M., Paik, W. K., and Cohen, P. P., *J. Biol. Chem.* **236**, 162 (1961).
724. Marshall, M., and Cohen, P. P., *J. Biol. Chem.* **236**, 718 (1961).
725. Schimke, R. T., *J. Biol. Chem.* **237**, 459, 1012, 1921 (1962).
726. Metzenberg, R. L., Hall, L. M., Marshall, M., and Cohen, P. P., *J. Biol. Chem.* **229**, 1019 (1957).
727. Marshall, M., Metzenberg, R. L., and Cohen, P. P., *J. Biol. Chem.* **233**, 102 (1958); **236**, 2229 (1961).
728. Grassl, M., and Bach, S. J., *Biochim. Biophys. Acta* **42**, 154 (1960).
729. Hall, L. M., Metzenberg, R. L., and Cohen, P. P., *J. Biol. Chem.* **230**, 1013 (1958).
730. Metzenberg, R. L., Marshall, M., Cohen, P. P., and Miller, W. G., *J. Biol. Chem.* **234**, 1534 (1959).
731. Reichard, P., *Proc. Inter. Congr. Biochem., 4th, Vienna,* 1958, Vol. 13, p. 119 (1959). Pergamon Press, New York.
732. Metzenberg, R. L., Marshall, M., and Cohen, P. P., *J. Biol. Chem.* **233**, 1560 (1958).
723. Jones, M. E., and Spector, L., *J. Biol. Chem.* **235**, 2897 (1960).
734. Schooler, J. M., Fahien, L. A., and Cohen, P. P., *J. Biol. Chem.* **238**, PC 1909 (1963).

735. Cohen, P. P., and Marshall, M., *in* " The Enzymes " (P. D. Boyer, H. Lardy, and K. Myrbäck, eds.), Vol. 6, p. 327. Academic Press, New York, 1962.

736. Jones, M. E., *Science* **140**, 1373 (1963).

737. Bowers, M. D., and Grisolia, S., *Comp. Biochem. Physiol.* **5**, 1 (1962).

738. Brown, G. W., Jr., and Cohen, P. P., *Biochem. J.* **75**, 82 (1960).

739. Jones, M. E., Anderson, D., Anderson, C., and Hodes, S., *Arch. Biochem. Biophys.* **95**, 499 (1961).

739a. Piérard, A., and Wiame, J. M., *Biochem. Biophys. Res. Commun.* **15**, 76 (1964).

740. Caravaca, J., and Grisolia, S., *J. Biol. Chem.* **235**, 684 (1960).

741. Oginsky, E. L., *in* "Amino Acid Metabolism " (W. D. McElroy and B. Glass, eds.), p. 300. Johns Hopkins Press, Baltimore, Maryland, 1955.

742. Slade, H. D., *in* "Amino Acid Metabolism " (W. B. McElroy and B. Glass, eds.), p. 321. Johns Hopkins Press, Baltimore, Maryland, 1955.

743. Korzenovsky, M., *in* "Amino Acid Metabolism" (W. D. McElroy and B. Glass, eds.), p. 309. Johns Hopkins Press, Baltimore, Maryland, 1955.

744. Ravel, J. M., Grona, M. L., Humphreys, J. S., and Shive, W., *J. Biol. Chem.* **234**, 1452 (1959).

745. Reichard, P., *Acta Chem. Scand.* **11**, 523 (1957).

746. Burnett, G. H., and Cohen, P. P., *J. Biol. Chem.* **229**, 337 (1957).

747. Joseph, R. L., Baldwin, E., and Watts, D. C., *Biochem. J.* **87**, 409 (1963).

748. Krebs, H. A., Jensen, P. K., and Eggleston, L. V., *Biochem. J.* **70**, 397 (1959).

749. Stulberg, M. P., and Boyer, P. D., *J. Am. Chem. Soc.* **76**, 5569 (1954).

750. Estes, J. M., Ravel, J. M., and Shive, W., *J. Am. Chem. Soc.* **78**, 6410 (1956).

751. Sund, R. F., Ravel, J. M., and Shive, W., *J. Biol. Chem.* **231**, 807 (1958).

752. Ravel, J. M., Mollenhauer, B. F., and Shive, W., *J. Biol. Chem.* **236**, 2268 (1961).

753. Grisolia, S., and Harmon, P., *Biochim. Biophys. Acta* **59**, 482 (1962).

754. Novoa, W. B., and Grisolia, S., *J. Biol. Chem.* **237**, PC 2710 (1962).

755. Grisolia, S., Amelunxen, R., and Raijman, L., *Biochem. Biophys. Res. Commun.* **11**, 75 (1963).

756. Ramponi, G., Melani, F., and Guerritore, A., *Italian J. Biochim.* **10**, 188 (1961).

757. Thorne, K. J. I., and Jones, M. E., *J. Biol. Chem.* **238**, 2992 (1963).

758. Schimke, R. T., *Biochim. Biophys. Acta* **62**, 599 (1962).

759. Cohen, P. P., and Sallach, H. J., *in* "Metabolic Pathways " (D. M. Greenberg, ed.), Vol. **2**, p. 60. Academic Press, New York, 1961.

760. Davies, R. K., DeFalco, A. J., Shander, D., Kopelman, A., and Kiyasu, J., *Nature* **191**, 288 (1961).

761. Ratner, S., Morell, H., and Carvalho, E., *Arch. Biochem. Biophys.* **91**, 280 (1960).

761a. Tamir, H., and Ratner, S., *Arch. Biochem. Biophys.* **102**, 249, 259 (1963).

762. Bronk, J. R., and Fisher, R. B., *Biochem. J.* **64**, 106, 111, 118 (1956).

763. Bach, S. J., and Smith, M., *Nature* **176**, 1126 (1955).

764. Burke, W. T., and Miller, L. L., *Federation Proc.* **15**, 227 (1956).

765. Cedrangolo, F., *Enzymologia* **19**, 335 (1958).

766. Cedrangolo, F., Della Pietra, G., Cittadini, D., Papa, S., and DeLorenzo, F., *Nature* **195**, 708 (1962).

767. Ory, R. L., Hood, D. W., and Lyman, C. M., *J. Biol. Chem.* **207**, 267 (1954).

768. Levenberg, B., *J. Biol. Chem.* **237**, 2590 (1962).

769. Szulmajster, J., *Biochim. Biophys. Acta* **30**, 154 (1958); **44**, 173 (1960).

770. Valentine, R. C., and Wolfe, R. S., *Biochem. Biophys. Res. Commun.* **2**, 384 (1960); *Biochim. Biophys. Acta* **45**, 389 (1960).
770a. Bojanowski, R., Gaudy, E., Valentine, R. C., and Wolfe, R. S., *J. Bacteriol.* **87**, 75 (1964).
771. Valentine, R. C., and Wolfe, R. S., *Nature* **191**, 925 (1961).
772. Cook, A. R., and Boulter, D., *Biochem. J.* **88**, 69 P (1963).
773. Hills, G. M., *Biochem. J.* **34**, 1057 (1940).
774. Horn, F., *Z. Physiol. Chem.* **216**, 244 (1953).
775. Oginsky, E. L., and Gehrig, R. F., *J. Biol. Chem.* **198**, 791 (1952).
776. Oginsky, E. L., and Gehrig, R. F., *J. Biol. Chem.* **198**, 799 (1952).
777. Stetten, D., Jr., and Bloom, B., *J. Biol. Chem.* **220**, 723 (1956).
778. Kihara, H., Prescott, J. M., and Snell, E. E., *J. Biol. Chem.* **217**, 497 (1955).
779. Kihara, H., and Snell, E. E., *J. Biol. Chem.* **226**, 485 (1957).
780. Kalyankar, G. D., Ikawa, M., and Snell, E. E., *J. Biol. Chem.* **233**, 1175 (1958).
781. Walker, J. B., and Walker, M. S., *J. Biol. Chem.* **234**, 1481 (1959).
782. Kitagawa, M., and Yamada, H., *J. Biochem. (Tokyo)* **16**, 339 (1932).
783. Walker, J. B., *J. Biol. Chem.* **218**, 549 (1956).
783a. Thiem, Ng.-V., Thoai, Ng.-V., and Roche, J., *Bull. Soc. Chim. Biol.* **44**, 285 (1962).
784. Lohmann, K., *Biochem. Z.* **282**, 109 (1935).
784a. Morrison, J. F., Griffiths, D. E., and Ennor, A. H., *Biochem. J.* **65**, 143 (1957).
785. Smith, T. A., and Richards, F. J., *Biochem. J.* **84**, 292 (1962).
786. Jakoby, W. B., and Fredericks, J., *J. Biol. Chem.* **234**, 2145 (1959).
787. Mothes, K., and Schütte, H. R., *Angew. Chem. Intern. Ed. Engl.* **2**, 341, 441 (1963).
788. Leete, E., *J. Am. Chem. Soc.*, **84**, 55 (1962).
789. Bothner-By, A. A., Schutz, R. S., Dawson, R. F., and Solt, M. L., *J. Am. Chem. Soc.* **84**, 52 (1962).
790. Vickery, H. B., *J. Biol. Chem.* **60**, 647 (1924).
791. Marion, L., *in* "The Alkaloids" (R. H. F. Manske and H. L. Holmes, eds.), Vol. 1, Pt. 1, p. 101. Academic Press, New York, 1950.
792. Leete, E., Marion, L., and Spenser, I. D., *J. Biol. Chem.* **214**, 71 (1955).
793. Essery, J. M., McCaldin, D. J., and Marion, L., *Phytochemistry* **1**, 209 (1962).
794. Robertson, A. V., and Marion, L., *Can. J. Chem.* **37**, 1197 (1959).
795. Robertson, A. V., and Marion, L., *Can. J. Chem.* **38**, 396 (1960).
796. Lamberts, B. L., Dewey, L. J., and Byerrum, R. U., *Biochim. Biophys. Acta* **33**, 22, (1959).
797. Dewey, L. J., Byerrum, R. U., and Ball, C. D., *Biochim. Biophys. Acta* **18**, 141 (1955).
798. Leete, E., *J. Am. Chem. Soc.*, **80**, 2162 (1958).
799. Lamberts, B. L., and Byerrum, R. U., *J. Biol. Chem.* **233**, 939 (1958).
800. Wu, P. H. L., Griffith, T., and Byerrum, R. U., *J. Biol. Chem.* **237**, 887 (1962).
801. Mann, P. J. G., and Smithies, W. R., *Biochem. J.* **61**, 89 (1955).
802. Hasse, K., and Maisack, H., *Naturwissenschaften* **42**, 627 (1955).
803. Hasse, K., and Maisack, H., *Biochem. Z.* **327**, 296 (1955).
804. Leete, E., *J. Am. Chem. Soc.* **78**, 3520 (1956).
805. Hasse, K., and Schmid, G., *Biochem. Z.* **337**, 480 (1963).
806. Thoai, Ng.-V., and Robin, Y., *Bull. Soc. Chim. Biol.* **41**, 735 (1959).

807. Thoai, Ng.-V., DiJeso, F., and Robin, Y., *Compt. Rend. Acad. Sci.* **256**, 4525 (1963).
808. Hunter, G. D., Herbert, M., and Hockenhull, D. J. D., *Biochem. J.* **58**, 249 (1954).
809. Thoai, Ng.-V., and Desvages, G., *Bull. Soc. Chim. Biol.* **45**, 413 (1963).
810. Vogel, H. J., and Davis, B. D., *J. Am. Chem. Soc.* **74**, 109 (1952).
811. Moe, O. A., and Warner, D. T., *J. Am. Chem. Soc.* **70**, 2763 (1948).
812. Shemin, D., and Rittenberg, D., *J. Biol. Chem.* **158**, 71 (1945).
813. Vogel, H. J., and Bonner, D. M., *Proc. Natl. Acad. Sci. U.S.* **40**, 688 (1954).
814. Abelson, P. H., and Vogel, H. J., *J. Biol. Chem.* **213**, 355 (1955).
815. Strecker, H. J., *J. Biol. Chem.* **235**, 2045 (1960).
816. Strecker, H. J., *J. Biol. Chem.* **225**, 825 (1957).
817. Yura, T., and Vogel, H. J., *Biochim. Biophys. Acta* **17**, 582 (1955).
818. Yura, T., and Vogel, H. J., *Biochim. Biophys. Acta* **24**, 648 (1957).
819. Yura, T., and Vogel, H. J., *J. Biol. Chem.* **234**, 335, 339 (1959).
820. Meister, A., Radhakrishnan, A. N., and Buckley, S. D., *J. Biol. Chem.* **229**, 789 (1957).
821. Vogel, H. J., *Proc. Natl. Acad. Sci. U.S.* **39**, 578 (1953).
822. Vogel, H. J., Abelson, P. H., and Bolton, E. T., *Biochim. Biophys. Acta* **11**, 584 (1953).
823. Vogel, H. J., and Bonner, D. M., *J. Biol. Chem.* **218**, 97 (1956).
824. Vogel, H. J., *in* "Amino Acid Metabolism" (W. D. McElroy and B. Glass, eds.), p. 335. Johns Hopkins Press, Baltimore, Maryland, 1955.
825. Maas, W. K., Novelli, G. D., and Lipmann, F., *Proc. Natl. Acad. Sci. U.S.* **39**, 1004 (1953).
826. Vyas, S., and Maas, W. K., *Arch. Biochem. Biophys.* **100**, 542 (1963).
827. Udaka, S., and Kinoshita, S., *J. Gen. Appl. Microbiol.* (*Tokyo*) **4**, 272 (1958).
828. Baich, A., and Vogel, H. J., *Biochem. Biophys. Res. Commun.* **7**, 491 (1962).
829. Vogel, R. H., and Vogel, H. J., *Biochim. Biophys. Acta* **69**, 174 (1963).
830. Fincham, J. R. S., *Biochem. J.* **53**, 313 (1953).
831. Vogel, R. H., and Kopac, M. J., *Biochim. Biophys. Acta* **36**, 505 (1959).
832. DeDeken, R. H., *Biochem. Biophys. Res. Commun.* **8**, 462 (1962).
832a. Vogel, R. H., and Vogel, H. J., *Genetics* **48**, 914 (1963).
833. Gorini, L., *Proc. Natl. Acad. Sci. U.S.* **46**, 682 (1960).
834. Gorini, L., Gundersen, W., and Burger, M., *Cold Spring Harbor Symp. Quant. Biol.* **26**, 173 (1961).
835. Vogel, H. J., "The Chemical Basis of Heredity," p. 276. Johns Hopkins Press, Baltimore, Maryland (1956).
836. Vogel, H. J., *Cold Spring Harbor Symp. Quant. Biol.* **26**, 163 (1961).
837. Maas, W. K., *Cold Spring Harbor Symp. Quant. Biol.* **26**, 183 (1961).
838. Gorini, L., and Maas, W. K., *Biochim. Biophys. Acta* **25**, 208 (1957).
839. Mahler, I., Newmann, J., and Marmur, J., *Biochim. Biophys. Acta* **72**, 69 (1963).
840. Vogel, H. J., Bacon, D. F., and Baich, A., *in* "Informational Macromolecules" (H. J. Vogel, V. Bryson, and J. O. Lampen, eds.), p. 293. Academic Press, New York, 1963.
841. Depocas, F., and Bouthillier, L. P., *Extrait Rev. Can. Biol.* **10**, 289 (1951).
842. Sallach, H. J., Koeppe, R. E., and Rose, W. C., *J. Am. Chem. Soc.* **73**, 4500 (1951).
843. Stetten, M. R., and Schoenheimer, R., *J. Biol. Chem.* **153**, 113 (1944).

844. Roloff, M., Ratner, S., and Schoenheimer, R., *J. Biol. Chem.* **136**, 561 (1940).
845. Weil-Malherbe, H., and Krebs, H. A., *Biochem. J.* **29**, 2077 (1935).
846. Neber, M., *Z. Physiol Chem.* **240**, 70 (1936).
847. Srb, A. M., Fincham, J. R. S., and Bonner, D. M., *Am. J. Botany* **37**, 533 (1950).
848. Forbes, M., and Sevag, M. G., *Arch. Biochem. Biophys.* **31**, 406 (1951).
849. Krebs, H. A., *Enzymologia* **7**, 53 (1939).
850. Blanchard, M., Green, D. E., Nocito, V., and Ratner, S., *J. Biol. Chem.* **155**, 421 (1944).
851. Macholan, L., and Skursky, L., *Chem. Listy* **49**, 1385 (1955); *Chem. Abstr.* **50**, 5572 (1956).
852. Hasse, K., and Wieland, A., *Ber.* **93**, 1686 (1960).
853. Stetten, M. R., *J. Biol. Chem.* **189**, 499 (1951).
854. Taggart, J. V., and Krakaur, R. B., *J. Biol. Chem.* **177**, 641 (1949).
855. Lang, K., and Schmidt, G., *Biochem. Z.* **322**, 1 (1951).
856. Johnson, A. B., and Strecker, H. J., *J. Biol. Chem.* **237**, 1876 (1962).
857. Smith, M. E., and Greenberg, D. M., *J. Biol. Chem.* **226**, 317 (1957).
858. Peisach, J., and Strecker, H. J., *J. Biol. Chem.* **237**, 2255 (1962).
859. Strecker, H. J., *J. Biol. Chem.* **235**, 3218 (1960).
860. Gustavson, K. H., "The Chemistry and Reactivity of Collagen." Academic Press, New York, 1956.
861. Steward, F. C., Bidwell, R. G. S., and Yemm, E. W., *Nature* **178**, 789 (1956).
862. Steward, F. C., and Thompson, J. F., *Ann. Rev. Plant Physiol.* **1**, 233 (1950).
863. Lamport, D. T. A., and Northcote, D. H., *Nature* **188**, 665 (1960); *Biochem. J.* **76**, 52 P. (1960).
864. Dougall, D. K., and Shimbayashi, K., *Plant Physiol.* **35**, 396 (1960).
865. Lenhoff, H. M., Kline, E. S., and Hurley, R., *Biochem. Biophys. Acta* **26**, 204 (1957).
866. Maser, M. D., and Rice, R. V., *Biochim. Biophys. Acta* **63**, 255 (1962).
867. Hoare, D. S., *J. Gen. Microbiol.* **12**, 534 (1955).
868. Stetten, M. R., *J. Biol. Chem.* **181**, 31 (1949).
869. Womack, M., and Rose, W. C., *J. Biol. Chem.* **171**, 37 (1947).
870. Pederson, S., Lewis, H. B., *J. Biol. Chem.* **154**, 705 (1944).
871. Simmonds, S., and Fruton, J. S., *J. Biol. Chem.* **174**, 705 (1948).
872. Green, N. M., and Lowther, D. A., *Biochem. J.* **71**, 55 (1959).
873. Mitoma, C., Smith, T. E., Friedberg, F., and Rayford, C. R., *J. Biol. Chem.* **234**, 78 (1959).
874. Prockop, D. J., Peterkofsky, B., and Udenfriend, S., *J. Biol. Chem.* **237**, 1581 (1962).
875. Hausmann, E., and Neuman, W. F., *J. Biol. Chem.* **236**, 149 (1961).
876. Robertson, W. van B., Hiwett, J., and Herman, C., *J. Biol. Chem.* **234**, 105 (1959).
877. Mitoma, C., and Smith, T. E., *J. Biol. Chem.* **235**, 426 (1960).
878. Stone, N., and Meister, A., *Nature* **194**, 555 (1962).
879. Wolbach, S. B., and Howe, P. R., *Arch. Pathol. Lab. Med.* **1**, 1 (1926).
880. Robertson, W. van B., and Schwarz, B., *J. Biol. Chem.* **201**, 689 (1953).
881. Gould, B. S., and Woessner, J. F., *J. Biol. Chem.* **226**, 289 (1957).
882. Robertson, W. van B., Hiwett, J., and Herman, C., *J. Biol. Chem.* **234**, 105 (1959).
883. Robertson, W. van B., *Ann. N.Y. Acad. Sci.* **92**, 159 (1961).

884. Robertson, W. van B., *J. Biol. Chem.* **196**, 403 (1952).
885. Gould, B. S., Manner, G., Goldman, H. M., and Stolman, J. M., *Ann. N.Y. Acad. Sci.* **85**, 385 (1960).
886. Gould, B. S., *Ann. N.Y. Acad. Sci.* **92**, 168 (1961).
887. Gould, B. S., *J. Biol. Chem.* **232**, 637 (1958).
888. Gross, J., *J. Exptl. Med.* **109**, 557 (1959).
889. Chvapil, M., and Hurych, J., *Nature* **184**, 1145 (1959).
890. Breslow, R., and Lukens, L. N., *J. Biol. Chem.* **235**, 292 (1960).
891. Robertson, W. van B., *Biochim. Biophys. Acta* **74**, 137 (1963).
892. Daughaday, W. H., and Mariz, I. K., *J. Biol. Chem.* **237**, 2831 (1962).
893. Kivirikko, K. I., *Nature* **197**, 593 (1963); *Acta Chem. Scand.* **17**, 270 (1963); *Acta Physiol. Scand.* **60**, Suppl. 219 (1963).
894. Hurych, J., and Chvapil, M., *Biochim. Biophys. Acta* **65**, 170 (1962).
895. Lindstedt, S., and Prockop, D. J., *J. Biol. Chem.* **236**, 1399 (1961).
896. Ziff, M., Kibrick, A. C., Dresner, E., and Gribetz, H. J., *J. Clin. Invest.* **35**, 579 (1956).
897. Mechanic, G., Skupp, S. J., Safier, L. B., and Kibrick, A. C., *Arch. Biochem. Biophys.* **86**, 71 (1960).
898. Meilman, E., and Urivetzky, M. M., *Arthritis Rheum.* **4**, 119 (1961).
899. Prockop, D. J., and Sjoerdsma, A., *J. Clin. Invest.* **40**, 843 (1961).
900. Kibrick, A. C., Hashiro, C. Q., and Safier, L. B., *Proc. Soc. Exptl. Biol. Med.* **109**, 473 (1962).
901. Jasin, H. E., Fink, C. W., Wise, W., and Ziff, M., *J. Clin. Invest.* **41**, 1928 (1962).
902. Meilman, E., Urivetzky, M. M., and Rapoport, C. M., *J. Clin. Invest.* **42**, 40 (1963).
903. Ebert, P. S., and Prockop, D. J., *Biochem. Biophys. Res. Commun.* **8**, 305 (1962).
903a. Lamport, D. T. A., *Nature* **202**, 293 (1964).
904. Fujimoto, D., Osawa, H., and Tamiya, H., *Symp. Enzyme Chem.* (*Tokyo*) Preliminary Issue **14**, 28 (1962).
905. Fujimoto, D., and Tamiya, N., *Biochem. J.* **84**, 333 (1962).
906. Prockop, D. J., Kaplan, A., and Udenfriend, S., *Biochem. Biophys. Res. Commun.* **9**, 162 (1962).
907. Scharpenseel, H. W., and Wolf, G., *Z. Tierphysiol. Tierernaehr. Futtermittelk.* **14**, 347 (1959).
908. Lamport, D. T. A., *J. Biol. Chem.* **238**, 1438 (1963).
909. Witkop, B., *Chem. Soc.* (*London*) *Spec. Publ.* **3**, 60 (1955).
910. Witkop, B., and Beiler, T., *J. Am. Chem. Soc.* **78**, 2822 (1956).
911. Robertson, A. V., Katz, E., and Witkop, B., *J. Org. Chem.* **27**, 2676 (1962).
912. Robertson, A. V., Francis, J. E., and Witkop, B., *J. Am. Chem. Soc.* **84**, 1709 (1962).
913. Robertson, A. V., and Witkop, B., *J. Am. Chem. Soc.* **84**, 1697 (1962).
914. Patchett, A. A., and Witkop, B., *J. Am. Chem. Soc.* **79**, 185 (1957).
915. Smith, T. E., and Mitoma, C., *J. Biol. Chem.* **237**, 1177 (1962).
916. Peterkofsky, B., and Udenfriend, S., *Biochem. Biophys. Res. Commun.* **6**, 184 (1961); **12**, 257 (1963).
917. Manner, G., and Gould, B. S., *Biochim. Biophys. Acta* **72**, 243 (1963).
918. Coronado, A., Mardones, E., and Allende, J. E., *Biochem. Biophys. Res. Commun.* **13**, 75 (1963).

919. Jackson, D. S., Watkins, D., and Winkler, A., *Biochim. Biophys. Acta* **87**, 152 (1964).

920. Urivetzky, M., Kranz, V., and Meilman, E., *Arch. Biochem. Biophys.* **100**, 478 (1963).

921. Katz, E., Prockop, D. J., and Udenfriend, S., *J. Biol. Chem.* **237**, 1585 (1962).

922. Kapfhammer, J., and Bischoff, C., *Z. Physiol. Chem.* **172**, 251 (1927).

923. Hess, W. C., and Shaffran, I. P., *J. Am. Chem. Soc.* **73**, 474 (1951).

924. Gianetto, R., and Bouthillier, L. P., *Can. J. Biochem. Physiol.* **32**, 154 (1954).

925. Wolf, G., Heck, W. W., and Leak, J. C., *J. Biol. Chem.* **223**, 95 (1956).

926. Lang, K., and Mayer, U., *Biochem. Z.* **324**, 237 (1953).

927. Adams, E., and Goldstone, A., *J. Biol. Chem.* **235**, 3492 (1960).

928. Adams, E., and Goldstone, A., *J. Biol. Chem.* **235**, 3499 (1960).

929. Adams, E., Friedman, R., and Goldstone, A., *Biochim. Biophys. Acta* **30**, 212 (1958).

930. Adams, E., and Goldstone, A., *J. Biol. Chem.* **235**, 3504 (1960).

931. Wolf, G., and Berger, C. R. A., *J. Biol. Chem.* **230**, 231 (1958).

932. Benoiton, L., and Bouthillier, L. P., *Can. J. Biochem. Physiol.* **34**, 661 (1956).

933. Goldstone, A., and Adams, E., *J. Biol. Chem.* **237**, 3476 (1962).

934. Dekker, E. E., *Biochim. Biophys. Acta* **40**, 174 (1960).

935. Dekker, E. E., and Maitra, U., *J. Biol. Chem.* **237**, 2218 (1962).

936. Kuratomi, K., and Fukunaga, K., *Biochim. Biophys. Acta* **43**, 562 (1960); **78**, 617 (1963).

937. Bouthillier, L. P., Binette, Y., and Pouliot, G., *Can. J. Biochem. Physiol.* **39**, 1595 (1961).

937a. Virtanen, A. I., and Hietala, P. K., *Acta Chem. Scand.* **9**, 549 (1955).

938. Maitra, U., and Dekker, E. E., *Biochim. Biophys. Acta* **51**, 416 (1961).

938a. Homola, A. D., and Dekker, E. E., *Biochim. Biophys. Acta* **82**, 207 (1964).

938b. Morton, R. K., and Wells, J. R. E., *Nature* **201**, 477 (1964).

939. Adams, E., *J. Am. Chem. Soc.* **79**, 6338 (1957).

939a. Goldstone, A., and Adams, E., *Biochem. Biophys. Res. Commun.* **16**, 71 (1964).

940. Adams, E. *J. Biol. Chem.* **234**, 2073 (1959).

941. Yoneya, T., and Adams, E., *J. Biol. Chem.* **236**, 3272 (1961).

942. Radhakrishnan, A. N., and Meister, A., *J. Biol. Chem.* **226**, 559 (1957).

943. Corrigan, J. J., Wellner, D., and Meister, A., *Biochim. Biophys. Acta* **73**, 50 (1963).

944. Gottschalk, A., *Biochem. J.* **61**, 298 (1955); *Nature* **176**, 881 (1955).

945. Bonner, D., Tatum, E. L., and Beadle, G. W., *Arch. Biochem.* **3**, 71 (1943).

946. Umbarger, H. E., and Mueller, J. H., *J. Biol. Chem.* **189**, 287 (1951).

947. Bonner, D., *J. Biol. Chem.* **166**, 545 (1946).

948. Umbarger, H. E., and Mueller, J. H., *J. Biol. Chem.* **189**, 277 (1951).

949. Umbarger, H. E., and Adelberg, E. A., *J. Biol. Chem.* **192**, 883 (1951).

950. Singh, R. M. M., and Adams, E., *Science* **144**, 67 (1964).

951. Rudman, D., and Meister, A., *J. Biol. Chem.* **200**, 591 (1953).

952. Adelberg, E. A., and Umbarger, H. E., *J. Biol. Chem.* **205**, 475 (1953).

953. Fincham, J. R. S., and Boulter, A. B., *Biochem. J.* **62**, 72 (1956).

954. Seecof, R. L., and Wagner, R. P., *J. Biol. Chem.* **234**, 2689, 2694 (1959).

955. Adelberg, E. A., Bonner, D. M., and Tatum, E. L., *J. Biol. Chem.* **190**, 837 (1951).

956. Adelberg, E. A., and Tatum, E. L., *Arch. Biochem.* **29**, 235 (1950).

957. Sjolander, J. R., Folkers, K., Adelberg, E. A., and Tatum, E. L., *J. Am. Chem. Soc.* **76**, 1085 (1954).

958. Myers, J. W., and Adelberg, E. A., *Proc. Natl. Acad. Sci. U.S.* **40**, 493 (1954).

959. Adelberg, E. A., *in* "Amino Acid Metabolism" (W. D. Elroy and B. Glass, eds.), p. 419. Johns Hopkins Press, Baltimore, Maryland, 1955.

960. Wixom, R. L., Wikman, J. H., and Howell, G. B., *J. Biol. Chem.* **236**, 3257 (1961).

961. Myers, J. W., *J. Biol. Chem.* **236**, 1414 (1961).

962. Wixom, R. L., Shatton, J. B., and Strassman, M., *J. Biol. Chem.* **235**, 128 (1960).

963. Tatum, E. L., and Adelberg, E. A., *J. Biol. Chem.* **190**, 843 (1951).

964. Strassman, M., Thomas, A. J., and Weinhouse, S., *J. Am. Chem. Soc.* **75**, 5135 (1953).

965. Strassman, M., Thomas, A. J., and Weinhouse, S., *J. Am. Chem. Soc.* **77**, 1261 (1955).

966. Rafelson, M. E., Jr., *J. Am. Chem. Soc.* **77**, 4679 (1955).

967. Adelberg, E. A., Coughlin, C. A., and Barratt, R. W., *J. Biol. Chem.* **216**, 425 (1955).

968. McManus, I. R., *J. Biol. Chem.* **208**, 639 (1954).

969. Willson, C. D., and Adelberg, E. A., *J. Biol. Chem.* **229**, 1011 (1957).

970. Umbarger, H. E., Brown, B., and Eyring, E. J., *J. Am. Chem. Soc.* **79**, 2980 (1957).

971. Umbarger, H. E., and Brown, B., *J. Biol. Chem.* **233**, 1156 (1958).

972. Lewis, K. F., and Weinhouse, S., *J. Am. Chem. Soc.* **80**, 4913 (1958).

973. Strassman, M., Shatton, J. B., Corsey, M. E., and Weinhouse, S., *J. Am. Chem. Soc.* **80**, 1771 (1958).

974. Juni, E., *J. Biol. Chem.* **195**, 715, 727 (1952).

975. Juni, E., and Heym, G. A., *J. Biol. Chem.* **218**, 365 (1956).

976. Halpern, Y. S., and Umbarger, H. E., *J. Biol. Chem.* **234**, 3067 (1959).

977. Krampitz, L. O., Gruell, G., Miller, C. S., Bicking, J. B., Skeggs, H. R., and Sprague, J. M., *J. Am. Chem. Soc.* **80**, 5893 (1958).

978. Carlson, G. L., and Brown, G. M., *J. Biol. Chem.* **235**, PC 3 (1960).

979. Wagner, R. P., Radhakrishnan, A. N., and Snell, E. E., *Proc. Natl. Acad. Sci. U.S.* **44**, 1047 (1958).

980. Wagner, R. P., Bergquist, A., and Forrest, H. S., *J. Biol. Chem.* **234**, 99 (1959).

981. Radhakrishnan, A. N., and Snell, E. E., *J. Biol. Chem.* **235**, 2316 (1960).

982. Leavitt, R. I., and Umbarger, H. E., *J. Biol. Chem.* **236**, 2486 (1961).

983. Watanabe, Y., Hayashi, K., and Shimura, K., *Biochim. Biophys. Acta* **31**, 583 (1959).

984. Leavitt, R. I., and Umbarger, H. E., *J. Bacteriol.* **83**, 624 (1962).

985. Umbarger, H. E., Brown, B., and Eyring, E. J., *J. Biol. Chem.* **235**, 1425 (1960).

986. Radhakrishnan, A. N., Wagner, R. P., and Snell, E. E., *J. Biol. Chem.* **235**, 2322 (1960).

987. Strassman, M., Shatton, J. B., and Weinhouse, S., *J. Biol. Chem.* **235**, 700 (1960).

988. Armstrong, F. B., and Wagner, R. P., *J. Biol. Chem.* **236**, 2027, 3252 (1961).

989. Meister, A., *J. Biol. Chem.* **184**, 117 (1950).

990. Cahn, R. D., Kaplan, N. O., Levine, L., and Zwilling, E., *Science* **136**, 962 (1962).

991. Adelberg, E. A., *J. Am. Chem. Soc.* **76**, 4241 (1954).

992. Adelberg, E. A., *J. Biol. Chem.* **216**, 431 (1955).

993. Strassman, M., Thomas, A. J., Locke, L. A., and Weinhouse, S., *J. Am. Chem. Soc.* **76**, 4241 (1954).

994. Umbarger, H. E., and Brown, B., *J. Bacteriol.* **71**, 443 (1956); **73**, 105 (1957); *J. Biol. Chem.* **233**, 415 (1958).

995. Abramsky, T., Rowland, L. P., and Shemin, D., *J. Biol. Chem.* **237**, PC 265 (1962).

996. Kanamori, M., and Wixom, R. L., *J. Biol. Chem.* **238**, 998 (1963).

997. Satyanarayana, T., and Radhakrishnan, A. N., *Biochim. Biophys. Acta* **56**, 197 (1962); **77**, 121 (1963).

998. Kretovich, W. L., and Kagan, Z. S., *Nature* **195**, 81 (1962).

999. Kretovich, W. L., Kagan, Z. S., and Tscheuschner, G., *Nahrung* **6**, 609 (1962).

1000. Strassman, M., Locke, L. A., Thomas, A. J., and Weinhouse, S., *Science* **121**, 303 (1955); *J. Am. Chem. Soc.* **79**, 1599 (1956).

1001. Reiss, O., and Bloch, K., *J. Biol. Chem.* **216**, 703 (1955).

1002. Rafelson, M. E., Jr., *Arch. Biochem. Biophys.* **72**, 376 (1957).

1003. Jungwirth, C., Gross, S. R., Margolin, P., and Umbarger, H. E., *Biochemistry* **2**, 1 (1963).

1004. Calvo, J. M., Kalyanpur, M. G., and Stevens, C. M., *Biochemistry* **1**, 1157 (1962).

1005. Martin, W. R., Coleman, W. H., Wideburg, N. E., Cantrell, R., Jackson, M., and Denison, F. W., Jr., *Biochim. Biophys. Acta* **62**, 165 (1962).

1006. Yamashita, M., *J. Org. Chem.* **23**, 835 (1953).

1007. Strassman, M., and Ceci, L. N., *J. Biol. Chem.* **238**, 2445 (1963).

1008. Gross, S. R., Burns, R. O., and Umbarger, H. E., *Biochemistry* **2**, 1046 (1963).

1009. Burns, R. O., Umbarger, H. E., and Gross, S. R., *Biochemistry* **2**, 1053 (1963).

1010. Ingraham, J. L., Guymon, J. F., and Crowell, E. A., *Arch. Biochem. Biophys.* **88**, 157 (1960); **95**, 169 (1961).

1011. Webb, M., *Biochem. J.* **70**, 472 (1958).

1012. Butler, G. W., and Shen, L., *Biochim. Biophys. Acta* **71**, 456 (1963).

1013. Allison, M. J., Bryant, M. P., Doetsch, R. N., *Arch. Biochem. Biophys.* **84**, 245 (1959); *J. Bacteriol.* **83**, 523 (1962).

1013a. Yoshizawa, K., *Agr. Biol. Chem. (Tokyo)* **27**, 162 (1963).

1014. Embden, G., Salomon, H., and Schmidt, F., *Beitr. Chem. Physiol. Pathol.* **8**, 129 (1906).

1015. Ringer, A. I., Frankel, E. M., and Jonas, L., *J. Biol. Chem.* **14**, 525 (1913).

1016. Cohen, P. P., *J. Biol. Chem.* **119**, 333 (1937).

1017. Bloch, K., *J. Biol. Chem.* **155**, 255, (1944).

1018. Coon, M. J., and Gurin, S., *J. Biol. Chem.* **180**, 1159 (1949).

1019. Coon, M. J., *J. Biol. Chem.* **187**, 71 (1950).

1020. Zabin, I., and Bloch, K., *J. Biol. Chem.* **185**, 117 (1950).

1021. Plaut, G. W. E., and Lardy, H. A., *J. Biol. Chem.* **192**, 435 (1951).

1022. Coon, M. J., *Federation Proc.* **14**, 762 (1955).

1023. Bachhawat, B. K., Woessner, J. F., Jr., and Coon, M. J., *Federation Proc.* **15**, 214 (1956).

1024. Bachhawat, B. K., Robinson, W. G., and Coon, M. J., *J. Am. Chem. Soc.* **76**, 3098 (1954); *J. Biol. Chem.* **216**, 727 (1955); **219**, 539 (1956).

1025. Coon, M. J., *in* "Amino Acid Metabolism" (W. D. McElroy and B. Glass, eds.), p. 431. Johns Hopkins Press, Baltimore, Maryland, 1955.

1026. Seubert, W., and Lynen, F., *J. Am. Chem. Soc.* **75**, 2787 (1953).

1027. Green, D. E., Mii, S., and Mahler, H. R., *J. Biol. Chem.* **206**, 1 (1954).
1028. Sasaki, S., *Nature* **189**, 400 (1961); *Biochem. J.* **51**, 335 (1962).
1029. Rilling, H. C., and Coon, M. J., *J. Biol. Chem.* **235**, 3087 (1960).
1030. Lynen, F., Henning, U., Bublitz, C., Sorbo, B., and Kroplin-Ruess, L., *Biochem. Z.* **330**, 269 (1958).
1031. Himes, R. H., Young, D. L., Ringelmann, E., and Lynen, F., *Biochem. Z.* **337**, 48 (1963).
1032. Del Campillo-Campbell, A., Dekker, E. E., and Coon, M. J., *Biochim. Biophys. Acta* **31**, 290 (1959).
1033. Knappe, J., Ringelmann, E., and Lynen, F., *Biochem. Z.* **335**, 168 (1961).
1034. Knappe, J., Biederbick, K., and Brümmer, W., *Angew. Chem.* **74**, 432 (1962).
1035. Lane, M. D., and Lynen, F., *Proc. Natl. Acad. Sci. U.S.* **49**, 379 (1963).
1036. Kosow, D. P., and Lane, M. D., *Biochem. Biophys. Res. Commun.* **7**, 439 (1962).
1037. Halenz, D. R., Feng, J.-Y., Hegre, C. S., and Lane, M. D., *J. Biol. Chem.* **237**, 2140 (1962).
1038. Kaziro, Y., and Ochoa, S., *J. Biol. Chem.* **236**, 3131 (1961).
1039. Kaziro, Y., Hass, L. F., Boyer, P. D., and Ochoa, S., *J. Biol. Chem.* **237**, 1460 (1962).
1040. Lane, M. D., Halenz, D. R., Kosow, D. P., and Hegre, C. S., *J. Biol. Chem.* **235**, 3082 (1960).
1041. Seubert, W., and Remberger, U., *Biochem. Z.* **334**, 401 (1961).
1042. Waite, M., and Wakil, S. J., *J. Biol. Chem.* **238**, 77, 81 (1963).
1043. Woessner, J. F., Jr., Bachhawat, B. K., and Coon, M. J., *J. Biol. Chem.* **233**, 520 (1958).
1044. Kupiecki, F. P., and Coon, M. J., *J. Biol. Chem.* **235**, 1944 (1960).
1045. Dekker, E. E., Schlesinger, M. J., and Coon, M. J., *J. Biol. Chem.* **233**, 434 (1958).
1046. Rudney, H., *J. Biol. Chem.* **227**, 363 (1957).
1047. Durr, I. F., and Rudney, H., *J. Biol. Chem.* **235**, 2572 (1960).
1048. Knappe, J., Ringelmann, E., and Lynen, F., *Biochem. Z.* **332**, 195 (1959).
1049. Wright, L. B., *Ann. Rev. Biochem.* **30**, 525 (1961).
1050. Park, R. B., and Bonner, J., *J. Biol. Chem.* **233**, 340 (1958).
1051. Zabin, I., and Bloch, K., *J. Biol. Chem.* **185**, 131 (1950).
1052. Bloch, K., Clark, L. C., and Harary, I., *J. Biol. Chem.* **211**, 687 (1954).
1053. Chichester, C. O., Yokoyama, H., Nakayama, T. O. M., Lukton, A., and Mac-Kinney, G., *J. Biol. Chem.* **234**, 598 (1959).
1054. Ehrenberg, L., and Daniel, A. F., *Acta Chem. Scand.* **16**, 1523 (1962).
1055. Rose, W. C., Johnson, J. E., and Haines, W. J., *J. Biol. Chem.* **145**, 679 (1942).
1056. Gray, I., Adams, P., and Hauptmann, H., *Experientia* **6**, 430 (1950).
1057. Fones, W. S., Waalkes, T. P., and White, J., *Arch. Biochem. Biophys.* **32**, 89 (1951).
1058. Peterson, E. A., Fones, W. S., and White, J., *Arch. Biochem. Biophys.* **36**, 323 (1952).
1059. Kinnory, D. S., Takeda, Y., and Greenberg, D. M., *J. Biol. Chem.* **212**, 379 (1955)
1060. Atchley, W. A., *J. Biol. Chem.* **176**, 123 (1948).
1061. Robinson, W. G., Nagle, R., Bachhawat, B. K., Kupiecki, F. P., and Coon, M. J., *J. Biol. Chem.* **224**, 1 (1957).
1062. Crane, F. L., Mii, S., Hauge, J. G., Green, D. E., and Beinert, H., *J. Biol. Chem.* **218**, 701 (1956).

1063. Robinson, W. G., and Coon, M. J., *J. Biol. Chem.* **225**, 511 (1957).
1064. Tietz, A., and Ochoa, S., *J. Biol. Chem.* **234**, 1394 (1959).
1065. Beck, W. S., and Ochoa, S., *J. Biol. Chem.* **232**, 931 (1958).
1065a. Allen, S. H. G., Kellermeyer, R., Stjernholm, R., Jacobson, B., and Wood, H. G., *J. Biol. Chem.* **238**, 1637 (1963).
1065b. Sprecher, M., Clark, M. J., and Sprinson, D. B., *Biochem. Biophys. Res. Commun.* **15**, 581 (1964).
1065c. Retey, J., and Lynen, F., *Biochem. Biophys. Res. Commun.* **16**, 358 (1964).
1066. Beck, W. S., Flavin, M., and Ochoa, S., *J. Biol. Chem.* **229**, 997 (1957).
1067. Flavin, M., and Ochoa, S., *J. Biol. Chem.* **229**, 965 (1957).
1068. Eggerer, H., Overath, P., Lynen, F., and Stadtman, E. R., *J. Am. Chem. Soc.* **82**, 2643 (1960).
1069. Swick, R. W., and Wood, H. G., *Proc. Natl. Acad. Sci. U.S.* **46**, 28 (1960).
1070. Kellermeyer, R. W., and Wood, H. G., *Biochemistry* **1**, 1124 (1962).
1071. Mazumder, R., Sasakawa, T., Kaziro, Y., and Ochoa, S., *J. Biol. Chem.* **237**, 3065 (1962).
1072. Hegre, C. S., Miller, S. J., and Lane, M. D., *Biochim. Biophys. Acta* **56**, 538 (1962).
1073. Marston, H. R., *Med. J. Australia*, **2**, 105 (1959).
1074. Smith, R. M., and Monty, K. J., *Biochem. Biophys. Res. Commun.* **1**, 105 (1959).
1075. Stern, J. R., and Friedman, D. L., *Biochem. Biophys. Res. Commun.* **2**, 82 (1960).
1076. Lengyel, P., Mazumder, R., and Ochoa, S., *Proc. Natl. Acad. Sci. U.S.* **46**, 1312 (1960).
1077. Gurnani, S., Mistry, S. P., and Johnson, B. C., *Biochim. Biophys. Acta* **38**, 187 (1960).
1078. Marston, H. R., Allen, S. H., and Smith, R. M., *Nature* **190**, 1085 (1961).
1079. Den, H., Robinson, W. G., and Coon, M. J., *J. Biol. Chem.* **234**, 1666 (1959).
1080. Giovanelli, J., and Stumpf, P. K., *J. Biol. Chem.* **231**, 411 (1958).
1081. Vagelos, P. R., and Earl, J. M., *J. Biol. Chem.* **234**, 2272 (1959).
1082. Butts, J. S., Blunden, H., and Dunn, M. S., *J. Biol. Chem.* **120**, 289 (1937).
1083. Terriere, L. C., and Butts, J. S., *J. Biol. Chem.* **190**, 1 (1951).
1084. Edson, N. L., *Biochem. J.* **29**, 2498 (1935).
1085. Coon, M. J., Abrahamsen, N. S. B., and Greene, G. S., *J. Biol. Chem.* **199**, 75 (1954).
1086. Coon, M. J., and Abrahamsen, N. S. B., *J. Biol. Chem.* **195**, 805 (1952).
1087. Robinson, W. G., Bachhawat, B. K., and Coon, M. J., *J. Biol. Chem.* **218**, 391 (1956).
1088. Lynen, F., Wesseley, L., Wieland, O., and Rueff, L., *Angew. Chem.* **64**, 687 (1952).
1089. Hassan, M., and Greenberg, D. M., *Arch. Biochem. Biophys.* **39**, 129 (1952).
1090. Kinnory, D. S., Takeda, Y., Mohamed, M. S., and Greenberg, D. M., *Arch. Biochem. Biophys.* **55**, 546 (1955).
1091. Kinnory, D. S., Takeda, Y., and Greenberg, D. M., *Biochim. Biophys. Acta* **17**, 561 (1955).
1092. Brouwer, E., and Nijkamp, H. J., *Biochem. J.* **55**, 444 (1953).
1093. Maas, W. K., and Vogel, H. J., *J. Bacteriol.* **65**, 388 (1953).
1094. Nelson, E. V., Purko, M., Nelson, W. O., and Wood, W. A., *Bacteriol. Proc. (Soc. Am. Bacteriologists)*, p. 130 (1950).
1095. McIntosh, E. N., Purko, M., and Wood, W. A., *J. Biol. Chem.* **228**, 499 (1957).

1096. Baddiley, J., *Adv. Enzymol.* **16**, 1 (1955).

1097. MacDonald, J. C., *J. Biol. Chem.* **236**, 512 (1961); **237**, 1977 (1962).

1098. Lennarz, W. J., *Biochem. Biophys. Res. Commun.* **6**, 112 (1961).

1099. Kaneda, T., *Biochem. Biophys. Res. Commun.* **10**, 283 (1963).

1100. Stickings, C. E., and Townsend, R. J., *Biochem. J.* **78**, 412 (1961).

1101. Brand, E., Cahill, G. F., and Harris, M. M., *J. Biol. Chem.* **109**, 69 (1935).

1102. White, A., and Lewis, H. B., *J. Biol. Chem.* **98**, 607 (1932).

1103. Stekol, J. A., *J. Biol. Chem.* **117**, 147 (1937).

1104. Tarver, H., and Schmidt, C. L. A., *J. Biol. Chem.* **130**, 67 (1939).

1105. Brand, E., Cahill, G. F., and Block, R. J., *J. Biol. Chem.* **110**, 399 (1935).

1106. Brand, E., Block, R. J., Kassell, B., and Cahill, G. F., *Proc. Soc. Exptl. Biol. Med.* **35**, 501 (1936).

1107. du Vigneaud, V., Brown, G. B., and Chandler, J. P., *J. Biol. Chem.* **143**, 59 (1942).

1108. Binkley, F., Anslow, W. P., Jr., and du Vigneaud, V., *J. Biol. Chem.* **143**, 559 (1942).

1109. Binkley, F., and du Vigneaud, V., *J. Biol. Chem.* **144**, 507 (1942).

1110. Anslow, W. P., Jr., and du Vigneaud, V., *J. Biol. Chem.* **170**, 245 (1947).

1111. Binkley, F., and Okeson, D., *J. Biol. Chem.* **182**, 273 (1950).

1112. Rachele, J. R., Reed, L. J., Kidwai, A. R., Ferger, M. F., and du Vigneaud, V., *J. Biol. Chem.* **185**, 817 (1950).

1113. Anslow, W. P., Jr., Simmonds, S., and du Vigneaud, V., *J. Biol. Chem.* **166**, 35 (1946).

1114. Reed, L. J., Cavallini, D., Plum, F., Rachele, J. R., and du Vigneaud, V., *J. Biol. Chem.* **180**, 783 (1949).

1115. Jones, D. B., Caldwell, A., and Horn, M. J., *Federation Proc.* **7**, 162 (1948).

1116. Stekol, J. A., and Weiss, K., *J. Biol. Chem.* **175**, 405; **179**, 67 (1948).

1117. Stekol, J. A., and Weiss, K., *J. Biol. Chem.* **185**, 577 (1950).

1118. Carroll, W. R., Stacy, G. W., and du Vigneaud, V., *J. Biol. Chem.* **180**, 375 (1949).

1119. Matsuo, Y., and Greenberg, D. M., *J. Biol. Chem.* **215**, 547 (1955).

1120. Dent, C. E., *Biochem. J.* **40**, xliv (1946); *Science* **105**, 335 (1947).

1121. Hope, D. B., *Biochem. J.* **66**, 486 (1957).

1122. Hess, W. C., *Arch. Biochem. Biophys.* **40**, 127 (1952).

1123. Tabachnick, M., and Tarver, H., *Arch. Biochem. Biophys.* **56**, 115 (1955).

1123a. Kondo, Y., *Nippon Sanshigaku Zasshi* **28**, 1 (1959).

1124. Tallan, H. H., Moore, S., and Stein, W. H., *J. Biol. Chem.* **230**, 707 (1958).

1125. Gaitonde, M. K., and Richter, D., *Proc. Roy. Soc.* **B 145**, 83 (1956).

1126. Eagle, H., Piez, K. A., and Oyama, V. I., *J. Biol. Chem.* **236**, 1425 (1961).

1127. Braunstein, A. E., and Goryachenkova, E. V., *Doklady Akad. Nauk SSSR* **74**, 529 (1950).

1128. Binkley, F., Christensen, G. M., and Jensen, W. N., *J. Biol. Chem.* **194**, 109 (1952).

1129. Goryachenkova, E. V., *Doklady Akad. Nauk SSSR* **85**, 603 (1952).

1130. Binkley, F., *J. Biol. Chem.* **191**, 531 (1951).

1131. Selim, A. S. M., and Greenberg, D. M., *J. Biol. Chem.* **234**, 1474 (1959).

1132. Binkley, F., and Olson, C. K., *J. Biol. Chem.* **185**, 881 (1950).

1133. Binkley, F., *J. Biol. Chem.* **186**, 287 (1950); **192**, 209 (1951).

1134. Matsuo, Y., and Greenberg, D. M., *J. Biol. Chem.* **230**, 545, 561 (1958); **234**, 507, 516 (1959).
1135. Matsuo, Y., Rothstein, M., and Greenberg, D. M., *J. Biol. Chem.* **221**, 679 (1956).
1135a. Greenberg, D. M., Mastalerz, P., and Nagabhushanam, A., *Biochim. Biophys. Acta* **81**, 158 (1964).
1136. Horowitz, N. H., *J. Biol. Chem.* **171**, 255 (1947).
1137. Fischer, G. A., *Biochim. Biophys. Acta* **25**, 50 (1957).
1138. Lampen, J. O., Roepke, R. R., and Jones, M. J., *Arch. Biochem.* **13**, 55 (1947).
1139. Bolton, E. T., Cowie, D. B., and Sands, M. K., *J. Bacteriol.* **63**, 309 (1952).
1140. Cowie, D. B., Bolton, E. T., and Sands, M. K., *J. Bacteriol.* **62**, 63 (1951).
1141. Kalan, E. B., and Ceithaml, J., *J. Bacteriol.* **68**, 293 (1954).
1142. Harold, F. M., *J. Bacteriol.* **84**, 382 (1962).
1143. Flavin, M., *J. Biol. Chem.* **237**, 768 (1962).
1143a. Rowbury, R. J., *Biochem. J.* **81**, 42p (1961); *J. Gen. Microbiol.* **28**, v (1962).
1143b. Flavin, M., Delavier-Klutchko, C., and Slaughter, C., *Science* **143**, 50 (1964).
1144. Dyer, H. M., and du Vigneaud, V., *J. Biol. Chem.* **109**, 477 (1935).
1145. du Vigneaud, V., Dyer, H. M., and Kies, M. W., *J. Biol. Chem.* **130**, 325 (1939).
1146. Rose, W. C., and Rice, E. E., *J. Biol. Chem.* **130**, 305 (1939).
1147. du Vigneaud, V., Chandler, J. P., Moyer, A. W., and Keppel, D. M., *J. Biol. Chem.* **131**, 57 (1939).
1148. Hofmeister, H., *Arch. Exptl. Pathol. Pharmakol.* **33**, 198 (1894).
1149. du Vigneaud, V., Chandler, J. P., Cohn, M., and Brown, G. B., *J. Biol. Chem.* **134**, 787 (1940).
1150. McManus, I. R., *Federation Proc.* **15**, 312 (1956).
1151. Keller, E. B., Rachele, J. R., and du Vigneaud, V., *J. Biol. Chem.* **177**, 233 (1949).
1152. Toennies, G., Bennett, M. A., and Medes, G., *Growth* **7**, 251 (1943).
1153. Bennett, M. A., Medes, G., and Toennies, G., *Growth* **8**, 59 (1944).
1154. Bennett, M. A., *Federation Proc.* **4**, 83 (1945).
1155. du Vigneaud, V., Simmonds, S., Chandler, J. P., and Cohn, M., *J. Biol. Chem.* **159**, 755 (1945).
1156. du Vigneaud, V., Ressler, C., and Rachele, J. R., *Science* **112**, 267 (1950).
1156a. Sakami, W., and Welch, A. D., *J. Biol. Chem.* **187**, 379 (1950).
1157. Bird, H. R., Rubin, M., and Groschke, A. C., *J. Nutr.* **33**, 319 (1947).
1158. Gillis, M. B., and Norris, L. C., *J. Biol. Chem.* **179**, 487 (1949).
1159. Schaefer, A. E., Salmon, W. D., Strength, D. R., and Copeland, D. H., *J. Nutr.* **40**, 95 (1950).
1160. Stekol, J. A., and Weiss, K., *J. Biol. Chem.* **186**, 343 (1950).
1161. Bennett, M. A., *J. Biol. Chem.* **187**, 751 (1950).
1162. Jukes, T. H., Stokstad, E. L. R., and Broquist, H. P., *Arch. Biochem.* **25**, 453 (1950).
1163. Borsook, H., and Dubnoff, J. W., *J. Biol. Chem.* **160**, 247 (1947).
1164. Dubnoff, J. W., *Arch. Biochem.* **24**, 251 (1949).
1165. Muntz, J. A., *J. Biol. Chem.* **182**, 489 (1950).
1166. Ericson, L. E., Williams, J. N., Jr., and Elvehjem, C. A., *J. Biol. Chem.* **212**, 537 (1955).
1167. Cromwell, B. T., and Rennie, S. D., *Biochem. J.* **58**, 322 (1954).
1168. Cromwell, B. T., and Rennie, S. D., *Biochem. J.* **58**, 318 (1954).

1169. Stetten, D., Jr., *J. Biol. Chem.* **140**, 143 (1941).
1170. Dubnoff, J. W., and Borsook, H., *J. Biol. Chem.* **176**, 789 (1948).
1171. du Vigneaud, V., Moyer, A. W., and Chandler, J. P., *J. Biol. Chem.* **174**, 477 (1948).
1172. McRorie, R. A., Sutherland, G. L., Lewis, M. S., Barton, A. D., Glazener, M. G., and Shive, W., *J. Am. Chem. Soc.* **76**, 115 (1954).
1173. Bennett, M. A., *J. Biol. Chem.* **141**, 377 (1941).
1174. McRorie, R. A., Glazener, M. R., Skinner, C. G., and Shive, W., *J. Biol. Chem.* **211**, 489 (1954).
1175. Challenger, F., and Simpson, M. R., *J. Chem. Soc.*, p. 1591 (1948).
1176. Challenger, F., Bywood, R., Thomas, P., and Hayward, B. J., *Arch. Biochem. Biophys.* **69**, 514 (1957).
1177. Cantoni, G. L., and Anderson, D. G., *J. Biol. Chem.* **222**, 171 (1956).
1178. Greene, R. C., *J. Biol. Chem.* **237**, 2251 (1962).
1179. Durell, J., Anderson, D. G., and Cantoni, G. L., *Biochim. Biophys. Acta*, **26**, 270 (1957).
1180. Durell, J., and Cantoni, G. L., *Biochim. Biophys. Acta* **35**, 515 (1959).
1181. Borsook, H., and Dubnoff, J. W., *J. Biol. Chem.* **171**, 363 (1947).
1182. Cantoni, G. L., *J. Biol. Chem.* **189**, 203, 745 (1951).
1183. Cantoni, G. L., *in* "Phosphorus Metabolism" (W. D. McElroy and B. Glass, eds.), Vol. 1, p. 641. Johns Hopkins Press, Baltimore, Maryland, 1951; Vol. 2, p. 129, 1952.
1184. Cantoni, G. L., *J. Biol. Chem.* **204**, 403 (1953).
1185. Cantoni, G. L., and Vignos, P. J., Jr., *J. Biol. Chem.* **209**, 647 (1954).
1186. Cantoni, G. L., *J. Am. Chem. Soc.*, **74**, 2942 (1952).
1187. Cantoni, G. L., and Durell, J., *J. Biol. Chem.* **225**, 1033 (1957).
1188. Baddiley, J., and Jamieson, G. A., *J. Chem. Soc.*, p. 1085 (1955).
1189. Borsook, H., and Dubnoff, J. W., *J. Biol. Chem.* **132**, 559 (1940); **134**, 635 (1940).
1190. Sourkes, T. L., *Arch. Biochem.* **21**, 265 (1949).
1191. Barrenscheen, H. K., and Pany, J., *Z. Physiol. Chem.* **283**, 78 (1948).
1192. Stekol, J. A., Anderson, E. I., and Weiss, S., *J. Biol. Chem.* **233**, 425 (1958).
1193. Perlzweig, W. A., Bernheim, M. L. C., and Bernheim, F., *J. Biol. Chem.* **150**, 401 (1943).
1194. Ellinger, P., *Biochem. J.* **42**, 175 (1948).
1195. Mudd, S. H., and Cantoni, G. L., *J. Biol. Chem.* **231**, 481 (1958).
1196. Mudd, S. H., *J. Biol. Chem.* **237**, PC 1372 (1962); **238**, 2156 (1963).
1197. Mudd, S. H., and Mann, J. D., *J. Biol. Chem.* **238**, 2164 (1963).
1198. De La Haba, G., and Cantoni, G. L., *J. Biol. Chem.* **234**, 603 (1959).
1199. Duerre, J. A., and Schlenk, F., *Arch. Biochem. Biophys.* **96**, 575 (1962).
1200. De La Haba, G., Jamieson, G. A., Mudd, S. H., and Richards, H. H., *J. Am. Chem. Soc.* **81**, 3975 (1959).
1201. Schlenk, F., and DePalma, R. E., *J. Biol. Chem.* **229**, 1037, 1051 (1957).
1202. Suzuki, V., Odake, S., and Mori, T., *Biochem. Z.*, **154**, 278 (1924).
1203. Sato, K., and Makino, K., *Nature* **167**, 238 (1951).
1204. Baddiley, J., Trauth, O., and Weygand, F., *Nature* **167**, 359 (1951).
1205. Smith, R. L., and Schlenk, F., *Federation Proc.* **11**, 289 (1952).
1206. Weygand, F., Jung, R., and Leber, D., *Z. Physiol. Chem.* **291**, 155 (1952).

1207. Parks, L. W., and Schlenk, F., *J. Biol. Chem.* **230**, 295 (1958).

1208. Shapiro, S. K., and Mather, A. N., *J. Biol. Chem.* **233**, 631 (1958).

1209. Mudd, S. H., *J. Biol. Chem.* **234**, 87, 1784 (1959).

1210. Duerre, J. A., *J. Biol. Chem.* **237**, 3737 (1962).

1211. Baldessarini, R. J., and Kopin, I. J., *Anal. Biochem.* **6**, 289 (1963).

1212. Archer, S., Arnold, A., Kulnig, R. K., and Wylie, D. W., *Arch. Biochem. Biophys.* **87**, 153 (1960).

1213. Shapiro, S. K., and Yphantis, D. A., *Biochim. Biophys. Acta* **36**, 241 (1959).

1214. Sloane, N. H., and Boggiano, E. M., *Arch. Biochem. Biophys.* **87**, 217 (1960).

1215. Shapiro, S. K., and Schlenk, F., *Adv. Enzymol.* **22**, 237 (1960).

1216. Maw, G. A., *Biochem. J.* **70**, 168 (1958).

1217. Shapiro, S. K., *Biochim. Biophys. Acta* **29**, 405 (1958).

1218. Shapiro, S. K., Lohmar, P., and Hertenstein, M., *Arch. Biochem. Biophys.* **100**, 74 (1963).

1219. Pfeffer, M., and Shapiro, S. K., *Biochem. Biophys. Res. Commun.* **9**, 405 (1962).

1220. Brown, D. D., Tomchik, R., and Axelrod, J., *J. Biol. Chem.* **234**, 2948 (1959).

1221. Lindahl, K. M., *Acta Chem. Scand.* **12**, 1690, 2050 (1958).

1222. McManus, I. R., *J. Biol Chem.* **225**, 325 (1957); **237**, 1207 (1962).

1223. Winnick, T., and Winnick, R. E., *Nature* **183**, 1466 (1959); *Biochim. Biophys. Acta* **31**, 47 (1959).

1224. Keller, E. B., Boissonnas, R. A., and du Vigneaud, V., *J. Biol. Chem.* **183**, 627 (1950).

1225. Axelrod, J., *J. Biol. Chem.* **237**, 1657 (1962).

1226. Krüger, M., and Salomon, G., *Z. Physiol. Chem.* **26**, 350 (1898).

1227. Weissmann, B., Bromberg, P. A., and Gutman, A. B., *J. Biol. Chem.* **224**, 407 (1957).

1228. Littlefield, J. W., and Dunn, D. B., *Biochem. J.* **70**, 642 (1958).

1229. Adler, M., Weissmann, B., and Gutman, A. B., *J. Biol. Chem.* **230**, 717 (1958).

1230. Smith, J. D., and Dunn, D. B., *Biochim. Biophys. Acta* **31**, 573 (1959).

1231. Hall, R. H., *Biochem. Biophys. Res. Commun.* **12**, 429 (1963).

1232. Remy, C. N., *J. Biol. Chem.* **234**, 1485 (1959).

1233. Axelrod, J., and Daly, J., *Biochim. Biophys. Acta* **61**, 855 (1962).

1234. Biswas, B. B., Edmonds, M., and Abrams, R., *Biochem. Biophys. Res. Commun.* **6**, 146 (1961).

1235. Mandel, L. R., and Borek, E., *Biochem. Biophys. Res. Commun.* **6**, 138 (1961).

1236. Borek, E., Mandel, L. R., and Fleissner, E., *Federation Proc.* **21**, 379 (1962).

1237. Gold, M., Hurwitz, J., and Anders, M., *Biochem. Biophys. Res. Commun.* **11**, 107 (1963).

1238. Srinivasan, P. R., and Borek, E., *Proc. Natl. Acad. Sci. U.S.* **49**, 529 (1963).

1239. Starr, J. L., *Biochem. Biophys. Res. Commun.* **10**, 428 (1963).

1240. Fleissner, E., and Borek, E., *Biochemistry* **2**, 1093 (1963); *Proc. Natl. Acad. Sci. U.S.* **48**, 1199 (1962).

1241. Svensson, I., Boman, H. G., Eriksson, K. G., and Kjellin, K., *J. Mol. Biol.* **7**, 254 (1963).

1242. Mudd, S. H., *Biochim. Biophys. Acta* **37**, 164 (1960).

1243. Mann, J. D., and Mudd, S. H., *J. Biol. Chem.* **238**, 381 (1963).

1244. Mann, J. D., Steinhart, C. E., and Mudd, S. H., *J. Biol. Chem.* **238**, 676 (1963).

1245. Carter, H. E., Bhattacharyya, P. K., Weidman, K. R., and Fraenkel, G., *Arch. Biochem. Biophys.* **38**, 405 (1952).

1246. Wolf, G., and Berger, C. R. A., *Arch. Biochem. Biophys.* **92**, 360 (1961).

1247. Bremer, J., *Biochim. Biophys. Acta* **48**, 622 (1961).

1248. Lindstedt, G., and Lindstedt, S., *Biochem. Biophys. Res. Commun.* **7**, 394 (1962).

1249. Fritz, I. B., Schultz, S. K., and Srere, P. A., *J. Biol. Chem.* **238**, 2509 (1963).

1250. Bremer, J., *J. Biol. Chem.* **237**, 2228, 3628 (1962).

1251. Stockler, B. A. D., McDonough, M. W., and Ambler, R. C., *Nature* **189**, 556 (1961).

1252. McKennis, H., Jr., Turnbull, L. B., and Bowman, E. R., *J. Biol. Chem.* **238**, 719 (1963).

1252a. Blumenstein, J., and Williams, G. R., *Biochem. Biophys. Res. Commun.* **3**, 259 (1960).

1253. Alexander, G. J., Gold, A. M., and Schwenk, E., *J. Am. Chem. Soc.* **79**, 2967 (1957).

1254. Alexander, G. J., and Schwenk, E., *J. Am. Chem. Soc.* **79**, 4554 (1957).

1255. Parks, L. W., *J. Am. Chem. Soc.* **80**, 2023 (1958).

1256. Bray, R., and Shemin, D., *Biochim. Biophys. Acta* **30**, 647 (1958).

1257. Hodgkin, D. C., Pickworth, J., Robertson, J. H., Trueblood, K. N., Prosen, R. J., and White, J. G., *Nature* **176**, 325 (1955).

1258. Bonnett, R., Cannon, J. R., Johnson, A. W., Sutherland, I., Todd, A. R., and Smith, E. L., *Nature* **176**, 328 (1955).

1258a. Bonnett, R., *Chem. Rev.* **63**, 573 (1963).

1259. Gibson, K. D., Neuberger, A., and Tait, G. H., *Biochem. J.* **88**, 325 (1963).

1260. Axelrod, J., and Tomchik, R., *J. Biol. Chem.* **233**, 702 (1958).

1261. Fales, H. M., Mann, J. D., and Mudd, S. H., *J. Am. Chem. Soc.* **85**, 2025 (1963).

1262. Sato, C. S., Byerrum, R. U., and Ball, C. D., *J. Biol. Chem.* **224**, 717 (1957).

1263. Sato, C. S., Byerrum, R. U., Albersheim, P., and Bonner, J., *J. Biol. Chem.* **233**, 128 (1958).

1264. Byerrum, R. U., Flokstra, J. H., Dewey, L. J., and Ball, C. D., *J. Biol. Chem.* **210**, 633 (1954).

1265. Brown, S. A., and Byerrum, R. U., *J. Am. Chem. Soc.* **74**, 1523 (1952).

1266. Byerrum, R. U., and Wing, R. E., *J. Biol. Chem.* **205**, 637 (1953).

1267. Dubeck, M., and Kirkwood, S., *J. Biol. Chem.* **199**, 307 (1952).

1268. Sribney, M., and Kirkwood, S., *Nature* **171**, 931 (1953).

1269. Pettersson, G., *Acta Chem. Scand.* **17**, 1323 (1963).

1270. Challenger, F., Lisle, D. B., and Dransfield, P. B., *J. Chem. Soc.* p. 1760 (1954).

1271. Dransfield, P. B., and Challenger, F., *J. Chem. Soc.*, p. 1153 (1955).

1272. Challenger, F., *Chem. Rev.* **36**, 315 (1945); *Adv. Enzymol.* **12**, 429 (1951).

1273. McConnell, K. P., and Portman, O. W., *J. Biol. Chem.* **195**, 277 (1952).

1274. Mudd, S. H., and Cantoni, G. L., *Nature* **180**, 1052 (1957).

1275. Tuve, T., and Williams, H. H., *J. Biol. Chem.* **236**, 597 (1961).

1276. Liu, T. Y., and Hofmann, K., *Biochemistry* **1**, 189 (1962).

1277. O'Leary, W. M., *J. Bacteriol.*, **84**, 967 (1962).

1277a. Law, J. H., Zalkin, H., and Kaneshiro, T., *Biochim. Biophys. Acta* **70**, 143 (1963).

1277b. Pohl, S., Law, J. H., and Ryhage, R., *Biochim. Biophys. Acta* **70**, 583 (1963).

1277c. Zalkin, H., Law, J. H., and Goldfine, H., *J. Biol. Chem.* **238**, 1242 (1963).

1277d. Chung, A. E., and Law, J. H., *Biochemistry* **3**, 967 (1964).

1278. Remy, C. N., *J. Biol. Chem.* **238**, 1078 (1963).

1279. Tuppy, H., and Dus, K., *Monatsh.* **89**, 318 (1958).

1280. Davis, B. D., and Mingioli, E. S., *J. Bacteriol.* **60**, 17 (1950).

1281. Berg, P., *J. Biol. Chem.* **205**, 145 (1953).

1282. Nakao, A., and Greenberg, D. M., *J. Biol. Chem.* **230**, 603 (1958).

1283. Doctor, V. M., Patton, T. L., and Awapara, J., *Arch. Biochem. Biophys.* **67**, 404 (1957).

1284. Stevens, A., and Sakami, W., *J. Biol. Chem.* **234**, 2063 (1959).

1285. Helleiner, C. W., and Woods, D. D., *Biochem. J.* **63**, 26P (1956).

1286. Gibson, F., and Woods, D. D., *Biochem. J.* **74**, 160 (1960).

1287. Kisliuk, R. L., and Woods, D. D., *J. Gen. Microbiol.* **18**, XV (1957).

1288. Szulmajster, J., and Woods, D. D., *Biochem. J.* **75**, 3 (1960).

1289. Kisliuk, R., and Woods, D. D., *Biochem. J.* **75**, 467 (1960).

1290. Guest, J. R., Helleiner, C. W., Cross, M. J., and Woods, D. D., *Biochem. J.* **76**, 396 (1960).

1291. Guest, J. R., and Woods, D. D., *Biochem. J.* **77**, 422 (1960).

1292. Jones, K. M., Guest, J. R., and Woods, D. D., *Biochem. J.* **79**, 566 (1961).

1293. Foster, M. A., Jones, K. M., and Woods, D. D., *Biochem. J.* **80**, 519 (1961).

1294. Hatch, F. T., Takeyama, S., Cathou, R. E., Larrabee, A. R., and Buchanan, J. M., *J. Am. Chem. Soc.* **81**, 6525 (1959).

1295. Larrabee, A. R., Rosenthal, S., Cathou, R. E., and Buchanan, J. M., *J. Am. Chem. Soc.* **83**, 4094 (1961).

1296. Hatch, F. T., Larrabee, A. R., Cathou, R. E., and Buchanan, J. M., *J. Biol. Chem.* **236**, 1095 (1961).

1297. Takeyama, S., Hatch, F. T., and Buchanan, J. M., *J. Biol. Chem.* **236**, 1102 (1961).

1298. Donaldson, K. O., and Keresztesy, J. C., *J. Biol. Chem.* **237**, 1298 (1962).

1299. Sakami, W., and Ukstins, I., *J. Biol. Chem.* **236**, PC 50 (1961).

1300. Keresztesy, J. C., and Donaldson, K. O., *Biochem. Biophys. Res. Commun.* **5**, 286 (1961).

1301. Silverman, M., Law, L. W., and Kaufman, B., *J. Biol. Chem.* **236**, 2530 (1961).

1302. Herbert, V., Larrabee, A. R., and Buchanan, J. M., *J. Clin. Invest.* **41**, 1134 (1962).

1303. Kisliuk, R. L., *J. Biol. Chem.* **236**, 817 (1961).

1304. Kisliuk, R. L., *J. Biol. Chem.* **238**, 397 (1963).

1305. Buchanan, J. M., Larrabee, A. R., Rosenthal, S., and Cathou, R. E., *Intern. Symp. on the Chem. and Biol. Pteridines, Stuttgart,* 1962. See also Cathou, R. E., and Buchanan, J. M., *J. Biol. Chem.* **238**, 1746 (1963).

1306. Wilmanns, W., Rücker, B., and Jaenicke, L., *Z. Physiol. Chem.* **322**, 283 (1960).

1307. Larrabee, A. R., Rosenthal, S., Cathou, R. E., and Buchanan, J. M., *J. Biol. Chem.* **238**, 1025 (1963).

1308. Guest, J. R., Friedman, S., and Foster, M. A., *Biochem. J.* **84**, 93p (1962).

1309. Takeyama, S., and Buchanan, J. M., *J. Biochem.* (*Tokyo*) **49**, 578 (1961).

1310. Mangnum, J. H., and Scrimgeour, K. G., *Federation Proc.* **21**, 242 (1962).

1311. Rosenthal, S., and Buchanan, J. M., *Acta Chem. Scand.* Suppl. 1, **17**, 288 (1963).

1312. Guest, J. R., Friedman, S., Woods, D. E., and Smith, E. L., *Nature* **195**, 340 (1962).

1313. Baker, H., Frank, O., Pasher, I., Sobotka, H., Nathan, H. A., Hutner, S. H., and Aaronson, S., *Experientia* **16**, 187 (1960).

1314. Floyd, K. W., and Whitehead, R. W., *Biochem. Biophys. Res. Commun.* **12**, 215 (1963).

1315. Lockingen, L. S., *Proc. Nat. Acad. Sci. U.S.* **44**, 924 (1958).

1316. Wacker, A., Kirschfeld, S., and Trager, L., *Z. Naturforsch.* **14b**, 145 (1959).

1317. Abeles, R. H., and Lee, H. A., Jr., *J. Biol. Chem.* **236**, 2347 (1961).

1318. Dinning, J. S., Allen, B. K., Young, R. S., and Day, P. L., *J. Biol. Chem.* **233**, 674 (1958).

1319. Roberts, D., and Nichol, C. A., *J. Biol. Chem.* **237**, 2278 (1962).

1320. Peel, J. L., *J. Biol. Chem.* **237**, PC 263 (1962).

1321. Kisliuk, R. L., Sakami, W., and Patwardhan, M. V., *J. Biol. Chem.* **221**, 885 (1956).

1322. Medes, G., and Floyd, N. F., *Biochem. J.* **36**, 259 (1942).

1323. Fromageot, C., and Desnuelle, P., *Compt. rend. Acad. Sci.* **214**, 647 (1942); *Bull. Soc. Chim. Biol.* **24**, 2169 (1942).

1324. Kallio, R. E., *J. Biol. Chem.* **192**, 371 (1951).

1325. Desnuelle, P., *Bull. Soc. Chim. Biol.* **25**, 1001 (1943).

1326. Canellakis, E. S., and Tarver, H., *Arch. Biochem. Biophys.* **42**, 387 (1953).

1327. Canellakis, E. S., and Tarver, H., *Arch. Biochem. Biophys.* **42**, 446 (1953).

1328. Kallio, R. E., and Larson, A. D., *in* "Amino Acid Metabolism" (W. D. McElroy and B. Glass, eds.), p. 616. Johns Hopkins Press, Baltimore, Maryland, 1955.

1329. Ohigashi, K., Tsunetoshi, A., and Ichihara, K., *Med. J. Osaka Univ.* **2**, 111 (1951).

1330. Challenger, F., and Walshe, J. M., *Biochem. J.* **59**, 372 (1955).

1331. Stekol, J. A., *in* "Amino Acid Metabolism" (W. D. McElroy and B. Glass, eds.), Johns Hopkins Press, Baltimore, Maryland, 1955.

1332. Sourkes, T. L., and Trano, Y., *Arch. Biochem. Biophys.* **42**, 321 (1953).

1333. Black, S., Harte, E. M., Hudson, B., and Wartofsky, L., *J. Biol. Chem.* **235**, 2910 (1960).

1334. Tabor, H., Rosenthal, S. M., and Tabor, C. W., *J. Biol. Chem.* **233**, 907 (1958).

1335. Greene, R. C., *J. Am. Chem. Soc.* **79**, 3929 (1957).

1336. Dubin, D. T., and Rosenthal, S. M., *J. Biol. Chem.* **235**, 776 (1960).

1337. Bachrach, U., *J. Biol. Chem.* **237**, 3443 (1962).

1337a. Johnson, D. B., Howells, D. J., and Goodwin, T. W., *Biochem. J.* **91**, 8p (1964).

1337b. Leete, E., *J. Am. Chem. Soc.* **86**, 3162 (1964).

1338. Bachrach, U., *Biochem. J.* **77**, 417 (1960).

1339. Weaver, R. H., and Herbst, E. J., *J. Biol. Chem.* **231**, 637, 647 (1958).

1340. Razin, S., Gery, I., and Bachrach, U., *Biochem. J.* **71**, 551 (1959).

1341. Wolff, E. C., Black, S., and Downey, P. F., *J. Am. Chem. Soc.* **78**, 5958 (1956).

1342. Horner, W. H., and Kuchinskas, E. J., *J. Biol. Chem.* **234**, 2935 (1959).

1343. Hockenhull, D. J. D., *Biochim. Biophys. Acta* **3**, 326 (1949).

1344. Lampen, J. O., Roepke, R. R., and Jones, M. J., *Arch. Biochem.* **13**, 55 (1947).

1345. Horowitz, N. H., *Adv. Genet.* **3**, 33 (1950).

1346. De Meio, R. H., Wizerkaniuk, M., and Fabriani, E., *J. Biol. Chem.* **203**, 257 (1953).

1347. Robbins, P. W., and Lipmann, F., *J. Am. Chem. Soc.* **78**, 2652, 6410 (1956).

1348. Bandurski, R. S., Wilson, L. G., Squires, C. L., *J. Am. Chem. Soc.* **78**, 6408 (1956).

1349. Robbins, P. W., and Lipmann, F., *J. Biol. Chem.* **229**, 837 (1957).

1350. Robbins, P. W., and Lipmann, F., *J. Biol. Chem.* **233**, 681, 686 (1958).

1351. Gregory, J. D., and Lipmann, F., *J. Biol. Chem.* **229**, 1081 (1957).

1352. Ragland, J. B., *Arch. Biochem. Biophys.* **84**, 541 (1959).

1353. Dreyfuss, J., and Monty, K. J., *J. Biol. Chem.* **238**, 1019 (1963).

1354. Wilson, L. G., Asahi, T., and Bandurski, R. S., *J. Biol. Chem.* **236**, 1822 (1961).

1354a. Torii, K., and Bandurski, R. S., *Biochem. Biophys. Res. Commun.* **14**, 537 (1964).

1355. Hilz, H., Kittler, M., and Knape, G., *Biochem. Z.* **332**, 151 (1959).

1356. Asahi, T., Bandurski, R. S., and Wilson, L. G., *J. Biol. Chem.* **236**, 1830 (1961).

1357. Peck, H. D., Jr., *J. Biol. Chem.* **237**, 198 (1962).

1358. Ishimoto, M., Koyama, J., and Nagai, Y., *J. Biochem. (Tokyo)* **42**, 41 (1955).

1359. Kaji, A., and McElroy, W. D., *J. Bacteriol.* **77**, 630 (1959).

1360. Mager, J., *Biochim. Biophys. Acta* **41**, 553 (1960).

1361. Kemp, J. D., Atkinson, D. E., Ehret, A., and Lazzarini, R. A., *J. Biol. Chem.* **238**, 3466 (1963).

1362. Schlossmann, K., and Lynen, F., *Biochem. Z.* **328**, 591 (1957).

1363. Schlossmann, K., Brüggemann, J., and Lynen, F., *Biochem. Z.* **336**, 258 (1962).

1963a. Brüggemann, J., Schlossmann, K., Merkenschlager, M., and Waldschmidt, M., *Biochem. Z.* **335**, 392,408 (1962).

1363b. Sentenac, A., and Fromageot, P., *Biochim. Biophys. Acta* **81**, 289 (1964).

1364. Nakamura, T., and Sato, R., *Biochem. J.* **86**, 328 (1963); *Nature* **198**, 1198 (1963).

1365. Szczepkowski, T. W., *Nature* **182**, 934 (1958).

1366. Tarr, H. L. A., *Biochem. J.* **27**, 1869 (1933).

1367. Fromageot, C., *in* "The Enzymes" (J. B. Sumner and K. Myrbäck, eds.), Vol. 2, p. 248. Academic Press, New York, 1951.

1368. Fromageot, C., *Adv. Enzymol.* **7**, 369 (1947).

1369. Fromageot, C., Wookey, E., and Chaix, P., *Enzymologia* **9**, 198 (1940).

1370. Chatagner, F., and Fromageot, C., *Giornate Biochim. Italo-Franco-Elvetiche April* 21–24, p. 3 (1955).

1371. Smythe, C. V., *Ann. N. Y. Acad. Sci.* **45**, 425 (1944).

1372. Smythe, C. V., and Halliday, D., *J. Biol. Chem.* **144**, 237 (1942).

1373. Ohigashi, K., Tsunetoshi, A., Uchida, M., and Ichihara, K., *J. Biochem. (Tokyo)* **39**, 211 (1952).

1374. Meister, A., Morris, H. P., and Tice, S. V., *Proc. Soc. Exptl. Biol. Med.* **82**, 301 (1952).

1375. Delwiche, E. A., *J. Bacteriol.* **62**, 717 (1951).

1376. Braunstein, A. E., and Azarkh, R. M., *Doklady Akad. Nauk SSSR* **71**, 93 (1950).

1377. Suda, M., Saigo, T., and Ichihara, A., *Med. J. Osaka Univ.* **5**, 127 (1954).

1378. Metaxas, M. A., and Delwiche, E. A., *J. Bacteriol.* **70**, 735 (1955).

1379. Meister, A., Fraser, P. E., and Tice, S. V., *J. Biol. Chem.* **206**, 561 (1954).

1380. Anderson, K. E., and Ransford, R., *Sci. Studies St. Bonaventure Univ.* **15**, 87 (1953).

1381. Hanson, H., and Mantel, E., *Z. Physiol. Chem.* **295**, 141 (1953).

1382. Tamiya, N., *J. Chem. Soc. Japan Pure Chem. Sect.* **72**, 118 (1951).

1383. Tamiya, N., *J. Biochem. (Tokyo)* **41**, 199, 287 (1954).

1384. Ichihara, A., Saigo, T., and Suda, M., *Symp. Enzyme Chem. (Tokyo)* **10**, 43 (1954).

1385. Chatagner, F., and Sauret-Ignazi, G., *Bull. Soc. Chim. Biol.* **38**, 415 (1956).

1386. Cavallini, D., Mondovi, B., DeMarco, C., and Scioscia-Santoro, A., *Enzymologia* **24**, 253 (1962).

1387. Cavallini, D., Mondovi, B., DeMarco, C., and Scioscia-Santoro, A., *Arch. Biochem. Biophys.* **92**, 456 (1962).

1388. Cavallini, D., DeMarco, C., Mondovi, B., and Mori, B. G., *Enzymologia* **21**, 11 (1960).

1389. Jolles-Bergeret, B., Brun, D., Labouesse, J., and Chatagner, F., *Bull. Soc. Chim. Biol.* **45**, 397 (1963).

1390. Desnuelle, P., Wookey, E., and Fromageot, C., *Enzymologia* **8**, 225 (1940).

1391. Saz, A. K., and Brownell, L. W., *Arch. Biochem. Biophys.* **52**, 291 (1954).

1392. Stekol, J. A., Weiss, S., and Anderson, E. I., *J. Biol. Chem.* **233**, 936 (1958).

1393. Chapeville, F., and Fromageot, P., *Bull. Soc. Chim. Biol.* **42**, 877 (1960); *Biochim. Biophys. Acta.* **49**, 328 (1961).

1394. Ratsisalovanina, O., Chapeville, F., and Fromageot, P., *Biochim. Biophys. Acta* **49**, 322 (1961).

1395. Wood, J. L., and Cooley, S. L., *J. Biol. Chem.* **218**, 449 (1956).

1396. Fiedler, H., and Wood, J. L., *J. Biol. Chem.* **222**, 387 (1956).

1397. Hylin, J. W., and Wood, J. L., *J. Biol. Chem.* **234**, 2141 (1959).

1398. Fanshier, D. W., and Kun, E., *Biochim. Biophys. Acta* **58**, 266 (1962).

1399. Kun, E., and Fanshier, D. W., *Biochim. Biophys. Acta* **27**, 658 (1958); **32**, 338; **33**, 28 (1959).

1400. Kun, E., and Fanshier, D. W., *Biochim. Biophys. Acta* **48**, 187 (1961).

1401. Sorbo, B., *Biochim. Biophys. Acta* **24**, 324 (1957).

1402. Maloof, F., and Spector, L., *J. Biol. Chem.* **234**, 949 (1959).

1403. Maloof, M., and Soodak, M., *J. Biol. Chem.* **236**, 1689 (1961).

1404. Stoll, A., and Seebeck, E., *Adv. Enzymol.* **11**, 377 (1951).

1405. Klein, P., and Souverein, C., *Biochem. Z.* **326**, 123 (1954).

1406. Kupiecki, F. P., and Virtanen, A. I., *Acta Chem. Scand.* **14**, 1913 (1960).

1407. Goryachenkova, E. V., *Doklady Acad. Nauk SSSR* **87**, 457 (1952).

1408. Schwimmer, S., and Mazelis, M., *Arch. Biochem. Biophys.* **100**, 66 (1963).

1409. Keilin, D., *Proc. Roy. Soc.* **B106**, 418 (1930).

1410. Nickerson, W. J., and Romano, A. H., *Science* **115**, 676 (1952).

1411. Romano, A. H., and Nickerson, W. J., *J. Biol. Chem.* **208**, 409 (1954).

1412. Conn, E. E., and Vennesland, B., *J. Biol. Chem.* **192**, 17 (1951).

1413. Mapson, L. W., and Goddard, D. R., *Biochem. J.* **49**, 592 (1951).

1414. Rall, T. W., and Lehninger, A. L., *J. Biol. Chem.* **194**, 119 (1952).

1415. Racker, E., *J. Biol. Chem.* **217**, 855 (1955).

1416. Asnis, R. E., *J. Biol. Chem.* **213**, 77 (1955).

1417. Black, S., *Ann. Rev. Biochem.* **32**, 399, 1963.

1418. Mize, C. E., Thompson, T. E., and Langdon, R. G., *J. Biol. Chem.* **237**, 1589, 1596 (1962).

1419. Mapson, L. W., and Isherwood, F. A., *Biochem. J.* **86**, 173 (1963).

1420. Pirie, N. W., *Biochem. J.* **28**, 305 (1934).

1421. Medes, G., *Biochem. J.* **33**, 1559 (1939).

1421a. Schubert, M. P., *J. Am. Chem. Soc.* **55**, 3336 (1933).

1422. Lavine, T. F., *J. Biol. Chem.* **113**, 580, 583 (1936).

1423. Bennett, M. A., *Biochem. J.* **31**, 962 (1937).

1424. Fromageot, C., and Royane, M. A., *Helv. Chim. Acta* **26**, 1279 (1946).
1425. Fromageot, C., Chatagner, F., and Bergeret, B., *Biochim. Biophys. Acta* **2**, 294 (1948).
1426. Chapeville, F., and Fromageot, C., *Biochim. Biophys. Acta* **14**, 415 (1954).
1427. Fromageot, P., Chapeville, F., and Petit, L., *Biochim. Biophys. Acta* **23**, 12 (1957).
1428. Singer, T. P., and Kearney, E. B., *in* "Amino Acid Metabolism" (W. D. McElroy and B. Glass, eds.), p. 558. Johns Hopkins Press, Baltimore, Maryland, 1955.
1429. Kearney, E. B., and Singer, T. P., *Biochim. Biophys. Acta* **8**, 698 (1952); **11**, 270, 276, 290 (1953).
1430. Singer, T. P., and Kearney, E. B., *Biochim. Biophys. Acta* **14**, 570 (1954).
1431. Singer, T. P., and Kearney, E. B., *Adv. Enzymol.* **15**, 79 (1954).
1432. Chatagner, F., Bergeret, B., Séjourné, T., and Fromageot, C., *Biochim. Biophys. Acta* **9**, 340 (1952).
1433. Singer, T. P., and Kearney, E. B., *Arch. Biochem. Biophys.* **61**, 397 (1956).
1434. Perez-Milan, H., Schliack, J., and Fromageot, P., *Biochim. Biophys. Acta* **36**, 73 (1959).
1435. Fromageot, P., and Chapeville, F., *Biochim. Biophys. Acta* **50**, 325, 334 (1961).
1436. Fridovich, I., and Handler, P., *J. Biol. Chem.* **235**, 1835 (1960).
1437. MacLeod, R. M., Farkas, W., Fridovich, I., and Handler, P., *J. Biol. Chem.* **236**, 1841 (1961).
1438. MacLeod, R. M., Fridovich, I., and Handler, P., *J. Biol. Chem.* **236**, 1847 (1961).
1439. Heimberg, M., Fridovich, I., and Handler, P., *J. Biol. Chem.* **204**, 913 (1953).
1440. Leinweber, F.-J., and Monty, K. J., *Biochim. Biophys. Acta* **63**, 171 (1962).
1441. Soda, K., Novogrodsky, A., and Meister, A., *Biochemistry* **3**, 1450 (1964).
1442. Sumizu, K., *Biochim. Biophys. Acta* **53**, 435 (1961).
1443. Machlin, L. J., Pearson, P. B., and Denton, C. A., *J. Biol. Chem.* **212**, 469 (1955).
1444. Lowe, I. P., and Roberts, E., *J. Biol. Chem.* **212**, 477 (1955).
1445. Chapeville, F., and Fromageot, P., *Biochim. Biophys. Acta* **26**, 538 (1957).
1446. Chapeville, F., and Fromageot, P., *Bull. Soc. Chim. Biol.* **40**, 1965 (1958).
1447. Simonnet, G., Chapeville, F., and Fromageot, P., *Bull. Soc. Chim. Biol.* **42**, 891 (1960).
1448. Virtue, R. W., and Doster-Virtue, M. E., *J. Biol. Chem.* **127**, 431 (1939).
1449. Blaschko, H., *Biochem. J.* **36**, 571 (1942).
1450. Awapara, J., *Nature* **165**, 76 (1950).
1451. Awapara, J., *J. Biol. Chem.* **203**, 183 (1953).
1452. Bergeret, B., Chatagner, F., and Fromageot, C., *Biochim. Biophys. Acta* **9**, 147 (1952).
1453. Chatagner, F., and Bergeret, B., *Compt. Rend. Acad. Sci.* **232**, 448 (1951).
1454. Chatagner, F., Tabechian, H., and Bergeret, B., *Biochim. Biophys. Acta* **13**, 313 (1954).
1455. Cavallini, D., Mondovi, B., and De Marco, C., *J. Biol. Chem.* **216**, 577 (1955).
1456. Ouchi, S., *J. Biochem. (Tokyo)* **46**, 765 (1959).
1457. Cavallini, D., De Marco, C., and Mondovi, B., *Giorn. Biochim.* **4**, 338 (1953).
1458. Bricas, E., Kieffer, F., and Fromageot, C., *Biochim. Biophys. Acta* **18**, 358 (1955).
1459. Davison, A. N., *Biochim. Biophys. Acta* **19**, 66 (1956).
1460. Hope, D. B., *Biochem. J.* **59**, 497 (1955).
1461. Blaschko, H., Datta, S. P., and Harris, H., *Brit. J. Nutr.* **7**, 364 (1953).

1462. Bergeret, B., Chatagner, F., and Fromageot, C., *Biochim. Biophys. Acta* **22**, 329 (1956).

1462a. Sumizu, K., *Biochim. Biophys. Acta* **63**, 210 (1962).

1463. Jacobsen, J. G., and Smith, L. H., Jr., *Nature* **200**, 575 (1963).

1463a. Sörbo, B., and Heyman, T., *Biochim. Biophys. Acta* **23**, 624 (1957).

1464. Medes, G., *Biochem. J.* **31**, 1330 (1937).

1465. Sörbo, B., *Biochim. Biophys. Acta* **22**, 570 (1956).

1466. Sweetman, B. J., *Nature* **183**, 744 (1959).

1467. Toennies, G., and Lavine, T. F., *J. Biol. Chem.* **113**, 571 (1936).

1468. Brown, G. M., *J. Biol. Chem.* **226**, 651 (1957).

1469. Brown, G. M., and Snell, E. E., *J. Am. Chem. Soc.* **75**, 2782 (1953).

1470. Hoagland, M. B., and Novelli, G. D., *J. Biol. Chem.* **207**, 767 (1954).

1471. Brown, G. M., *J. Am. Chem. Soc.* **80**, 3161 (1958).

1472. Novelli, G. D., Schmetz, F. J., Jr., and Kaplan, N. O., *J. Biol. Chem.* **206**, 533 (1954).

1473. Cavallini, D., Mondovi, B., and De Marco, C., *Biochim. Biophys. Acta* **18**, 122 (1955).

1474. Eldjarn, L., *J. Biol. Chem.* **206**, 483 (1954); *Scand. J. Clin. Lab. Invest.* **6**, (13), 96 (1954).

1475. Cavallini, D., Mondovi, B., and De Marco, C., *Giorn. Biochim.* **1**, 455, 465 (1952); **2**, 13 (1953).

1476. Cavallini, D., De Marco, C., Mondovi, B., and Tentori, L., *J. Chromatog.* **3**, 20 (1960).

1477. Cavallini, D., De Marco, C., and Mondovi, B., *J. Biol. Chem.* **230**, 25 (1958).

1478. Eldjarn, L., and Pihl, A., *J. Biol. Chem.* **223**, 341 (1956).

1479. Eldjarn, L., Pihl, A., and Sverdrup, A., *J. Biol. Chem.* **223**, 353 (1956).

1480. Cavallini, D., De Marco, C., and Mondovi, B., *Biochim. Biophys. Acta* **24**, 353 (1957).

1481. De Marco, C., Coletta, M., Mondovi, B., *Italian J. Biochem.* **9**, 77 (1960).

1482. Cavallini, D., De Marco, C., and Mondovi, B., *Nature* **192**, 557 (1961).

1483. Cavallini, D., De Marco, C., Mondovi, B., *Enzymologia* **23**, 101 (1961).

1484. De Marco, C., *Italian J. Biochem.* **10**, 196 (1961).

1485. Cavallini, D., De Marco, C., and Scandurra, R., *Italian J. Biochem.* **11**, 196 (1962).

1486. De Marco, C., Mondovi, B., Scandurra, R., and Cavallini, D., *Enzymologia* **25**, 94 (1962).

1487. Cavallini, D., Scandurra, R., and De Marco, C., *J. Biol. Chem.* **238**, 2999 (1963).

1488. Mondovi, B., and Tentori, L., *Italian J. Biochem.* **10**, 436 (1961).

1489. Cavallini, D., De Marco, C., and Mondovi, B., *J. Biol. Chem.* **234**, 854 (1959).

1490. Mondovi, B., and De Marco, C., *Enzymologia* **23**, 156 (1961).

1491. Cavallini, D., De Marco, C., and Mondovi, B., *Bull. Soc. Chim. Biol.* **40**, 1711 (1958).

1492. Sörbo, B., *Acta Chem. Scand.* **12**, 146; *Bull. Soc. Chim. Biol.* **40**, 1859 (1958).

1493. De Marco, C., Coletta, M., Mondovi, B., and Cavallini, D., *Italian J. Biochem.* **9**, 3 (1960).

1494. De Marco, C., Bagnolo, D., and Coletta, M., *Ital. J. Biochem* **11**, 221 (1962).

1495. Awapara, J., *J. Biol. Chem.* **225**, 877 (1957).

1496. Pentz, E. I., Davenport, C. H., Glover, W., and Smith, D. D., *J. Biol. Chem.* **228**, 433 (1957).
1497. Gilbert, J. B., Ku, Y., Rogers, L. L., and Williams, R. J., *J. Biol. Chem.* **235**, 1055 (1960).
1498. Koechlin, B. A., *J. Biophys. Biochem. Cytol.* **1**, 511 (1955).
1499. Welty, J. D., Read, W. O., and Shaw, E. H., Jr., *J. Biol. Chem.* **237**, 1160 (1962).
1500. Read, W. O., and Welty, J. D., *J. Biol. Chem.* **237**, 1521 (1962).
1501. Braun, R., and Fromageot, P., *Biochim. Biophys. Acta* **62**, 548 (1962).
1501a. Ikeda, K., Yamada, H., and Tanaka, S., *J. Biochem. (Tokyo)* **54**, 312 (1963).
1502. Elliott, W. H., *Biochem. J.* **62**, 427, 433 (1956); **65**, 315 (1957).
1503. Thoai, Ng.-V., and Robin, Y., *Biochim. Biophys. Acta* **13**, 533 (1954).
1504. Hobson, G. E., and Rees, K. R., *Biochem. J.* **65**, 305 (1957).
1505. Ackermann, D., *Z. Physiol. Chem.* **232**, 206; **234**, 208; **235**, 115, 233 (1935).
1506. Robin, Y., and Thoai, Ng.-V., *Biochim. Biophys. Acta* **63**, 481 (1962).
1507. Thoai, Ng.-V., Robin, Y., and Pradel, L.-A., *Biochim. Biophys. Acta* **73**, 437 (1963).
1507a. Thoai, Ng.-V., Zappacosta, S., and Robin, Y., *Comp. Biochem. Physiol.* **10**, 209 (1963).
1508. Lindberg, B., *Acta Chem. Scand.* **9**, 1323 (1955).
1509. Coletta, M., Mari, S., and De Marco, C., *Italian J. Biochem.* **10**, 411 (1962).
1510. De Marco, C., Coletta, M., and Mari, S., *Italian J. Biochem.* **10**, 446 (1962).
1511. Sörbo, B., *Acta Chem. Scand.* **12**, 1990 (1958).
1512. Coletta, M., Benerecetti, S. A., and De Marco, C., *Italian J. Biochem.* **10**, 244 (1961).
1513. De Marco, C., and Coletta, M., *Biochim. Biophys. Acta* **47**, 262 (1961).
1514. Lang, K., *Biochem. Z.* **259**, 243 (1933).
1515. Gal, E. M., Fung, F.-H., and Greenberg, D. M., *Cancer Res.* **12**, 574 (1952).
1516. Sörbo, B. H., *Svensk Kem. Tidskr.* **65**, 169 (1953).
1517. Westley, J., and Green, J. R., *J. Biol. Chem.* **234**, 2325 (1959).
1518. Sörbo, B. H., *Acta Chem. Scand.* **5**, 724, 1218 (1951); **7**, 32, 238, 1129, 1137 (1953); **8**, 694 (1954).
1519. Sörbo, B., *Acta Chem. Scand.* **16**, 243 (1962).
1520. Wood, J. L., and Fiedler, H., *J. Biol. Chem.* **205**, 231 (1953).
1521. Westley, J., *J. Biol. Chem.* **234**, 1857 (1959).
1522. Westley, J., and Nakamoto, T., *J. Biol. Chem.* **237**, 547 (1962).
1523. Baxter, C. F., Van Reen, R., Pearson, P. B., and Rosenberg, C., *Biochim. Biophys. Acta* **27**, 584; **28**, 567, 573 (1958).
1524. Vishniac, W., and Santer, M., *Bacteriol. Rev.* **21**, 195 (1957).
1525. Lees, H., *Ann. Rev. Microbiol.* **14**, 83 (1960).
1526. Young, L., and Maw, G. A., "The Metabolism of Sulphur Compounds." Wiley, New York, 1958.
1527. Skarzynski, B., and Ostrowski, W., *Nature* **182**, 933 (1958).
1528. Skarzynski, B., Szczepkowski, T. W., and Weber, M., *Nature* **184**, 994 (1959).
1529. Schneider, J. F., and Westley, J., *J. Biol. Chem.* **238**, PC 3516 (1963).
1530. Schubert, M. P., *J. Biol. Chem.* **114**, 341 (1936).
1531. Ratner, S., and Clarke, H. T., *J. Am. Chem. Soc.* **59**, 200 (1937).
1532. MacKenzie, C. G., and Harris, J., *J. Biol. Chem.* **227**, 393 (1957).
1533. Wriston, J. C., Jr., and Mackenzie, C. G., *J. Biol. Chem.* **225**, 607 (1957).

1534. Wolen, R. L., and Wriston, J. C., Jr., *J. Biol. Chem.* **238**, 377 (1963).
1535. Neely, W. B., *J. Bacteriol.* **85**, 1420 (1963).
1536. Dann, J. R., Oliver, G. L., and Gates, J. W., Jr., *J. Am. Chem. Soc.* **79**, 1644 (1957).
1537. Dann, J. R., and Gates, J. W., Jr., *J. Am. Chem. Soc.* **79**, 1650 (1957).
1538. Wood, J. L., and Cooley, S. L., *J. Biol. Chem.* **218**, 449 (1956).
1539. Voegtlin, C., Johnson, J. M., and Dyer, H. M., *J. Pharmacol. Exptl. Therap.* **27**, 467 (1926).
1540. Smith, R. A., Frank, I. F., and Gunsalus, I. C., *Federation Proc.* **16**, 251 (1957).
1541. Feuer, Gy., and Wollemann, M., *Acta Physiol. Acad. Sci. Hung.* **7**, 343 (1955); **10**, 1 (1956).
1542. Kaufman, S., *J. Biol. Chem.* **216**, 153 (1955).
1543. Levy, H. M., and Koshland, D. E., *J. Biol. Chem.* **234**, 1102 (1959).
1544. Binkley, F., *J. Biol. Chem.* **181**, 317 (1949); **195**, 283 (1952).
1545. Akerfeldt, S., *Acta Chem. Scand.* **14**, 1019 (1960).
1546. Jaffe, M., *Ber.* **12**, 1092 (1879).
1547. Baumann, E., and Schmitz, P., *Z. Physiol. Chem.* **20**, 586 (1895).
1548. Stekol, J. A., *J. Biol. Chem.* **121**, 87, 93 (1937); **122**, 333; **124**, 129 (1938); **127**, 131; **128**, 199 (1939); **138**, 225; **140**, 827 (1941); **164**, 651 (1946); **167**, 637 (1947).
1549. Williams, R. T., "Detoxication Mechanisms," 2nd ed. Wiley, New York, 1959.
1550. Knight, R. H., and Young, L., *Biochem. J.* **70**, 111 (1958).
1551. Boyland, E., and Simms, P., *Biochem. J.* **68**, 440 (1958).
1552. Smith, J. T., and Wood, J. L., *J. Biol. Chem.* **234**, 3192 (1959).
1553. Mills, G. C., and Wood, J. L., *J. Biol. Chem.* **204**, 547; **207**, 695; **219**, 1 (1956).
1554. Bray, H. G., and Franklin, T. J., *Biochem. J.* **66**, 3p (1957).
1555. Booth, J., Boyland, E., and Sims, P., *Biochem. J.* **79**, 516 (1961).
1556. Al-Kassab, S., Boyland, E., and Williams, K., *Biochem. J.* **87**, 4 (1963).
1557. Combes, B., and Stakelum, G. S., *J. Clin. Invest.* **40**, 981 (1961).
1558. Moxon, A. L., Schaefer, A. E., Lardy, H. A., DuBois, K. P., and Olson, O. E., *J. Biol. Chem.* **132**, 785 (1940).
1559. Lemley, R. E. J., *Lancet* **60**, 528 (1940).
1560. Harrow, B., and Sherwin, C. P., *J. Biol. Chem.* **70**, 683 (1926).
1561. Cox, G. J., and Rose, W. C., *J. Biol. Chem.* **68**, 781 (1926).
1562. Conrad, R. M., and Berg, C. P., *J. Biol. Chem.* **117**, 351 (1936).
1563. Neuberger, A., and Webster, T. A., *Biochem. J.* **40**, 576 (1946).
1564. Celander, D. R., and Berg, C. P., *J. Biol. Chem.* **202**, 339, 351 (1953).
1565. Broquist, H. P., and Snell, E. E., *J. Biol. Chem.* **180**, 59 (1949).
1566. Vogel, H. J., Davis, B. D., and Mingioli, E. S., *J. Am. Chem. Soc.* **73**, 1897 (1951).
1567. Ames, B. N., and Mitchell, H. K., *J. Am. Chem. Soc.* **74**, 252 (1952).
1568. Ames, B. N., Mitchell, H. K., and Mitchell, M. B., *J. Am. Chem. Soc.* **75**, 1015 (1953).
1569. Ames, B. N., and Mitchell, H. K., *J. Biol. Chem.* **212**, 687 (1955).
1570. Ames, B. N., *in* "Amino Acid Metabolism" (W. D. McElroy and B. Glass, eds.), p. 357. Johns Hopkins Press, Baltimore, Maryland, 1955.
1571. Adams, E., *J. Biol. Chem.* **209**, 829 (1954); **217**, 317, 325 (1955).
1572. Ames, B. N., *J. Biol. Chem.* **228**, 131 (1957).
1573. Ames, B. N., and Horecker, B. L., *J. Biol. Chem.* **220**, 113 (1956).
1574. Ames, B. N., *J. Biol. Chem.* **226**, 583 (1957).

1575. Westley, J., and Ceithaml, J., *Arch. Biochem. Biophys.* **60**, 215 (1956).
1576. Ames, B. N., Garry, B. J., and Herzenberg, L. A., *J. Gen. Microbiol.* **22**, 369 (1960).
1577. Luzzati, D., and Guthrie, R., *J. Biol. Chem.* **216**, 1 (1955).
1578. Balis, M. E., Levin, D. H., and Luzzati, D., *J. Biol. Chem.* **216**, 9 (1955).
1579. Levy, L., and Coon, M. J., *J. Biol. Chem.* **192**, 807 (1951); **208**, 691 (1954).
1580. Mitoma, C., and Snell, E. E., *Proc. Natl. Acad. Sci. U.S.* **41**, 891 (1955).
1581. Magasanik, B., Moyed, H. S., and Karibian, D., *J. Am. Chem. Soc.* **78**, 1510 (1956).
1582. Magasanik, B., *J. Am. Chem. Soc.* **78**, 5449 (1956).
1583. Neidle, A., and Waelsch, H., *J. Biol. Chem.* **234**, 586 (1959).
1584. Neidle, A., and Waelsch, H., *J. Am. Chem. Soc.* **78**, 1767 (1956).
1585. Moyed, H. S., and Magasanik, B., *J. Biol. Chem.* **235**, 149 (1960).
1586. Ames, B. N., Martin, R. G., and Garry, B. J., *J. Biol. Chem.* **236**, 2019 (1961).
1587. Martin, R. G., *J. Biol. Chem.* **238**, 257 (1963).
1588. Shedlovsky, A. E., and Magasanik, B., *J. Biol. Chem.* **237**, 3725, 3731 (1962).
1589. Broquist, H. P., *Arch. Biochem. Biophys.* **70**, 210 (1957).
1590. Moyed, H. S., *J. Biol. Chem.* **236**, 2261 (1961).
1591. Ames, B. N., and Garry, B., *Proc. Natl. Acad. Sci. U.S.* **45**, 1453 (1959).
1592. Ames, B. N., Garry, B., and Herzenberg, L. A., *J. Gen. Microbiol.* **22**, 369 (1960).
1593. György, P., and Röthler, H., *Biochem. Z.* **173**, 334 (1926).
1594. Edlbacher, S., *Z. Physiol. Chem.* **157**, 106 (1926).
1595. Edlbacher, S., and Kraus, J., *Z. Physiol. Chem.* **191**, 225 (1927); **195**, 267 (1931).
1596. Leuthardt, F., *in* "The Enzymes" (J. B. Sumner and K. Myrbäck, eds.), Vol. 1, Pt. 2, p. 1156. Academic Press, New York, 1951.
1597. Edlbacher, S., *Ergeb. Enzymforsch.* **9**, 131 (1943).
1598. Edlbacher, S., and Neber, M., *Z. Physiol. Chem.* **225**, 261 (1934).
1599. Walker, A. C., and Schmidt, C. L. A., *Arch. Biochem.* **5**, 445 (1944).
1600. Jaffe, M., *Ber.* **7**, 1669 (1874).
1601. Raistrick, H., *Biochem. J.* **11**, 71 (1917).
1602. Darby, W. J., and Lewis, H. B., *J. Biol. Chem.* **146**, 225 (1942).
1603. Siegfried, M., *Z. Physiol. Chem.* **24**, 399 (1898).
1604. Hunter, A., *J. Biol. Chem.* **11**, 537 (1912).
1605. Swain, R. L., *Am. J. Physiol.* **13**, 30 (1905).
1606. Hunter, A., and Givens, M. H., *J. Biol. Chem.* **8**, 449 (1910).
1607. Kotake, K., and Konishi, M., *Z. Physiol. Chem.* **122**, 230 (1922).
1608. Konishi, M., *Z. Physiol. Chem.* **122**, 237 (1922).
1609. Kiyokawa, M., *Z. Physiol. Chem.* **214**, 38 (1933).
1610. Sera, Y., and Yada, S., *J. Osaka Med. Soc.* **38**, 1107 (1939).
1611. Sera, Y., and Aihara, D., *J. Osaka Med. Soc.* **41**, 745 (1942).
1612. Takeuchi, M., *J. Biochem.* (*Tokyo*), **34**, 1 (1941).
1613. Akamatsu, S., *J. Japan. Biochem. Soc.* **17**, 75 (1943).
1614. Oyamada, Y., *J. Biochem.* (*Tokyo*) **36**, 227 (1944).
1615. Parshin, A. N., *Doklady Akad. Nauk SSSR* **58**, 621 (1947).
1616. Parshin, A. N., and Goryukhina, T. A., *Biokhimiya* **15**, 499 (1950).
1617. Sera, Y., *Med. J. Osaka Univ.* **4**, 1 (1951).
1618. Hall, D. A., *Biochem. J.* **51**, 499 (1952).
1619. Goryukhina, T. A., *Doklady Akad. Nauk SSSR* **87**, 645 (1952).

1620. Tabor, H., and Hayaishi, O., *J. Biol. Chem.* **194**, 171 (1952).
1621. Tabor, H., Mehler, A. H., Hayaishi, O., and White, J., *J. Biol. Chem.* **196**, 121 (1952).
1622. Mehler, A. H., and Tabor, H., *J. Biol. Chem.* **201**, 775 (1953).
1623. Abrams, A., and Borsook, H., *J. Biol. Chem.* **198**, 205 (1952).
1624. Fournier, J. P., and Bouthillier, L. P., *J. Am. Chem. Soc.* **74**, 5210 (1952).
1625. Wolf, G., *J. Biol. Chem.* **200**, 637 (1953).
1626. Tabor, H., Silverman, M., Mehler, A. H., Daft, F. S., and Bauer, H., *J. Am. Chem. Soc.* **75**, 756 (1953).
1627. Morel, C. J., *Helv. Chim. Acta* **29**, 905 (1946).
1628. Matsuda, K., Itagaki, J., Wachi, T., and Uchida, M., *J. Biochem. (Tokyo)* **39**, 40 (1952).
1629. Suda, M., Tomihata, K., Nakaya, A., and Kato, A., *J. Biochem. (Tokyo)* **40**, 257 (1953).
1630. Wickremasinghe, R. L., and Fry, B. A., *Biochem. J.* **58**, 268 (1954).
1631. Peterkofsky, A., *J. Biol. Chem.* **237**, 787 (1962).
1632. Borek, B. A., and Waelsch, H., *J. Biol. Chem.* **205**, 459 (1953).
1633. Kumagai, N., *J. Japan. Biochem. Soc.* **21**, 191 (1949).
1634. Peterkofsky, A., and Mehler, L. N., *Biochem. Biophys. Acta* **73**, 159 (1963).
1635. Ichihara, K., Uchida, M., Matsuda, K., Kmajari, N., and Kikuoka, H., *Z. Physiol. Chem.* **295**, 220 (1953).
1636. Erspamer, V., and Benati, O., *Biochem. Z.* **324**, 66 (1953).
1637. Erspamer, V., and Benati, O., *Science* **117**, 161 (1953).
1638. Zenisek, A., and Kral, J. A., *Biochim Biophys. Acta* **12**, 479 (1953).
1639. Zenisek, A., Kral, J. A., and Hais, I. M., *Biochim. Biophys. Acta* **18**, 589 (1955).
1640. Borek, B. A., and Waelsch, H., *J. Am. Chem. Soc.* **75**, 1772 (1953).
1641. Tabor, H., and Mehler, A. H., *J. Biol. Chem.* **210**, 559 (1954).
1642. Silverman, M., Bakerman, H. A., and Daft, F. S., *Procl Soc. Exptl. Biol. Med.* **87**, 451 (1954).
1643. Miller, A., and Waelsch, H., *J. Am. Chem. Soc.* **76**, 6195 (1954).
1644. Seegmiller, J. E., Silverman, M., Tabor, H., and Mehler, A. H., *J. Am. Chem. Soc.* **76**, 6205 (1954).
1645. Revel, H. R. B., and Magasanik, B., *J. Biol. Chem.* **233**, 930 (1958).
1646. Feinberg, R. H., and Greenberg, D. M., *J. Biol. Chem.* **234**, 2670 (1959).
1647. Freter, K., Rabinowitz, J. C., and Witkop, B., *Ann.* **607**, 174 (1957).
1648. Kny, H., and Witkop, B., *J. Am. Chem. Soc.* **81**, 6245 (1959).
1649. Brown, D. D., and Kies, M. W., *J. Biol. Chem.* **234**, 3188 (1959).
1650. Miller, A., and Waelsch, H., *J. Biol. Chem.* **228**, 365 (1957).
1650a. Hassall, H., and Greenberg, D. M., *J. Biol. Chem.* **238**, 1423 (1963).
1651. Gupta, K., and Robinson, W. G., *Federation Proc.* **20**, 4 (1961).
1652. Snyder, S. H., Silva, O. L., and Kies, M. W., *J. Biol. Chem.* **236**, 2996 (1961).
1653. Rao, D. R., and Greenberg, D. M., *J. Biol. Chem.* **236**, 1758 (1961).
1654. Baldridge, R. C., *J. Biol. Chem.* **231**, 207 (1958).
1655. Silverman, M., Gardiner, R. C., and Bakerman, H. A., *J. Biol. Chem.* **194**, 815 (1952).
1656. Bakerman, H., Silverman, M., and Daft, F. S., *J. Biol. Chem.* **188**, 117 (1951).
1657. Rabinowitz, J. C., and Tabor, H., *J. Biol. Chem.* **233**, 252 (1958).

1658. Bennett, M. C., and Chanarin, I., *Nature* **196**, 271 (1962).
1659. Miller, A., and Waelsch, H., *Biochim. Biophys. Acta* **17**, 278 (1955); *Arch. Biochem. Biophys.* **63**, 262 (1956).
1660. Miller, A., and Waelsch, H., *J. Biol. Chem.* **228**, 383 (1957).
1661. Miller, A., and Waelsch, H., *J. Biol. Chem.* **228**, 397 (1957).
1662. Tabor, H., and Wyngarden, L., *J. Biol. Chem.* **234**, 1830 (1959).
1663. Sagers, R. D., Beck, J. V., Gruber, W., and Gunsalus, I. C., *J. Am. Chem. Soc.* **78**, 694 (1956).
1664. Magasanik, B., *J. Biol. Chem.* **213**, 557 (1955).
1665. Magasanik, B., and Bowser, H. R., *J. Biol. Chem.* **213**, 571 (1955).
1666. Wachsman, J. T., and Barker, H. A., *J. Bacteriol.* **69**, 83 (1955).
1667. Nishizawa, Y., *Med. J. Osaka Univ.* **5**, 105 (1954).
1668. Suda, M., Miyahara, I., Tomihata, K., and Kato, A., *Med. J. Osaka Univ.* **3**, 115 (1952).
1669. Suda, M., Nakaya, A., Hara, M., Kato, A., and Ikenaka, T., *Med. J. Osaka Univ.* **4**, 107 (1953).
1670. Silverman, M., Keresztesy, J. C., Koval, G. J., and Gardiner, R. C., *J. Biol. Chem.* **226**, 83 (1957).
1671. Silverman, M., and Pitney, A. J., *J. Biol. Chem.* **233**, 1179 (1958).
1672. Brown, D. D., Silva, O. L., Gardiner, R. C., and Silverman, M., *J. Biol. Chem.* **235**, 2058 (1960).
1673. Brown, D. D., and Kies, M. W., *J. Biol. Chem.* **234**, 3182 (1959).
1674. Hassall, H., and Greenberg, D. M., *Biochim. Biophys. Acta* **67**, 507 (1963).
1675. Hassall, H., and Greenberg, D. M., *J. Biol. Chem.* **238**, 3325 (1963).
1676. Tabor, H., *Pharmacol. Revs.* **6**, 299 (1954).
1677. Tabor, H., *J. Biol. Chem.* **188**, 125 (1951).
1678. Mehler, A. H., Tabor, H., and Bauer, H., *J. Biol. Chem.* **197**, 475 (1952).
1679. Schayer, R. W., *J. Biol. Chem.* **196**, 469 (1952).
1680. Schayer, R. W., *J. Biol. Chem.* **203**, 787 (1953).
1681. Schayer, R. W., Kennedy, J., and Smiley, R. L., *J. Biol. Chem.* **205**, 739 (1953).
1682. Tabor, H., Mehler, A. H., and Schayer, R. W., *J. Biol. Chem.* **200**, 605 (1953).
1683. Bouthillier, L. P., and Goldner, M., *Arch. Biochem. Biophys.* **44**, 251 (1953).
1684. Tabor, H., and Hayaishi, O., *J. Am. Chem. Soc.* **77**, 505 (1955).
1685. Karjala, S. A., *J. Am. Chem. Soc.* **77**, 504 (1955).
1686. Bauer, H., *Biochim. Biophys. Acta* **30**, 219 (1958).
1687. Alivisatos, S. G. A., and Woolley, D. W., *J. Am. Chem. Soc.* **77**, 1065 (1955).
1688. Alivisatos, S. G. A., and Woolley, D. W., *J. Biol. Chem.* **221**, 651 (1956).
1689. Alivisatos, S. G. A., Ungar, F., Lukacs, L., and LaMantia, L., *J. Biol. Chem.* **235**, 1742 (1962).
1690. Abdel-Latif, A. A., and Alivisatos, S. G. A., *J. Biol. Chem.* **236**, 2710 (1961).
1691. Alivisatos, S. G. A., Abdel-Latif, A. A., Ungar, F., and Mourkides, G. A., *Nature* **199**, 907 (1963).
1691a. Crowley, G. M., *Federation Proc.* **19**, 309 (1960).
1691b. Jones, O. W., Jr., Ashton, D. M., and Wyngaarden, J. B., *J. Clin. Invest.* **41**, 1805 (1962).
1692. Hayaishi, O., Tabor, H., and Hayaishi, T., *J. Am. Chem. Soc.* **76**, 5570 (1954).
1693. Hayaishi, O., Tabor, H., and Hayaishi, T., *J. Biol. Chem.* **227**, 161 (1957).

1694. Ohmura, E., and Hayaishi, O., *J. Biol. Chem.* **227**, 181 (1957).
1695. Rothberg, S., and Hayaishi, O., *J. Biol. Chem.* **229**, 897 (1957).
1696. Tabor, H., and Mosettig, E., *J. Biol. Chem.* **180**, 703 (1949).
1697. Tabor, H., Mehler, A. H., and Stadtman, E. R., *J. Biol. Chem.* **204**, 127 (1953).
1698. Stadtman, E. R., and White, F. H., Jr., *J. Am. Chem. Soc.* **75**, 2022 (1953).
1699. Kinsky, S. C., *J. Biol. Chem.* **235**, 94 (1960).
1700. Schayer, R. W., *Brit. J. Pharmacol.* **11**, 472 (1956).
1700a. Schayer, R. W., and Karjala, S. A., *J. Biol. Chem.* **221**, 307 (1956).
1701. Brown, D. D., Axelrod, J., and Tomchick, R., *Nature* **183**, 680 (1959).
1702. Roche, J., Thoai, Ng.-V., and Glahn, P. E., *Compt. Rend. Soc. Biol.* **148**, 481 (1954).
1703. Thoai, Ng.-V., Glahn, P. E., Hedegaard, J., Manchon, P., and Roche, J., *Biochim. Biophys. Acta* **15**, 87 (1954).
1704. Wolf, G., Wu, P.-H. L., and Heck, W. W., *J. Biol. Chem.* **222**, 159 (1956).
1705. Baldridge, R. C., and Tourtellotte, C. D., *J. Biol. Chem.* **233**, 125 (1958).
1706. Brown, D. D., Silva, O. L., McDonald, P. B., Snyder, S. H., and Kies, M. W., *J. Biol. Chem.* **235**, 154 (1960).
1707. Sen, N. P., McGeer, P. L., and Paul, R. M., *Biochem. Biophys. Res. Commun.* **9**, 257 (1962).
1707a. Nakajima, T., and Sano, L., *Biochim. Biophys. Acta* **82**, 260 (1964).
1708. Cowgill, R. W., and Freeburg, B., *Arch. Biochem. Biophys.* **71**, 466 (1957).
1709. Hanson, H., and Smith, E. L., *J. Biol. Chem.* **179**, 789 (1949).
1710. Shabanova, I. A., *Biokhimiya* **18**, 385 (1953); *Chem. Abstr.* **48**, 4681 (1954).
1711. Fink, K., Williams, A. D., and Fink, R. M., *J. Biol. Chem.* **234**, 1182 (1959).
1712. McManus, I. R., *J. Biol. Chem.* **235**, 1398 (1960).
1713. Rathlev, T., and Rosenberg, T., *Arch. Biochem. Biophys.* **65**, 319 (1956).
1714. Goldman, L., Marsico, J. W., and Anderson, G. W., *J. Am. Chem. Soc.* **82**, 2969 (1960).
1715. Baddiley, J., Buchanan, J. G., and Letters, R., *J. Chem. Soc.* **3**, 2812 (1956).
1716. Schaller, H., Staab, H. A., and Cramer, F., *Ber.* **94**, 1621 (1961).
1717. Boyer, P. D., DeLuca, M., Ebner, K. E., Hultquist, D. E., and Peter, J. B., *J. Biol. Chem.* **238**, PC 3306 (1963).
1718. Boyer, P. D., *Science* **141**, 1147 (1963).
1718a. Pressman, B. C., *Biochem. Biophys. Res. Commun.* **15**, 556 (1964).
1718b. Perlgut, L. E., and Wainio, W. W., *Biochem. Biophys. Res. Commun.* **16**, 227 (1964).
1719. Tanret, M. C., *Compt. Rend. Acad. Sci.* **149**, 222 (1909).
1720. Melville, D. B., Horner, W. H., and Lubschez, R., *J. Biol. Chem.* **206**, 221 (1954).
1721. Touster, O., and Yarbro, M. C., *J. Lab. Clin. Med.* **39**, 720 (1952).
1722. Melville, D. B., Otken, C. C., and Kovalenko, V., *J. Biol. Chem.* **216**, 325 (1955).
1723. Melville, D. B., Horner, W. H., Otken, C. C., and Ludwig, M. L., *J. Biol. Chem.* **213**, 61 (1955).
1724. Mackenzie, J. B., and Mackenzie, C. G., *J. Biol. Chem.* **225**, 651 (1957).
1725. Heath, J., and Wildy, J., *Nature* **179**, 196 (1957); *Biochem. J.* **64**, 612 (1956); **65**, 220 (1957); **68**, 407 (1958).
1726. Melville, D. B., Genghof, D. S., Inamine, E., and Kovalenko, V., *J. Biol. Chem.* **223**, 9 (1956).

1727. Melville, D. B., Eich, S., and Ludwig, M. L., *J. Biol. Chem.* **224**, 871 (1957).

1728. Melville, D. B., Ludwig, M. L., Inamine, E., and Rachele, J. R., *J. Biol. Chem.* **234**, 1195 (1959).

1729. Askari, A., and Melville, D. B., *J. Biol. Chem.* **237**, 1615 (1962).

1729a. Genghof, D. S., and Van Damme, O., *J. Bacteriol.* **87**, 852 (1964).

1730. Yanasugondha, D., and Appleman, M. D., *J. Bacteriol.* **74**, 381 (1957).

1731. Kelly, B., and Appleman, M. D., *J. Bacteriol.* **81**, 715 (1961).

1732. Booth, J. S., and Appleman, M. D., *J. Bacteriol.* **85**, 654 (1963).

1733. Wolff, J. B., *J. Biol. Chem.* **237**, 874 (1962).

1733a. Ackermann, D., and Hoppe-Seyler, G., *Z. Physiol. Chem.* **336**, 283 (1964).

1734. Fildes, P., *Brit. J. Exptl. Pathol.* **22**, 293 (1941).

1735. Snell, E. E., *Arch. Biochem.* **2**, 389 (1943).

1736. Tatum, E. L., Bonner, D. M., and Beadle, G. W., *Arch. Biochem.* **3**, 477 (1944).

1737. Haskins, F. A., and Mitchell, H. K., *Proc. Natl. Acad. Sci. U.S.* **35**, 500 (1949).

1738. Trudinger, P. A., *Biochem. J.* **62**, 480 (1956).

1739. Umbreit, W. W., Wood, W. A., and Gunsalus, I. C., *J. Biol. Chem.* **165**, 731 (1946).

1740. Yanofsky, C., *J. Biol. Chem.* **194**, 279 (1952).

1741. Tatum, E. L., and Shemin, D., *J. Biol. Chem.* **209**, 671 (1954).

1742. Nyc, J. F., Mitchell, H. K., Liefer, E., and Langham, W. H., *J. Biol. Chem.* **179**, 783 (1949).

1743. Partridge, C. W. H., Bonner, D. M., and Yanofsky, C., *J. Biol. Chem.* **194**, 269 (1952).

1744. Yanofsky, C., *J. Biol. Chem.* **217**, 345 (1955).

1745. Yanofsky, C., *Biochim. Biophys. Acta* **20**, 438 (1956).

1746. Srinivasan, P. R., and Rivera, A., Jr., *Biochemistry* **2**, 1059 (1963).

1747. Rivera, A., Jr., and Srinivasan, P. R., *Biochemistry* **2**, 1063 (1963).

1748. Yanofsky, C., *J. Biol. Chem.* **223**, 171 (1956).

1749. Yanofsky, C., *J. Biol. Chem.* **224**, 783 (1957).

1750. Gots, J. S., and Roth, S. H., *Biochim. Biophys. Acta* **24**, 429 (1957).

1751. Yanofsky, C., *Science* **121**, 138 (1955).

1752. Doy, C. H., and Gibson, F. W., *Biochem. J.* **72**, 586 (1959).

1753. Smith, O. H., and Yanofsky, C., *J. Biol. Chem.* **235**, 2051 (1960).

1754. Doy, C. H., *Nature* **189**, 461 (1961).

1755. Doy, C. H., Rivera, A., Jr., and Srinivasan, P. R., *Biochem. Biophys. Res. Commun.* **4**, 83 (1961).

1756. Parks, L. W., and Douglas, H. C., *Biochim. Biophys. Acta* **23**, 207 (1957).

1757. Lingens, F., Hildinger, M., and Hellmann, H., *Biochim. Biophys. Acta* **30**, 668 (1958).

1757a. Lingens, F., and Lück, W., *Z. Physiol. Chem.* **333**, 190 (1963).

1758. Yanofsky, C., and Rachmeler, M., *Biochim. Biophys. Acta* **28**, 640 (1958).

1759. Crawford, I. P., and Yanofsky, C., *Proc. Natl. Acad. Sci. U.S.* **44**, 1161 (1958).

1760. Yanofsky, C., *Bacteriol. Rev.* **24**, 221 (1960).

1761. Suskind, S. R., Yanofsky, C., and Bonner, D. M., *Proc. Natl. Acad. Sci. U.S.* **41**, 577 (1955).

1762. Yanofsky, C., and Stadler, J., *Proc. Natl. Acad. Sci. U.S.* **44**, 245 (1958).

1763. Hatanaka, M., White, E. A., Horibata, K., and Crawford, I. P., *Arch. Biochem. Biophys.* **97**, 596 (1962).

1764. Henning, U., Helinski, D. R., Chao, F. C., and Yanofsky, C., *J. Biol. Chem.* **237**, 1523 (1962).

1765. Carlton, B. C., and Yanofsky, C., *J. Biol. Chem.* **237**, 1531 (1962).

1765a. Garrick, M. D., Elberfeld, H., and Suskind, S. R., *Science* **145**, 491 (1964).

1766. Matchett, W. H., and De Moss, J. A., *Biochim. Biophys. Acta* **71**, 632 (1963).

1767. Tatum, E. L., Gross, S. R., Ehrensvärd, G., and Garnjobst, L., *Proc. Natl. Acad. Sci. U.S.* **40**, 271 (1954).

1768. Nair, P. M., and Vaidyanathan, C. S., *Arch. Biochem. Biophys.* **93**, 262 (1961).

1769. Liebig, J., *Ann.* **86**, 125 (1853).

1770. Matsuoka, Z., and Yoshimatsu, S., *Z. Physiol. Chem.* **143**, 206 (1925).

1771. Ellinger, A., *Z. Physiol. Chem.* **43**, 325 (1904).

1772. Kotake, Y., and Kawase, M., *Z. Physiol. Chem.* **214**, 6 (1933).

1773. Kotake, Y., and Masayama, T., *Z. Physiol. Chem.* **243**, 237 (1936).

1774. Knox, W. E., and Mehler, A. H., *J. Biol. Chem.* **187**, 419 (1950).

1775. Mehler, A. H., and Knox, W. E., *J. Biol. Chem.* **187**, 431 (1950).

1776. Knox, W. E., *Biochim. Biophys. Acta* **14**, 117 (1954).

1777. Mehler, A. H., *in* "Amino Acid Metabolism" (W. D. McElroy and B. Glass, eds.), p. 882. Johns Hopkins Press, Baltimore, Maryland, 1955.

1778. Dalgliesh, C. E., Knox, W. E., and Neuberger, A., *Nature* **168**, 20 (1951).

1779. Ek, A., Kissman, A., Patrick, J. B., and Witkop, B., *Experientia* **8**, 36 (1952).

1780. Jayson, G. G., Scholes, G., and Weiss, J., *Biochem. J.* **57**, 386 (1954).

1781. Sakan, T., and Hayaishi, O., *J. Biol. Chem.* **186**, 177 (1950).

1782. Mason, M., and Berg, C. P., *J. Biol. Chem.* **188**, 783 (1951).

1783. Hayaishi, O., Rothberg, S., Mehler, A. H., and Saito, Y., *J. Biol. Chem.* **229**, 889 (1957).

1784. Hayaishi, O., and Stanier, R. Y., *J. Bacteriol.* **62**, 691 (1951).

1785. Tanaka, T., and Knox, W. E., *J. Biol. Chem.* **234**, 1162 (1959).

1786. Greengard, O., and Feigelson, P., *J. Biol. Chem.* **237**, 1903 (1962).

1786a. Tokuyama, K., and Knox, W. E., *Biochim. Biophys. Acta* **81**, 201 (1964).

1787. Nemeth, A. M., *J. Biol. Chem.* **234**, 2921 (1959).

1788. Knox, W. E., and Mehler, A. H., *Science* **113**, 237 (1951).

1789. Efimochkina, E. F., *Biokhimiya* **19**(1), 68 (1954).

1790. Knox, W. E., and Auerbach, V. H., *J. Biol. Chem.* **214**, 307 (1955).

1791. Geschwind, I. I., and Li, C. H., *Nature* **172**, 732 (1953).

1792. Lee, N. D., and Williams, R. H., *Biochim. Biophys. Acta* **9**, 698 (1952); *J. Biol. Chem.* **204**, 477 (1953).

1793. Feigelson, P., and Greengard, O., *J. Biol. Chem.* **236**, 153 (1961); **237**, 1908 (1962).

1794. Greengard, O., and Feigelson, P., *J. Biol. Chem.* **236**, 158 (1961).

1795. Nemeth, A. M., and De La Haba, G., *J. Biol. Chem.* **237**, 1190 (1962).

1796. Nemeth, A. M., *J. Biol. Chem.* **237**, 3703 (1962).

1797. Price, J. B., Jr., and Dietrich, L. S., *J. Biol. Chem.* **227**, 633 (1957).

1798. Civen, M., and Knox, W. E., *J. Biol. Chem.* **234**, 1787 (1959).

1799. Schor, J. M., and Frieden, E., *J. Biol. Chem.* **233**, 612 (1958).

1800. Jakoby, W. B., *J. Biol. Chem.* **207**, 657 (1954).

References 1001

1801. Krehl, W. A., Teply, L. J., Sarma, P. S., and Elvehjem, C. A., *Science* **101**, 489 (1945); *J. Nutr.* **31**, 85 (1946).
1802. Spector, H., *J. Biol. Chem.* **173**, 659 (1948).
1803. Sarett, H. P., *J. Biol. Chem.* **182**, 659, 671 (1950).
1804. Dalgliesh, C. E., *Quart. Rev. (London)* **5**, 227 (1951).
1805. Rosen, F., Huff, J. W., and Perlzweig, W. A., *J. Biol. Chem.* **163**, 343 (1946).
1806. Beadle, G. W., Mitchell, H. K., and Nyc, J. F., *Proc. Natl. Acad. Sci. U.S.* **33**, 155 (1947).
1807. Mitchell, H. K., and Nyc, J. F., *Proc. Natl. Acad. Sci. U.S.* **34**, 1 (1948).
1808. Rosen, F., Huff, J. W., and Perlzweig, W. A., *J. Biol. Chem.* **167**, 511 (1947).
1809. Bonner, D., and Yanofsky, C., *Proc. Natl. Acad. Sci. U.S.* **35**, 576 (1949).
1810. Bonner, D., and Beadle, G. W., *Arch. Biochem.* **11**, 319 (1946).
1811. Yanofsky, C., Wasserman, E., and Bonner, D., *Science* **111**, 61 (1950).
1812. Nyc, J. F., and Mitchell, H. K., *J. Am. Chem. Soc.* **70**, 1847 (1948).
1813. Sarett, H. P. and Goldsmith, G. A., *J. Biol. Chem.* **182**, 679 (1950).
1814. Bonner, D. M., *Proc. Natl. Acad. Sci. U.S.* **34**, 5 (1948).
1815. Bonner, D. M., and Wasserman, E., *J. Biol. Chem.* **185**, 69 (1950).
1816. Mitchell, H. K., Nyc, J. F., and Owen, R. D., *J. Biol. Chem.* **175**, 433 (1948).
1817. Sarett, H. P., *J. Biol. Chem.* **182**, 691 (1950).
1818. Williams, R. C., "The United States Public Health Service, 1798–1950." Commissioned Officers Association of the U.S. Public Health Service, Bethesda, Maryland, 1951; Goldberger, J., and Tanner, W. F., *Public Health Rept.* **37**, 462 (1922).
1819. Heidelberger, C., Gullberg, M. E., Morgan, A. F., and Lepkovsky, S., *J. Biol. Chem.* **179**, 143 (1949).
1820. Heidelberger, C., Abraham, E. P., and Lepkovsky, S., *J. Biol. Chem.* **179**, 151 (1949).
1821. Hundley, J. M., and Bond, H. W., *Arch. Biochem.* **21**, 313 (1949).
1822. Schayer, R. W., *J. Biol. Chem.* **187**, 777 (1950).
1823. Henderson, L. M., and Ramasarma, G. B., *J. Biol. Chem.* **181**, 687 (1949).
1824. Yanofsky, C., and Bonner, D. M., *J. Nutr.* **44**, 603 (1951).
1825. Charconnet-Harding, F., Dalgliesh, C. E., and Neuberger, A., *Biochem. J.* **53**, 513 (1953).
1826. Mason, M., *J. Biol. Chem.* **201**, 513 (1953).
1827. Henderson, L. M., Koski, R. E., and D'Angeli, F., *J. Biol. Chem.* **215**, 369 (1955).
1828. DeCastro, F. T., Price, J. M., and Brown, R. R., *J. Am. Chem. Soc.* **78**, 2904 (1956).
1829. Saito, Y., Hayaishi, O., and Rothberg, S., *J. Biol. Chem.* **229**, 921 (1957).
1830. Stevens, C. O., and Henderson, L. M., *J. Biol. Chem.* **234**, 1191 (1959).
1831. Butenandt, A., Wiedel, W., and Schlossberger, H. G., *Z. Naturforsch.* **46**, 242 (1949).
1832. Sundaram, T. K., and Sarma, P. S., *Nature* **172**, 627 (1953).
1833. Makino, K., Takahashi, H., Satoh, K., and Inagami, K., *Nature* **173**, 586 (1954).
1834. Wiltshire, G. H., *Biochem. J.* **55**, 408 (1953).
1835. Dalgliesh, C. E., and Tekman, S., *Biochem. J.* **56**, 458 (1954).
1836. Brown, R. R., *J. Biol. Chem.* **227**, 649 (1957).
1837. Hellmann, H., and Wiss, O., *Helv. Physiol. Pharmacol. Acta* **10**, C16, C35 (1952).

1838. Wiss, O., and Hellmann, H., *Z. Naturforsch.* **8b**, 70 (1953).

1839. Yanofsky, C., and Bonner, D. M., *Proc. Natl. Acad. Sci. U.S.* **36**, 167 (1950).

1840. Umebachi, Y., and Takahashi, H., *J. Biochem. (Tokyo)* **43**, 73 (1956).

1841. Wiss, O., and Fuchs, H., *Helv. Chim. Acta* **32**, 2553 (1949).

1842. Wiss, O., and Hatz, F., *Helv. Chim. Acta* **32**, 532 (1949).

1843. Wiss, O., *Helv. Chim. Acta* **32**, 1694 (1949).

1844. Braunstein, A. E., Goryachenkova, E. V., and Paskhina, T. S., *Biokhimiya* **14**, 163 (1949).

1845. Kotake, Y., Chikano, M., and Ichihara, K., *Z. Physiol. Chem.* **143**, 218 (1925).

1846. Kotake, Y., *J. Chem. Soc. (Japan)* **60**, 632 (1939).

1847. Knox, W. E., *Biochem. J.* **53**, 379 (1953).

1848. Wiss, O., and Weber, F., *Z. Physiol. Chem.* **304**, 232 (1956).

1849. Jakoby, W. B., and Bonner, D. M., *J. Biol. Chem.* **205**, 709 (1953).

1850. Braunstein, A. E., and Shemyakin, M. M., *Biokhimiya* **18**, 393 (1953).

1851. Longenecker, J. B., and Snell, E. E., *J. Biol. Chem.* **213**, 229 (1955).

1852. Jakoby, W. B., and Bonner, D. M., *J. Biol. Chem.* **205**, 699 (1953).

1853. Hayaishi, O., *in* "Amino Acid Metabolism" (W. D. McElroy and B. Glass, eds.), p. 914. Johns Hopkins Press, Baltimore, Maryland, 1955.

1854. Jakoby, W. B., Ph.D. Dissertation, Yale Univ. (1954).

1855. Decker, R. H., Brown, R. R., and Price, J. M., *J. Biol. Chem.* **238**, 1049 (1963).

1856. Mitchell, H. K., and Nyc, J. F., *Proc. Natl. Acad. Sci. U.S.* **34**, 1 (1948).

1857. Mitchell, H. K., Nyc, J. F., and Owen, R. D., *J. Biol. Chem.* **175**, 433 (1948).

1858. Wiss, O., Viollier, G., and Müller, M., *Helv. Chim. Acta* **33**, 171 (1950).

1859. Henderson, L. M., Koski, R. E., and D'Angeli, F., *J. Biol. Chem.* **223**, 479 (1956).

1860. Henderson, L. M., *J. Biol. Chem.* **178**, 1005 (1949).

1861. Henderson, L. M., *J. Biol. Chem.* **181**, 677 (1949).

1862. Hankes, L. V., and Henderson, L. M., *J. Biol. Chem.* **225**, 349 (1957).

1863. Schayer, R. W., and Henderson, L. M., *J. Biol. Chem.* **195**, 657 (1952).

1864. Partridge, C. W. H., Bonner, D. M., and Yanofsky, C., *J. Biol. Chem.* **194**, 269, (1952).

1865. Bokman, A. H., and Schweigert, B. S., *J. Biol. Chem.* **186**, 153 (1950).

1866. Long, C. L., Hill, H. N., Weinstock, I. M., and Henderson. L. M., *J. Biol. Chem.* **211**, 405 (1954).

1867. Miyake, A., Bokman, A. H., and Schweigert, B. S., *J. Biol. Chem.* **211**, 391 (1954).

1868. Wiss, O., and Bettendorf, G., *Z. Physiol. Chem.* **306**, 145 (1957).

1869. Mehler, A. H., *J. Biol. Chem.* **218**, 241 (1956).

1870. Kalckar, H. M., Strominger, J. L., and Gewirtz, N. R., *Biol. Bull.* **105**, 391 (1953).

1871. Mehler, A. H., and May, E. L., *J. Biol. Chem.* **223**, 449 (1956).

1872. Mehler, A. H., McDaniel, E. G., and Hundley, J. M., *J. Biol. Chem.* **232**, 323 (1958).

1873. Mehler, A. H., McDaniel, E. G., and Hundley, J. M., *J. Biol. Chem.* **232**, 331 (1958).

1874. Suhadolnik, R. J., Stevens, C. O., Decker, R. H., Henderson, L. M., and Hankes, L. V., *J. Biol. Chem.* **228**, 973 (1957).

1875. Hayaishi, O., Rothberg, S., and Mehler, A. H., *Abstr. 130th Meeting Am. Chem. Soc., September*, 1956, 53C.

1876. Mason, H. S., *Adv. Enzymol.* **19**, 79 (1957).

1877. Moline, S. W., Walker, H. C., and Schweigert, B. S., *J. Biol. Chem.* **234**, 880 (1959).
1878. Stevens, C. O., and Henderson, L. M., *J. Biol. Chem.* **234**, 1188 (1959).
1879. Decker, R. H., Kang, H. H., Leach, F. R., and Henderson, L. M., *J. Biol. Chem.* **236**, 3076 (1961).
1880. Mitchell, R. A., Kang, H. H., and Henderson, L. M., *J. Biol. Chem.* **238**, 1151 (1963).
1881. Vescia, A., and di Prisco, G., *J. Biol. Chem.* **237**, 2318 (1962).
1882. Gholson, R. K., and Henderson, L. M., *Biochim. Biophys. Acta* **30**, 424 (1958).
1883. Gholson, R. K., Rao, D. R., Henderson, L. M., Hill, R. J., and Koeppe, R. E., *J. Biol. Chem.* **230**, 179 (1958).
1884. Henderson, L. M., and Hankes, L. V., *J. Biol. Chem.* **222**, 1069 (1956).
1885. Gholson, R. K., Henderson, L. M., Mourkides, G. A., Hill, R. J., and Koeppe, R. E., *J. Biol. Chem.* **234**, 96 (1959).
1886. Rothstein, M., and Greenberg, D. M., *Biochim. Biophys. Acta* **34**, 598 (1959).
1887. Gholson, R. K., Hankes, L. V., and Henderson, L. M., *J. Biol. Chem.* **235**, 132 (1960).
1888. Gholson, R. K., Nishizuka, Y., Ichiyama, A., Kawai, H., Nakamura, A., and Hayaishi, O., *J. Biol. Chem.* **237**, PC 2043 (1962).
1889. Nishizuka, Y., and Hayaishi, O., *J. Biol. Chem.* **238**, PC 483 (1963).
1890. Nishizuka, Y., and Hayaishi, O., *J. Biol. Chem.* **238**, 3369 (1963).
1891. Nakamura, S., Ikeda, M., Tsuji, H., Nishizuka, Y., and Hayaishi, O., *Biochem. Biophys. Res. Commun.* **13**, 285 (1963).
1892. Hankes, L. V., and Schmaeler, M. A., *Biochem. Biophys. Res Commun.* **2**, 468 (1960).
1893. Huff, J. W., and Perlzweig, W. A., *Science,* **97**, 538 (1943).
1894. Huff, J. W., and Perlzweig, W. A., *J. Biol. Chem.* **167**, 157 (1947).
1895. Perlzweig, W. A., Rosen F., and Pearson, P. B., *J. Nutrition* **40**, 453 (1950).
1896. Dann, W. J., and Huff, J. W., *J. Biol. Chem.* **168**, 121 (1947).
1897. Jones, K. M., and Elliott, W. H., *Biochim. Biophys. Acta* **14**, 586 (1954).
1898. Knox, W. E., and Grossman, W. I., *J. Biol. Chem.* **166**, 391 (1946).
1899. Hunter, S. F., and Handler, P., *Arch. Biochem. Biophys.* **35**, 377 (1952).
1900. Holman, W. I. M., and deLange, D. J., *Nature* **165**, 604 (1950).
1901. Walters, C. J., Brown, R. R., Kaihara, M., and Price, J. M., *J. Biol. Chem.* **217**, 489 (1955).
1902. Sarett, H. P., *J. Biol. Chem.* **193**, 627 (1951).
1903. Knox, W. E., and Grossman, W. I., *J. Biol. Chem.* **168**, 363 (1947).
1904. Lindenblad, G. E., Kaihara, M., and Price, J. M., *J. Biol. Chem.* **219**, 893 (1956).
1905. Wu Chang, M. L., and Johnson, B. C., *J. Biol. Chem.* **234**, 1817 (1959); **236**, 2096 (1961).
1906. Abelson, D., Boyle, A., and Seligson, H., *J. Biol. Chem.* **238**, 717 (1963).
1907. Joshi, J. G., and Handler, P., *J. Biol. Chem.* **235**, 2981 (1960).
1908. Böddeker, H., and Mishkin, A. R., *Anal. Chem.* **35**, 1662 (1963).
1909. Joshi, J. G., and Handler, P., *J. Biol. Chem.* **237**, 3185 (1962).
1910. Behrman, E. J., and Stanier, R. Y., *J. Biol. Chem.* **228**, 923 (1957).
1911. Yanofsky, C., *in* "Amino Acid Metabolism" (W. D. McElroy and B. Glass, eds.), p. 930. Johns Hopkins Press, Baltimore, Maryland, 1955.

1912. Yanofsky, C., *J. Bacteriol.* **68**, 577 (1954).

1913. Volcani, B. E., and Snell, E. E., *Proc. Soc. Exptl. Biol. Med.* **67**, 511 (1948).

1914. Stanier, R. Y., and Tsuchida, M., *J. Bacteriol.* **58**, 45 (1949).

1915. Henderson, L. M., Someroski, J. F., Rao, D. R., Wu, P.-H. L., Griffith, T., and Byerrum, R. U., *J. Biol. Chem.* **234**, 93 (1959).

1916. Ortega, M. V., and Brown, G. M., *J. Biol. Chem.* **235**, 2939 (1960).

1917. Christman, D. R., and Dawson, R. F., *Biochemistry* **2**, 182 (1963).

1918. Dawson, R. F., Christman, D. R., Anderson, R. C., Solt, M. L., D'Adamo, A. F., and Weiss, U., *J. Am. Chem. Soc.* **78**, 2645 (1956).

1919. Dawson, R. F., Christman, D. R., D'Adamo, A., Solt, M. L., and Wolf, A. P., *J. Am. Chem. Soc.* **82**, 2628 (1960).

1920. Waller, G. R., and Henderson, L. M., *J. Biol. Chem.* **236**, 1186 (1961).

1921. Hadwiger, L. A., Badiei, S. E., Waller, G. R., and Gholson, R. K., *Biochem. Biophys. Res. Commun.* **13**, 466 (1963).

1922. Brown, R. R., and Price, J. M., *J. Biol. Chem.* **219**, 985 (1956).

1923. DeCastro, F. T., Brown, R. R., and Price, J. M., *J. Biol. Chem.* **228**, 777 (1957).

1924. Langner, R. R., and Berg, C. P., *J. Biol. Chem.* **214**, 699 (1955).

1925. Mason, M., and Berg, C. P., *J. Biol. Chem.* **195**, 515 (1952).

1926. Dalgliesh, C. E., and Tekman, S., *Biochem. J.* **56**, 458 (1954).

1927. Price, J. M., and Brown, R. R., *J. Biol. Chem.* **222**, 835 (1956).

1928. Luckner, M., *Z. Allgem. Mikrobiol.* **3** (1), 93 (1963).

1929. Makino, K., and Arai, K., *Science* **121**, 143 (1955).

1929a. Weissbach, H., Smith, T. E., Daly, J. W., Witkop, B., and Udenfriend, S., *J. Biol. Chem.* **235**, 1160 (1960).

1929b. Kanaoka, Y., Weissbach, H., Smith, T. E., and Witkop, B., *J. Am. Chem. Soc.* **83**, 732 (1961).

1929c. Makino, K., Joh, Y., Hasegawa, F., Takahashi, H., *Biochim. Biophys. Acta* **86**, 191 (1964).

1930. Johnston, C. C., and Mason, M., *J. Biol. Chem.* **237**, 29 (1962).

1931. Kido, R., Tsuji, T., and Matsumura, Y., *Biochem. Biophys. Res. Commun.* **13**, 428 (1963).

1932. Price, J. M., and Dodge, L. W., *J. Biol. Chem.* **223**, 699 (1956).

1933. Murachi, T., Tsukada, K., and Hayaishi, O., *Biochemistry* **2**, 304 (1963).

1934. Kaihara, M., and Price, J. M., *J. Biol. Chem.* **237**, 1727 (1962).

1935. Kaihara, M., *J. Biol. Chem.* **235**, 136 (1960).

1936. Takahashi, H., and Price, J. M., *J. Biol. Chem.* **233**, 150 (1958).

1937. Takahashi, H., Kaihara, M., and Price, J. M., *J. Biol. Chem.* **223**, 705 (1956).

1938. Kaihara, M., and Price, J. M., *J. Biol. Chem.* **236**, 508 (1961).

1939. Hayaishi, O., Taniuchi, H., Tashiro, M., and Kuno, S., *J. Biol. Chem.* **236**, 2492 (1961).

1940. Horibata, K., Taniuchi, H., Tashiro, M., Kuno, S., and Hayaishi, O., *J. Biol. Chem.* **236**, 2991 (1961).

1941. Taniuchi, H., and Hayaishi, O., *J. Biol. Chem.* **238**, 283 (1963).

1942. Behrman, E. J., and Tanaka, T., *Biochem. Biophys. Res. Commun.* **1**, 257 (1959).

1943. Stanier, R. Y., *J. Bacteriol.* **54**, 339 (1947).

1944. Stanier, R. Y., and Tsuchida, M., *J. Bacteriol.* **58**, 45 (1949).

1945. Suda, M., Hayaishi, O., and Oda, Y., *J. Biochem.* **37**, 355 (1950).

References

1946. Hayaishi, O., and Hashimoto, K., *J. Biochem.* **37**, 371 (1950).
1947. Suda, M., Hashimoto, K., Natsuoka, H., and Kamahora, T., *J. Biochem.* **37**, 355 (1951).
1948. Stanier, R. Y., Hayaishi, O., and Tsuchida, M., *J. Bacteriol.* **62**, 355 (1951).
1949. Hayaishi, O., and Stanier, R. Y., *J. Bacteriol.* **62**, 367 (1951).
1950. Stanier, R. Y., and Hayaishi, O., *Science* **114**, 2961 (1951).
1951. Sistrom, W. R., and Stanier, R. Y., *J. Biol. Chem.* **210**, 821 (1954).
1952. Stanier, R. Y., and Ingraham, J. L., *J. Biol. Chem.* **210**, 799 (1954).
1953. MacDonald, D. L., Stanier, R. Y., and Ingraham, J. L., *J. Biol. Chem.* **210**, 809 (1954).
1954. Hayaishi, O., and Stanier, R. Y., *J. Bacteriol.* **62**, 691 (1951).
1955. Ichihara, A., Adachi, K., Hosokawa, K., and Takeda, Y., *J. Biol. Chem.* **237**, 2296 (1962).
1956. Nakagawa, H., Inoue, H., and Takeda, Y., *J. Biochem. (Tokyo)* **54**, 65 (1963).
1957. Hayaishi, O., Katagiri, M., and Rothberg, S., *J. Biol. Chem.* **229**, 905 (1957).
1958. Katagiri, M., and Hayaishi, O., *J. Biol. Chem.* **226**, 439 (1957).
1959. Werle, E., and Mennicken, G., *Biochem. Z.* **291**, 325 (1937).
1960. Udenfriend, S., Clark, C. T., and Titus, E., *J. Am. Chem. Soc.* **75**, 501 (1953).
1961. Clark, C. T., Weissbach, H., and Udenfriend, S., *J. Biol. Chem.* **210**, 139 (1954).
1962. Erspamer, V., *Experientia* **10**, 471 (1954).
1963. Rapport, M. M., Green, A. A., and Page, I. H., *J. Biol. Chem.* **174**, 735; **176**, 1237, 1243 (1948).
1964. Rapport, M. M., Green, A. A., and Page, I. H., *Science* **108**, 329 (1948).
1965. Page, I. H., *Physiol. Rev.* **34**, 563 (1954).
1966. Udenfriend, S., Titus, E., Weissbach, H., and Peterson, R. E., *J. Biol. Chem.* **219**, 335 (1956).
1967. Udenfriend, S., Weissbach, H., and Bogdanski, D. F., *J. Biol. Chem.* **224**, 803 (1957).
1968. Udenfriend, S., and Titus, E., *in* "Amino Acid Metabolism" (W. D. McElroy and B. Glass, eds.), p. 945. Johns Hopkins Press, Baltimore, Maryland, 1955.
1969. Mitoma, C., Weissbach, H., and Udenfriend, S., *Nature* **175**, 994 (1955).
1970. Beer, R. J. S., Jennings, B. E., and Robertson, A., *J. Chem. Soc.*, p. 2679 (1954).
1971. Freedland, R. A., Wadzinski, I. M., and Waisman, H. A., *Biochem. Biophys. Res. Commun.* **5**, 94 (1961); **6**, 227 (1961).
1972. Renson, J., Weissbach, H., and Udenfriend, S., *J. Biol. Chem.* **237**, 2261 (1962).
1973. Schindler, R., *Biochem. Pharmacol.* **1**, 323 (1959).
1974. Dalgliesh, C. E., and Dutton, R. W., *Biochem. J.* **65**, 21p (1957).
1975. Cooper, J. R., and Melcer, I., *J. Pharmacol. Exptl. Therap.* **132**, 265 (1961).
1976. Weber, L. J., and Horita, A., *Federation Proc.* **22**, 625 (1963).
1977. Cooper, J., *Ann. N. Y. Acad. Sci.* **92**, 208 (1961).
1978. Gal, E. M., Poczik, M., and Marshall, F. D., Jr., *Biochem. Biophys. Res. Commun.* **12**, 39 (1963).
1979. Chari-Bitron, A., *Biochem. Biophys. Res. Commun.* **12**, 310 (1963).
1980. Pare, C. M. B., Sandler, M., and Stacey, R. S., *Lancet* **ii**, 1099 (1958).
1981. Udenfriend, S., *Vitamins Hormones* **17**, 133 (1959).
1982. Buzard, J. A., and Nytch, P. D., *J. Biol. Chem.* **227**, 225; **229**, 409 (1957).

1983. Weissbach, H., Bogdanski, D. F., Redfield, B. G., and Udenfriend, S., *J. Biol. Chem.* **227**, 617 (1957).

1984. Oates, J. A., and Sjoerdsma, A., *Proc. Soc. Exptl. Biol. Med.* **108**, 264 (1961).

1985. Page, I. H., *Physiol. Rev.* **38**, 277 (1958).

1986. Lingjaerde, P., and Skaug, O. E., *J. Biol. Chem.* **226**, 33 (1957).

1987. Udenfriend, S., Clark, C. T., and Titus, E., *Federation Proc.* **12**, 282 (1953).

1988. Udenfriend, S., Titus, E., and Weissbach, H., *J. Biol. Chem.* **216**, 499 (1955).

1989. Armstrong, M. D., *Federation Proc.* **13**, 175 (1954).

1990. Schayer, R. W., Wu, K. Y. T., Smiley, R. L., and Kobayashi, Y., *J. Biol. Chem.* **210**, 259 (1954).

1991. Ewin, A. J., and Laidlaw, P. P., *Biochem. J.* **7**, 18 (1913).

1992. Anderson, J. A., Ziegler, M. R., and Doeden, D., *Science* **127**, 236 (1958).

1993. McIsaac, W. M., and Page, I. H., *J. Biol. Chem.* **234**, 858 (1959).

1994. Kveder, S., Iskric, S., and Keglevic, D., *Biochem. J.* **85**, 447 (1962).

1995. Lerner, A. B., Case, J. D., Heinzelman, R. V., *J. Am. Chem. Soc.* **81**, 6084 (1959).

1996. Axelrod, J., and Weissbach, H., *J. Biol. Chem.* **236**, 211 (1961).

1997. Kveder, S., and McIsaac, W. M., *J. Biol. Chem.* **236**, 3214 (1961).

1998. Jensen, H., and Chen, K. K., *J. Biol. Chem.* **116**, 87 (1936).

1999. Wieland, H., *Ann.* **513**, 1 (1934).

2000. Erspamer, V., *Rend. Sci. Farmitalia* **1** (1954).

2001. Stromberg, V. L., *J. Am. Chem. Soc.* **76**, 1707 (1954).

2002. Wieland, T., Motzel, W., and Merz, H., *Ann.* **581**, 10 (1953).

2003. Wieland, H., Hesse, G., and Mittasch, H., *Ber.* **64**, 2099 (1931).

2004. Wieland, H., Konz, W., and Mittasch, H., *Ann.* **513**, 1 (1934).

2005. Jensen, H., *J. Am. Chem. Soc.* **57**, 1765 (1935).

2006. Wieland, H., and Wieland, T., *Ann.* **528**, 234 (1937).

2006a. Märki, F., Robertson, A. V., and Witkop, B., *J. Am. Chem. Soc.* **83**, 3341 (1961).

2007. Kögl, F., Haagen-Smit, A. J., and Erxleben, H., *Z. Physiol. Chem.* **228**, 90, 104 (1934).

2008. Gordon, S. A., and Nieva, F. S., *Arch. Biochem.* **20**, 367 (1949).

2009. Thimann, K. V., *J. Biol. Chem.* **109**, 279 (1935).

2010. Gordon, S. A., and Nieva, F. S., *Arch. Biochem.* **20**, 356 (1949).

2011. Wildman, S. G., Ferri, M. G., and Bonner, J., *Arch. Biochem.* **13**, 131 (1947).

2012. Thimann, K. V., *Ann. Rev. Plant Physiol.* **14**, 1 (1963).

2013. White, E. P., *New Zealand J. Sci. Technol.* **B25**, 137 (1944).

2014. Stowe, B. B., and Thimann, K. V., *Nature* **172**, 764 (1953).

2015. Larsen, P., *Ann. Rev. Plant Physiol.* **2**, 169 (1951).

2016. Skoog, F., *J. Gen. Physiol.* **20**, 311 (1937).

2017. Kaper, J. M., and Veldstra, H., *Biochim. Biophys. Acta* **30**, 401 (1958).

2018. Ludwig, G. D., and Rusk, J. M., *Acta. Chem. Scand. Suppl.* 1, **17**, 325 (1963).

2019. Stowe, B. B., and Thimann, K. V., *Arch. Biochem. Biophys.* **51**, 499 (1954).

2020. Jones, E. R. H., Henbest, H. B., Smith, G. F., and Bentley, J. A., *Nature* **169**, 485 (1952).

2021. Gmelin, R., and Virtanen, A. I., *Ann. Acad. Sci. Fennicae Ser. A. II* **107** (1961); *Suomen Kemistilehti* **B34**, 15 (1961).

2022. Good, N. E., Andreae, W. A., and Van Ysselstein, M. W. H., *Plant Physiol.* **31**, 231 (1956).

2023. Tang, Y. W., and Bonner, J., *Arch. Biochem.* **13**, 11 (1947).
2024. Wagenknecht, A. C., and Burris, R. H., *Arch. Biochem.* **25**, 30 (1949).
2025. Galston, A. W., Bonner, J., and Baker, R. S., *Arch. Biochem. Biophys.* **42**, 456 (1953).
2026. Kefford, N. P., Kaur-Sawhney, R., and Galston, A. W., *Acta. Chem. Scand. Suppl.* **1**, **17**, 313 (1963).
2027. Hopkins, F. G., and Cole, S. W., *J. Physiol.* (*London*) **29**, 451 (1903).
2028. Happold, F. C., and Hoyle, L., *Biochem. J.* **29**, 1918 (1935).
2029. Happold, F. C., *Adv. Enzymol.* **10**, 51 (1950).
2030. Wood, W. A., Gunsalus, I. C., and Umbreit, W. W., *J. Biol. Chem.* **170**, 313 (1947).
2031. Dawes, E. A., and Happold, F. C., *Biochem. J.* **44**, 349 (1949).
2032. Metzler, D. E., Ikawa, M., and Snell, E. E., *J. Am. Chem. Soc.* **76**, 648 (1954).
2033. Newton, W. A., and Snell, E. E., *Proc. Natl. Acad. Sci. U.S.* **48**, 1431 (1962).
2033a. Newton, W. A., and Snell, E. E., *Proc. Natl. Acad. Sci. U.S.* **51**, 382 (1964).
2034. Hoppe-Seyler, G., *Z. Physiol. Chem.* **7**, 423 (1883).
2035. Neuberg, C., and Schwenck, E., *Biochem. Z.* **79**, 387 (1917).
2036. Dalgliesh, C. E., *J. Clin. Pathol.* **8**, 73 (1955).
2036a. Posner, H. S., Mitoma, C., and Udenfriend, S., *Arch. Biochem. Biophys.* **94**, 269 (1961).
2037. Sakamoto, Y., Uchida, M., and Ichihara, K., *Med. J. Osaka Univ.* **3**, 477 (1953).
2038. McMenamy, R. H., Lund, C. C., and Oncley, J. L., *J. Clin. Invest.* **36**, 1672 (1957).
2039. McMenamy, R. H., and Oncley, J. I., *J. Biol. Chem.* **233**, 1436 (1958).
2040. Armstrong, M. D., and Robinson, K. S., *Federation Proc.* **13**, 175 (1954).
2041. Baron, D. N., Dent, C. E., Harris, H., Hart, E. W., and Jepson, J. B., *Lancet* **ii**, 421 (1956).
2042. Weissbach, H., King, W., Sjoerdsma, A., and Udenfriend, S., *J. Biol. Chem.* **234**, 81 (1959).
2043. Hankes, L. V., Schmaeler, M. A., and Rai, K., *Proc. Soc. Exptl. Biol. Med.* **110**, 420 (1962).
2044. Winterstein, E., and Trier, G., "Die Alkaloide." Borntraeger, Berlin, 1910.
2045. Woodward, R. B., *Nature* **162**, 155 (1948).
2046. von Tamelen, E. E., *Experientia* **9**, 457 (1953).
2047. Brack, A., Hofmann, A., Kalberer, F., Knobel, H., and Rutschmann, J., *Arch. Pharm.* **294**, 230 (1961).
2048. O'Donovan, D., and Leete, E., *J. Am. Chem. Soc.* **85**, 461 (1963).
2049. Wenkert, E., *J. Am. Chem. Soc.* **84**, 98 (1962).
2050. Mudd, S. H., *Biochim. Biophys. Acta* **37**, 164 (1960).
2050a. Gower, B. G., and Leete, E., *J. Am. Chem. Soc.* **85**, 3683 (1963).
2051. Kikkawa, H., Ogita, Z., and Fujito, S., *Proc. Japan Acad.* **30**, 30 (1954); *Science* **121**, 43 (1955).
2052. Butenandt, A., Schiedt, U., and Biekert, E., *Ann.* **586**, 229 (1954).
2053. Butenandt, A., Schiedt, U., Biekert, E., and Kornmann, P., *Ann.* **586**, 217 (1954).
2054. Kikkawa, H., *Adv. Genet.* **5**, 107 (1953).
2055. Butenandt, A., Schiedt, U., and Biekert, E., *Ann.* **588**, 106 (1954).
2056. Kühn, A., *Naturwissenschaften* **43**, 25 (1956).

2057. Butenandt, A., Schiedt, U., Biekert, E., and Cromartie, R. J. T., *Ann.* **590**, 75 (1954).

2058. Butenandt, A., and Beckmann, R., *Z. Physiol. Chem.* **301**, 115 (1955).

2059. Butenandt, A., and Neubert, G., *Z. Physiol. Chem.* **301**, 109 (1955).

2060. Butenandt, A., Biekert, E., and Linzen, B., *Z. Physiol. Chem.* **312**, 227 (1958).

2061. Yoshi, S., and Brown, R. L., *Federation Proc.* **18**, 255 (1959).

2062. Butenandt, A., Biekert, E., and Linzen, B., *Z. Physiol. Chem.* **305**, 284 (1956).

2063. Davis, B. D., *J. Biol. Chem.* **191**, 315 (1951).

2064. Davis, B. D., *Nature* **166**, 1120 (1950).

2065. Davis, B. D., *J. Bacteriol.* **64**, 729 (1952).

2066. Davis, B. D., *Harvey Lectures Ser.* **50**, 230 (1956).

2067. Davis, B. D., *Bull. Soc. Chim. Biol.* **36**, 947 (1954).

2068. Davis, B. D., *Proc. Natl. Acad. Sci. U. S.* **39**, 363 (1953).

2069. Davis, B. D., *Experientia* **6**, 41 (1950).

2070. Tatum, E. L., Gross, S. R., Ehrensvärd, G., and Garnjobst, L., *Proc. Natl. Acad. Sci. U.S.* **40**, 271 (1954).

2071. Davis, B. D., *in* "Amino Acid Metabolism" (W. D. McElroy and B. Glass, eds.), p. 779. Johns Hopkins Press, Baltimore, Maryland, 1955.

2072. Gilvarg, C., *in* "Amino Acid Metabolism" (W. D. McElroy and B. Glass, eds.), p. 812. Johns Hopkins Press, Baltimore, Maryland, 1955.

2073. Srinivasan, P. R., Shigeura, H. T., Sprecher, M., Sprinson, D. B., and Davis, B. D., *J. Biol. Chem.* **220**, 477 (1956).

2074. Salamon, I. I., and Davis, B. D., *J. Am. Chem. Soc.* **75**, 5567 (1953).

2075. Davis, B. D., and Weiss, U., *Arch. Exptl. Pathol. Pharmakol.* **220**, 1 (1953).

2076. Weiss, U., Davis, B. D., and Mingioli, E. S., *J. Am. Chem. Soc.* **75**, 5572 (1953).

2077. Gordon, M., Haskins, F. A., and Mitchell, H. K., *Proc. Natl. Acad. Sci. U.S.* **36**, 427 (1950).

2078. Mitsuhashi, S., and Davis, B. D., *Biochim. Biophys. Acta* **15**, 54, 268 (1954).

2079. Carr, J. G., Pollard, A., Whiting, G. C., and Williams, A. H., *Biochem. J.* **66**, 283 (1957).

2080. Weinstein, L. H., Porter, C.A ., and Laurencot, H. J., Jr., *Nature* **183**, 326 (1959).

2081. Yaniv, H., and Gilvarg, C., *J. Biol. Chem.* **213**, 787 (1955).

2082. Baddiley, J., Ehrensvärd, G., Klein, E., Reio, L., and Saluste, E., *J. Biol. Chem.* **183**, 777 (1950).

2083. Ehrensvärd, G., *Congr. Intern. Biochim.*, 2, Paris, 1952 p. 72 (1952). Masson, Paris.

2084. Gilvarg, C., and Bloch, K., *J. Biol. Chem.* **193**, 339 (1951); **199**, 689 (1952).

2085. Thomas, R. C., Cheldelin, V. H., Christensen, B. E., and Wang, C. H., *J. Am. Chem. Soc.* **75**, 5554 (1953).

2086. Rafelson, M. E., Jr., Ehrensvärd, G., and Reio, L., *Exptl. Cell Res. Suppl.* **3**, 281 (1955).

2087. Srinivasan, P. R., Katagiri, M., and Sprinson, D. B., *J. Am. Chem. Soc.* **77**, 4943 (1955).

2088. Kalan, E. B., Davis, B. D., Srinivasan, P. R., and Sprinson, D. B., *J. Biol. Chem.* **223**, 907 (1956).

2089. Srinivasan, P. R., Sprinson, D. B., Kalan, E. B., and Davis, B. D., *J. Biol. Chem.* **223**, 913 (1956).

2090. Srinivasan, P. R., Katagiri, M., and Sprinson, D. B., *J. Biol.Chem.* **234**, 713 (1959).
2091. Srinivasan, P. R., and Sprinson, D. B., *J. Biol. Chem.* **234**, 716 (1959).
2092. Weissbach, A., and Hurwitz, J., *J. Biol. Chem.* **234**, 705 (1959).
2093. Hurwitz, J., and Weissbach, A., *J. Biol. Chem.* **234**, 710 (1959).
2094. Sprinson, D. B., Rothschild, J., and Sprecher, M., *J. Biol.Chem.* **238**, 3170 (1963).
2095. Srinivasan, P. R., Rothschild, J., and Sprinson, D. B., *J. Biol. Chem.* **238**, 3176 (1963).
2096. Davis, B. D., and Mingioli, E. S., *J. Bacteriol.* **66**, 129 (1953).
2097. Weiss, U., and Mingioli, E. S., *J. Am. Chem. Soc.* **78**, 2894 (1956).
2098. Levin, J. G., and Sprinson, D. B., *Biochem. Biophys. Res. Commun.* **3**, 157 (1960); *J. Biol. Chem.* **239**, 1142 (1964).
2099. Davis, B. D., *Science* **118**, 251 (1953).
2100. Katagiri, M., and Sato, R., *Science* **118**, 250 (1953).
2101. Katagiri, M., *J. Biochem.* **40**, 629 (1953).
2102. Simmonds, S., *J. Biol. Chem.* **185**, 755 (1950).
2103. Plieninger, H., *Angew. Chem.* **1**, 367 (1962).
2104. Weiss, U., Gilvarg, C., Mingioli, E. S., and Davis, B. D., *Science* **119**, 774 (1954).
2105. Gibson, M. I., and Gibson, F., *Biochim. Biophys. Acta* **65**, 160 (1962).
2106. Gibson, M. I., Gibson, F., Doy, C. H., and Morgan, P., *Nature* **195**, 1173 (1962).
2106a. Gibson, F., *Biochem. J.* **90**, 256 (1964).
2106b. Gibson, F., Gibson, M., and Cox, G. B., *Biochim. Biophys. Acta* **82**, 637 (1964).
2107. Schwinck, I., and Adams, E., *Biochim. Biophys. Acta* **36**, 102–117 (1959).
2108. Metzenberg, R. L., and Mitchell, H. K., *Biochem. J.* **68**, 168 (1958).
2109. Gross, S. R., *J. Biol. Chem.* **233**, 1146 (1958).
2110. Smith, L. C., Ravel, J. M., Lax, S. R., and Shive, W., *J. Biol. Chem.* **237**, 3566 (1962).
2111. Brown, K. D., and Doy, C. H., *Biochim. Biophys. Acta* **77**, 170 (1963).
2112. Moyed, H. S., *J. Biol. Chem.* **235**, 1098 (1960).
2113. Beerstecher, E., Jr., and Shive, W., *J. Biol. Chem.* **164**, 53 (1946); **167**, 49, 527 (1947).
2114. Bergmann, E. D., Sicher, S., and Volcani, B. E., *Biochem. J.* **54**, 1 (1953).
2115. Simmonds, S., Dowling, M. T., and Stone, D., *J. Biol. Chem.* **208**, 701 (1954).
2116. Miller, D. A., and Simmonds, S., *Science* **126**, 445 (1957).
2117. Haddox, C. H., *Proc. Natl. Acad. Sci. U.S.* **38**, 482 (1952).
2118. Mitoma, C., and Leeper, L. C., *Federation Proc.* **13**, 266 (1954).
2119. Beer, C. T., Dickens, F., and Pearson, J., *Biochem. J.* **48**, 222 (1951).
2120. Neubauer, O., *Deut. Arch. Klin. Med.* **95**, 211 (1909).
2121. Embden, G., and Baldes, K., *Biochem. Z.* **55**, 301 (1913).
2122. Embden, G., Salomon, H., and Schmidt, F., *Beitr. Chem. Physiol. Pathol.* **8**, 129 (1906).
2123. Falta, W., and Langstein, L., *Z. Physiol. Chem.* **37**, 513 (1903).
2124. Abbot, L. D., Jr., and Salmon, C. L., Jr., *J. Biol. Chem.* **150**, 339 (1943).
2125. Butts, J. S., Dunn, M. S., and Hallman, L. F., *J. Biol. Chem.* **123**, 711 (1938).
2126. Fölling, A., and Closs, K., *Z. Physiol. Chem.* **227**, 169 (1934).
2127. Sealock, R. R., and Silberstein, H. E., *J. Biol. Chem.* **135**, 251 (1940).
2128. Sealock, R. R., Perkinson, J. D., and Basinski, D. H., *J. Biol. Chem.* **140**, 153 (1941).
2129. Medes, G., *Biochem. J.* **26**, 917 (1932).

2130. Levine, S. Z., Marples, E., and Gordon, H. H., *J. Clin. Invest.* **20**, 199, 209 (1941).

2131. Levine, S. Z., Dann, M., and Marples, E., *J. Clin. Invest.* **22**, 551 (1943).

2132. Moss, A. R., and Schoenheimer, R., *J. Biol. Chem.* **135**, 415 (1940).

2133. Grau, C. R., and Steele, R., *J. Nutr.* **53**, 59 (1954).

2134. Bernheim, M. L. C., and Bernheim, F., *J. Biol. Chem.* **152**, 481 (1944).

2135. Udenfriend, S., and Cooper, J. R., *J. Biol. Chem.* **194**, 503 (1952).

2136. Mitoma, C., Posner, H. S., Reitz, H. C., and Udenfriend, S., *Arch. Biochem. Biophys.* **61**, 431 (1956).

2137. Mitoma, C., *Arch. Biochem. Biophys.* **60**, 476 (1956).

2138. Kaufman, S., *Biochim. Biophys. Acta* **23**, 445 (1957); *J. Biol. Chem.* **226**, 511 (1957); **230**, 931 (1958); **234**, 2677 (1959).

2139. Kaufman, S., *J. Biol. Chem.* **236**, 804 (1961).

2140. Kaufman, S., *J. Biol. Chem.* **237**, PC 2712 (1962).

2141. Kaufman, S., *Proc. Natl. Acad. Sci. U.S.* **50**, 1085 (1963).

2141a. Kaufman, S., *J. Biol. Chem.* **239**, 332 (1964).

2142. Nawa, S., *Bull. Chem. Soc. Japan* **33**, 1555 (1960).

2143. Kaufman, S., and Levenberg, B., *J. Biol. Chem.* **234**, 2683 (1959).

2143a. Kaufman, S., Bridges, W. F., Eisenberg, F., and Friedman, S., *Biochem. Biophys. Res. Commun.* **9**, 497 (1962).

2143b. Takashima, K., Fumimoto, D., and Tamiya, N., *J. Biochem. (Tokyo)* **55**, 122 (1964).

2144. Kaufman, S., *in* "The Enzymes" (P. D. Boyer, H. Lardy, and K. Myrbäck, eds.), Vol. 8, p. 373. Academic Press, New York, 1963.

2145. Freedland, R. A., *Biochim. Biophys. Acta* **73**, 71 (1963).

2146. Freedland, R. A., Krakowski, M. C., and Waisman, H. A., *Am. J. Physiol.* **202**, 145 (1962).

2147. Fellman, J. H., and Devlin, M. K., *Biochim. Biophys. Acta* **28**, 328 (1958).

2148. Fukuda, T., *Nature* **177**, 429 (1956).

2149. Guroff, G., and Ito, T., *Biochim. Biophys. Acta* **77**, 159 (1963).

2150. Schepartz, B., and Gurin, S., *J. Biol. Chem.* **180**, 663 (1949).

2151. Winnick, T., Friedberg, F., and Greenberg, D. M., *J. Biol. Chem.* **173**, 189 (1948).

2152. Weinhouse, S., and Millington, R. H., *J. Biol. Chem.* **175**, 995 (1948).

2153. Weinhouse, S., and Millington, R. H., *J. Biol. Chem.* **181**, 645 (1949).

2154. Dische, R., and Rittenberg, D., *J. Biol. Chem.* **211**, 199 (1954).

2155. Lerner, A. B., *J. Biol. Chem.* **181**, 281 (1949).

2156. Meyer, E., *Deut. Arch. Klin. Med.* **70**, 1443 (1901).

2157. Friedmann, E., *Beitr. Chem. Physiol. Pathol.* **11**, 304 (1908).

2158. La Du, B. N., Jr., and Greenberg, D. M., *J. Biol. Chem.* **190**, 245 (1951).

2159. LeMay-Knox, M., and Knox, W. E., *Biochem. J.* **49**, 686 (1951).

2160. Schepartz, B., *J. Biol. Chem.* **193**, 293 (1951).

2161. Canellakis, Z. N., and Cohen, P. P., *J. Biol. Chem.* **222**, 63 (1956).

2162. Kenney, F. T., *J. Biol. Chem.* **234**, 2707 (1959).

2163. Lin, E. C. C., Civen, M., and Knox, W. E., *J. Biol. Chem.* **233**, 1183 (1958).

2164. Lin, E. C. C., and Knox, W. E., *J. Biol. Chem.* **233**, 1186 (1958).

2165. Neuberger, A., Rimington, C., and Wilson, J. M. G., *Biochem. J.* **41**, 438 (1947).

2166. Nishimura, N., Shibata, Y., Yasui, M., and Okamoto, H., *Proc. Japan Acad.* **32**, (9) (1956).

2167. Nishimura, N., Yasui, M., Okamoto, H., Kanazawa, M., Kotake, Y., and Shibata, Y., *A.M.A. Arch. Dermatol.* **77**, 255 (1958).
2168. Tye, M. J., Masters, S., Appel, B., White, H., Tanaka, T., Knox, W. E., Cullen, A., and Rosen, B., *A.M.A. Arch. Dermatol.* **81**, 447 (1960).
2169. Neuberger, A., *Ann. Rev. Biochem.* **18**, 243 (1949).
2170. Witkop, B., and Goodwin, S., *Experientia* **8**, 377 (1952).
2171. Williams, J. N., Jr., and Sreenivasan, A., *J. Biol. Chem.* **203**, 109 (1953).
2172. Williams, J. N., Jr., and Sreenivasan, A., *J. Biol. Chem.* **203**, 613 (1953).
2173. Williams, J. N., Jr., and Sreenivasan, A., *J. Biol. Chem.* **203**, 605 (1953).
2174. Uchida, M., Suzuki, S., and Ichihara, K., *J. Biochem. (Tokyo)* **41**, 41 (1954).
2175. La Du, B. N., Jr., and Greenberg, D. M., *Science* **117**, 111 (1953).
2176. La Du, B. N., Jr., and Zannoni, V. G., *J. Biol. Chem.* **217**, 777 (1955).
2177. Sealock, R. R., and Goodland, R. L., *Science* **114**, 645 (1951).
2178. Udenfriend, S., Clark, C. T., Axelrod, J., and Brodie, B. B., *J. Biol. Chem.* **208**, 731 (1954).
2179. Brodie, B. B., Axelrod, J., Shore, P. A., and Udenfriend, S., *J. Biol. Chem.* **208**, 741 (1954).
2180. Green, J. H., Ralph, B. J., and Schofield, P. J., *Nature* **195**, 1309 (1962).
2181. Gerthsen, T., *Biochem. Z.* **336**, 251 (1962).
2182. Morris, J. E., Harpur, E. R., and Goldbloom, A., *J. Clin. Invest.* **29**, 225 (1950).
2183. Woodruff, C. W., Cherrington, M. E., Stockell, A. K., and Darby, W. J., *J. Biol. Chem.* **178**, 861 (1949).
2184. Rodney, G., Swendseid, M. E., and Swanson, A. L., *J. Biol. Chem.* **168**, 395 (1947).
2185. Rodney, G., Swendseid, M. E., and Swanson, A. L., *J. Biol. Chem.* **179**, 19 (1949).
2186. Salmon, R. J., and May, C. D., *J. Lab. Clin. Med.* **36**, 591 (1950).
2187. Salmon, R. J., and May, C. D., *Arch. Biochem. Biophys.* **32**, 220 (1951).
2188. LaDu, B. N., and Zannoni, V. G., *J. Biol. Chem.* **219**, 273 (1956).
2189. Hager, S. E., Gregerman, R. I., and Knox, W. E., *J. Biol. Chem.* **225**, 935 (1957).
2190. Zannoni, V. G., and LaDu, B. N., *J. Biol. Chem.* **234**, 2925 (1959).
2191. Zannoni, V. G., *J. Biol. Chem.* **237**, 1172 (1962).
2192. Knox, W. E., and Goswami, M. N. D., *J. Biol. Chem.* **235**, 2662 (1960).
2193. Zannoni, V. G., and LaDu, B. N., *J. Biol. Chem.* **235**, 2667 (1960).
2194. Zannoni, V. G., and LaDu, B. N., *J. Biol. Chem.* **235**, 165 (1960).
2195. Zannoni, V. G., Jacoby, G. A., Malawista, S. E., and La Du, B. N., *J. Biol. Chem.* **237**, 3506 (1962).
2196. Ravdin, R. G., and Crandall, D. I., *J. Biol. Chem.* **189**, 137 (1951).
2197. Suda, M., and Takeda, Y., *Med. J. Osaka Univ.* **2**, 37, 41 (1950).
2198. Suda, M., Takeda, Y., Sujishi, K., and Tanaka, T., *J. Biochem. (Tokyo)* **38**, 297 (1951).
2199. Crandall, D. I., and Halikis, D. N., *J. Biol. Chem.* **208**, 629 (1954).
2200. Crandall, D. I., *J. Biol. Chem.* **212**, 565 (1955).
2201. Schepartz, B., *J. Biol. Chem.* **205**, 185 (1953).
2202. Knox, W. E., and Edwards, S. W., *J. Biol. Chem.* **216**, 479 (1955).
2203. Tokuyama, K., *J. Biochem. (Tokyo)* **46**, 1379, 1453, 1559 (1959).
2204. Crandall, D. I., Krueger, R. C., Anan, F., Yasunobu, K., and Mason, H. S., *J. Biol. Chem.* **235**, 3011 (1960).

2205. LaDu, B. N., and Zannoni, V. G., *Biochim. Biophys. Acta* **67**, 281 (1963).

2206. Seegmiller, J. E., Zannoni, V. G., Laster, L., and La Du, B. N., *J. Biol. Chem.* **236**, 774 (1961).

2207. Knox, W. E., and Edwards, S. W., *J. Biol. Chem.* **216**, 489 (1955).

2208. Edwards, S. W., and Knox, W. E., *J. Biol. Chem.* **220**, 79 (1956).

2209. Meister, A., and Greenstein, J. P., *J. Biol. Chem.* **175**, 573 (1948).

2210. Witter, R. F., and Stotz, E., *J. Biol. Chem.* **176**, 501 (1948).

2211. Meister, A., *J. Biol. Chem.* **178**, 577 (1949).

2211a. Kanda, M., Watanabe, H., Nakata, Y., Higashi, T., and Sakamoto, Y., *J. Biochem. (Tokyo)* **55**, 65 (1964).

2212. Lack, L., *Biochim. Biophys. Acta* **34**, 117 (1959).

2213. Tanaka, H., Sugiyama, S., and Arima, K., *Bull. Agr. Chem. Soc. Japan* **21**, 67 (1957).

2214. Sugiyama, K., Yano, K., Tanaka, H., Komagata, K., and Arima, K., *J. Gen. Appl. Microbiol. (Tokyo)* **4**, 223 (1958).

2215. Lack, L., *J. Biol. Chem.* **236**, 2835 (1961).

2216. Knox, W. E., and Pitt, B. M., *J. Biol. Chem.* **225**, 675 (1957).

2217. Woolf, L. I., *Biochem. J.* **49**, ix (1951).

2218. Stein, W. H., Paladini, A. C., Hirs, C. H. W., and Moore, S., *J. Am. Chem. Soc.* **76**, 2848 (1954).

2219. Thierfelder, H., and Sherwin, C. P., *Ber.* **47**, 2630 (1914).

2220. Ambrose, A. M., Power, F. W., and Sherwin, C. P., *J. Biol. Chem.* **101**, 669 (1933).

2221. Sherwin, C. P., *J. Biol. Chem.* **31**, 307 (1917).

2222. Sherwin, C. P., Wolf, M., and Wolf, W., *J. Biol. Chem.* **37**, 113 (1919).

2223. Shiple, G. J., and Sherwin, C. P., *J. Am. Chem. Soc.* **44**, 618 (1922).

2224. Shiple, G. J., and Sherwin, C. P., *J. Am. Chem. Soc.* **53**, 463 (1922).

2225. Power, F. W., *Proc. Soc. Exptl. Biol. Med.* **33**, 598 (1935).

2226. Moldave, K., and Meister, A., *J. Biol. Chem.* **229**, 463 (1957).

2227. Schreier, K., Altman, K. I., and Hempelmann, L. H., *Proc. Soc. Exptl. Biol. Med.* **87**, 61 (1954).

2228. Armstrong, M. D., Chao, F.-C., Parker, V. J., and Wall, P. E., *Proc. Soc. Exptl. Biol. Med.* **90**, 675 (1955).

2229. Bruns, F. H., Haberland, G. L., and Altman, K. I., *Biochem. Z.* **331**, 446 (1959).

2230. Bernhard, K., Vuilleumier, J. P., and Brubacher, G., *Helv. Chim. Acta* **38**, 1438 (1955).

2231. Grümer, H. D., *Nature* **189**, 63 (1961).

2232. Pitt, B. M., *Nature* **196**, 272 (1962).

2232a. Taniguchi, K., and Armstrong, M. D., *J. Biol. Chem.* **238**, 4091 (1963).

2233. Seidenberg, M., Martinez, R. J., Guthrie, R., Minnemeyer, H., and Tieckelmann, H., *Arch. Biochem. Biophys.* **97**, 470 (1962).

2234. Gurin, S., and Delluva, A. M., *J. Biol. Chem.* **170**, 545 (1947).

2235. Udenfriend, S., Cooper, J. R., Clarke, C. T., and Baer, J. E., *Science* **117**, 663 (1953).

2236. Udenfriend, S., and Wyngaarden, J. B., *Biochim. Biophys. Acta* **20**, 48 (1956).

2237. Leeper, L. C., and Udenfriend, S., *Federation Proc.* **15**, 298 (1956).

2238. Goodall, McC., and Kirshner, N., *J. Biol. Chem.* **226**, 213 (1957).

2239. Kirshner, N., and Goodall, McC., *Biochim. Biophys. Acta* **24**, 658 (1957).

2240. Hartman, W. J., Pogrund, R. S., Drell, W., and Clark, W. G., *J. Am. Chem. Soc.* **77**, 816 (1955).
2241. Kirshner, N., *J. Biol. Chem.* **226**, 821 (1957).
2241a. Nagatsu, T., Levitt, M., and Udenfriend, S., *Biochem. Biophys. Res. Commun.* **14**, 543 (1964).
2242. Hagen, P., *J. Pharmacol. Exptl. Therap.* **116**, 26 (1956).
2243. Neri, R., Hayano, M., Stone, D., Dorfman, R. I., and Elmadjian, F., *Arch. Biochem. Biophys.* **60**, 297 (1956).
2244. Levin, E. Y., Levenberg, B., and Kaufman, S., *J. Biol. Chem.* **235**, 2080 (1960).
2245. Levin, E. Y., and Kaufman, S., *J. Biol. Chem.* **236**, 2043 (1961).
2246. Goldstein, M., McKereghan, M. R., and Lauber, E., *Biochim. Biophys. Acta* **77**, 161 (1963).
2247. Senoh, S., Creveling, C. R., Udenfriend, S., and Witkop, B., *J. Am. Chem. Soc.* **81**, 6236 (1959).
2248. Smith, W. J., and Kirshner, N., *J. Biol. Chem.* **237**, 1890 (1962).
2249. Goldstein, M., and Contrera, J. F., *J. Biol. Chem.* **237**, 1898 (1962).
2250. Creveling, C. R., Daly, J. W., Witkop, B., and Udenfriend, S., *Biochim. Biophys. Acta* **64**, 125 (1962).
2251. Waalkes, T. P., Sjoerdsma, A., Creveling, C. R., Weissbach, H., and Udenfriend, S., *Science* **127**, 648 (1958).
2252. Smith, W. J., and Kirshner, N., *J. Biol. Chem.* **235**, 3589 (1960).
2253. Axelrod, J., *Physiol. Rev.* **39**, 751 (1959).
2254. Daly, J. W., and Witkop, B., *Angew. Chem.* **2**, 421 (1963).
2255. Green, D. E., and Richter, D. E., *Biochem. J.* **31**, 596 (1937).
2256. Mazur, A., Green, S., and Shorr, E., *J. Biol. Chem.* **220**, 227 (1956).
2257. Shaw, K. N. F., McMillan, A., and Armstrong, M. D., *J. Biol. Chem.* **226**, 255 (1957).
2258. Williams, C. M., Babuscio, A. A., and Watson, R., *Am. J. Physiol.* **199**, 722 (1960).
2259. Goldstein, M., Friedhoff, A. J., and Simmons, C., *Biochim. Biophys. Acta* **33**, 572 (1959).
2260. Goldstein, M., Friedhoff, A. J., Pomerantz, S., and Contrera, J. F., *J. Biol. Chem.* **236**, 1816 (1961).
2261. Senoh, S., Creveling, C. R., Udenfriend, S., and Witkop, B., *J. Am. Chem. Soc.* **81**, 1768 (1959).
2262. Daly, J. W., Horner, L., and Witkop, B., *J. Am. Chem. Soc.* **83**, 4787 (1961).
2263. Friedhoff, A. J., and Van Winkle, E., *Nature* **199**, 1271 (1963).
2264. Märki, F., Axelrod, J., and Witkop, B., *Biochim. Biophys. Acta* **58**, 367 (1962).
2265. Bridges, W. F., and Kaufman, S., *J. Biol. Chem.* **237**, 526 (1963).
2266. Armstrong, M. D., McMillan, A., and Shaw, K. N. F., *Biochim. Biophys. Acta* **25**, 422 (1957).
2267. Goodall, M., Kirschner, M., and Rosen, L., *J. Clin. Invest.* **38**, 707 (1959).
2268. Axelrod, J., Kopin, I. J., and Mann, J. D., *Biochim. Biophys. Acta* **36**, 576 (1959).
2269. Smith, A. A., and Wortis, S. B., *Biochim. Biophys. Acta* **60**, 420 (1962).
2270. Weissbach, H., Redfield, B. G., and Axelrod, J., *Biochim. Biophys. Acta* **54**, 190 (1961).
2270a. Senoh, S., Creveling, C. R., Udenfriend, S., and Witkop, B., *J. Am. Chem. Soc.* **81**, 6236 (1959).

2271. Rosen, L., and Goodall, M., *Proc. Soc. Exptl. Biol. Med.* **110**, 767 (1962).

2272. Axelrod, J., Senoh, S., and Witkop, B., *J. Biol. Chem.* **233**, 697 (1958).

2273. Axelrod, J., and Tomchick, R., *J. Biol. Chem.* **233**, 702 (1958).

2274. Kopin, I. J., *Methods Biochem. Anal.* **11**, 247 (1963).

2275. Erspaner, V., *Nature* **169**, 375 (1952).

2276. Kakimoto, Y., and Armstrong, M. D., *J. Biol. Chem.* **237**, 422 (1962).

2277. Pisano, J. J., Oates, J. A., Jr., Karmen, A., Sjoerdsma, A., and Udenfriend, S., *J. Biol. Chem.* **236**, 898 (1961).

2278. Smith, A., Fabrykant, M., Gitlow, S., and Wortis, S. B., *Nature* **193**, 577 (1962).

2279. Smith, A. A., *Biochim. Biophys. Acta* **69**, 203 (1963).

2280. Armstrong, M. D., Shaw, K. N. F., and Wall, P. E., *J. Biol. Chem.* **218**, 293 (1956).

2281. Goldstein, M., and Musacchio, J. M., *Biochim. Biophys. Acta* **58**, 607 (1962).

2282. Karlson, P., *Angew. Chem. Intern. Ed. Engl.* **2**, 175 (1963).

2283. Karlson, P., and Liebau, H., *Z. Physiol. Chem.* **326**, 135 (1961).

2284. Taurog, A., Potter, G. D., and Chaikoff, I. L., *J. Biol. Chem.* **213**, 119 (1955).

2285. Tong, W., Taurog, A., and Chaikoff, I. L., *J. Biol. Chem.* **227**, 773 (1957).

2286. Fawcett, D. N., and Kirkwood, S., *J. Biol. Chem.* **205**, 795 (1953).

2287. Fawcett, D. M., and Kirkwood, S., *J. Biol. Chem.* **209**, 249 (1954).

2288. Serif, G. S., and Kirkwood, S., *J. Biol. Chem.* **233**, 109 (1958).

2289. Cunningham, B. A., and Kirkwood, S., *J. Biol. Chem.* **236**, 485 (1961).

2290. Taurog, A., Potter, G. D., Tong, W., and Chaikoff, I. L., *Endocrinology* **58**, 132 (1956).

2291. Potter, G. D., Tong, W., and Chaikoff, I. L., *J. Biol. Chem.* **234**, 350 (1959).

2292. Alexander, N. M., *J. Biol. Chem.* **234**, 1530 (1959).

2293. Klebanoff, S. J., Yip, C., and Kessler, D., *Biochim. Biophys. Acta* **58**, 563 (1962).

2294. deGroot, L. J., and Davis, A. M., *Endocrinology* **70**, 492 (1962).

2295. Alexander, N. M., and Corcoran, B. J., *J. Biol. Chem.* **237**, 243 (1962).

2296. Roche, J., and Michel, R., *Physiol. Rev.* **35**, 583 (1955).

2297. Gross, J., and Pitt-Rivers, R., *Lancet* **ii**, 766 (1951).

2298. Gross, J., and LeBlond, C. P., *Proc. Soc. Exptl. Biol. Med.* **76**, 686 (1951).

2299. Albright, E. C., Larson, F. C., and Tust, R. H., *Proc. Soc. Exptl. Biol. Med.* **86**, 137 (1954).

2300. Hogness, J. R., Berg, M., Van Arsdel, P. P., Jr., and Williams, R. H., *Proc. Soc. Exptl. Med.* **90**, 93 (1955).

2301. Pitt-Rivers, R., Stanbury, J. B., and Rapp, B., *J. Clin. Endocrinol. Metab.* **15**, 616 (1955).

2302. Johnson, T. B., and Tewkesbury, L. B., Jr., *Proc. Natl. Acad. Sci. U.S.* **28** 73 (1943).

2303. Harington, C. R., *J. Chem. Soc.*, p. 193 (1944).

2304. Pitt-Rivers, R., *Physiol. Rev.* **30**, 194 (1950); *Biochem. Soc. Symp. (Cambridge, Engl.)* **5**, 55 (1950).

2305. Matsuura, T., and Nishinaga, A., *J. Org. Chem.* **27**, 3072 (1962).

2306. Matsuura, T., and Cahnmann, H. J., *J. Am. Chem. Soc.* **82**, 2055 (1960).

2307. Matsuura, T., and Cahnmann, H. J., *J. Am. Chem. Soc.* **81**, 871 (1959).

2308. Cahnmann, H. J., and Matsuura, T., *J. Am. Chem. Soc.* **82**, 2050 (1960).

2309. Shiba, T., and Cahnmann, H. J., *Biochim. Biophys. Acta* **58**, 609 (1962).

2310. Meltzer, R. I., and Stanaback, R. J., *J. Org. Chem.* **26**, 1977 (1961).

2311. Yip,C., and Klebanoff, S. J., *Biochim. Biophys. Acta* **74**, 747 (1963); **82**, 276 (1964).
2311a. Toi, K., Salvatore, G., and Cahnmann, H. J., *Biochim. Biophys. Acta* **78**, 805 (1963).
2311b. Maloof, F., Sato, G., and Soodak, M., *Medicine* **43**, 375 (1964).
2312. Fawcett, D. M., and Kirkwood, S., *J. Biol. Chem.* **209**, 249 (1954).
2313. Stanbury, J. B., *J. Biol. Chem.* **228**, 801 (1957).
2314. Stanbury, J. B., and Morris, M. L., *J. Biol. Chem.* **233**, 106 (1958).
2315. Querido, A., Stanbury, J. B., Kassenaar, A. A. H., and Meiger, J. W. A., *J. Clin. Endocrinol. Metab.* **16**, 1096 (1956).
2316. Wynn, J., and Gibbs, R., *J. Biol. Chem.* **237**, 3499 (1962).
2317. Wynn, J., Gibbs, R., and Royster, B., *J. Biol. Chem.* **237**, 1892 (1962).
2318. Plaskett, L. G., *Biochem. J.* **78**, 652 (1961).
2319. De Escobar, G. M., Rodriguez, P. L., Jolin, T., and Del Rey, F. E., *J. Biol. Chem.* **238**, 3508 (1963).
2320. Tomita, K., Lardy, H. A., Larson, F. C., and Albright, E. C., *J. Biol. Chem.* **224**, 387 (1957).
2321. Tong, W., Taurog, A., and Chaikoff, I. L., *J. Biol. Chem.* **207**, 59 (1954).
2322. Thibault, O., and Pitt-Rivers, R., *Lancet* ii, 285 (1955).
2323. Ljunggren, J.-G., *Acta Chem. Scand.* **17**, 567 (1963).
2324. Roche, J., Lissitzky, S., and Michel, R., *Compt. Rend. Acad. Sci.* **234**, 997, 1228 (1952).
2325. Gross, J., and Pitt-Rivers, R., *Biochem. J.* **53**, 645 (1953).
2326. Gross, J., and Pitt-Rivers, R., *Recent Progr. Hormone Res.* **10**, 109 (1954).
2327. Roche, J., and Michel, R., *Recent Progr. Hormone Res.* **12**, 1 (1956).
2328. Roche, J., and Michel, R., *Physiol Rev.* **35**, 583 (1955); *Adv. Protein Chem.* **6**, 253 (1951).
2329. Raper, H. S., *Biochem. J.* **21**, 89 (1927); *J. Chem. Soc.*, p. 125 (1938).
2330. Raper, H. S., *Biochem. J.* **20**, 735 (1926); **26**, 2000 (1932).
2331. Mason, H. S., *J. Biol. Chem.* **168**, 433 (1947); **172**, 83 (1948); **181**, 803 (1949).
2332. Bu'Lock, J. D., and Harley-Mason, J., *J. Chem. Soc.*, p. 703 (1951).
2333. Lerner, A. B., *Adv. Enzymol.* **14**, 73 (1953).
2334. Lerner, A. B., Fitzpatrick, T. B., Calkins, E., and Summerson, W. H., *J. Biol. Chem.* **178**, 185 (1949).
2335. Nelson, J. M., and Dawson, C. R., *Adv. Enzymol.* **4**, 99 (1944).
2336. Mason, H. S., *Adv. Enzymol.* **16**, 105 (1955).
2337. Lerner, A. B., and Fitzpatrick, T. B., *Physiol. Rev.* **30**, 91 (1950).
2338. Dawson, C. R., and Tarpley, W. B., *in* "The Enzymes" (J. B. Sumner and K. Myrbäck, eds.), 1st ed., Vol. 2, Pt. 1, p. 454. Academic Press, New York, 1951.
2339. Knox, W. E., *Am. J. Human Genet.* **10**, 249 (1958).
2340. Horowitz, N. H., Fling, M., Macleod, H., and Watanabe, Y., *Cold Spring Harbor Symp. Quant. Biol.* **26**, 233 (1961).
2341. Fling, M., Horowitz, N. H., and Heinemann, S. F., *J. Biol. Chem.* **238**, 2045 (1963).
2342. Foster, M., and Brown, S. R., *J. Biol. Chem.* **225**, 247 (1957).
2343. Kim, K. H., and Tchen, T. T., *Biochim. Biophys. Acta* **59**, 569 (1962).
2344. Karkhanis, Y., and Frieden, E., *J. Biol. Chem.* **236**, PC 1 (1961).

2345. Kubowitz, F., *Biochem. Z.* **299**, 32 (1938).

2346. Sizer, I. W., *Adv. Enzymol.* **14**, 129 (1953).

2347. Yasunobu, K. T., and Dandliker, W. B., *J. Biol. Chem.* **224**, 1065 (1957).

2348. Cory, J. G., Bigelow, C. C., and Frieden, E., *Biochemistry* **1**, 419 (1962).

2349. Lissitzky, S., and Rolland, M., *Biochim. Biophys. Acta* **56**, 95 (1962).

2350. Bruce, J. M., *J. Appl. Chem.* (*London*), 469 (1954).

2351. Axelrod, J., and Lerner, A. B., *Biochim. Biophys. Acta* **71**, 650 (1963).

2352. Hirai, K., *Biochem. Z.*, **135**, 299 (1923).

2353. Hirai, K., *Biochem. Z.* **114**, 71 (1921).

2354. Koukol, J., and Conn, E. E., *J. Biol. Chem.* **236**, 2692 (1961).

2355. Neish, A. C., *Phytochemistry* **1**, 1 (1961).

2356. Neish, A. C., *Ann. Rev. Plant Physiol.* **11**, 55 (1960).

2357. Brown, S. A., *Science* **134**, 305 (1961).

2358. MacLeod, N. J., and Pridham, J. B., *Biochem. J.* **88**, 45 p (1963).

2359. Baumann, E., *Ber.* **12**, 1450 (1879).

2360. Baumann, E., *Z. Physiol. Chem.* **1**, 244 (1877).

2361. Uchida, U., Takemoto, Y., Kakihara, Y., and Ichihara, K., *Med. J. Osaka Univ.* **3**, 509 (1953).

2362. Armstrong, M. D., Shaw, K. N. F., and Wall, P. E., *J. Biol. Chem.* **218**, 293 (1956).

2363. Tallan, H. H., Bella, S. T., Stein, W. H., and Moore, S., *J. Biol. Chem.* **217**, 703 (1955).

2364. Bettelheim, F. R., *J. Am. Chem. Soc.* **76**, 2838 (1954).

2365. Blombäck, B., and Sjoquist, J., *Acta Chem. Scand.* **14**, 493 (1960).

2366. Blombäck, B., Blombäck, M., and Searle, J., *Biochim. Biophys. Acta* **74**, 148 (1963).

2367. Blombäck, B., Blombäck, M., Edman, P., and Hessel, B., *Nature* **193**, 883 (1962).

2368. Segal, H. L., and Mologne, L. A., *J. Biol. Chem.* **234**, 909 (1959).

2369. Kittredge, J. S., Simonsen, D. G., Roberts, E., and Jelinek, B., "Amino Acid Pools," p. 176. Elsevier, Amsterdam, 1962.

2370. Powell, G. M., Rose, F. A., and Dodgson, K. S., *Biochem. J.* **87**, 545 (1963).

2371. Jones, J. G., Dodgson, K. S., Powell, G. M., and Rose, F. A., *Biochem. J.* **87**, 548 (1963).

2371a. Mitchell, H. K., and Lunan, K. D., *Arch. Biochem. Biophys.* **106**, 219 (1964).

2372. Birkinshaw, J. H., and Mohammed, Y. S., *Biochem. J.* **85**, 523 (1962).

2373. Battersby, A. R., and Gavrat, S., *Quart. Rev.* (*London*) **15**, 272 (1961).

2374. Gross, S., and Dawson, R. F., *Biochemistry* **2**, 186 (1963).

2375. Leete, E., *J. Am. Chem. Soc.* **82**, 612 (1960).

2376. Leete, E., and Louden, M. L., *Chem. Ind.* (*London*), p. 1405 (1961).

2377. Louden, M. L., and Leete, E., *J. Am. Chem. Soc.* **84**, 1510, 4507 (1962).

2378. Goodeve, A. M., and Ramstad, E., *Experientia* **17**, 124 (1961).

2379. Leete, E., Kirkwood, S., and Marion, L., *Can. J. Chem.* **30**, 749 (1952).

2380. Leete, E., and Marion, L., *Can. J. Chem.* **31**, 126 (1953).

2381. Kirkwood, S., and Marion, L., *Can. J. Chem.* **29**, 30 (1951).

2382. Matchett, T. J., Marion, L., and Kirkwood, S., *Can. J. Chem.* **31**, 488 (1953).

2383. Leete, E., and Marion, L., *Can. J. Chem.* **32**, 646 (1954).

2384. Mudd, S. H., *Biochim. Biophys. Acta* **37**, 164 (1960).

2385. Sribney, M., and Kirkwood, S., *Can. J. Chem.* **32**, 918 (1954).

2386. Leete, E., *Chem. Ind. (London)*, p. 604 (1959).

2387. Leete, E., and Németh, P. E., *J. Am. Chem. Soc.* **82**, 6055 (1960).

2388. Leete, E., and Németh, P. E., *J. Am. Chem. Soc.* **83**, 2192 (1961).

2389. Olson, R. E., Bently, R., Aiyar, A. S., Dialameh, G. H., Gold, P. H., Ramsey, V. G., and Springer, C. M., *J. Biol. Chem.* **238**, PC 3146 (1963).

2390. Work, E., *Biochim. Biophys. Acta* **3**, 400 (1949).

2391. Work, E., *Biochem. J.* **49**, 17 (1951).

2392. Work, E., and Dewey, D. L., *J. Gen. Microbiol.* **9**, 394 (1953).

2393. Work, E., Birnbaum, S. M., Winitz, M., and Greenstein, J. P., *J. Am. Chem. Soc.* **77**, 1916 (1955).

2394. Ikawa, M., and O'Barr, J. S., *J. Biol. Chem.* **213**, 877 (1955).

2395. Dougherty, E. C., Gordon, H. T., and Allen, M. B., *Exptl. Cell. Res.* **13**, 171 (1957).

2396. Hoare, D. S., and Work, E., *Biochem. J.* **65**, 441 (1957).

2397. Meadow, P., Hoare, D. S., and Work, E., *Biochem. J.* **66**, 270 (1957).

2398. Wright, L. D., and Cresson, E. L., *Proc. Soc. Exptl. Biol. Med.* **82**, 354 (1953).

2399. Asselineau, J., Choucroun, N., and Lederer, E., *Biochim. Biophys. Acta* **5**, 197 (1950).

2400. Dewey, D. L., and Work, E., *Nature* **169**, 533 (1952).

2401. Davis, B. D., *Nature* **169**, 534 (1952).

2402. Abelson, P. H., Bolton, E. T., Britten, R. J., Cowie, D. B., and Roberts, R. B., *Proc. Natl. Acad. Sci. U.S.* **39**, 1020 (1953).

2403. Gilvarg, C., *Federation Proc.* **15**, 261 (1956); *J. Biol. Chem.* **233**, 1501 (1958).

2404. Rhuland, L. E., and Bannister, B., *J. Am. Chem. Soc.* **78**, 3548 (1956).

2405. Gilvarg, C., *Biochim. Biophys. Acta* **24**, 216 (1957).

2406. Gilvarg, C., *J. Biol. Chem.* **234**, 2955 (1959).

2407. Kindler, S. H., and Gilvarg, C., *J. Biol. Chem.* **235**, 3532 (1960).

2408. Smith, E. L., *J. Biol. Chem.* **176**, 21 (1948).

2409. Gilvarg, C., *J. Biol. Chem.* **236**, 1429 (1961).

2410. Peterkofsky, B., and Gilvarg, C., *J. Biol. Chem.* **236**, 1432 (1961).

2411. Edelman, J. C., and Gilvarg, C., *J. Biol. Chem.* **236**, 3295 (1961).

2412. Gilvarg, C., *J. Biol. Chem.* **237**, 482 (1962).

2413. Yugari, Y., and Gilvarg, C., *Biochim. Biophys. Acta* **62**, 612 (1962).

2414. Dewey, D. L., Hoare, D. S., and Work, E., *Biochem. J.* **58**, 532 (1954).

2415. Hoare, D. S., and Work, E., *Biochem. J.* **61**, 562 (1955).

2416. Patte, J.-C., Loviny, T., and Cohen, G. N., *Biochim. Biophys. Acta* **58**, 359 (1962).

2417. Antia, M., Hoare, D. S., and Work, E., *Biochem. J.* **65**, 448 (1957).

2418. Meadow, P., and Work, E., *Biochem. J.* **72**, 400 (1959).

2419. Rhuland, L. E., and Hamilton, R. B., *Biochim. Biophys. Acta* **51**, 525 (1961).

2420. Perry, J. J., and Foster, J. W., *J. Bacteriol.* **69**, 337 (1955).

2421. Martin, H. H., and Foster, J. W., *J. Bacteriol.* **76**, 167 (1958).

2422. Powell, J. F., and Strange, R. E., *Biochem. J.* **65**, 700 (1957).

2422a. Powell, J. F., and Strange, R. E., *Nature* **184**, 878 (1959).

2423. Vogel, H. J., *Biochim. Biophys. Acta* **34**, 282 (1959); **41**, 172 (1960); *Proc. Natl. Acad. Sci. U.S.* **45**, 1717 (1959).

2424. Gill, J. W., and Vogel, H. J., *Biochim. Biophys. Acta* **56**, 200 (1962); *J. Protozool.* **10**, 148 (1963).

2425. Vogel, H. J., *Proc. 5th Intern. Congr. Biochem., Moscow 1963*, Vol. 3, p. 341 (1963).

2426. Mitchell, H. K., and Houlahan, M. B., *J. Biol. Chem.* **174**, 883 (1948).

2427. Windsor, E., *J. Biol. Chem.* **192**, 607 (1951).

2428. Bergström, S., and Rottenberg, M., *Acta Chem. Scand.* **4**, 553 (1950).

2429. Good, N., Heilbronner, R., and Michell, H. K., *Arch. Biochem.* **28**, 464 (1950).

2430. Ehrensvärd, G., Reio, L., and Saluste, E., *Acta Chem. Scand.* **3**, 645 (1949).

2431. Gilvarg, C., and Bloch, K., *J. Biol. Chem.* **193**, 339 (1951).

2432. Strassman, M., and Weinhouse, S., *J. Am. Chem. Soc.* **75**, 1680 (1953).

2433. Strassman, M., and Weinhouse, S., *J. Am. Chem. Soc.* **74**, 3457 (1952).

2433a. Weber, M. A., Hoagland, A. N., Klein, J., and Lewis, K., *Arch. Biochem. Biophys.* **104**, 257 (1964).

2433b. Strassman, M., and Ceci, L. N., *Biochem. Biophys. Res. Commun.* **14**, 262 (1964).

2433c. Strassman, M., Ceci, L. N., and Silverman, B. E., *Biochem. Biophys. Res. Commun.* **14**, 268 (1964).

2434. Sagisaka, S., and Shimura, K., *J. Agr. Chem. Soc. Japan* **31**, 110 (1957).

2435. Sagisaka, S., and Shimura, K., *J. Biochem. (Tokyo)* **49**, 392 (1961).

2436. Larson, R. L., Sandine, W. D., and Broquist, H. P., *J. Biol. Chem.* **238**, 275 (1963).

2437. Sagisaka, S., and Shimura, K., *Nature* **184**, 1709 (1959).

2438. Sagisaka, S., and Shimura, K., *J. Biochem. (Tokyo)* **51**, 398 (1962).

2439. Sagisaka, S., and Shimura, K., *J. Biochem. (Tokyo)* **52**, 155 (1962).

2440. Kuo, M. H., Saunders, P., and Broquist, H. P., *Biochem. Biophys. Res. Commun.* **8**, 227 (1962); *J. Biol. Chem.* **239**, 508 (1964).

2440a. Broquist, H. P., *Proc. 6th Intern. Congr. Biochem., New York*, 1964; Symposium V, p. 363 (1964).

2441. Aspen, A. J., and Meister, A., *Biochemistry* **1**, 600, 606 (1962).

2442. Mattoon, J. R., and Haight, R. D., *J. Biol. Chem.* **237**, 3486 (1962).

2443. Geiger, E., and Dunn, H. J., *J. Biol. Chem.* **178**, 877 (1949).

2444. Lewis, H. B., and Root, L. E., *J. Biol. Chem.* **43**, 79 (1920).

2445. McGinty, D. A., Lewis, H. B., and Marvel, C. S., *J. Biol. Chem.* **62**, 75 (1924–5).

2446. Stevens, C. M., and Ellman, P. B., *J. Biol. Chem.* **182**, 75 (1950).

2447. Page, E., Gaudry, R., and Gingras, R., *J. Biol. Chem.* **171**, 831 (1947).

2448. Stevens, C. M., and Bush, J. A., *J. Biol. Chem.* **183**, 139 (1950).

2449. Berg, C. P., *J. Nutr.* **12**, 671 (1936).

2450. Neuberger, A., and Sanger, F., *Biochem. J.* **38**, 125 (1944).

2451. Neuberger, A., and Sanger, F., *Biochem. J.* **37**, 515 (1943).

2452. Gordon, W. O., *J. Biol. Chem.* **127**, 487 (1939).

2453. Michi, K., and Tsuda, H., *Bull. Agr. Chem. Soc. Japan*, **22**, 283 (1958).

2454. Neuberger, A., and Sanger, F., *Biochem. J.* **38**, 119 (1944).

2455. Clark, I., and Rittenberg, D., *J. Biol. Chem.* **189**, 521 (1951).

2456. Bloch, K., and Rittenberg, D., *J. Biol. Chem.* **169**, 467 (1949).

2457. Paik, W. K., Bloch-Frankenthal, L., Birnbaum, S. M., Winitz, M., and Greenstein, J. P., *Arch. Biochem. Biophys.* **69**, 56 (1957).

2458. Chibata, I., Watanabe, A., and Yamada, S., *Bull. Agr. Chem. Soc. Japan* **21**, 296, 300, 304 (1957).

2459. Michi, K., and Tsuda, H., *J. Biochem. (Tokyo)* **45**, 745 (1958).

2460. Chibata, I., Ishikawa, T., and Tosa, T., *Bull. Agr. Chem. Soc. Japan* **24**, 31, 37 (1960).

2461. Chibata, I., Ishikawa, T., and Tosa, T., *Nature* **195**, 80 (1962).
2462. Weissman, N., and Schoenheimer, R., *J. Biol. Chem.* **140**, 779 (1941).
2463. Foster, G. L., Schoenheimer, R., and Rittenberg, D., *J. Biol. Chem.* **127**, 319 (1939).
2464. Elliott, D. F., and Neuberger, A., *Biochem. J.* **46**, 207 (1950).
2465. Aspen, A. J., Ph.D. Dissertation, Tufts Univ. (1961).
2466. Borsook, H., Deasy, C. L., Haagen-Smit, A. J., Keighley, G., and Lowy, P. H., *J. Biol. Chem.* **176**, 1395 (1948).
2467. Borsook, H., Deasy, C. L., Haagen-Smit, A. J., Keighley, G., and Lowy, P. H., *J. Biol. Chem.* **173**, 423 (1948).
2468. Borsook, H., Deasy, C. L., Haagen-Smit, A. J., Keighley, G., and Lowy, P. H., *J. Biol. Chem.* **176**, 1383 (1948).
2469. Boulanger, P., and Biserte, G., *Compt. Rend. Acad. Sci.* **232**, 1451 (1951).
2470. Cavallini, D., and Mondovi, B., *Arch. Sci. Biol.* (*Bologna*) **35**, 468 (1952).
2471. Ringer, A. I., Frankel, E. M., and Jonas, L., *J. Biol. Chem.* **14**, 539 (1913).
2472. Rothstein, M., and Miller, L. L., *J. Am. Chem. Soc.* **75**, 4371 (1953); **76**, 1459 (1954); *J. Biol. Chem.* **206**, 243; **211**, 851, 859 (1954).
2473. Rothstein, M., and Greenberg, D. M., *J. Biol. Chem.* **235**, 714 (1960).
2474. Hobbs, D. C., and Koeppe, R. E., *J. Biol. Chem.* **230**, 655 (1958).
2475. Bagchi, S. P., Mushhwar, I. K., Chang, T., Koeppe, R. E., and Mourkides, G. A., *J. Biol. Chem.* **236**, 370 (1961).
2476. Nishizuka, Y., Kuno, S., and Hayaishi, O., *Biochim. Biophys. Acta* **43**, 357 (1960).
2477. Morrison, R. I., *Biochem. J.* **50**, xiv (1952).
2478. Morrison, R. I., *Biochem. J.* **53**, 474 (1953).
2479. Grobbelaar, N., Zacharius, R. M., and Steward, F. C., *J. Am. Chem. Soc.* **76**, 2912 (1954).
2480. Zacharius, R. M., Thompson, J. F., and Steward, F. C., *J. Am. Chem. Soc.* **74**, 2949 (1952).
2481. Zacharius, R. M., Thompson, J. F., and Steward, F. C., *J. Am. Chem. Soc.* **76**, 2908 (1954).
2482. Grobbelaar, N., and Steward, F. C., *J. Am. Chem. Soc.* **75**, 4341 (1953).
2483. Lowy, P., *Arch. Biochem. Biophys.* **47**, 228 (1953).
2484. Schweet, R. S., Holden, J. T., and Lowy, P. H., *in* "Amino Acid Metabolism" (W. D. McElroy and B. Glass, eds.), p. 496. Johns Hopkins Press, Baltimore, Maryland, 1955.
2485. Rothstein, M., and Greenberg, D. M., *J. Biol. Chem.* **235**, 714 (1960).
2486. Ishikawa, T., Tosa, T., and Chibata, I., *Agr. Biol. Chem.* (*Tokyo*) **26**, 43, 412, 581 (1962).
2487. Paik, W. K., *Biochim. Biophys. Acta* **65**, 518 (1962).
2488. Meister, A., and Buckley, S. D., *Biochim. Biophys. Acta* **23**, 202 (1957).
2489. Rothstein, M., Cooksey, K. E., and Greenberg, D. M., *J. Biol. Chem.* **237**, 2828 (1962).
2490. Rao, D. R., and Rodwell, V. W., *J. Biol. Chem.* **237**, 2232 (1962).
2491. Basso, L. V., Rao, D. R., and Rodwell, V. W., *J. Biol. Chem.* **237**, 2239 (1962).
2492. Schweet, R. S., Holden, J. T., and Lowy, P. H., *J. Biol. Chem.* **211**, 517 (1954).
2493. Rothstein, M., and Miller, L. L., *Arch. Biochem. Biophys.* **54**, 1 (1955).
2494. Roberts, E., *Arch. Biochim. Biophys.* **48**, 395 (1954).

2495. Suda, M., Kamahora, T., and Hagihira, H., *Med. J. Osaka Univ.* **5**, 119 (1954).
2496. Wright, L. D., Cresson, E. L., Skeggs, H. R., Peck, R. L., Wolf, D. E., Wood, T. R., Valiant, J., and Folkers, K., *Science* **114**, 635 (1951).
2497. Wright, L. D., Driscoll, C. A., and Boger, W. P., *Proc. Soc. Exptl. Biol. Med.* **86**, 335 (1954).
2498. Wright, L. D., Cresson, E. L., and Driscoll, C. A., *Proc. Soc. Exptl. Biol. Med.* **91**, 248 (1956).
2499. Doty, J. R., and Eaton, A. G., *Am. J. of Physiol.* **119**, 296, 301 (1937).
2500. Ratner, S., Weissman, N., and Schoenheimer, R. J., *J. Biol. Chem.* **147**, 549 (1943).
2501. Rothstein, M., Bly, C. G., and Miller, L. L., *Arch. Biochem. Biophys.* **50**, 252 (1954).
2502. Hasse, K., Homann, P., and Schührer, K., *Naturwissenschaften* **48**, 51 (1961).
2503. Hasse, K., and Wieland, A., *Naturwissenschaften* **47**, 303 (1960).
2504. Stadtman, T. C., *in* "Amino Acid Metabolism" (W. D., McElroy and B. Glass, eds.), p. 493. Johns Hopkins Press, Baltimore, Maryland, 1955.
2505. Stadtman, T. C., and White, F. H., Jr., *J. Bacteriol.* **67**, 651 (1954).
2506. Stadtman, T. C., *J. Biol. Chem.* **237**, PC 2409 (1962).
2507. Lecte, E., *J. Am. Chem. Soc.* **78**, 3520 (1956); **80**, 4393 (1958).
2508. Solt, M. L., Dawson, R. F., and Christman, D. R., *Plant Physiol.* **35**, 887 (1960).
2509. Mothes, K., Schütte, H. R., Simon, H., and Weygand, F., *Z. Naturforsch.* **14b**, 49 (1959).
2510. Clarke, A. J., and Mann, P. J. G., *Biochem. J.* **71**, 596 (1959).
2511. Sinex, F. M., and Van Slyke, D. D., *J. Biol. Chem.* **216**, 245 (1955).
2512. Piez, K. A., and Likins, R. C., *J. Biol. Chem.* **229**, 101 (1957).
2513. Sinex, F. M., Van Slyke, D. D., and Christman, D. R., *J. Biol. Chem.* **234**, 918 (1959).
2514. Popenoe, E. A., and Van Slyke, D. D., *J. Biol. Chem.* **237**, 3491 (1962).
2515. Van Slyke, D. D., and Sinex, F. M., *J. Biol. Chem.* **232**, 797 (1958).
2516. Fujimoto, D., and Tamiya, N., *Biochem. Biophys. Res. Commun.* **10**, 498 (1963).
2517. Tsung, C. M., Smith, W. G., Leach, F. R., and Henderson, L. M., *J. Biol. Chem.* **237**, 1194 (1962).
2518. Smith, W. G., Newman, M., Leach, F. R., and Henderson, L. M., *J. Biol. Chem.* **237**, 1198 (1962).
2519. Lindstedt, S., and Lindstedt, G., *Arch. Biochem. Biophys.* **85**, 565 (1959).
2520. Boulanger, P., Osteux, R., and Bertrand, J., *Biochim. Biophys. Acta* **29**, 534 (1958).

CHAPTER VII

Some Disorders of Amino Acid Metabolism in Man

"... the anomalies of which I propose to treat ... may be classed together as inborn errors of metabolism. Some of them are certainly, and all of them are probably, present from birth ... they are characterized by wide departures from the normal of the species far more conspicuous than any ordinary individual variations, and one is tempted to regard them as metabolic sports, the chemical analogues of structural malformations. ... It may well be that the intermediate products formed at the several stages [in metabolism] have only momentary existence as such, being subjected to further change almost as soon as they are formed; and that the course of metabolism along any particular path should be pictured as in continuous movement rather than as a series of distinct steps. If any one step in the process fail, the intermediate product in being at the point of arrest will escape further change, just as when the film of a biograph is brought to a standstill the moving figures are left foot in air." ... GARROD (1923).

A. Introduction

In this chapter some of the abnormalities of amino acid metabolism which have been observed in man will be surveyed. It is probable that virtually all human disease involves some alteration of amino acid metabolism; many human diseases are genetically determined and therefore reflect the translation of genetic information into abnormalities of protein synthesis. The present discussion will be restricted to disorders in which the defect can be related with reasonable certainty to specific enzymatic events. The material considered here is therefore primarily intended to supplement the body of information on amino acid metabolism reviewed in the preceding chapter.

Most of the human disorders considered below are "inborn errors of metabolism" (1, 2) and are associated with the absence of or marked reduction in the activity of a particular enzyme. Although direct examina-

1021

tion of the structures of these enzymes has not yet been carried out, it seems probable that in many cases "abnormal" enzymes are synthesized in which there are particular amino acid replacements. In some instances there may be complete failure of enzyme synthesis. Many human diseases are now known in which the basic defect is synthesis of an abnormal protein. Thus, Itano et al. (3) demonstrated that sickle cell hemoglobin and normal hemoglobin exhibited different electrophoretic mobilities, and subsequent work by Ingram (4) provided the explanation for the electrophoretic data. It was found that a specific glutamic acid residue in normal hemoglobin is replaced by a valine residue in hemoglobin S. Different specific amino acid replacements occur in other hemoglobin diseases, and there are now a number of human conditions known in which there is abnormal synthesis of various blood serum proteins and in some cases complete failure of the synthesis of a particular protein.

Many metabolic defects due to specific enzymatic blocks have been observed in studies on microorganisms such as *Escherichia coli* and *Neurospora crassa* (Chapter VI). However, the occurrence of such genetically induced enzymatic deficiency in man justifies separate and special consideration. The biochemical data now available concerning the translation of genetic information into the specific amino acid sequences of proteins (Chapter V), and the extensive knowledge of the metabolism of amino acids (Chapter VI) and many other cellular constituents suggest the need for a reexamination of the etiological and therapeutic aspects of human disease, and further development of the field of "molecular medicine". The concept of inborn errors was expressed many years ago by Sir Archibald Garrod (1, 2), who anticipated many of the developments of the subsequent half-century. Garrod studied diseases such as cystinuria, albinism, pentosuria, and alcaptonuria, and postulated that these were "errors of metabolism" in which there was a congenital failure of the body to carry out a particular reaction in the normal metabolic sequence. His prediction concerning the defect in alcaptonuria was fulfilled by direct enzymatic study as recently as 1958. Forty years after Garrod's important contributions, the closely related "one-gene-one enzyme" hypothesis was proposed by Beadle (5), and the many ramifications and exploitations of this idea have led to accumulation of much data about metabolism. Recent refinements in thought and experiment have made it possible to define a unit of heredity in chemical terms, and the prospect for future developments in the understanding of metabolic phenomena in terms of protein synthesis and genetic information are truly exciting. Despite these impressive advances, there has been a tendency to regard human "inborn errors of metabolism" and "metabolic diseases" as rather special and perhaps unusual types of human disease. However, the realization that many human diseases can be understood in molecular terms has recently become more general.

In considering enzymatic blocks in man it is necessary (and possible) to go beyond the mere demonstration of the nature of the enzymatic deficiency. In contrast to many of the studies on mutations in microorganisms, studies on man compel one to consider the phenomena that are secondary to enzymatic defects. Thus, a straightforward block in a biosynthetic reaction in *Escherichia coli* or *Neurospora crassa* has generally sufficed to explain a given nutritional requirement. On the other hand, analogous defects in the synthesis of a particular enzyme in man usually do not lead to an immediate understanding of the symptomatology. For example, it is not clear why the absence of phenylalanine hydroxylase activity in patients with phenylpyruvic oligophrenia should cause mental retardation. Much work remains to be done to elucidate the complexities of the phenotypic expression of mutations in man. The studies on microorganisms offer a number of possible explanations; for example, a block of a given enzymatic reaction leads to failure of formation of a particular product which may be needed for synthesis of an essential metabolite or macromolecule. The absence of this product can lead to loss of feedback control of enzymatic activity or enzyme synthesis. The accumulation of the precursor of this product may provide additional metabolic embarrassment so that exaggerated formation of side products or perhaps formation of a new product may take place. After accumulation of sufficient concentrations of the precursor, it may be acted upon by another enzyme or serve as an antagonist of a different enzymatic reaction or transport mechanism. Clearly other phenomena can occur secondary to a single enzymatic block. The occurrence of a particular enzymatic defect at an early stage in the development of a multicellular organism such as man can provide opportunity for a large number of associated defects since it is likely that the processes of differentiation and development offer many opportunities for interactions involving a variety of metabolic phenomena.

It may be postulated that many of the metabolic defects considered below are associated with a change in a single nucleic acid nucleotide residue. A consideration of the many metabolic pathways now known, the large number of enzymes involved in these reactions, and the much larger numbers of amino acid residues present in each of these enzymes, together with the thought that each amino acid residue may be determined by a specific triplet of nucleic acid nucleotides, indicates that the theoretical possibilities for the production of a metabolic disease are enormous. Undoubtedly some mutational changes are lethal, and some do not lead to abnormal phenotypes but represent the basis for biochemical individuality (6). The "one-gene-one enzyme" phenomenon may be found to represent a rather special and relatively uncommon situation when all of the data on the determination of the amino acid sequences of proteins are known. However, it seems likely that many additional inborn errors of metabolism will be discovered in the near future, and it is not impossible that blocks or partial blocks in virtually all of the known metabolic pathways will eventually be discovered in man. In microorganisms where relatively short generation times have permitted more extensive study, the available data indicate that an extremely large number of mutations occur with associated defects or changes in protein structure. Until relatively recently, detailed chemical studies on the amino acids of human tissues and body fluids have not been carried out, and it is to be expected that with the application of modern techniques many more abnormalities of amino acid metabolism will come to light.

Complete understanding of the pathogenesis of these conditions requires much additional study, especially of the processes involved in tissue and cell differentiation. It is of considerable interest that certain enzymatic deficiencies affect a wide variety of tissues [e.g., total albinism, galactosemia (7)], while other defects appear to be restricted to a particular organ or tissue. Little is now known about the manner in which genetic information is reflected in the embryological development of a multicellular organism such as man. It is noteworthy that a very large number of the inborn errors of amino acid metabolism are associated with defects in central nervous system function. Even if one allows for the fact that normal individuals are not generally studied in detail, and that many such patients have been discovered in the course of screening programs in mental hospitals, the findings suggest that normal cerebral function is crucially dependent upon a favorable tissue environment. The studies on phenylketonuria and galactosemia suggest that if such environmental factors can be controlled during the period of brain development, normal function may be possible. On the other hand, the association of certain symptoms and signs in patients with aminoaciduria, amino-

Table I

Some Disorders of Amino Acid Metabolism and Transport in Man

Disease	Probable site of defect	Major chemical findings	Major clinical findings
Albinism	Tyrosinase	—	Absence of melanin
Alcaptonuria	Homogentisic acid oxidase	Urinary excretion of homogentisic acid	Ochronosis
β-Aminoisobutyric aciduria	(?)β-Aminoisobutyrate-glutamate transaminase	Increased urinary excretion of β-aminoiso-butyric acid	None (see p. 1035)
Ammonemia	(?)Ornithine transcarbamylase	Increased urinary excretion of glutamine; increased concentration of glutamine in blood and spinal fluid; high concentration of ammonia in blood and spinal fluid	Mental retardation (no obvious generalized liver damage)
Argininosuccinic aciduria	Argininosuccinase	Urinary excretion of argininosuccinate; increased concentration of this amino acid in blood	Mental retardation, hair defect
Carcinoid	5-Hydroxytryptophan formation and decarboxylation (excess)	Increased excretion of serotonin and 5-hydroxyindoleacetic acid; increased blood concentration of serotonin	Weight loss, flushes, diarrhea, heart disease, respiratory distress, pellagra-like condition
Cerebromacular degeneration	(?) Renal transport system for imidazole compounds	Increased urinary excretion of carnosine, anserine, histidine, methylhistidine	Blindness, central nervous system disease (Tay-Sachs disease)
Citrullinuria	(?) Argininosuccinate synthetase	High concentrations of citrulline in blood, urine, and spinal fluid. High post-prandial blood ammonia concentration	Mental retardation
Cystathioninuria	(?) Cystathionase	Increased blood concentration and urinary excretion of cystathionine	Mental retardation and aberrations
Cystinuria	Renal and intestinal transport systems for several diamino acids	Abnormally high urinary excretion of cystine, lysine, arginine, and ornithine	Renal calculi

Table I—*continued*

Disease	Probable site of defect	Major chemical findings	Major clinical findings
Fanconi Syndrome	Renal reabsorption systems for all amino acids secondary to unknown defect	Generalized aminoaciduria	Osteomalacia, cystinosis, liver damage
Galactosemia	Galactose 1-phosphate uridyl transferase; renal reabsorption systems for all amino acids	Generalized aminoaciduria; galactosuria, galactosemia	Liver damage, mental retardation, cataracts
Glycinemia	Unknown	Increased blood glycine concentration	Mental retardation, ketosis, blood dyscrasia, hypogammaglobulinemia
Glycinuria	Renal transport system for glycine	Abnormally high urinary excretion of glycine	Nephrolithiasis
Hartnup disease	Renal and intestinal transport systems for a number of neutral amino acids	Abnormally high urinary excretion of neutral amino acids (except glycine and imino acids); excretion of indole compounds	Pellagra-like rash, mental retardation and aberrations
Hepatolenticular degeneration (Wilson's disease)	Copper metabolism; ceruloplasmin; renal reabsorption systems for amino acids	Generalized aminoaciduria; decreased plasma ceruloplasmin; evidence of increased copper in plasma, tissues, and urine	Symptoms of central nervous system disease; cirrhosis
Histidinemia	Histidase	Increased urinary excretion of histidine, imidazolepyruvic acid, imidazolelactic acid, and imidazoleacetic acid. Increased blood concentration of histidine	Speech defect, mental retardation
Homocystinuria	Cystathionine synthetase	Increased urinary excretion of homocystine; increased blood concentration of methionine	Convulsions and mental retardation, mottled red skin, lens dislocation, fine sparse hair

		excretion of hydroxyproline	
Hyperoxaluria	Oxidation of glyoxylate to CO_2	Excessive urinary excretion of oxalate and glycolate	Genitourinary tract disease, calculi
Hypophosphatasia	Alkaline phosphatase	Decreased blood and tissue alkaline phosphatase and increased blood and urine phosphoaminoethanol	Bone lesions, central nervous system disease, anemia
Maple syrup urine disease	Enzymatic decarboxylation of the branched-chain α-keto acids to the corresponding acyl-coenzyme A derivatives	Increased blood concentrations of leucine, isoleucine, and valine. Presence of these amino acids and alloisoleucine in blood, urine, and spinal fluid. Urinary excretion of the corresponding α-keto acids	Convulsions, mental retardation, respiratory distress
Mastocytosis	Histidine decarboxylase (excess)	Increased amounts of histamine and 1-methylimidazole-4-acetic acid in urine	Erythema, edema, urticaria, tachycardia, gastrointestinal symptoms
Phenylpyruvic oligophrenia (phenylketonuria)	Phenylalanine hydroxylase	Increased blood concentration of phenylalanine; increased excretion of phenylalanine, phenylpyruvate, phenyllactate, phenylacetylglutamine, o-hydroxyphenylpyruvate and other compounds. Decreased blood concentration of serotonin	Mental retardation, convulsions, eczema, abnormal muscle tone and tendon reflexes
Pheochromocytoma	Enzyme(s) that catalyze catecholamine formation from tyrosine (excess)	Increased urinary excretion of epinephrine, norepinephrine, and related compounds	Paroxysmal hypertension
Prolinemia	Proline oxidase (in some cases) and (?) Δ^1-pyrroline-5-carboxylate dehydrogenase in another type	Abnormally high blood concentration of proline and urinary excretion of proline, glycine, and hydroxyproline	Mental retardation, convulsions, renal disease
"Tyrosinosis"	(?) p-Hydroxyphenylpyruvic acid oxidase	Excretion of p-hydroxyphenylpyruvate and tyrosine	Variable; see (301–303)
Vitamin B_{12} deficiency	Methylmalonyl-coenzyme A isomerase	Urinary excretion of methylmalonic acid	Pernicious anemia

acidemia, and other chemical manifestations of specific enzymatic blocks is not always easy to explain; the simultaneous occurrence of apparently unrelated phenomena may be due in some cases to fortuitous association of two or more genetically induced abnormalities, or to genetically induced aberrations in the process of tissue differentiation. Although many metabolic pathways are now understood, it is apparent that our knowledge of metabolism is far from complete. In particular, there are huge gaps in our understanding of the relative quantitative significance of various pathways and in the relationships between metabolic pathways, specific enzymatic reactions, and physiological phenomena. The likelihood that a large proportion of all human disease is associated with qualitative or quantitative changes in the cellular enzymatic machinery amply justifies further research.

A summary of most of the metabolic disorders considered in this chapter is given in Table I.

B. Aminoaciduria

"The urine of man is one of the animal matters that have been the most examined by chemists, and of which the examination has at the same time furnished the most singular discoveries to chemistry, and the most useful application to physiology, as well as the art of healing. This liquid, which commonly inspires men only with contempt and disgust, which is generally ranked amongst vile and repulsive matters, has become, in the hands of the chemists, a source of important discoveries. . . ."

FOURCROY (1801).

Introduction

From earliest times, human urine has been the subject of considerable attention by chemists and others, and many clues to the nature of human disease have come from the detection of urinary metabolites. The preoccupation of early chemists and physicians with urine is perhaps reflected in the fact that the second natural amino acid was obtained from a urinary calculus. Urine has long been known as an extraordinarily complex solution containing a large number of substances; it is of interest to compare Fourcroy's early discussion of the chemistry of urine with our presently still incomplete knowledge of urinary constituents. Several years after Fourcroy's masterful eleven-volume treatise "A General System of Chemical Knowledge; and Its Application to the Phenomena of Nature and Art" was published (8), Wollaston (9) reported the isolation of a urinary calculus containing cystine. The patient who passed this stone undoubtedly had the inborn error cystinuria and probably also excreted arginine, ornithine, and lysine, but the detection of all of these amino acids in the urine of patients with cystinuria had to await the application of chromatographic procedures almost a century and a half later. (It may be noted, however, that evidence for the presence of lysine in cystinuric urine was published many years before chromatographic methods were generally used.)

Although the urinary amino acids are derived from the amino acids of the blood plasma, the concentrations of the various amino acids in these fluids are quite different. The major amino acid constituents of normal human urine are not those which are present in highest concentrations in the blood plasma (see Table IV, Chapter I). Furthermore, in man the concentrations of the amino acids of the blood plasma seem to be much more constant than those of the urine; there may be considerable variation in the urinary excretion of amino acids due to several factors including the nature of the diet and genetic differences. Normally, amino acids comprise less than 3% of urinary nitrogen; thus, in man about 80 to 300 mg. of amino acid nitrogen are excreted daily. There are profound species differences in the urinary excretion of amino acids (10); remarkable is the excretion by cats of felinine, an amino acid not present in the urine of other species (see p. 74). The amino acids found in greatest abundance in normal human urine include glycine, histidine, 1-methylhistidine, 3-methylhistidine, taurine, glutamine, asparagine, alanine, and serine. A detailed and informative discussion of the effects of diet, age, nutritional state, sex, and other factors on the urinary excretion of amino acids has been provided by Scriver (11). It is of interest that there is a relatively greater excretion of aminoethanol, proline, hydroxyproline, and occasionally other amino acids in infants (12). No major sex differences have been observed except for increased excretion of histidine during pregnancy. Variations in amino acid excretion have been observed during the human reproductive cycle (13). 5-Hydroxypipecolic acid has been found in the urine after ingestion of dates (14) and urinary excretion of homocitrulline follows ingestion of milk preparations containing this amino acid (see p. 99); these amino acids (and probably certain others) seem not to be significantly metabolized. Presumably most of the excreted amino acids are of the L-configuration, but it is possible that some D-amino acids are present in the urine; these might arise from dietary constituents or represent products of the metabolism of the bacterial flora. Freshly voided human urine has been found to contain D-pyrrolidone carboxylic acid but very little of the corresponding L-isomer (15).

Aminoaciduria (i.e., excretion of amino acids in a pattern that differs significantly from the normal) may occur when (a) the concentrations of amino acids in the blood plasma are elevated, or (b) there is failure of the renal reabsorption process. An example of the first mechanism ["over-flow" (16, 17)] is the excretion of phenylalanine in phenylpyruvic oligophrenia. In hepatic disease, there is commonly a general increase in the concentration of amino acids of the plasma, and an associated generalized aminoaciduria (17–24). This is not surprising in view of the fact that the liver is the chief organ for the metabolism of amino acids. Dent and Walshe (18) found increased urinary excretion of cystine, taurine, β-aminoisobutyric acid, methylhistidine, aminoethanol, and methionine in patients with mild hepatic disease. In more advanced liver disease, the excretion of all of the amino acids was greatly increased, a finding similar to the excretion of amino acids after hepatectomy in animals (25). In other conditions associated with increased concentrations of blood plasma amino acids [e.g., wasting disease, malnutrition (26), muscular atrophy (27, 28), hyperthyroidism, trauma (29)], there may also be generalized aminoaciduria (30).

The extent of tubular reabsorption may significantly influence the excretion of amino acids (16, 31–39). In general, amino acids are normally reabsorbed efficiently in the kidney. Although the chemical details of the process of amino acid transport are not yet known, there is substantial basis for the belief that there are several different amino acid-specific systems for amino acid transport and that these are under genetic control (see Chapter IV, Section A).

Cystinuria

Cystinuria, the first aminoaciduria to be observed, was extensively considered in the classical lectures of Garrod (1, 2), who believed it to be an inborn error of metabolism. Subsequent work has shown that cystinuria is associated with a defect in the tubular reabsorption system for this amino acid as well as ornithine, arginine, and lysine (40–45). Patients with this disorder are usually normal except for a tendency to form cystine stones. The available data indicate that all of these diamino acids are reabsorbed by the same transport system. However, studies on the mode of inheritance of cystinuria have indicated that there is some variation in the excretion of amino acids by the parents of affected individuals. One observed inheritance pattern suggests that the condition is recessive and that heterozygous individuals exhibit little if any cystinuria. An apparently incompletely recessive form has also been observed in which heterozygous individuals excrete cystine and lysine, and homozygous individuals excrete all four of the diamino acids. The genetic analysis of cystinuria has revealed a rather complex picture, which has been reviewed by Harris (46, 47).

The daily urinary excretion of cystine in cystinuria is frequently of the order of 1 g. and similar amounts of the basic amino acids may be excreted. Several early studies revealed that putrescine and cadaverine were present in the urine of cystinuric patients (48–50) and it is certainly of note that early investigators found evidence of nitrogen-containing products other than cystine, urea, ammonia, etc., as well as lysine in the urine of cystinurics (50–53). More recent work has indicated that there is also a defect in the intestinal transport of diamino acids in this disease (54–54b); formation of putrescine and cadaverine may be explained by the action of the corresponding amino acid decarboxylases of the intestinal microorganisms.

Cystinuria also occurs in dogs, where the syndrome seems to have the same basis as in man (54c). It is of interest that dogs have been found that excrete lysine and cystine, but not arginine and ornithine (55). Cystine calculi have also been found in the bladder of the mink (56). The Kenya genet normally excretes cystine in the urine (57), but apparently not the other diamino acids, suggesting that a special transport system for cystine may exist in this animal. The concentration of cystine in genet urine is extremely high (e.g., 0.2%); stones do not seem to be formed, suggesting that cystine is solubilized by the presence of other substances in the urine.

Humans and dogs with cystinuria have been found to excrete the asymmetrical disulfide of L-cysteine and L-homocysteine (58). This disulfide has also been found in the urine of patients with Fanconi syndrome and Wilson's disease. It is of interest that cysteine, although present in blood plasma, does not occur in urine. Administration of cystine does not lead to increased excretion of cystine in patients with cystinuria, and most of the administered sulfur appears as urinary sulfate (59). On the other hand, the classical studies of Brand and his collaborators (59–61) (which led to postulation of the intermediate later established and named cystathionine; see p. 758) showed that administration of cysteine, methionine, the α-hydroxy acid analog of methionine, or homocysteine to cystinurics led to increased excretion of cystine. Recently it has been found that administration of D-penicillamine leads to excretion of

L-cysteine-D-penicillamine disulfide and a reduction of cystine excretion in cystinuria (62). The mixed disulfide is more soluble than cystine indicating a potential therapeutic procedure. These findings and studies on the concentrations of amino acids in the renal venous and arterial blood in cystinuria (58) suggest that plasma cysteine rather than cystine is the precursor of urinary cystine. It is of associated interest that cystine does not compete with lysine, arginine, and ornithine for uptake in rat kidney slices, although there is mutual competition between the basic amino acids (63). These findings suggest further questions about the nature of an amino acid transport system that seems to be specific for diamino acids. Rapid administration of a large amount (5 g.) of lysine to normal individuals was reported to be followed by cystinuria as well as excretion of arginine and ornithine (64), suggesting again that a single transport system is involved. Lysine infusion did not affect the excretion of other amino acids.

Glycinuria

Excessive urinary excretion of glycine was found in four female members of a single family in which the trait was found in three generations (65). The information available suggested transmission of the trait as a sex-linked Mendelian dominant. All four of these patients excreted from about 0.5 to 1 g. of glycine per day, but exhibited normal blood serum concentrations of glycine. Three of the four affected individuals experienced nephrolithiasis, and examination of one stone showed that it contained calcium oxalate as well as a small amount of glycine. Administration of glycine to one patient resulted in much greater excretion of glycine than observed in two normal individuals; the urinary excretion of glycine by the subject was not affected by feeding a low protein diet. The data indicate that the excretion of glycine is due to a specific renal defect in the reabsorption of this amino acid. Glycinuria also occurs in other conditions some of which are considered below.

Scriver et al. (66, 67) have found evidence for a renal tubular transport system that is common to glycine, proline, and hydroxyproline. They studied patients with abnormally high concentrations of blood plasma L-proline (see below) and found that these individuals excreted greater than normal quantities of glycine, hydroxyproline, and proline. Renal clearance studies suggested that glycine, proline, and hydroxyproline share a common transport system.

Generalized Aminoaciduria

A condition in which generalized aminoaciduria occurs in association with mental retardation and other clinical and chemical phenomena has been reported by Lowe *et al.* and others (68, 69). All but one of the reported cases were males, and the information available suggests that the disease is transmitted as a sex-linked recessive trait. In addition to mental retardation, a number of these patients exhibited ocular abnormalities, developed hypophosphatemic rickets, and showed considerable evidence of renal tubular malfunction. The aminoaciduria is general; it is accompanied by proteinuria and occasionally by glycosuria. Such patients commonly develop hyperchloremic acidosis of renal origin, which apparently results from defective production of ammonia. Although the concentration of glutamine in the blood is normal, considerable amounts of this amino acid are found in the urine. It seems probable that the aminoaciduria in this condition is secondary to a profound renal tubular defect, which may conceivably be associated with lack of glutaminase, but this seems not to have been studied as yet. The relationship between the renal and ocular findings and the mental deficiency is not yet clear.

Aminoaciduria has been observed in a number of other relatively uncommon conditions, which are not yet completely understood. The Fanconi syndrome and related disorders (11, 30, 70–82) are associated with aminoaciduria and urinary excretion of peptides, bicarbonate, and phosphate. Patients with this syndrome may also exhibit osteomalacia or rickets, and liver damage. Some forms of Fanconi syndrome are accompanied by cystinosis in which there is accumulation of cystine in the tissues. This condition is clearly not identical with uncomplicated cystinuria; cystinosis is a much more serious condition than cystinuria and leads to early death. Scriver (11) has recently reviewed the several forms of the Fanconi syndrome and cystinosis. At the present time the reason for the aminoaciduria is not known, but the reported findings suggest that there is generalized failure of tubular reabsorption of amino acids [see also (39)]. Generalized aminoaciduria has also been observed in vitamin D deficiency and in several other conditions (11).

In hepatolenticular degeneration (Wilson's disease), a generalized aminoaciduria occurs in association with liver damage (11, 83–86). There is some evidence that the aminoaciduria of this disease may occur prior to the development of substantial evidence of liver damage; aminoaciduria is not accompanied by increased concentrations of amino acids in the blood. There is also evidence suggesting urinary excretion of peptides in this disorder. Patients with Wilson's disease exhibit marked abnormalities of copper metabolism (86–94). Deposition of copper occurs in the lenticulate nucleus of the brain, the liver, and the cornea, and abnormally large quantities of copper are excreted in the urine in the form of copper-dicarboxylic amino acid-peptide chelates. Copper is normally bound to the serum protein ceruloplasmin, whose concentration is reduced in most cases of Wilson's disease. The total copper content of the serum may be normal or higher than normal and there seems to be a parallel between the excretion of amino acids and copper; thus, increase of amino acid excretion induced by ingestion of high protein diets leads to increased excretion of copper. The basic etiology of Wilson's disease is not yet known; although much attention has been given to the possibility that this disorder is due to a defect in ceruloplasmin, other hypotheses have also been considered. It seems probable that the aminoaciduria of Wilson's disease is due to a generalized defect of amino acid reabsorption, probably related to the effect of copper. It is of interest that renal damage induced by metals (uranium, lead, cadmium, mercury) (95–97) and other agents (98, 99) has been reported to lead to aminoaciduria.

Hereditary galactosemia is also associated with aminoaciduria, which disappears when galactose is eliminated from the diet (100–102). In this condition also, aminoaciduria appears to be due to failure of renal absorption. However, the mechanism by which galactose affects amino acid reabsorption is not known.

The aminoaciduria of Hartnup disease (see below) is characteristic in that there is relatively little increased excretion of glycine, imino acids, ornithine, arginine, cystine, and lysine. On the other hand, all of the other amino acids are excreted in considerable quantity. There is substantial evidence that the tubular reabsorption of the excreted amino acids is markedly impaired. Recent studies indicate that patients with Hartnup disease have both renal and intestinal defects in the reabsorption of most of the neutral amino acids (54). The abnormalities of tryptophan metabolism associated with Hartnup disease are considered below.

Aminoaciduria of the "Overflow" Type

Aminoaciduria associated with increased formation or accumulation of amino acids may be due to abnormalities of metabolism in which specific enzymatic steps are affected. In some cases amino acids are formed which are not normally present in significant quantities in the blood plasma and for which there seem to be no renal reabsorptive mechanisms. Examples of this type of aminoaciduria are considered below.

C. Excretion of β-Aminoisobutyric Acid

Levorotatory β-aminoisobutyric acid occurs in the urine of certain clinically normal individuals in amounts ranging from approximately 50 to 300 mg. per day (103–107a). It has been estimated that 5–10% of the population excrete β-aminoisobutyric acid; the amount excreted per day is constant for a given individual and there seems to be no obvious relationship between such excretion and diet or sex (107, 108). The excretion of β-aminoisobutyric acid exhibits a familial incidence, and there is evidence indicating that the variation in excretion of β-amino-isobutyric acid is controlled by a single pair of alleles (107, 109). The trait seems to be more common in individuals of Chinese and Japanese origin (107a).

β-Aminoisobutyric acid arises in the degradation of thymine (see p. 602) and valine (see p. 748). The naturally occurring levorotatory isomer can be considered either as an L-amino acid or as a D-amino acid (see p. 152). Although early studies suggested the possibility that the excretion of β-aminoisobutyric acid was related to a specific renal tubular reabsorption deficiency, more recent studies appear to support an explanation based on a metabolic imbalance. Very little if any β-aminoisobutyric acid is found in the tissues or blood plasma, and it appears that there may be no renal threshold or a very low threshold for this amino acid. There is some evidence that β-aminoisobutyric acid is transported in the kidney by the same system that transports taurine and β-alanine (110).

The most likely explanation for the urinary excretion of β-aminoiso-butyric acid is that it arises from the degradation of thymine. Admin-istration of DNA, dihydrothymine, or thymine to rats was followed by urinary excretion of β-aminoisobutyric acid; enzymatic studies have elucidated the pathway from thymine to β-aminoisobutyric acid, car-bon dioxide, and ammonia [see p. 602 and also (111)]. Administration of thymine in man increased the blood concentration of β-aminoisobutyric acid (109, 112), and administration of thymidine, thymine, dihydrothy-mine, or β-ureidoisobutyric acid led to increased excretion of β-aminoisobutyric acid. Thus far, attempts to increase excretion of β-aminoisobutyric acid by administration of valine have not succeeded.

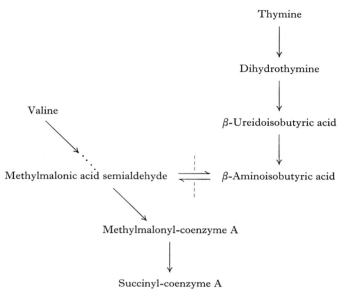

As indicated in the accompanying metabolic scheme, a block in the conversion of β-aminoisobutyric acid to methylmalonic acid semialdehyde by transamination would explain accumulation of the β-amino acid. Were the block subsequent to methylmalonic acid semialdehyde it might be expected that valine administration would lead to excretion of β-aminoisobutyric acid. Although the findings would seem to exclude the valine as a significant precursor of urinary β-aminoisobutyric acid, definitive studies with labeled valine and thymine would clearly be of value in order to settle this point. If, as supposed, the same enzyme catalyzes transamination of β-aminoisobutyric acid and β-alanine (see p. 603), it might be expected that the excretion of β-alanine would accompany that of β-aminoisobutyric acid. Since there is no evidence for parallel excretion of these β-amino acids, one must consider the possibility that separate transaminases are involved. A single transaminase exhibiting a much higher affinity for β-alanine than for β-aminoisobutyric acid might explain the findings, but it is also possible that the alternative pathways of β-alanine metabolism are sufficiently active to dispose of accumulated β-alanine. The possibility that separate transaminases exist for β-alanine and β-aminoisobutyric acid should be considered, however, and it would be of interest to carry out enzymatic studies on individuals who excrete large amounts of β-aminoisobutyric acid to determine whether the β-alanine-transaminase activity is present.

The excretion of β-aminoisobutyric acid is not associated with clinical symptoms, and it therefore appears that the accumulation of this amino acid neither reflects nor produces a significant disturbance of metabolism. β-Aminoisobutyric acid excretion has also been reported in starvation (113) and in patients with various diseases including cancer, tuberculosis, liver disease, lead poisoning, and others (107); in such individuals the occurrence of urinary β-aminoisobutyric acid is consistent with increased destruction of tissue associated with degradation of DNA thymine.

D. Disorders of Glycine and Glyoxylate Metabolism

Glycinemia

Childs et al. (114) have described an infant who exhibited increased serum glycine concentration (as high as 11.2 mg. per 100 ml.) and glycinuria. The clinical findings included mental retardation, episodes of vomiting, lethargy, ketosis, neutropenia, periodic thrombocytopenia, and hypogammaglobulinemia. Although the blood plasma concentrations of several other amino acids (serine, alanine, isoleucine, and valine) were also increased, only glycine was excreted in abnormal amounts in the urine. When the dietary intake of protein was restricted, the glycinuria and aminoacidemia tended to revert to normal values, and the symptoms were improved. Attempts to reduce the blood plasma concentration of glycine by administration of benzoate did not affect symptomatology, and data were obtained suggesting that the leucine present in dietary protein was a factor in the development of symptoms. The metabolic defect (or defects) associated with this disorder is not clear.

Hyperoxaluria

In primary hyperoxaluria there is progressive deposition of calcium oxalate in the kidneys and other tissues (oxalosis) and extensive formation of calcium oxalate stones (115). The disease leads to extensive genito-urinary tract difficulty and may cause early death. Calcium oxalate crystals have been found in various tissues and many of the renal stones formed contain almost pure calcium oxalate. There is some evidence that the blood concentration of oxalate is elevated (116), and the urinary excretion of oxalate may be as high as several hundred milligrams per day. Oral administration of sodium oxalate has been reported to increase the excretion of oxalate, and a transient decrease in oxalate excretion follows administration of large amounts of sodium benzoate. Oxalate excretion has also been observed after oral administration of glycine, glycolic acid, and ascorbic acid. When glycine-1-C^{13} was administered to patients with this condition, relatively rapid incorporation of the isotope into urinary oxalate occurred (117, 118), and a similar result was obtained in another study with glycine-1-C^{14} (119, 120). Recent studies have shown that glycolic acid, a normal urinary constituent, is excreted in much larger amounts by patients with hyperoxaluria (121). When C^{14}-glyoxylate was administered to such patients the rate of respiratory C^{14}-carbon dioxide formation was markedly reduced as compared to control individuals. Isotopic glyoxylate was incorporated into urinary oxalate and glycolate at a more rapid rate in patients with hyperoxaluria than in their parents, or in control subjects. The metabolism of glyoxylate is summarized in the accompanying diagram (see also p. 673). It seems probable that oxalate, an end product of metabolism, is formed by oxidation of glyoxylate, and that in hyperoxaluria there is increased formation of oxalate from glyoxylate. Although it is conceivable that the metabolic defect is associated with increased activity of the system that catalyzes oxidation of glyoxylate to oxalate, other possibilities appear more likely. Thus, overproduction of oxalate is probably related to decreased conversion of glyoxylate to other products. The data indicating conversion of glycine carbon to oxalate carbon and the finding that labeled glyoxylate is converted to glycolate in this condition offer no reason to believe that the transaminase- or dehydrogenase-catalyzed pathways are blocked. The possibility that there is excessive degradation

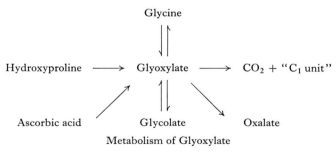

Metabolism of Glyoxylate

of hydroxyproline (see p. 729) or of ascorbic acid [carbon atoms 1 and 2 of this molecule are converted in man to oxalic acid (122)] must be considered. However, the studies on the conversion of C^{14}-glyoxylate to respiratory carbon dioxide point to a defect in the oxidation of glyoxylate. The enzymatic oxidative decarboxylation of glyoxylate (see p. 639) has not yet been thoroughly examined at the enzymatic level and the mechanism of this reaction requires further study. As yet there seems to be no definitive evidence for the nature of the enzymatic defect involved in the conversion of glyoxylate to carbon dioxide in patients with hyperoxaluria (123).

E. Phosphoaminoethanol Metabolism

Hypophosphatasia

This condition, which has been studied in a number of clinics (124, 125), is associated with accumulation of phosphoaminoethanol. The major clinical features are associated with abnormalities in the deposition of apatite which result in a number of bone lesions. The skeletal defects are extensive and depend to some extent on the age at which the condition develops. Infants with this condition experience additional difficulties such as central nervous system symptoms, feeding problems, anemia, and tendency to frequent infections. In some patients calcium is deposited in the renal tubular epithelium and in the surrounding interstitial tissues.

The main known biochemical features of hypophosphatasia are a marked decrease in the activity of serum alkaline phosphatase and elevated concentrations of phosphoaminoethanol (126) in the blood and urine. It has been reported that the alkaline phosphatase activity of bone and other tissues is also reduced in patients with this condition. The disorder appears to be inherited as a Mendelian recessive trait, and examination of heterozygous individuals has shown moderate reduction in serum alkaline phosphatase activity, and greater than normal concentrations of phosphoaminoethanol in the urine and blood. Phosphoaminoethanol is also excreted in the urine of patients with other disorders in which there is a reduction of serum alkaline phosphatase (e.g., hepatic disease, scurvy). The relationship of the clinical to the biochemical findings requires further investigation. It is logical to suppose that at least one of the physiological functions of alkaline phosphatase is to catalyze the hydrolysis of phosphoaminoethanol, but the relationship of this enzyme and its presumed substrate to the processes involved in ossification is not yet known.

F. Metabolism of Ammonia, Arginine, Citrulline, and Ornithine

Introduction

The enzymatic reactions involved in the metabolism of ammonia have been considered above (Chapter IV, Section B; Chapter VI, Sections E and H). In mammals, most of the nitrogen excreted in the urine is in the form of urea, whose nitrogen atoms are derived from carbamyl phosphate and the α-amino group of aspartate. Aspartate nitrogen can arise from ammonium ion by the coupled activity of glutamate dehydrogenase and glutamate-aspartate transaminase. Some ammonium ion is excreted in the urine, thereby replacing sodium and potassium ions, and also serving to excrete hydrogen ions in acidosis. At physiological values of pH, ammonia exists predominantly in the form of ammonium ion, but it has been suggested that un-ionized ammonia (in equilibrium with NH_4^+) is the form which diffuses through the kidney tubules. The excretion of ammonia conserves base by exchanging ammonium ions for sodium or potassium ions (127, 128). The excretion of ammonia, which takes place by passive diffusion (129–133), can result in reabsorption of sodium ion in exchange for hydrogen ion by reducing the pH gradient between the tubule cells and the urine (32, 129). Urinary ammonia is derived from the nitrogen atoms of glutamine and to some extent from other amino acids (see p. 287). There is evidence that the ammonia-producing enzyme systems are increased in activity by chronic acidosis and decreased by chronic alkalosis (127, 134–136).

Ammonia is also absorbed from the intestine, where it is formed by bacterial urease and by other reactions. It is carried via the portal blood to the liver, where it is converted to urea. Ammonia is utilized for glutamine synthesis in the liver and other tissues (e.g., brain). The mechanisms responsible for utilization of ammonia are exceedingly efficient and there is normally little free ammonia in mammalian blood and tissues [(137); see p. 286]. The liver plays a highly significant role in ammonia metabolism; in experiments in which the portal circulation was shunted directly into the vena cava, the peripheral blood concentration of ammonia increased appreciably (138, 139). In man, elevated blood concentrations of ammonia are commonly observed in liver disease (139–146) and similar findings have been made in experiments on animals (147). In the classical studies of Kirk and Sumner (148), injection of urease produced rapid ammonia intoxication. Administration of ammonium chloride to normal human subjects had relatively little effect on the concentration of blood ammonia, whereas increased concentrations of ammonia were observed in patients with liver damage (148). In general, the depth of coma in terminal hepatic disease is proportional to the peripheral venous and arterial blood concentrations of ammonia. Normally, the arterial blood concentration is higher than that of the venous blood. Bessman and associates (149, 150) showed that there is an increase in the cerebral arteriovenous difference in ammonia in hepatic disease, and that the brain takes up ammonia when the concentration of ammonia in the blood rises above approximately 1 μg. per milliliter. The concentration of amino acids in the blood often rises in hepatic disease (151, 152), and after hepatectomy in animals (153). However, the blood concentrations of glutamine have been reported to remain relatively constant in hepatic disease (154).

Although it is not at all certain that ammonia is the only toxic agent of significance in the development of hepatic coma, there is reason to believe that increased concentrations of ammonia could interfere with utilization of α-ketoglutarate (150). Such interference might result in inhibition of the citric acid cycle, and thus with the oxidative metabolism of the brain. According to this interpretation, high concentrations of ammonia would lead to increased formation of glutamate from α-ketoglutarate. This reaction, catalyzed by glutamic dehydrogenase, would effectively remove α-ketoglutarate. Recknagel and Potter (155), in an investigation of the ketogenic effect of ammonia on liver minces, found that conversion of α-ketoglutarate to glutamate occurred in the presence of ammonium chloride; this resulted in reduced formation of oxaloacetate, with a resultant shunt of metabolites in the direction of acetoacetate formation. Consistent with this explanation of the mechanism of hepatic coma is the observation that the oxygen consumption of the brain is decreased in hepatic coma (137, 156). Increased levels of blood ammonia have occasionally been observed in other disorders, e.g., shock (157) and psychosis associated with liver disease (158).

High blood and tissue ammonia concentrations might conceivably lead to increased glutamine formation from glutamate and adenosine triphosphate and thus reduce the quantity of adenosine triphosphate available for other reactions, e.g., acetylcholine synthesis (159). Tigerman and Mac Vicar (160) found that tissue glutamine was increased in rats by feeding ammonium carbonate and glutamate for a period of 10 days; on the other hand, administration of ammonium carbonate or of glutamate separately did not increase tissue glutamine. Since brain contains a high concentration of glutamate, it is possible that increased glutamine synthesis might occur in the presence of "extra" ammonia.

Glutamate administration has been used in the therapy of hepatic coma [see, for example (161–166)]. Although glutamate appears to be effective in preventing ammonia-induced convulsions and coma in animals (147), its use in the treatment of hepatic coma has not produced striking results, probably because of the reduction in liver function and associated decrease in total activity of glutamine synthetase. Furthermore, administered glutamate does not reach the brain to an appreciable extent (160, 167).

Greenstein and collaborators (168–170) found that the toxicity to rats of relatively large doses of individual amino acids or of an amino acid mixture was reduced by simultaneous or prior administration of L-arginine. Subsequent study revealed that arginine exerted a protective effect against toxic doses of ammonium acetate. L-Arginine was more effective than was D-arginine or L-ornithine, although these compounds afforded some protection. Glutamate, aspartate, and α-ketoglutarate were relatively ineffective. Presumably the effect of arginine is related to an increase of the activity of the urea cycle. Attempts to use arginine therapy clinically have been accompanied by variable degrees of success [see, for example (171–172b)]. It is evident that hepatic disease is often associated with a general reduction of liver enzyme activity and that administration of "extra" substrate for the urea cycle therefore might be ineffective in increasing the total formation of urea. Despite these considerations, trial of glutamate and arginine therapy may be worthwhile in particular cases of hepatic coma, but restriction of dietary protein and antibiotic therapy (to reduce bacterial flora urease) may often be more effective measures.

Argininosuccinic Aciduria

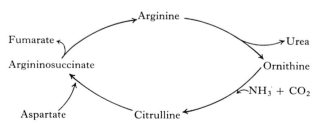

Several genetically determined defects that seem to involve enzymatic reactions of the Krebs-Henseleit urea cycle have been discovered in man during the last few years. The first of these to be found was argininosuccinic aciduria, a condition in which there is mental retardation and other symptomatology in association with the urinary excretion of argininosuccinic acid (39, 173–178). Individuals afflicted with this condition develop evidence of mental retardation within the first few years of life, often in association with epilepsy, ataxia, and other abnormalities including hepatomegaly. About half of the patients that have thus far been seen also exhibit a characteristic deformity of the hair, which becomes brittle and tufted; histological examination shows small nodes in the hair shafts associated with splitting of the hairs. Mental retardation is generally severe, although one patient with an intelligence quotient of 92 has been reported. Most of the patients with this condition have been found to excrete several grams of argininosuccinic acid per day; one patient was reported to excrete almost 10 g. per day. Argininosuccinic acid has apparently not been detected in the urine, blood plasma, or cerebrospinal fluid of normal individuals or animals. In this disease, the blood plasma concentration of argininosuccinic acid may be several milligrams per 100 ml.; somewhat higher concentrations have been found in the cerebrospinal fluid. The renal clearance of argininosuccinic acid is high and it has been concluded that there is little or no renal tubular reabsorption.

The fact that the concentration of argininosuccinic acid is higher in cerebrospinal fluid than in blood serum suggests that the primary defect is localized in the brain. There is evidence that arginine can be formed in the brain and that it can be cleaved to urea in this tissue [(179–181); see p. 696]. Normal human brain can catalyze the synthesis and cleavage of argininosuccinic acid (181). The defect in argininosuccinic aciduria might logically be ascribed to decreased or absent brain argininosuccinase. The argininosuccinase activity of rat brain was found to be approximately 1% of that of rat liver; activity is also present in blood, but this is less than 5% of that of brain (182). Studies on blood hemolysates from normal individuals and patients with argininosuccinic aciduria have shown that only the preparations obtained from the patients are completely lacking in this activity (183). It is of interest that the parents of children afflicted with this condition showed decreased argininosuccinase activity. These findings are consistent with recessive Mendelian inheritance. In a recent study, the urine of fifty members of a family of an individual with this disease was examined; a number of these apparently normal individuals excreted argininosuccinic acid, although in smaller quantities than did the patient (184). Administration of citrulline increases the excretion of argininosuccinate in patients with the disease, and the same phenomenon was observed in studies on the mother of such a patient. Much smaller amounts of argininosuccinate are excreted by normal individuals after ingestion of citrulline.

Although the data point to a defect in argininosuccinase as the primary factor in this disease, a number of interesting questions remain to be answered. It is evident that some urea formation can be catalyzed by the brain; the presence of arginase and the enzymes necessary for the formation and cleavage of argininosuccinate has been demonstrated, but there seem to be no data as to whether the brain can synthesize citrulline. It is clear that the urea synthesized by the brain does not represent a significant fraction of total urea formation. Since the concentration of urea in the peripheral blood is apparently normal in this condition, it may be postulated that the genetic block is restricted to the brain argininosuccinase. On the other hand, the absence of this activity in the blood cells of patients with this disorder suggests that there may be a generalized deficiency of the enzyme. Thus, the activity of liver argininosuccinase may also be reduced, but such reduction may be insufficient to affect the over-all production of urea. Other data suggest that argininosuccinase is present in the liver in considerable excess as compared to the other enzymes of the urea cycle (185). Direct enzymatic studies of the liver and brain of patients with argininosuccinic aciduria should help to answer these questions. It seems unlikely that there is complete absence of liver argininosuccinase activity; such a finding would necessitate considerable revision of current ideas concerning the mechanism of urea formation in mammals.

The biochemical findings offer no immediate clues to the major symptomatology of this disorder. Thus, the cerebral symptoms (epilepsy, ataxia, retardation), the peculiar hair defect, and the enlarged liver observed in many of these patients requires explanation and study. It is of interest that examination of the chromosomes of one patient revealed that the modal chromosome number was 47 rather than the usual 46; in studies on heterozygous individuals chromosome numbers of 45 and 47 were found (184). The siblings of one patient with this disorder were found to be mentally retarded but they did not excrete argininosuccinic acid.

Ammonemia

This disease, which has been described in two infants who are first cousins, is marked by mental retardation associated with cerebral cortical atrophy (186). Paper chromatographic examination of the urine was reported to show an increase in the excretion of glutamine, and the concentration of glutamine in the cerebrospinal fluid was four to five times the normal value. Higher than normal concentrations of ammonia were found in the blood and cerebrospinal fluid. Study of these patients revealed no evidence of gross liver failure or cirrhosis, nor was there apparently unduly large absorption of ammonia from the gut.

Examination of a liver biopsy obtained from one of these cases was reported to show that the ornithine transcarbamylase activity was about 10% of that of two control autopsy samples. Carbamyl phosphate synthetase activity of the biopsy sample was about 50% of that of one control autopsy sample, but approximately the same as that of another. These findings were interpreted to indicate a genetic block in the urea cycle at the step catalyzed by ornithine transcarbamylase; the data were considered to support the view that a cycle other than the generally accepted one is operative in these patients. The latter suggestion follows from the statement that the concentration of blood urea was normal in these patients. No information seems to be available about the ornithine concentration of the blood and urine. The few data available seem to be consistent with a partial genetic block of ornithine transcarbamylase activity. However, if there is a huge (over one hundredfold) excess of ornithine transcarbamylase in human liver [cf. (185)], one would not expect even a 90% block of this enzyme to decrease urea formation or lead to an accumulation of ammonia, since the rates at which all of the reactions of the urea cycle normally proceed would presumably be the same and therefore be equal to that of the slowest step. Definite conclusions about the defect in ammonemia must await acquisition of more data about the activities of the several enzymes of the urea cycle *in vivo*, and also about the nature of this disorder. In this disease, and in others that seem to involve the urea cycle, there is a paucity of published information on the urea concentrations of the blood and urine. Although urea values are stated to be normal, it would seem necessary to obtain detailed quantitative data on blood and urine urea concentrations at various time intervals after ingestion of nitrogen-containing dietary constituents. It is conceivable that the fasting blood urea concentration and the total daily excretion of urea could be within normal limits even in the presence of partial blocks of the cycle which might delay urea formation after feeding without affecting the over-all daily formation of urea. It must be admitted that the findings in this condition can be explained by postulating the existence of an alternative pathway of urea formation as suggested (186), but there are at this time no definitive data for such a pathway. The observations on these patients indicate that there is excessive formation of ammonia, and this is associated with increased cerebrospinal fluid glutamine and increased excretion of glutamine. The formation of glutamine can be viewed as a compensatory mechanism for removal of ammonia; other data have shown that glutamine formation can provide a mechanism for ammonia utilization (187). On the other hand, it is possible that a mechanism exists in man (similar to that in *E. coli* and in the mushroom, see p. 697) that utilizes glutamine for citrulline formation. The accumulation of glutamine might then be due to its failure to be used for carbamyl phosphate formation.

Citrullinuria

This condition has been described in an infant that exhibited convulsions and alkalotic coma early in life; the patient subsequently showed evidence of severe retardation and diffusely abnormal electroencephalographic findings (188–190). Considerable amounts of citrulline were found in the blood, cerebrospinal fluid, and urine. The daily excretion of citrulline varied from 0.48 to 2.15 g. per day; this amino acid is not normally detectable in urine. The blood concentration of citrulline varied between 20 to 30 mg. per 100 ml. or approximately 50 times the normal value, and the concentration of citrulline in the cerebrospinal fluid was 6 mg. per 100 ml., which is also far above the normal concentration. The patient was stated to excrete normal amounts of urea, and no abnormalities were observed in relation to the concentration of the other amino acids in the body fluids. When the dietary intake of protein was reduced, the excretion of both citrulline and urea decreased. Increase of dietary protein led to increased urea and citrulline excretion, as well as an increase in the plasma concentration of citrulline. The postprandial blood ammonia concentration was extremely high (approximately 1 mg. per 100 ml.). A considerable portion of ingested citrulline could be accounted for in the urine. Although ingestion of glutamate, ornithine, arginine, and proline did not change the blood concentration or urinary excretion of citrulline, it did increase urinary excretion of urea.

It is possible that patients with citrullinuria are blocked in argininosuccinate synthetase, but it would appear that such a block is not complete since urea formation takes place. Argininosuccinate synthetase is thought to be one of the slowest steps of the urea cycle and might therefore be rate-limiting. The large postprandial increase in the concentration of blood ammonia would be consistent with a partial block, but eventually most of the ammonia must be converted to urea. Perhaps the symptomatology is related to delayed formation of urea and consequently retardation of ammonia utilization. Further studies on such patients are required, especially investigations in which enzymatic activities are determined. Several other cases of citrullinuria have been reported (191).

The excretion of citrulline is sometimes accompanied by other amino acids (192, 193) and the condition therefore appears to differ from that described above. In cystinuria, citrulline excretion may occur along with excretion of lysine, cystine, arginine, and ornithine; the possibility that the urinary citrulline in such cases arises from arginine by the action of arginine desimidase (see p. 699) present in the organisms of the bacterial flora must be considered.

G. Metabolism of Hydroxyproline and Proline

Hydroxyprolinemia

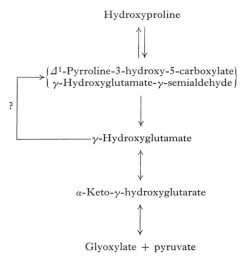

Hydroxyproline

$\left\{\begin{matrix}\Delta^1\text{-Pyrroline-3-hydroxy-5-carboxylate}\\\gamma\text{-Hydroxyglutamate-}\gamma\text{-semialdehyde}\end{matrix}\right\}$

?

γ-Hydroxyglutamate

α-Keto-γ-hydroxyglutarate

Glyoxylate + pyruvate

Efron *et al.* (194) have described a patient, the apparent offspring of siblings, who was severely retarded mentally and excreted large amounts of hydroxyproline in the urine. The excretion of hydroxyproline averaged 267 mg. of hydroxyproline per day and the urine contained normal amounts of hydroxyproline-containing peptides. The blood concentration of hydroxyproline varied between 0.2 and 0.41 μmole per ml. (normal, less than 0.01), and was not affected by ingestion of a hydroxyproline-free diet or supplementation of the diet with proline. The concentrations of the other amino acids of the blood and urine were within normal ranges. Efron (195) has reported that normal individuals excrete Δ^1-pyrroline-3-hydroxy-5-carboxylate, γ-hydroxyglutamate, and α-keto-γ-hydroxyglutarate after ingestion of L-hydroxyproline (100 mg. per kg.). In contrast, the patient with hydroxyprolinemia, even after ingestion of twice this amount of hydroxyproline, did not excrete detectable quantities of any of these metabolites. An oral proline tolerance test on the patient showed no abnormality as compared to a control individual, suggesting that the degradative pathway for L-proline is not impaired in hydroxyprolinemia. If the first step in hydroxyproline degradation is blocked in this patient (as seems probable) the findings would suggest that in man there are separate proline and hydroxyproline oxidase systems (see p. 714). The data indicate that dietary hydroxyproline is probably not a significant source of blood or urine hydroxyproline in this patient. Furthermore, there is no evidence for an abnormality of collagen metabolism. Although the origin of the blood and urinary hydroxyproline in this patient is not yet fully explained, two observations (195) are of considerable interest. In the course of an oral proline tolerance test, evidence was obtained for a significant increase in the plasma concentration of hydroxyproline; this observation suggests that free proline may be converted to free hydroxyproline. It was also observed that after administration of C^{14}-glyoxylate, radioactivity was found in urinary α-keto-γ-hydroxyglutarate, γ-hydroxyglutamate, and hydroxyproline. The recovery of label in hydroxyproline was approximately twice that found in the urinary glycine; this suggests that free hydroxyproline may be synthesized by the pathway considered elsewhere (see p. 725) in which glyoxylate and pyruvate condense to yield α-keto-γ-hydroxyglutarate, which is converted to the corresponding amino acid and thence to hydroxyproline. The relationship of the accumulation of hydroxyproline to the clinical symptomatology is not yet clear.

In the Marfan syndrome, there is also considerable excretion of hydroxyproline, apparently in the form of peptides (11, 196); in contrast to the hydroxyprolinemia syndrome discussed above, the Marfan syndrome (the basic metabolic defect of which is not yet understood) involves an abnormality of collagen synthesis associated with increased collagen turnover.

Prolinemia

Studies have been carried out on several patients with an inborn condition associated with prolinemia (195, 197, 198). One form of this condition occurs in conjunction with hereditary renal disease involving congenital anomalies of the kidney. A patient with this type of disease and three of his similarly affected siblings exhibited blood plasma proline concentrations of 0.56–1.75 μmoles per ml. compared to normal values in the range 0.09 to 0.29. These patients excreted proline, hydroxyproline, and glycine in the urine when the blood concentration of proline exceeded 0.86 μmole per ml. There is evidence that proline, hydroxyproline, and glycine share the same renal transport system (see p. 273); in the presence of a high concentration of proline in the glomerular filtrate, glycine and hydroxyproline, as well as proline, are incompletely reabsorbed. A convulsive syndrome has been observed in infants possessing apparently normal concentrations of amino acids in the blood plasma, in which proline, hydroxyproline, and glycine are excreted in the urine; this condition seems to be due to a genetic defect involving a specific renal transport system (199). Presumably the excretion of hydroxyproline and glycine observed in patients with prolinemia has a similar basis; thus the competitive effect of proline on transport of hydroxyproline and glycine would be expected to result in some excretion of the latter two amino acids. It is of interest that intravenous administration of proline to normal individuals leads to excretion of proline as well as glycine and hydroxyproline (67).

A liver homogenate prepared from a liver sample obtained from a patient with prolinemia did not form appreciable quantities of Δ^1-pyrroline-5-carboxylate from L-proline; in contrast, this conversion was observed with liver preparations obtained from control liver samples (195). When the liver homogenate obtained from this prolinemic patient was incubated with hydroxyproline, the extent of Δ^1-pyrroline-3-hydroxy-5-carboxylate formation was appreciable and about the same as observed with control liver preparations. The liver homogenate obtained from the patient converted little, if any, C^{14}-proline carbon to glutamate carbon in contrast to the controls, but both the prolinemic liver homo-genate and control homogenates catalyzed substantial conversion of C^{14}-hydroxyproline to C^{14}-γ-hydroxyglutamic acid. A liver homogenate obtained from the father of the patient exhibited some reduction in proline oxidase activity and in the conversion of C^{14}-proline to C^{14}-glutamate. These observations provide a reasonable basis for the con-clusion that, in this form of prolinemia, the enzymatic defect is a deficiency of proline oxidase. It is of interest that the proline oxidase activity of the heterozygous individual studied was somewhat lower than that of the controls, and the findings therefore suggest that the disease is transmitted as a recessive Mendelian trait.

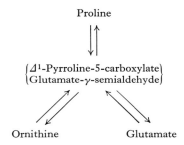

Proline

$$\updownarrow$$

$\begin{Bmatrix} \varDelta^1\text{-Pyrroline-5-carboxylate} \\ \text{Glutamate-}\gamma\text{-semialdehyde} \end{Bmatrix}$

Ornithine   Glutamate

A patient with another type of prolinemia associated with convulsive disease and mental retardation was found to excrete large amounts of proline, hydroxyproline, and glycine in the urine (195). The blood plasma concentration of proline was markedly elevated, reaching a value of 3.69 μmoles per ml. at one time. The urinary excretion of proline was about 1.4 g. per day, and smaller but abnormally large amounts of hydroxy-proline and glycine were also found in the urine. Chromatography of the urine revealed a compound with the properties of $\varDelta^1$-pyrroline-5-carboxylate; thus, it reacted with o-aminobenzaldehyde (see p. 708). Although no enzymatic studies have been carried out on this patient, the findings are consistent with the conclusion that there is a metabolic block of $\varDelta^1$-pyrroline-5-carboxylate dehydrogenase.

The relationship between prolinemia, the apparently associated enzymatic deficiencies, and the symptomatology is not yet clear. There is evidence that the renal disease is not directly associated with proline metabolism, since it can be inherited separately. A heterozygous individual who exhibited a partial deficiency of proline oxidase was apparently free of renal disease, and prolinemia has been observed without renal disease.

H. Metabolism of Isoleucine, Leucine, and Valine

Maple Syrup Urine Disease

Menkes *et al.* (201) reported observations on four infants in the same family who exhibited severe central nervous system symptoms and excreted urine that possessed an odor similar to that of maple syrup. Later, Westall *et al.* (202, 203) found a somewhat older mentally retarded infant with similar symptoms and findings, and subsequently a number of other cases of maple syrup urine disease were reported (204–206). The symptoms, which are generally seen early in life, include convulsions, mental retardation, respiratory distress, and feeding difficulties; many such patients die within a few weeks of birth. However, older patients have been observed whose principal difficulty is mental retardation. The blood plasma concentrations of valine, leucine, and isoleucine are greatly elevated in this disorder and there may be a reduction in the concentrations of certain other amino acids including cystine, alanine, serine, and threonine. Alloisoleucine (207) (originally thought to be methionine) (204) is also found in the blood plasma. These amino acids are present in increased amounts in the urine, cerebrospinal fluid, and saliva. The α-keto analogs of isoleucine, leucine, and valine have been found in the blood plasma and urine, and there is also evidence for the occurrence of corresponding α-hydroxy acids. Dancis *et al.* (208–211) have examined the ability of white blood cells and skin fibroblasts (grown in tissue culture) from patients with maple syrup urine disease to catalyze the decarboxylation of α-ketoisocaproic acid (see p. 744). They found that this enzyme activity was not present in such preparations obtained from patients, but was present in comparable preparations from control individuals. It seems probable that the same enzyme catalyzes the oxidative decarboxylation of α-ketoisocaproic acid, α-keto-β-methyl-valeric acid, and α-ketoisovaleric acid.

$$\underset{\underset{NH_2}{|}}{RCHCOOH} \rightleftharpoons \underset{\underset{O}{\|}}{RCCOOH} \rightarrow \underset{\underset{O}{\|}}{RC}\!-\!S\!-\!CoA + CO_2$$

The nature of the enzymatic block explains the accumulation of the α-keto acid analogs of leucine, isoleucine, and valine, as well as the corresponding amino acids. Conversion of the α-keto acids to the corresponding α-hydroxy acids is probably a side reaction catalyzed by lactic dehydrogenase (212) or a similar activity. The presence of alloisoleucine in the body fluids of patients with this disorder is probably due to racemization of α-keto-β-methylvaleric acid followed by transamination of D-α-keto-β-methylvaleric acid to L-alloisoleucine (see p. 165). Some patients with maple syrup urine disease have been found to exhibit hypoglycemia; this phenomenon may be related to other observations which indicate that leucine and α-ketoisocaproic acid can induce hypoglycemia (213–215). "Idiopathic hypoglycemia" has been observed in infants and children who do not have maple syrup urine disease, and in some such patients administration of leucine induces a striking decrease in the blood glucose concentration; the explanation for this effect is not known. However, it seems quite possible that there is a relationship between leucine metabolism and the synthesis of steroid hormones. As discussed elsewhere (see p. 747), the degradation of leucine leads to formation of β-hydroxy-β-methylglutaryl-coenzyme A, which is the precursor of mevalonate. Perhaps administration of leucine stimulates the production of steroids by this pathway.

It is difficult to explain the maple syrup odor of the urine of these patients. Some impure preparations of the branched-chain amino acids exhibit an odor which resembles that of certain samples of maple syrup. A similar odor is sometimes noted with preparations of α-keto-β-methylvaleric acid. The relationship of the biochemical defect to the clinical symptomatology is not yet clear. Post-mortem studies have revealed a number of pathological changes in the central nervous system.

Propionate Metabolism

The metabolism of propionic acid, which is formed in the degradation of several amino acids, is significantly affected by vitamin B_{12} deficiency. In vitamin B_{12} deficiency in sheep, the primary metabolic disturbance appears to be a block in conversion of methylmalonyl-coenzyme A to succinyl-coenzyme A, a reaction catalyzed by a cobamide enzyme (see p. 750). When the dietary intake of cobalt is reduced in sheep, synthesis of vitamin B_{12} by the rumen bacteria decreases, and the animals develop a characteristic deficiency syndrome (216). Ruminants obtain a considerable portion of their energy from acetate and propionate produced by fermentation of ingested carbohydrate. In early studies (217, 218), methylmalonic acid was found in the urine of rats with liver necrosis or after treatment with carcinogenic agents. Increased urinary excretion of methylmalonic acid has been observed in patients with pernicious anemia (219–221). In addition to megaloblastic anemia, patients with vitamin B_{12} deficiency commonly experience central nervous system disease, glossitis, and gastrointestinal symptoms. Such individuals exhibit a prompt reticulocyte response when treated with folic acid, but this therapy does not influence neurological symptoms or excretion of methylmalonic acid. The latter phenomena are reversed by administration of vitamin B_{12}. The possibility that the block of methylmalonylcoenzyme A isomerase is related to the nervous system disease is attractive, but requires further investigation.

I. Methionine Metabolism

Cystathioninuria

$$
\left.\begin{array}{c}\text{Homocysteine} \\ + \\ \text{serine}\end{array}\right\} \longrightarrow \text{cystathionine} \longrightarrow \left\{\begin{array}{c}\alpha\text{-ketobutyrate} \\ + \\ \text{cysteine} \\ + \\ \text{ammonia}\end{array}\right.
$$

Harris *et al.* (222) have described a 64-year-old female imbecile who excreted about 0.5 g. of cystathionine per day in the urine. Feeding methionine increased the excretion of cystathionine, and cystathioninuria of lesser extent was found in two of the patient's relatives who did not exhibit clinical symptoms. Subsequently, Frimpter *et al.* (223) observed a 44-year-old man with acromegaly, congenital defects, and mental aberrations, who excreted approximately 1 g. of cystathionine per day. Administration of pyridoxine reduced the excretion of cystathionine. This patient exhibited an elevated plasma concentration of cystathionine (0.45 mg. per 100 ml.), but the concentrations of the other amino acids were normal. The patient's sister and her four children exhibited lesser degrees of cystathioninuria, but were apparently clinically normal. Although urinary excretion of cystathionine has been observed in vitamin B_6 deficiency in the rat (224) and in man (225), no obvious evidence for vitamin B_6 deficiency was found in these patients. Considerable amounts of cystathionine are present in human brain (226) and cerebrospinal fluid (227), suggesting that this compound may play a role in cerebral function. Other tissues have little if any cystathionine. Examination of the tissues of the patient reported by Harris *et al.* (222) revealed considerable amounts of cystathionine. The possibility that this condition is associated with a hereditary deficiency of cystathionase must be considered, but as yet no direct enzymatic investigations have been carried out, and the relationship of cystathionine to cerebral function requires further study. It may be of significance that chromosome culture study of one patient showed a very large Y chromosome (223), but this has sometimes been found in the absence of disease. The finding that vitamin B_6 therapy reduced cystathioninuria in this patient suggests that cystathionase is present, but the enzyme may be synthesized in an abnormal form or in markedly reduced amounts.

Homocystinuria

Carson *et al.* (228) have described homocystinuria in two sisters who exhibited convulsive disease and mental retardation. A liver biopsy from one of these children showed extensive fatty change but no necrosis or cirrhosis, and examination of the eyes of both children showed lens dislocation. These patients had fine, dry, sparse hair, red mottled skin, and excreted 50–100 mg. of urinary homocystine per day. The results of methionine tolerance tests were not conclusive, but some evidence was obtained suggesting that the affected children and their mother exhibited slightly reduced ability to metabolize methionine; they showed a larger excretion of methionine than found in normal individuals. Administration of methionine increased homocystine excretion only slightly. Analysis of the cystine content of the hair of one child gave a value of 16.6 mg. per 100 mg. of dry hair, which is considered to be normal. Treatment of one patient with cystine did not seem to have a significant effect on the symptomatology. In these and other patients increased blood concentrations of homocystine and methionine were observed (229). Examination of a liver biopsy obtained from one patient failed to reveal cystathionine synthetase activity, while this activity was found in biopsy samples from controls (229a). In another study no cystathionine was found in the brain of a patient with this disease (200). The chemical findings are consistent with a complete or nearly complete absence of cystathionine synthetase. For such patients cystine (or cysteine) must be considered as an essential dietary amino acid. It is of interest that only a small fraction of dietary methionine is excreted as homocystine in this disorder suggesting that larger than normal amounts of methionine are metabolized by alternate pathways. The mechanisms responsible for the clinical findings are not yet clear. However, it seems likely that cystathionine is essential for normal brain function. Although it is possible that such patients are deficient in cystine, it is probable that sufficient amounts of this amino acid are available in the diet. The possibility that other metabolites of methionine are produced in toxic quantities must also be considered. The excretion of urinary homocystine is apparently not accompanied by calculus formation, and it is of note that the daily excretion of homocystine in these patients is much less than that of cystine in cystinuria.

J. Histidine Metabolism

Histidinemia

In 1961 Ghadimi et al. (230, 231) reported histidinemia and histidin-uria in two sisters, the youngest of which (age 3) exhibited a speech defect. Their urine gave a green color when treated with ferric chloride, a finding consistent with the presence of imidazolepyruvic acid (see below). It was suggested that the condition might be associated with a deficiency of either histidine deaminase or urocanase. Later, other patients with this disorder were observed, and it was found that they excreted imidazole-pyruvic acid, imidazolelactic acid, and imidazoleacetic acid in the urine (232–235a). Intravenous administration of urocanic acid led to urinary excretion of formiminoglutamic acid, suggesting that urocanase is not blocked in histidinemia (232, 233). Studies by LaDu et al. (233–235) showed that the enzymatic defect in histidinemia is the absence of histidase; thus, examination of the stratum corneum obtained by skin biopsy failed to reveal histidase activity. Histidase was found in similar biopsies obtained from normal individuals, and it was also found that an unaffected sibling and the father of a patient with this disorder exhibited skin histidase activity values that were somewhat lower than the normal range. The sweat and skin of patients with this disorder do not contain urocanic acid, in contrast to normal controls; heterozygous individuals show reduced amounts of urocanic acid. Although it has been suggested that urocanic acid protects the skin from ultraviolet radiation (236), histidinemic patients seem to show no unusual sensitivity to ultraviolet light. The blood plasma histidine concentrations of patients with this disease may be as much as fifteen times the normal value, and administra-tion of histidine increases the blood plasma histidine concentration to some extent; in contrast, normal individuals show an immediate rise which is followed by a rapid fall to normal levels within several hours.

It is of interest that many of the patients with histidinemia exhibit impairment of speech. Speech is said to be not completely intelligible, and there are defects in articulation and retardation in the development of language skills. The relationship between histidine metabolism and the symptomatology is not clear.

Cerebromacular Degeneration

Bessman and Baldwin (237) have observed abnormal excretion of carnosine, anserine, histidine, 1-methylhistidine, and several other compounds in patients with cerebromacular degeneration. The parents and siblings of such individuals exhibited similar urinary findings, but did not have neurological or retinal disease. The blood concentration of histidine is not increased in this type of disorder in which there may be a defect in the renal tubular transport system for these imidazole compounds. Cerebromacular degeneration is inherited as a dominant trait.

Mastocytosis

Relatively large quantities of histamine are produced in the mast cells, which contain considerable amounts of histidine decarboxylase (see p. 326); these cells also contain heparin and (in certain species) serotonin. In urticaria pigmentosa, there is an infiltration of mast cells into the skin; the clinical symptoms include erythema, edema, and the occurrence of multiple nodular lesions (238, 239). In systemic mast cell disease there is infiltration of mast cells into the liver, spleen, and other organs (240–242). Patients with this condition experience local and generalized flushing, urticaria, tachycardia, shock, and various gastrointestinal symptoms. The liver and spleen may be considerably enlarged and have been found to contain unusually high concentrations of histamine. The clinical findings are associated with an excess of histidine decarboxylase due to extensive proliferation of the mast cells. There seems to be no evidence for the occurrence of serotonin in human mast cells, but it is possible that histamine may be responsible for serotonin release from the platelets; serotonin and histamine are both released in anaphylaxis in the rabbit (243). Patients with mastocytosis frequently excrete increased amounts of histamine and 1-methylimidazole-4-acetic acid in the urine; excretion of the latter compound supports the view that the condition is related to an overproduction of histamine rather than to a block in its degradation.

K. Tryptophan Metabolism

Hartnup Disease

A condition known as H disease (Hartnup disease, Hart's syndrome) was first described by Baron *et al.* (244), who observed a family, some of whose members exhibited pellagra-like skin rashes, temporary cerebellar ataxia, and aminoaciduria. A number of other patients with this disorder have been described; several of these individuals exhibit psychiatric disturbances as well as the characteristic skin condition (245). Although the clinical manifestations are variable, aminoaciduria is relatively constant and characterized by increased excretion of alanine, serine, glutamine, asparagine, leucine, isoleucine, valine, phenylalanine, tyrosine, tryptophan, and histidine. The excretion of cystine, lysine, and glycine is moderately increased, but little if any proline, hydroxyproline, methionine, and arginine are found in the urine. Investigations of the renal clearance of amino acids in this condition revealed impaired tubular reabsorption of those amino acids excreted in abnormally large amounts (39).

Early studies revealed that patients with this condition excreted indolylacetylglutamine, indican, and other indole compounds in the urine (246). These observations, as well as the clinical finding of a pellagra-like skin rash, suggested an abnormality of tryptophan metabolism. However, administration of antibiotics rapidly decreases excretion of indole compounds in the urine, suggesting that these arise as a result of bacterial metabolism in the gastrointestinal tract. Subsequent work indicates that there is an intestinal defect in absorption of tryptophan and other neutral amino acids (54, 247). Failure of tryptophan to be absorbed by the intestine might under certain dietary conditions be responsible for a relative deficiency of nicotinic acid, thereby explaining the pellagra-like condition. It appears probable that the disease is associated with a defect of amino acid transport both in the renal tubules and in the intestine. It would be of interest to learn whether the transport defects in this condition and in cystinuria are restricted to the kidney and intestine, or whether the deficiencies affect other cells as well.

Carcinoid

In patients with advanced malignant carcinoid (tumors derived from the enterochromaffin or argentaffin cells), tryptophan metabolism often takes place predominantly by the serotonin route (248). When the dietary intake of nicotinic acid is low, interference with the conversion of tryptophan to niacin can result in a deficiency of this vitamin. Patients with carcinoid characteristically experience loss of weight, flushes, chronic diarrhea, respiratory distress, and cardiac valvular disease (249–253). Serotonin is produced by the chromaffin cells of the gastro-

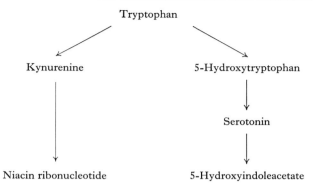

intestinal tract (254, 255) and the carcinoid tumors derived from these cells contain considerable amounts of serotonin (248, 256–258). Patients with malignant carcinoid excrete large amounts of 5-hydroxyindole-acetic acid (see p. 873), and the blood concentrations of serotonin in such patients are considerably higher than normal; serotonin and other 5-hydroxyindole compounds may be excreted in considerable quantity in the urine. Carcinoid tumors contain high concentrations of 5-hydroxy-indole derivatives, the major component of which is serotonin. When carcinoid tumors are excised, there is characteristically a reduction in the urinary excretion of 5-hydroxyindoleacetic acid; however, persistence of the excretion of abnormally large amounts of 5-hydroxyindoleacetic acid has been found to be related to the presence of metastases. The clinical findings in patients with malignant carcinoid tumors appear to be explained by (*a*) production of large quantities of serotonin by the tumor and metastases, (*b*) decreased formation of niacin, and (*c*) protein deficiency associated with lack of tryptophan. Normally only about 1% of dietary tryptophan is utilized for serotonin formation, whereas utilization of the order of 60% has been observed in some patients with malignant carcinoid.

Serotonin was independently isolated by Rapport and associates (259), and by Erspamer (254, 255, 260), who called this compound enteramine. Serotonin exerts a stimulatory effect on smooth muscle and produces increased motility of the intestine, bronchoconstriction, and vaso-constriction. Much of the serotonin of the blood is found in the platelets (255, 261). The release of serotonin from the platelets may be of significance in vasoconstriction associated with hemostasis (262, 263). The effects of serotonin on smooth muscle are probably responsible for many of the symptoms observed in patients with malignant carcinoid. The presence of serotonin in the brain has led to the suggestion that it may perform an important function in this organ. It is thought that reserpine causes the release of serotonin from the brain; administration of reserpine leads to increased urinary excretion of 5-hydroxyindoleacetic acid. Some of the effects of serotonin and reserpine are antagonized by lysergic acid diethylamide, a compound that produces hallucinations and other mental disturbances when administered to normal individuals in exceedingly low doses. There has been much speculation about the function of serotonin in the brain, and Woolley (264) has recently summarized evidence concerning the possible relationship between the metabolism of serotonin (and other compounds) and the development of psychoses.

There is now a very considerable literature on the urinary excretion of tryptophan metabolites in various human disorders including tuberculosis, diabetes, Hodgkin's disease, multiple myeloma, leukemia, bladder cancer, and other conditions. In some instances metabolism of tryptophan by organisms of the intestinal flora may be responsible for the appearance of urinary metabolites of this amino acid. In addition, it is known that tryptophan metabolites may be excreted in pregnancy and in vitamin B_6 deficiency. It would appear that tryptophan metabolism is a very sensitive indicator of disease, but it is not certain whether changes in tryptophan metabolism are responsible for certain conditions or whether they merely reflect the presence of disease. The availability of methods suitable for the detection of tryptophan metabolites has undoubtedly facilitated research in this area, but it is quite possible that the metabolism of all amino acids is affected by diseases that produce substantial systemic effects.

L. Phenylalanine and Tyrosine Metabolism

Alcaptonuria

The characteristic feature of this condition is urinary excretion of homogentisic acid; the disease is due to a genetic deficiency of homogentisic acid oxidase (see p. 903). Alcaptonuric individuals may excrete as much as 0.5 g. of homogentisic acid per day, and the urine characteristically becomes black on standing because of the oxidation of homogentisic acid by atmospheric oxygen. Oxidation takes place more rapidly in alkaline urine. That the disease has probably occurred for centuries

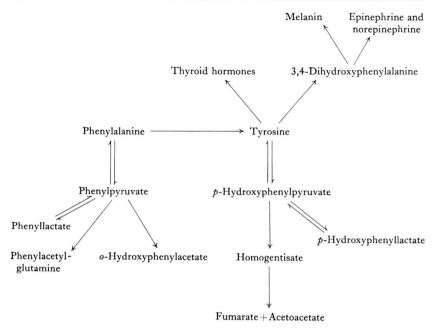

seems probable from early reports of patients who passed urine which darkened on standing. Garrod (2) refers to the case of a schoolboy (described in 1584) and that of a monk (described in 1609), who, although enjoying good health, continuously excreted urine which rapidly turned black. Alcaptonuria was first carefully described by Boedecker (265); subsequently, homogentisic acid was isolated and identified (266). This condition is often discovered early in life as a result of the observation that the infant's diapers turn black on exposure to air. Homogentisic acid also occurs in other body fluids (267). Alcaptonurics generally experience no other symptoms early in life, but later there is a darkening of the tendons and cartilages due to deposition of pigment, which is often associated with the development of arthritis. The latter condition is known as ochronosis, a condition in which there is a darkening of the nose, ears, and sclerae; at autopsy deposition of the pigment in cartilage may be readily apparent. No other metabolites of phenylalanine or tyrosine have been found in the urine of alcaptonuric individuals (268). The concentration of homogentisic acid in the blood is extremely low (267–269), suggesting that the renal threshold for this compound is very low.

The renal clearance of homogentisic acid is unusually high, and it has been suggested that the kidney may secrete as well as filter homogentisic acid. Urinary homogentisic acid may arise chiefly in the kidney (268, 270).

The characteristic pigmentation of the connective tissues was described by Virchow, who named the condition after the ochre color of the connective tissues observed microscopically (271). The relationship between ochronosis and alcaptonuria was first appreciated early in this century (272, 273). Ochronosis may also occur secondary to treatment with phenol, but this form of the condition is not associated with excretion of homogentisic acid (see p. 904).

When alcaptonuric patients are given homogentisic acid, it is completely excreted in the urine. In contrast, normal subjects metabolize homogentisic acid rapidly and can ingest as much as 5 g. of homogentisic acid in a single dose without exhibiting alcaptonuria (270, 274, 275). Alcaptonuric patients also excrete "extra" homogentisic acid after administration of tyrosine, p-hydroxyphenylpyruvate, phenyllactate, phenylalanine, phenylpyruvate, and 2,5-dihydroxyphenylpyruvate (268, 276–279). On the other hand, o-tyrosine, m-tyrosine, and the corresponding α-keto acids do not lead to increased alcaptonuria, nor does p-hydroxyphenyllactate administration result in excretion of homogentisic acid.

Alcaptonuria appears to be transmitted as a recessive Mendelian trait, but the available data are not completely consistent with this interpretation (280). It has been reported that the disease is more common in males than in females and that it is not sex-linked; these observations and data suggesting that the condition can occasionally be inherited in a dominant form may possibly reflect the incompleteness of information concerning the occurrence and incidence of this disorder. The clinical symptoms are often not impressive, and many cases may not be detected. It is also possible that the arthritis associated with ochronosis is more common in males than in females; consequently, the disease in females is not recognized as often.

Garrod (2) was the first to suggest that the basic defect in alcaptonuria is an inability to oxidize homogentisic acid, and many years later LaDu and his colleagues (281, 282) established that homogentisic acid oxidase (see p. 903) was not present in a liver homogenate prepared from a biopsy specimen obtained from an alcaptonuric patient. The same homogenate exhibited glutamate-tyrosine transaminase, p-hydroxyphenylpyruvic acid oxidase, maleylacetoacetic acid isomerase, and fumarylacetoacetic acid hydrolase activities. Liver preparations obtained from non-alcaptonuric individuals were shown to contain homogentisic acid oxidase. Subsequently, similar results were obtained in studies on the liver obtained at autopsy from another patient with alcaptonuria. Homogenates of kidney from alcaptonuric patients also lacked detectable homogentisic oxidase activity. The finding that this enzyme is absent in two tissues is of interest and suggests that the synthesis of the enzyme in both tissues is controlled by a single gene.

Although spontaneous alcaptonuria has not been found in species other than man, the condition can be induced experimentally in rats and mice by administration of large quantities of phenylalanine or tyrosine (283–290). In ascorbic acid-deficient guinea pigs and man, homogentisic acid excretion induced by feeding tyrosine was abolished by administration of ascorbic acid (291). Ascorbic acid deficiency also leads to the urinary excretion of p-hydroxyphenylpyruvate and p-hydroxyphenyllactate. Thus, ascorbic acid-deficient premature babies were found to excrete p-hydroxyphenylpyruvate and p-hydroxyphenyllactate, especially when high protein diets were administered; these metabolites disappeared from the urine after treatment with ascorbic acid (292). The effects observed in ascorbic acid deficiency are consistent with *in vitro* and *in vivo* studies on the oxidation of p-hydroxyphenylpyruvate (see p. 902). Ascorbic acid deficiency does not play a role in the genesis of hereditary alcaptonuria, and treatment with ascorbic acid does not alleviate the condition (268, 293, 294). Experimental alcaptonuria has also been induced in experimental animals by feeding diets deficient in sulfur-containing amino acids; administration of cysteine abolished the excretion of homogentisic acid and p-hydroxyphenylpyruvate observed in these animals (295, 296).

Excretion of Tyrosine and p-Hydroxyphenylpyruvic Acid

As discussed above, p-hydroxyphenylpyruvic acid has been found in the urine in ascorbic acid deficiency, but the excretion of p-hydroxyphenylpyruvic acid associated with scurvy disappears when ascorbic acid is administered. This keto acid is often also found in the urine of patients with hepatic disease (297–299); in such patients neither administration of ascorbic acid nor of tyrosine affects the excretion of p-hydroxyphenylpyruvate. The defect may probably be ascribed to liver cell damage and associated general reduction of enzymatic activity. p-Hydroxyphenylpyruvate excretion has also been observed in certain blood dyscrasias and infections (299, 300).

Levine and associates (292) found that premature infants given a high protein diet excreted *p*-hydroxyphenylpyruvate and *p*-hydroxyphenyllactate; premature and full-term babies also excreted these compounds after tyrosine or phenylalanine administration. The excretion of *p*-hydroxyphenylpyruvate and *p*-hydroxyphenyllactate disappeared after administration of ascorbic acid; these findings have been further elucidated by later studies on the enzymatic oxidation of *p*-hydroxyphenylpyruvate (see p. 903). Bloxam *et al.* (301) found that 14 infants out of 1,276 examined excreted large amounts of *p*-hydroxyphenylpyruvate, *p*-hydroxyphenyllactate, and tyrosine. These infants were fed a normal diet containing only a moderate amount of protein; in half of the cases ascorbic acid was also given. The observations suggest that the patients were probably deficient in *p*-hydroxyphenylpyruvate oxidase. A similar case was reported by Menkes and Jervis (302). It is probable that little if any *p*-hydroxyphenylpyruvate oxidase is present in the fetus and that these observations reflect delayed development of enzymatic activity.

A very large daily excretion of *p*-hydroxyphenylpyruvate was found in a 49-year-old male patient studied much earlier by Medes (303) and considered to have "tyrosinosis." When tyrosine was administered to this patient there was an increased excretion of *p*-hydroxyphenylpyruvate as well as tyrosine, *p*-hydroxyphenyllactate, and 3,4-dihydroxyphenylalanine. Increased excretion of tyrosine and *p*-hydroxyphenylpyruvate was also noted after phenylalanine administration. Administration of 3,4-dihydroxyphenylalanine led to excretion of tyrosine and *p*-hydroxyphenylpyruvate, and feeding of the latter compound led to its excretion and that of the corresponding α-hydroxy acid. The patient apparently oxidized homogentisic acid, inasmuch as feeding of this compound did not result in alcaptonuria. The site of the metabolic block in tyrosinosis is not known with certainty; however, the findings are consistent with a deficiency in *p*-hydroxyphenylpyruvate oxidase. The formation of *p*-hydroxyphenyllactate is probably due to the action of lactic dehydrogenase (212) on the accumulated α-keto acid. The presence of tyrosine in the urine suggests the possibility of a partial defect in the transaminase-catalyzed step. It is of interest that significant amounts of 3,4-dihydroxyphenylalanine were excreted; this seems to reflect exaggeration of an alternative pathway of tyrosine metabolism (see p. 909).

It has been reported that *p*-hydroxyphenylpyruvate and *p*-hydroxyphenyllactate are minor constituents of normal human urine, and that *p*-hydroxyphenylacetate and occasionally other *p*-hydroxyphenyl compounds are also found (304). Apparently a number of factors can influence the excretion of these compounds; the enzymatic phenomena involved are not yet entirely clear.

Albinism

Albinism was one of the inborn errors of metabolism considered by Garrod (1, 2), who correctly concluded that the condition was due to the lack of an intracellular enzyme necessary for the formation of melanin. Albinism may be "complete" (universal), in which case melanin is absent from the hair, skin, uveal tract, and retina. "Incomplete albinism" (generalized) may involve the skin, hair, and retinal pigment epithelium only. These forms of albinism are usually inherited as Mendelian recessive traits, whereas partial albinism, in which the absence of melanin is restricted to particular areas of the skin and hair, is a dominant trait. Ocular albinism, in which melanin is absent from the retinal pigment epithelium, is a sex-linked recessive trait (305). There is no evidence that the formation of epinephrine and norepinephrine is abnormal in albino individuals. The metabolic defect seems to be associated with failure of the melanocyte to synthesize tyrosinase. Fitzpatrick and colleagues (305) were unable to detect this enzyme by a radioautographic technique in the melanocytes of the skin or hair bulb of patients with generalized albinism. Thus no melanin was formed by albino melanocytes from tyrosine or 3,4-dihydroxyphenylalanine. These findings suggested that there is a failure either of tyrosinase synthesis or of melanin polymerization in albinism. Preparations of fetal albino guinea pig skin did not utilize oxygen in the presence of tyrosine, suggesting that the enzymatic defect is in the oxidative step rather than in the polymerization of indole-5,6-quinone.

Pheochromocytoma and Neuroblastoma

Pheochromocytomas are norepinephrine- and epinephrine-producing tumors which arise from the adrenal medulla or ganglia of the sympathetic nervous system. The symptomatology associated with such tumors may be explained in terms of increased secretion of epinephrine and norepinephrine. Successful excision of the tumor results in abolition of the syndrome, which is characterized by hypertension, often paroxysmal, and other symptoms. Patients with pheochromocytoma (306–309) and some with neuroblastoma (310) commonly excrete excessive amounts of norepinephrine, epinephrine, metanephrine, normetanephrine, and

3-methoxy-4-hydroxymandelic acid in the urine. There is much variability in the catecholamine content of such tumors, and the rate of turnover of catecholamines and of their metabolism by the tumor is also subject to considerable variation. The binding of catecholamines in pheochromocytomas appears to differ significantly from that of these amines in normal cells. Studies on the catecholamine content of such tumors and on the excretion of catecholamines and their derivatives in patients with these tumors indicate that these compounds follow metabolic pathways that have been considered above (Chapter VI, Section O). In general, the data indicate increased formation of 3,4-dihydroxyphenylalanine from tyrosine in the tumor and release of 3,4-dihydroxyphenylalanine and its metabolic products into the blood. Certain tumors catalyze reactions leading to the inactivation of catecholamines, and in some patients increased blood concentrations of tyramine have also been observed. The study of patients with such tumors has provided useful information about the metabolism of the catecholamines since many of the normal pathways are exaggerated.

Thyroid Hormones

Although the metabolic reactions involving the thyroid hormones are far from being completely understood (see p. 916), there is evidence that certain types of thyroid dysfunction are inborn errors of metabolism and therefore probably associated with specific enzymatic defects. Stanbury (311) has recently reviewed several types of familial goiter in which the findings suggested metabolic deficiencies. In one type of goitrous cretinism there is lack of thyroid gland dehalogenase activity (312–315). Such individuals exhibit abnormally large amounts of monoiodotyrosine and diiodotyrosine in the blood and urine after administration of iodine, and when monoiodotyrosine or diiodotyrosine are given, these compounds are excreted in the urine. Slices of thyroid from these patients do not catalyze the dehalogenation of diiodotyrosine; this reaction was observed with thyroid slices obtained from patients with nodular goiter and Graves' disease. The condition seems to be associated with chronic loss of iodine from the body in the form of iodinated tyrosine with consequent compensatory thyroid hyperplasia.

In another type of familial goiter associated with hypothyroidism there is a defect in the utilization of iodide (311, 316). Administered iodide is rapidly taken up by the thyroid gland but it is not effectively converted to organically bound forms. Administration of potassium thiocyanate immediately discharges the accumulated iodide. Failure of iodination of tyrosyl compounds leads to compensatory hyperplasia followed by degeneration of the gland and replacement by fibrous tissue. Patients with one form of this disease also have congenital nerve deafness. Other metabolic defects have also been detected (311, 317, 318) including some in which there seems to be failure of triiodothyronine and thyroxine formation.

Phenylpyruvic Oligophrenia (Phenylketonuria)

This condition, first described in 1934 by Fölling, is characterized by mental deficiency and urinary excretion of phenylpyruvic acid (319–322). The disease does not lead to early death provided that the patients, who often are unable to care for themselves, are protected from infection and nutritional deficiency. Many patients with this disorder have eczema, convulsive disease, and exhibit abnormal electroencephalograms. In addition, the majority of patients exhibit increased muscle tone and abnormally active tendon reflexes, and some have a decrease in pigmentation of the hair and skin. The mental defect is often very severe, but a few patients with this disorder have been found to exhibit only slight or moderate reduction in mental capacity; several have been found to have normal intelligence quotients (323, 324). Phenylpyruvic oligophrenia is transmitted as a recessive Mendelian trait. It has been estimated that the disease occurs once in 25,000 births, but it is possible that some cases are not recognized. This inborn error of metabolism has been detected in patients throughout the world and has been the subject of extensive study by a large number of investigators (325–327).

The urine of patients with phenylpyruvic oligophrenia characteristically contains large amounts of phenylpyruvic acid, and this finding in the presence of mental deficiency provides strong indication of the disease. However, phenylpyruvic acid excretion has been observed in other conditions; thus, a mentally deficient child who excreted α-hydroxybutyric acid as well as phenylpyruvic acid has been described (328, 329). Other α-keto acids may sometimes be confused with phenylpyruvate; for example, imidazolepyruvate (excreted in histidinemia; see above) and phenylpyruvate both give a green color on treatment with ferric chloride. In addition to phenylpyruvic acid, patients with phenylpyruvic oligophrenia also excrete phenyllactic acid, phenylalanine, and phenylacetylglutamine in relatively large quantities (320–322, 325–327, 330–336). The daily excretion of phenylpyruvate and phenyllactate may each be of the order of magnitude of 1 or 2 g.; as much as 1 g. of phenylalanine and 2–3 g. of phenylacetylglutamine may be excreted per day. Of these compounds, only small amounts of phenylalanine and perhaps several hundred milligrams of phenylacetylglutamine are normally excreted per day. Phenylalanine accumulates in the blood, reaching concentrations of the order of 10–60 mg. per 100 ml. of plasma, compared to a normal value of approximately 1–2 mg. per 100 ml. The concentration of phenylalanine in the cerebrospinal fluid is often about the same as that of the blood plasma (332, 337–339). In newborn infants with phenylpyruvic oligophrenia, there may be no characteristic urinary findings, and the diagnosis must therefore be made on the basis of an elevated concentration of phenylalanine in the blood. The blood contains very little phenylpyruvate and phenyllactate (337, 340). The concentrations of the other amino acids of the blood are probably reduced in phenylketonuria; detailed studies of the concentrations of the blood amino acids have not been reported.

Administration of phenylalanine to phenylketonuric patients results in increased excretion of phenylpyruvate and elevated phenylalanine blood concentrations; however, feeding of other amino acids produces no such effects (332–337, 341, 342). The early suggestion that D-phenylalanine might be formed in this disorder was based on the finding that phenylpyruvic acid was more readily formed from D-phenylalanine than from the L-isomer. However, subsequent study failed to reveal the presence of D-phenylalanine in the blood or urine of phenylketonuric patients (343, 344). The idea that phenylpyruvic oligophrenia was due to racemization or inversion of L-phenylalanine was therefore abandoned. The formation of phenylpyruvate from D-phenylalanine may be ascribed to the action of D-amino acid oxidase. On the other hand, the hypothesis that the conversion of phenylalanine to tyrosine is blocked in this disease has received substantial support. Jervis noted that while normal individuals exhibited an increase in the Millon-reactive substances of blood after administration of phenylalanine, phenylketonuric individuals did not (345). Udenfriend and Bessman provided conclusive proof for a deficiency in the conversion of phenylalanine to tyrosine in phenylketonurics in studies in which C^{14}-phenylalanine was administered (346). Their data, however, indicate that some conversion of isotopic phenylalanine to tyrosine does occur in this disorder. Thus, in control patients the ratio of the specific activities of tyrosine to phenylalanine was about 0.2, while in two phenylketonuric siblings ratios of about 0.02 were obtained. These workers suggested that the results might be explained by (a) diminished (but not absent) phenylalanine hydroxylase, (b) conversion of phenylalanine to tyrosine by intestinal bacteria or by another enzyme system such as a nonspecific aromatic hydroxylase, (c) absence of a cofactor for phenylalanine hydroxylase, or (d) the presence of an inhibitor of this enzyme. Enzymatic studies have shown that phenylalanine hydroxylase activity is not present in the liver of patients with phenyl-ketonuria (347–350) and that the more labile protein component required for hydroxylation (see p. 896) which is found only in the liver is absent (348, 349). There is no evidence that the pteridine cofactor for this reaction is absent (350).

Although the data (346) do not indicate a complete block of the conversion of phenylalanine to tyrosine, they seem to explain most of the chemical findings. Thus, reduction in conversion of phenylalanine to tyrosine would be expected to cause accumulation of phenylalanine. Transamination of phenylalanine would lead to phenylpyruvate formation with subsequent metabolism of this keto acid by known pathways to phenyllactate and phenylacetylglutamine.

Transamination of phenylalanine is undoubtedly responsible for the formation of phenylpyruvate in this disease. That transamination is involved in the formation of phenylpyruvic acid is consistent with the effect of orally administered glutamine, glutamate, or asparagine in reducing the urinary excretion of phenylpyruvate. It has been postulated that the administered amino acids shift the *in vivo* transamination reaction in the direction of phenylalanine. Glutamine administration did not significantly affect the excretion of phenylacetylglutamine, suggesting that excretion of this compound does not result in a significant loss of body glutamine (351).

The presence of phenylacetic acid in the urine of phenylketonurics may probably be ascribed to decarboxylation of phenylpyruvate, a reaction known to occur nonenzymatically, but its enzymatic catalysis would be consistent with that is known about the metabolism of other α-keto acids. It is well known that orally administered phenylacetic acid is excreted in man as phenylacetylglutamine (see p. 907). There seems to be no evidence for the presence of appreciable free phenylacetate in tissues; it is possible that phenylacetate is formed but rapidly coupled with glutamine, or that phenylpyruvate is a direct precursor of phenylacetylglutamine via phenylacetyl-coenzyme A. An enzyme preparation obtained from a liver biopsy sample from a phenylketonuric patient was found to synthesize phenylacetylglutamine approximately five times faster than observed with comparable preparations from normal individuals (326, 352). This finding suggests that there is an adaptive increase in the enzymes of the "transamination" pathway of phenylalanine metabolism in this disorder. The formation of phenyllactic acid is consistent with the broad specificity of lactic dehydrogenase (212).

In addition to the phenomena described above, patients with phenyl-pyruvic oligophrenia characteristically exhibit other types of chemical abnormalities which also seem to be secondary to the primary enzymatic defect. Thus, the blood concentration of 5-hydroxytryptamine is lower than normal and the urinary excretion of 5-hydroxyindoleacetic acid is also reduced (354, 355). Several investigators have found that increased amounts of indolelactic, indoleacetic, and indolepyruvic acids are also present in the urine of patients with phenylketonuria (353, 355, 356); o- and p-hydroxyphenylacetate and p-hydroxyphenyllactate excretion may also be increased (357). Armstrong et al. (358, 359) found that patients with phenylketonuria excreted more than 100 times as much o-hydroxyphenylacetic acid than did normal individuals. They also found that the excretion of o-hydroxyphenylacetic acid was directly related to the concentration of phenylalanine in the blood and that its excretion accounted for about 10% of the dietary phenylalanine. Its presence in the urine may be more useful in diagnosis than that of phenylpyruvic acid, because in contrast to phenylpyruvate, o-hydroxyphenylacetate is excreted in the urine even when the blood concentration of phenylalanine is below 15 mg. per 100 ml. When o-tyrosine was administered to normal individuals and patients with phenylketonuria, increased amounts of o-hydroxyphenylacetic acid were found in the urine. DL-o-Tyrosine is oxidized by both D- and L-amino acid oxidases and o-tyrosine is decarboxylated by the aromatic amino acid decarboxylase. The conversion of o-tyrosine to o-hydroxyphenylacetate may occur by transamination and oxidative decarboxylation of the corresponding α-keto acid, or possibly by oxidation of o-tyramine formed by decarboxylation of o-tyrosine. However, there is no evidence for the presence or formation of o-tyrosine in phenylketonuria and the excretion of increased o-hydroxy-phenylacetic acid in this condition is probably due to oxidation of phenyl-pyruvate. There is evidence for conversion of C^{14}-phenylalanine to o-hydroxyphenylacetate in phenylketonuria (360), and administration of D-phenylalanine or phenylpyruvate to normal individuals is followed by increased excretion of o-hydroxyphenylacetate (361). A mammalian liver enzyme has been recently found that catalyzes the conversion of phenylpyruvate to o-hydroxyphenylacetate (362).

There is no clear-cut evidence for mental retardation or disease in heterozygous individuals. However, heterozygotes often exhibit a greater and more sustained increase of the blood phenylalanine concentration after administration of this amino acid than do normal individuals (363, 364). The fasting blood concentration of phenylalanine has been reported to be somewhat higher in heterozygotes (365), and such individuals also excrete increased amounts of o-hydroxyphenylpyruvate after administration of phenylalanine (366, 367).

The symptomatology in phenylketonuria cannot yet be explained in chemical terms, but the chemical phenomena provide a logical basis for approaching the problem. The chemical abnormalities can be explained in terms of the primary block of phenylalanine hydroxylase and the exaggeration of alternative pathways of phenylalanine metabolism. It seems probable that there is an adaptive increase in the activity of some of these enzymes, i.e., those responsible for phenylacetylglutamine formation (see above). Such an increase in transaminase could be responsible for extensive production of phenylpyruvate and also for the formation of p-hydroxyphenylpyruvate and indolepyruvate. It is possible that one or more of the compounds produced in excess have toxic effects on the central nervous system or skin. Such toxicity, at least in part, may be due to inhibitory effects of the accumulated metabolites. For example, the decrease in skin and hair pigment in phenylketonuria seems to be due to inhibition of tyrosinase. Phenylalanine has been found to inhibit tyrosinase of mushrooms (368) and mouse melanomas (369, 370). Phenylalanine also inhibits the metabolism of tyrosine in rat liver slices (371); thus, conversion of tyrosine to acetoacetate was reduced in the presence of high concentrations of phenylalanine, a finding that might explain formation of p-hydroxyphenylpyruvate and its metabolites in phenylketonuria. Several studies have suggested that the formation of epinephrine is reduced in phenylpyruvic oligophrenia. Phenylketonuric individuals have been found to exhibit an increased hypertensive response to administration of epinephrine (330, 372), and there are decreased concentrations of norepinephrine and epinephrine in the blood plasma and urine in phenylketonuria (373). Decreased formation of epinephrine might be due to a deficiency of tyrosine, but it seems unlikely that reduced dietary intake of tyrosine is responsible for the abnormalities found in this disease. There is evidence that phenylpyruvate, phenylacetate, and phenyllactate inhibit the decarboxylation of 3,4-dihydroxyphenyl-alanine (374, 375), and phenylpyruvate (but not phenylalanine) has been found to inhibit epinephrine formation, apparently at the stage of decarboxylation of 3,4-dihydroxyphenylalanine (376). It may be of significance that the production of phenylethylamine from phenylalanine is increased in patients with phenylketonuria (377).

The decreased blood concentration of 5-hydroxytryptamine and the urinary excretion of this compound and 5-hydroxyindoleacetic acid may reflect a decrease in the hydroxylation of tryptophan or in the decarboxylation of 5-hydroxytryptophan, or both (378–380). Intravenous injection of 5-hydroxytryptophan to phenylketonurics led to a smaller excretion of 5-hydroxyindole compounds than observed in normals (379), but when 5-hydroxytryptophan was given orally to patients, large amounts of 5-hydroxytryptamine were excreted (380). Phenylalanine may inhibit 5-hydroxylation of tryptophan and the decarboxylation step; patients fed diets containing little phenylalanine exhibit normal blood concentrations and urinary excretion of 5-hydroxyindole compounds, indicating that the enzymatic block in phenylketonuria does not directly affect hydroxylation of tryptophan. The urinary excretion of indican by patients with phenylketonuria (381) indicates additional evidence for disturbance of tryptophan metabolism in this disorder.

It is of interest that despite the extraordinarily high concentration of phenylalanine in the peripheral blood, the total amino acid concentration is not significantly increased in phenylketonuria. This observation and complete amino acid analysis of the blood serum indicates that the concentrations of virtually all of the amino acids (except perhaps glycine and histidine) are reduced (327). Such an amino acid imbalance might be expected to affect protein synthesis, but there seem to be no unequivocal data to support the conclusion that protein synthesis is decreased or that abnormal proteins are formed [see (382–385)]. On the other hand, electrophoretic studies on blood plasma have shown abnormal β-globulin components which disappear on reduction of dietary phenyl-alanine and return on addition of phenylalanine to the diet (386).

The wide variety of chemical abnormalities that occur in this disorder provides considerable impetus to speculation concerning its pathogenesis. It is significant that virtually all of the known chemical abnormalities are improved or eliminated by administration of a diet containing small quantities of phenylalanine. Restriction of dietary phenylalanine is followed by elimination of phenylpyruvate and phenylalanine excretion and return to a normal blood concentration of phenylalanine; this dietary therapy also results in a decrease in severity of certain symptoms, e.g., convulsions, abnormal muscle tone, hyperactive reflexes, and there may be an increase in pigmentation of the skin and hair (327, 387–390). It has been hoped that early diagnosis and institution of a low phenylalanine diet early in life might prevent development of mental retardation. Phenylalanine hydroxylase as well as several other enzymes (e.g., p-hydroxyphenylpyruvate oxidase, tyrosine-phenylalanine-glutamate transaminase) are apparently not active or only slightly active in fetal tissues; the activities of these enzymes normally increase after birth (391). It seems probable that newborn patients with phenylpyruvic oligophrenia have the potential for normal cerebral development, and if phenylalanine metabolism can be controlled normal development might be expected. Recent observations on patients given diets containing small amounts of phenylalanine within a few weeks of birth indicate that this procedure prevents or retards development of mental retardation; however, more experience is needed. Care must be taken in use of such diets that the amounts of tyrosine (which is an essential amino acid for phenylketonurics) and phenylalanine in the diets are sufficient to promote normal growth and development. Assuming that the therapy is successful, it is not clear as to how long phenylalanine restriction must be continued. If the cerebral defect is related to defective maturation of the brain, it might be expected that regular diets could be given to older patients without danger of producing mental retardation. On the other hand, administration of low phenylalanine diets to older patients has been found to reduce or eliminate convulsions and eczema, but these symptoms may return when regular diets are subsequently permitted. Undoubtedly clinical experience will guide future dietary management of patients with this disorder; it is amply clear that early diagnosis is of crucial importance.

Several attempts to produce phenylketonuria in animals have recently been reported (392–398). Administration of large amounts of L-phenylalanine to rats (392) and monkeys (393) leads to increased blood levels of phenylalanine and urinary excretion of phenylpyruvate. Such animals also exhibit reduced formation of 5-hydroxyindole compounds (394, 395). Evidence has been reported that phenylalanine-treated weanling rats exhibit decreased temporal discrimination learning (398). Such studies may provide insight into the mechanisms responsible for the cerebral defect in the human disease. The discovery of genetically determined phenylketonuria in an experimental animal or of a specific inhibitor of phenylalanine hydroxylase would undoubtedly be of importance.

References

1. Garrod, A. E., *Lancet* **ii**, 1, 73, 142, 214 (1908).
2. Garrod, A. E., "Inborn Errors of Metabolism," 1st and 2nd eds. Oxford Medical Publs., London, 1909, 1923.
3. Itano, H. A., and Pauling, L., *Federation Proc.* **8**, 209 (1949); Pauling, L., Itano, H. A., Singer, S. J., and Wells, I. C., *Science* **110**, 543 (1949).
4. Ingram, V. M., "Hemoglobin and its Abnormalities." Thomas, Springfield, Illinois, 1961.
5. Beadle, G. W., *Chem. Rev.* **37**, 15 (1945).
6. Williams, R. J., "Biochemical Individuality" Wiley, New York, 1956.
7. Isselbacher, K. J., "The Metabolic Basis of Inherited Disease," p. 208. McGraw-Hill, New York, 1960.
8. Fourcroy, A. F., "A General System of Chemical Knowledge; and its Application to the Phenomena of Nature and Art." W. Flint, Old Bailey (Eleven volumes; translated from the French by William Nicholson) 1804.
9. Wollaston, W. H., *Ann. Chim. (Paris)* **76**, 21 (1810).
10. Datta, S. P., and Harris, H., *Ann. Eugenics* **18**, 107 (1953).
11. Scriver, C. R., *Progr. Med. Genet.* **2**, 83 (1962).
12. Fowler, D. I., Norton, P. M., Cheung, M. W., and Pratt, E. L., *Arch. Biochem. Biophys.* **68**, 452 (1957).
13. Miller, S., Ruttinger, V., and Macy, I. G., *J. Biol. Chem.* **209**, 795 (1954).
14. Gartler, S. M., and Dobzhansky, T., *Nature* **174**, 533 (1954).
15. Meister, A., Bukenberger, M. W., and Strassburger, M., *Biochem. Z.* **338**, 217 (1963).
16. Evered, D. F., *Biochem. J.* **62**, 416 (1956).
17. Dent, C. E., and Walshe, J. M., *Brit. Med. Bull.* **10**, 247 (1954).
18. Dent, C. E., and Walshe, J. M., *Ciba Symposia Liver Disease*, p. 22 (1951).
19. Frankl, W., Martin, H., and Dunn, M. S., *Arch. Biochem.* **13**, 103 (1947).
20. Gabuzda, G. J., Jr., Eckhardt, R. D., and Davidson, C. S., *J. Clin. Invest.* **31**, 1015 (1952).
21. Walshe, J. M., *Quart. J. Med.* **22**, 483 (1953).
22. Walshe, J. M., and Senior, B., *J. Clin. Invest.* **34**, 302 (1955).
23. Hsia, D. Y.-Y., and Gellis, S. S., *J. Clin. Invest.* **33**, 1603 (1954).
24. Kirk, E., *Acta Med. Scand.* **77**, Suppl. 1 (1936).
25. Flock, E. V., Mann, F. C., and Bollman, J. L., *J. Biol. Chem.* **192**, 293 (1951).
26. Westall, R. G., Roitman, E., de la Peña, C., Rasmussen, H., Cravioto, J., Gomez, F., and Holt, L. E., Jr., *Arch. Disease Childhood* **33**, 499 (1958).
27. Blahd, W. H., Bloom, A., and Drell, W., *Proc. Soc. Exptl. Biol. Med.* **90**, 704 (1955).
28. Ames, S. R., and Risley, H. A., *Proc. Soc. Exptl. Biol. Med.* **68**, 131 (1948).
29. Eades, C. H., Jr., Pollack, R. L., and Hardy, J. D., *J. Clin. Invest.* **34**, 1756 (1955).
30. Brick, I. W., *New Engl. J. Med.* **247**, 635 (1952).
31. Pitts, R. F., *Am. J. Physiol.* **140**, 155, 535 (1944).

32. Lotspeich, W. D., and Pitts, R. F., *J. Biol. Chem.* **168**, 611 (1947).
33. Beyer, K. H., Wright, L. D., Skeggs, H. R., Russo, H. F., and Shaner, G. A., *Am. J. Physiol.* **151**, 202 (1947).
34. Wright, L. D., *Trans. N. Y. Acad. Sci.* **10**, 271 (1948).
35. Kirk, E., *Acta Med. Scand.* **89**, 450 (1936).
36. Doty, J. R., *Proc. Soc. Exptl. Biol. Med.* **46**, 129 (1941).
37. Goettsch, E., Lyttle, J. D., Grim, W. M., and Dunbar, P., *Am. J. Physiol.* **140**, 688 (1944).
38. Beyer, K. H., Wright, L. D., Russo, H. F., Skeggs, H. R., and Patch, E. A., *Am. J. Physiol.* **146**, 330 (1946).
39. Cusworth, D. C., and Dent, C. E., *Biochem. J.* **74**, 550 (1960).
40. Yeh, H. L., Frankl, W., Dunn, M. S., Parker, P., Hughes, B., and György, P., *Am. J. Med. Sci.* **214**, 507 (1947).
41. Stein, W. H., *Proc. Soc. Exptl. Biol. Med.* **78**, 705 (1951).
42. Dent, C. E., and Rose, G. A., *Quart. J. Med.* **20**, 205 (1951).
43. Dent, C. E., Heathcote, J. G., and Joron, G. E., *J. Clin. Invest.* **33**, 1210 (1954).
44. Dent, C. E., Senior, B., and Walshe, J. M., *J. Clin. Invest.* **33**, 1216 (1954).
45. Knox, W. E., "The Metabolic Basis of Inherited Disease," p. 1302. McGraw-Hill, New York, 1960.
46. Harris, H., "Human Biochemical Genetics." Cambridge Univ. Press, London and New York, 1959.
47. Harris, H., and Robson, E. B., *Am. J. Med.* **22**, 774 (1957).
48. Udransky, V. L., and Baumann, E., *Z. Physiol. Chem.* **13**, 562 (1889).
49. Garcia, S. A., *Z. Physiol. Chem.* **17**, 577 (1892).
50. Alsberg, C., and Folin, O., *Am. J. Physiol.* **14**, 45 (1905).
51. Wolf, C. G. L., and Shaffer, P. A., *J. Biol. Chem.* **4**, 439 (1908).
52. Ackermann, D., and Kutscher, F., *Z. Biol.* **57**, 355 (1911).
53. Hoppe-Seyler, F. A., *Z. Physiol. Chem.* **214**, 267 (1933).
54. Milne, M. D., Asatoor, A. M., and Loughridge, L. W., *Lancet* **i**, 51 (1961).
54a. McCarthy, C. F., Borland, J. L., Jr., Lynch, H. J., Jr., Owen, E. E., and Tyor, M. P., *J. Clin. Invest.* **43**, 1518 (1964).
54b. Thier, S., Fox, M., and Segal, S., *Science* **143**, 482 (1964).
54c. Treacher, R. J., *Biochem. J.* **90**, 494 (1964).
55. Crane, C. W., and Turner, A. W., *Nature* **177**, 237 (1956).
56. Oldfield, J. E., Allen, P. H., and Adair, J., *Proc. Soc. Exptl. Biol. Med.* **91**, 560 (1956).
57. Datta, S. P., and Harris, H., *Ann. Eugenics* **18**, 107 (1953).
58. Frimpter, G. W., *J. Clin. Invest.* **42**, 1956 (1963).
59. Brand, E., Cahill, G. F., and Harris, M. M., *J. Biol. Chem.* **109**, 69 (1935).
60. Brand, E., and Cahill, G. F., *Proc. Soc. Exptl. Biol. Med.* **31**, 1247 (1934).
61. Brand, E., Block, R. J., Kassell, B., and Cahill, G. F., *J. Biol. Chem.* **119**, 669, 681 (1937).
62. Crawhall, J. C., Scowen, E. F., and Watts, R. W. E., *Brit. Med. J.* **I**, 588 (1963).
63. Rosenberg, L. E., Downing, S. J., and Segal, S., *J. Biol. Chem.* **237**, 2265 (1962).
64. Robson, E. B., and Rose, G. A., *Clin. Sci.* **16**, 75 (1957).
65. DeVries, A., Kochwa, S., Lazebnik, J., Frank, M., and Djaldetti, M., *Am. J. Med.* **23**, 408 (1957).

66. Scriver, C. R., Schafer, I. A., and Efron, M. L., *Nature* **192**, 672 (1961).
67. Scriver, C. R., Efron, M. L., and Schafer, I. A., *J. Clin. Invest.* **43**, 374 (1964).
68. Lowe, C. U., Terrey, M., and MacLachlan, E. A., *Am. J. Diseases Children* **83**, 164 (1952).
69. Richards, W., Donnell, G. N., Wilson, W. A., and Stowens, D. S., *Am. J. Diseases Children* **100**, 707 (1960).
70. Fanconi, G., *Jahrb. Kinderheilk.* **147**, 299 (1936).
71. Fanconi, G., *Helv. Paediat. Acta* **1**, 183 (1945).
72. McCune, D. J., Mason, H. H., and Clarke, H. T., *Am. J.Diseases Children* **65**, 81 (1943).
73. de Toni, G., *Acta Paediat.* **16**, 479 (1933).
74. Dent, C. E., *Biochem. J.* **41**, 240 (1947).
75. King, F. P., and Lochridge, E. P., *Am. J. Diseases Children* **82**, 446 (1951).
76. Harper, H. A., Grossman, M., Henderson, P., and Steinbach, H., *Am. J. Diseases Children* **84**, 327 (1952).
77. Meyerson, R. M., and Pastor, B. H., *Am. J. Med. Sci.* **228**, 378 (1954).
78. Sirota, J. H., and Hamerman, D., *Am. J. Med.* **16**, 138 (1954).
79. Abderhalden, E., *Z. Physiol. Chem.* **38**, 557 (1903).
80. Burki, E., *Ann. Paediat.* **156**, 324 (1941).
81. Esser, M., *Ann. Paediat.* **156**, 344 (1941).
82. Wallis, L. A., and Engle, R. L., Jr., *Am. J. Med.* **22**, 13 (1957).
83. Baker, A. B., *Arch. Pathol.* **46**, 268 (1948).
84. Uzman, L. L., and Denny-Brown, D., *Am. J. Med. Sci.* **215**, 599 (1948).
85. Uzman, L. L., and Hood, B., *Am. J. Med. Sci.* **223**, 392 (1952).
86. Bearn, A. G., "The Metabolic Basis of Inherited Disease," p. 809. McGraw-Hill, New York, 1960.
87. Cumings, J. N., *Brain* **71**, 410 (1948); **74**, 10 (1951).
88. Porter, H., *Arch. Biochem. Biophys.* **31**, 262 (1951).
89. Spillane, J. D., Keyser, J. W., and Parker, R. A., *J. Clin. Pathol.* **5**, 16 (1952).
90. Scheinberg, I. H., and Gitlin, D., *Science* **116**, 484 (1952).
91. Bearn, A. G., and Kunkel, H. G., *J. Clin. Invest.* **33**, 400 (1954).
92. Uzman, L. L., *Am. J. Med. Sci.* **226**, 645 (1953).
93. Stein, W. H., Bearn, A. G., and Moore, S., *J. Clin. Invest.* **33**, 410 (1954).
94. Uzman, L. L., Iber, F. L., and Chalmers, T. C., *Am. J. Med. Sci.* **231**, 511 (1956).
95. Rothstein, A., and Berke, H., *J. Pharmacol. Exptl. Therap.* **96**, 179 (1949).
96. Wilson, V. K., Thomson, M. L., and Dent, C. E., *Lancet* **ii**, 66 (1953).
97. Clarkson, T. W., and Kench, J. E., *Biochem. J.* **62**, 361 (1956).
98. Spencer, A. G., and Franglen, G. T., *Lancet* **ii**, 190 (1952).
99. Van Creveld, S., and Arons, P., *Ann. Paediat.* **173**, 299 (1949).
100. Holzel, A., Kromrower, G. M., and Wilson, V. K., *Brit. Med. J.* **I**, 194 (1952).
101. Robertson, G. K., *Med. J. Australia* **i**, 698 (1954).
102. Bickel, H., and Thursby-Pelham, D. C., *Arch. Diseases Childhood* **29**, 224 (1954).
103. Crumpler, H. R., Dent, C. E., Harris, H., and Westall, R. G., *Nature* **167**, 307 (1951).
104. Harris, H., *Ann. Eugenics* **18**, 43 (1953).

105. Harris, H., *Eugenics Lab. Mem.* **37**, 1 (1953).
106. Fink, K., Henderson, R. B., and Fink, R. M., *Proc. Soc. Exptl. Biol. Med.* **78**, 135 (1951).
107. Sutton, H. E., "The Metabolic Basis of Inherited Disease," p. 792. McGraw-Hill, New York, 1960.
107a. Armstrong, M. D., Yates, K., Kakimoto, Y., Taniguchi, K., and Kappe, T., *J. Biol. Chem.* **238**, 1447 (1963).
108. Berry, H. K., *Metabolism* **9**, 373 (1960).
109. Gartler, S. M., *Am. J. Human Genet.* **11**, 257 (1959).
110. Gilbert, J. B., Ku, Y., Rogers, L. L., and Williams, R. J., *J. Biol. Chem.* **235**, 1055 (1960).
111. Gerber, G. B., Gerber, G., and Altman, K. I., *Nature* **187**, 956 (1960).
112. Gartler, S. M., *Arch. Biochem. Biophys.* **80**, 400 (1959).
113. Sandler, M., and Pare, C. M. B., *Lancet* **i**, 494 (1954).
114. Childs, B., Nyhan, W. L., Borden, M., Bard, L., and Cooke, R. E., *Pediatrics* **27**, 522, 539 (1961).
115. Wyngaarden, J. B., and Elder, T. D., "The Metabolic Basis of Inherited Disease," p. 449. McGraw-Hill, New York, 1960.
116. Marshall, V. F., and Horwith, M., *J. Urol.* **82**, 278 (1959).
117. Scowen, E. F., Crawhall, J. C., and Watts, R. W. E., *Lancet* **ii**, 300 (1958).
118. Crawhall, J. C., Scowen, E. F., and Watts, R. W. E., *Lancet* **ii**, 806 (1959).
119. Wyngaarden, J. B., and Verner, J. V., *Clin. Res.* **6**, 267 (1958).
120. Elder, T. D., and Wyngaarden, J. B., *J. Clin. Invest.* **38**, 1001 (1959).
121. Frederick, E. W., Rabkin, M. T., Richie, R. H., Jr., and Smith, L. H., Jr., *New Engl. J. Med.* **269**, 821 (1963).
122. Hellman, L., and Burns, J. J., *J. Biol. Chem.* **230**, 923 (1958).
123. Crawhall, J. C., and Watts, R. W. E., *Clin. Sci.* **23**, 163 (1962).
124. Fraser, D., *Am..J. Med.* **22**, 730 (1957).
125. Bartter, F. C., "The Metabolic Basis of Inherited Disease," p. 1367. McGraw-Hill, New York, 1960.
126. McCance, R. A., Morrison, A. B., and Dent, C. E., *Lancet* **i**, 131 (1955).
127. Rector, F. C., Jr., Seldin, D. W., and Copenhaver, J. H., Jr., *J. Clin. Invest.* **34**, 20 (1955).
128. Ryberg, C., *Acta Physiol. Scand.* **15**, 161 (1948).
129. Pitts, R. F., *Federation Proc.* **7**, 418 (1948).
130. Wolf, A. V., *Am. J. Physiol.* **148**, 54 (1947).
131. Ferguson, E. B., Jr., *J. Physiol.* (*London*) **112**, 420 (1951).
132. Gilman, A., and Brazeau, P., *Am. J. Med.* **15**, 765 (1953).
133. Orloff, J., and Berliner, R. W., *J. Clin. Invest.* **35**, 223 (1956).
134. Davies, B. M. A., and Yudkin, J., *Biochem. J.* **52**, 407 (1952).
135. Leonard, E., and Orloff, J., *Am. J. Physiol.* **182**, 131 (1955).
136. Goldstein, L., and Kensler, C. J., *J. Biol. Chem.* **235**, 1086 (1960).
137. Bessman, S. P., *in* "Inorganic Nitrogen Metabolism" (W. D. McElroy and B. Glass, eds.), p. 408. Johns Hopkins Press, Baltimore, Maryland, 1956.
138. Nencki, M., Pawlow, J. P., and Zaleski, J., *Arch. Exptl. Pathol. Pharmakol.* **39**, 26 (1895).
139. McDermott, W. V., Jr., and Adams, R. D., *J. Clin. Invest.* **33**, 1 (1954).

140. Phillips, G. B., Schwartz, R., Gabuzda, G. J., Jr., and Davidson, C. S., *New Engl. J. Med.* **247**, 239 (1952).
141. Riddell, A. G., and McDermott, W. V., Jr., *Lancet* **i**, 1263 (1954).
142. Sherlock, S., Summerskill, W. H. J., White, L. P., and Phear, E. A., *Lancet* **ii**, 453 (1954).
143. McDermott, W. V., Jr., Adams, R. D., and Riddell, A. G., *Trans. Am. Surg. Assoc.* **72**, 297 (1954).
144. Walshe, J. M., *Quart. J. Med.* **20**, 421 (1951).
145. van Caulaert, C., Deviller, C., and Halff, M., *Compt. Rend. Acad. Sci.* **111**, 739 (1932).
146. White, J., Phear, E. A., Summerskill, W. H. J., and Sherlock, S., *J. Clin. Invest.* **34**, 158 (1955).
147. Saperstein, M. R., *Proc. Soc. Exptl. Biol. Med.* **32**, 334 (1943).
148. Kirk, J. S., and Sumner, J. B., *J. Biol. Chem.* **94**, 21 (1931); *J. Immunol.* **26**, 495 (1934).
149. Bessman, S. P., Fazekas, J. F., and Bessman, A. N., *Proc. Soc. Exptl. Biol. Med.* **85**, 66 (1954).
150. Bessman, S. P., and Bessman, A. N., *J. Clin. Invest.* **32**, 622 (1955).
151. Hsia, D. Y.-Y., and Gellis, S. S., *J. Clin. Invest.* **33**, 1603 (1954).
152. Wu, C., Bollman, J. L., and Butt, H. R., *J. Clin. Invest.* **34**, 845 (1955).
153. Mann, F. C., *Medicine* **6**, 419 (1927).
154. Seegmiller, J. E., Schwartz, R., and Davidson, C. S., *J. Clin. Invest.* **33**, 984 (1954).
155. Recknagel, R. O., and Potter, V. R., *J. Biol. Chem.* **191**, 263 (1951).
156. Wechsler, R. L., Crum, W., and Roth, J. L. A., *Clin. Res. Proc.* **II**, 74 (1954).
157. Nelson, R. M., and Seligson, D., *Surgery* **34**, 1 (1953).
158. Havens, L. L., and Child, C. G., *New Engl. J. Med.* **252**, 756 (1955).
159. Braganca, B. M., Faulkner, P., and Quastel, J. H., *Biochim. Biophys. Acta* **10**, 83 (1953).
160. Tigerman, H., and Mac Vicar, R., *J. Biol. Chem.* **189**, 793 (1951).
161. Walley, R. V., *Lancet* **i**, 157 (1954).
162. Walshe, J. M., *Lancet* **i**, 1075 (1953).
163. Singh, I. D., Barclay, J. A., and Cooke, W. T., *Lancet* **i**, 1004 (1954).
164. Alexander, J. W., and Porter, C. E., *Gastroenterology* **26**, 926 (1954).
165. Webster, L. T., Jr., and Davidson, C. S., *J. Clin. Invest.* **35**, 191 (1956).
166. Iber, F. L., and Chalmers, T. C., *J. Clin. Invest.* **36**, 706 (1957).
167. Schwerin, P., Bessman, S. P., and Waelsch, H., *J. Biol. Chem.* **184**, 37 (1950).
168. Gullino, P., Winitz, M., Birnbaum, S. M., Otey, M. C., Cornfield, J., and Greenstein, J. P., *Arch. Biochem. Biophys.* **58**, 253, 255 (1955).
169. Greenstein, J. P., Winitz, M., Gullino, P., and Birnbaum, S. M., *Arch. Biochem. Biophys.* **59**, 301 (1955).
170. du Ruisseau, J. P., Greenstein, J. P., Winitz, M., and Birnbaum, S. M., *Arch. Biochem. Biophys.* **64**, 335 (1956).
171. Fahey, J. L., *J. Clin. Invest.* **36**, 1647 (1957).
172. McDermott, W. V., Jr., Henneman, D. H., and Laumont, C., *J. Clin. Invest.* **36**, 913 (1957).
172a. Fazekas, J. F., Ticktin, H. E., and Shea, J. G., *Am. J. Med. Sci.* **234**, 462 (1957).

172b. Young, W. K., Johnson, J. V. V., Ticktin, H. E., and Fazekas, J. F., *Am. J. Med. Sci.* **238**, 60 (1959).
173. Allan, J. D., Cusworth, D. C., Dent, C. E., and Wilson, V. K., *Lancet* i, 182 (1958).
174. Dent, C. E., *Proc. Roy. Soc. Med.* **52**, 885 (1959).
175. Westall, R. G., *Biochem. J.* **77**, 135 (1960).
176. Carson, N. A. J., and Neill, D. W., *Arch. Disease Childhood* **37**, 505 (1962).
177. Van Pilsum, J. F., and Halberg, F., *Am. J. Mental Deficiency* **67**, 82 (1962).
178. Levin, B., Mackay, M. M. H., and Oberholzer, V. G., *Arch. Disease Childhood* **36**, 622 (1961).
179. Sporn, M. B., Pingman, W., De Falco, A., and Davies, R. K., *J. Neurochem.* **5**, 62 (1959).
180. Davies, R. K., De Falco, A. J., Shander, D., Kopelman, A., and Kiyasu, J., *Nature* **191**, 288 (1961).
181. Ratner, S., Morell, H., and Carvalho, E., *Arch. Biochem. Biophys.* **91**, 280 (1960).
182. Tomlinson, S., and Westall, R. G., *Nature* **188**, 235 (1960).
183. Tomlinson, S., and Westall, R. G., *Clin. Sci.* In press. Cited by Efron (see ref. 191).
184. Coryell, M. E., Hall, W. K., Thevaos, G., Welter, D. A., Gatz, A. J., Horton, B. F., Sisson, B. D., Looper, J. W., Jr., and Farrow, R. T., *Biochem. Biophys. Res. Commun.* **14**, 307 (1964).
185. Kennan, A. L., and Cohen, P. P., *Proc. Soc. Exptl. Biol. Med.* **106**, 170 (1961).
186. Russell, A., Levin, B., Oberholzer, V. G., and Sinclair, L., *Lancet* **ii**, 699 (1962).
187. Meister, A., *Physiol. Rev.* **36**, 103 (1956).
188. McMurray, W. C., Mohyuddin, F., Rossiter, R. J., Rathburn, J. C., Valentine, G. H., Koegler, S. J., and Zarfas, D. E., *Lancet* i, 138 (1962).
189. McMurray, W. C., and Mohyuddin, F., *Lancet* **ii**, 352 (1962).
190. McMurray, W. C., Rathburn, J. C., Mohyuddin, F., and Koegler, S. J., *Pediatrics* **32**, 347 (1963).
191. Efron, M. L., Disorders of ammonia metabolism. *In* "The Metabolic Basis of Inherited Disease" (Stanbury *et al.*, eds.), 2nd ed., in press. McGraw-Hill, New York, 1965. (Kindly made available to the author by Dr. Mary Efron.)
192. Visakorpi, J. K., *Lancet* i, 1357 (1962).
193. Milne, M. D., London, D. R., and Asatoor, A. M., *Lancet* **ii**, 49 (1962).
194. Efron, M. L., Bixby, E. M., Palattao, L. G., and Pryles, C. V., *New Engl. J. Med.* **267**, 1193 (1962).
195. Efron, M. L., Disorders of proline and hydroxyproline metabolism. *In* "The Metabolic Basis of Inherited Disease" (Stanbury *et al.*, eds.), 2nd ed., in press. McGraw-Hill, New York, 1965. (Kindly made available to the author by Dr. Mary Efron.)
196. Sjoerdsma, A., Davidson, J. D., Udenfriend, S., and Mitoma, C., *Lancet* **ii**, 994 (1958).
197. Schafer, I. A., Scriver, C. R., and Efron, M. L., *New Engl. J. Med.* **267**, 51 (1962).
198. Schafer, I. A., Scriver, C. R., and Efron, M. L., *Am. J. Diseases Children* **102**, 632 (1961).
199. Joseph, R., Ribierre, M., Job, J.-C., and Girault, M., *Arch. Franç. Pédiat.* **15**, 374 (1958).
200. Gerritsen, T., and Waisman, H. A., *Science* **145**, 588 (1964).
201. Menkes, J. H., Hurst, P. L., and Craig, J. M., *Pediatrics* **14**, 462 (1954).

References 1079

202. Westall, R. G., Dancis, J., and Miller, S., *A.M.A. J. Diseases Children* **94**, 571 (1957).
203. Dancis, J., Levitz, M., Miller, S., and Westall, R. G., *Brit. Med. J.* **I**, 91 (1959).
204. Dancis, J., and Levitz, M., "The Metabolic Basis of Inherited Disease," p. 473. McGraw-Hill, New York, 1960.
205. Menkes, J. H., *Pediatrics* **23**, 348 (1959).
206. Mackenzie, D. Y., and Woolf, L. I., *Brit. Med. J.* **I**, 90 (1959).
207. Norton, P. M., Roitman, E., Snyderman, S. E., and Holt, L. E., Jr., *Lancet* **i**, 26 (1962).
208. Dancis, J., Hutzler, J., and Levitz, M., *Biochim. Biophys. Acta* **43**, 342 (1960).
209. Holt, L. E., Jr., Snyderman, S. E., Dancis, J., and Norton, P., *Federation Proc.* **19**, 1 (1960).
210. Dancis, J., Hutzler, J., and Levitz, M., *Biochim. Biophys. Acta* **52**, 60 (1961).
211. Dancis, J., Jansen, V., Hutzler, J., and Levitz, M., *Biochim. Biophys. Acta* **77**, 523 (1963).
212. Meister, A., *J. Biol. Chem.* **184**, 117 (1950).
213. Cochrane, W. A., Payne, W. W., Simpkiss, M. J., and Woolf, L. I., *J. Clin. Invest.* **35**, 411 (1956).
214. Cochrane, W. A., *Metabolism* **9**, 386 (1960).
215. DiGeorge, A. M., and Auerbach, V. H., *Am. J. Med. Sci.* **240**, 160 (1960).
216. Marston, H. R., Allen, S. H., and Smith, R. M., *Nature* **190**, 1085 (1961).
217. Boyland, E., and Levi, A. A., *Biochem. J.* **30**, 2007 (1936).
218. Barness, L. A., Moeksi, H., and György, P., *J. Biol. Chem.* **221**, 93 (1956).
219. White, A. M., *Biochem. J.* **84**, 41P (1962).
220. Cox, E. V., and White, A. M., *Lancet* **ii**, 853 (1962).
221. Barness, L. A., Young, D., Mellman, W. J., Kahn, S. B., and Williams, W. J., *New Engl. J. Med.* **268**, 144 (1963).
222. Harris, H., Penrose, L. S., and Thomas, D. H. H., *Ann. Human Genet.* **23**, 442 (1959).
223. Frimpter, G. W., Haymovitz, A., and Horwith, M., *New Engl. J. Med.* **268**, 333 (1963).
224. Hope, D. B., *Biochem. J.* **66**, 486 (1957).
225. Scriver, C. R., Hutchison, J. H., and Coursin, D. B., *Am. J. Diseases Children* **102**, 632 (1961).
226. Tallan, H. H., Moore, S., and Stein, W. H., *J. Biol. Chem.* **230**, 707 (1958).
227. Perry, T. L., and Jones, R. T., *J. Clin. Invest.* **40**, 1363 (1961).
228. Carson, N. A. J., Cusworth, D. C., Dent, C. E., Field, C. M. B., Neill, D. W., and Westall, R. G., *Arch. Disease Children* **38**, 425 (1963).
229. Gerritsen, T., Vaughn, J. C., and Waisman, H. A., *Biochem. Biophys. Res. Commun.* **9**, 493 (1962).
229a. Mudd, S. H., Finkelstein, J. D., Irreverre, F., and Laster, L., *Science* **143**, 1443 (1964).
230. Ghadimi, H., Partington, M. W., and Hunter, A., *New Engl. J. Med.* **265**, 221 (1961).
231. Ghadimi, H., Partington, M. W., and Hunter, A., *Pediatrics* **29**, 714 (1962).
232. Auerbach, V. H., DiGeorge, A. M., Baldridge, R. C., Tourtellotte, C. D., and Brigham, M. P., *J. Pediat.* **60**, 487 (1962).

233. La Du, B. N., Howell, R. R., Jacoby, G. A., Seegmiller, J. E., Sober, E. K., Zannoni, V. G., Canby, J. P., and Ziegler, L. K., *Pediatrics* **32**, 216 (1963).

234. La Du, B. N., Howell, R., Jacoby, G. A., Seegmiller, J. E., and Zannoni, V. G., *Biochem. Biophys. Res. Commun.* **7**, 398 (1962).

235. Zannoni, V. G., and La Du, B. N., *Biochem. J.* **88**, 160 (1963).

235a. Baldridge, R. C., and Auerbach, V. H., *J. Biol. Chem.* **239**, 1557 (1964).

236. Zenisek, A., Kral, J. A., and Hais, I. M., *Biochim. Biophys. Acta* **18**, 589 (1955).

237. Bessman, S. P., and Baldwin, R., *Science* **135**, 789 (1962).

238. Ellis, J. M., *Arch. Pathol.* **48**, 426 (1949).

239. Gardner, L. I., and Tice, A. A., *Pediatrics* **21**, 805 (1958).

240. Szweda, J. A., Abraham, J. P., Fine, G., Nixon, R. K., and Rupe, C. E., *Am. J. Med.* **32**, 227 (1962).

241. Pastras, T., and Beerman, H., *Am. J. Med. Sci.* **244**, 510 (1962).

242. Demis, D. J., *Ann. Internal Med.* **59**, 194 (1963).

243. Waalkes, T. P., Weissbach, H., Boziecevich, J., and Udenfriend, S., *J. Clin. Invest.* **36**, 1115 (1957).

244. Baron, D. N., Dent, C. E., Harris, H., Hart, E. W., and Jepson, J. B., *Lancet* **ii**, 421 (1956).

245. Jepson, J. B., and Spiro, M. J., "The Metabolic Basis of Inherited Disease," p. 1338. McGraw-Hill, New York, 1960.

246. Jepson, J. B., *Biochem. J.* **64**, 14 P (1956).

247. Milne, M. D., Crawford, M. A., Girao, C. B., and Loughridge, L. W., *Quart. J. Med.* **29**, 407 (1960).

248. Sjoerdsma, A., Weissbach, H., and Udenfriend, S., *Am. J. Med.* **20**, 520 (1956).

249. Biörck, G., Axen, O., and Thorson, A., *Am. Heart J.* **44**, 143 (1952).

250. Branwood, A. W., and Bain, A. D., *Lancet* **ii**, 1259 (1954).

251. Jenkins, J. S., and Butcher, P. J. A., *Lancet* **i**, 331 (1955).

252. Bean, W. B., Olch, D., and Weinberg, H. S., *Circulation* **12**, 1 (1955).

253. Thorson, A., Biörck, G., Bjorkman, G., and Waldenström, J., *Am. Heart J.* **47**, 795 (1954).

254. Vialli, M., and Erspamer, V., *Z. Zellforsch. Mikroskop. Anat.* **19**, 743 (1933).

255. Erspamer, V., *Rend. Sci. Farmitalia* **1**, 1 (1954).

256. Lewbeck, F., *Nature* **172**, 910 (1953).

257. Ratzenhofer, M., and Lewbeck, F., *Z. Krebsforsch.* **60**, 169 (1954).

258. Bumpus, F. M., and Page, I. H., *J. Biol. Chem.* **212**, 111 (1955).

259. Rapport, M. M., Green, A. A., and Page, I. H., *J. Biol. Chem.* **174**, 735; **176**, 1237, 1243 (1948); *Science* **108**, 329 (1948).

260. Erspamer, V., *Arch. Intern. Pharmacodyn.* **76**, 308 (1948).

261. Page, I. H., *Physiol. Rev.* **34**, 563 (1954).

262. Fenichel, R. L., and Seegers, W. H., *Am. J. Physiol.* **181**, 19 (1955).

263. Zucker, M. B., *Am. J. Physiol.* **148**, 275 (1947).

264. Woolley, D. W., "The Biochemical Bases of Psychoses." Wiley, New York, 1962.

265. Boedeker, C., *Z. Rat. Med.* **7**, 130 (1859).

266. Wolkow, M., and Baumann, E., *Z. Physiol. Chem.* **15**, 228 (1891).

267. Lanyar, F., and Lieb, H., *Z. Physiol. Chem.* **203**, 135 (1931).

268. Neuberger, A., Rimington, C., and Wilson, J. M. G., *Biochem. J.* **41**, 438 (1947).

269. Katsch, G., and Metz, E., *Deut. Arch. Klin. Med.* **157**, 143 (1927).

270. Leaf, G., and Neuberger, A., *Biochem. J.* **43**, 606 (1948).
271. Virchow, R., *Arch. Pathol. Anat. Physiol.* **37**, 212 (1866).
272. Albrecht, H., *Z. Heilk.* **23**, 366 (1902).
273. Osler, W., *Lancet* **i**, 10 (1904).
274. Falta, W., *Deut. Arch. Klin. Med.* **81**, 231 (1904).
275. Embden, G., *Z. Physiol. Chem.* **17**, 182 (1893).
276. Neubauer, O., *Deut. Arch. Klin. Med.* **95**, 211 (1909).
277. Neubauer, O., "Handbuch der Normalen und Pathologischen Physiologie," Vol. 5. Springer, Berlin, 1928.
278. Neubauer, O., and Falta, W., *Z. Physiol. Chem.* **42**, 81 (1904).
279. Fromherz, K., and Hermanns, L., *Z. Physiol. Chem.* **91**, 194 (1914).
280. Hogben, L., Worall, R. L., and Zieve, I., *Proc. Roy. Soc. Edinburgh* **52**, 264 (1932).
281. La Du, B. N., Zannoni, V. G., Laster, L., and Seegmiller, J. E., *J. Biol. Chem.* **230**, 251 (1958).
282. Zannoni, V. G., Seegmiller, J. E., and La Du, B. N., *Nature* **193**, 952 (1962).
283. Falta, W., and Langstein, L., *Z. Physiol. Chem.* **37**, 513 (1903).
284. Abbot, L. D., Jr., and Salmon, C. L., Jr., *J. Biol. Chem.* **150**, 339 (1943).
285. Butts, J. S., Dunn, M. S., and Hallman, L. F., *J. Biol. Chem.* **123**, 711 (1938).
286. Lin, E. C. C., and Knox, W. E., *Proc. Soc. Exptl. Biol.* **96**, 501 (1957).
287. Sealock, R. R., and Silberstein, H. E., *J. Biol. Chem.* **135**, 251 (1940).
288. Sealock, R. R., Perkinson, J. D., and Basinski, D. H., *J. Biol. Chem.* **140**, 153 (1941).
289. Lanyar, F., *Z. Physiol. Chem.* **275**, 225 (1942); **278**, 155 (1943).
290. Papageorge, E., and Lewis, H. B., *J. Biol. Chem.* **123**, 211 (1938).
291. Sealock, R. R., and Silberstein, H. E., *Science* **90**, 517 (1939).
292. Levine, S. Z., Marples, E., and Gordon, H. H., *Science* **90**, 620 (1939); *J. Clin. Invest.* **20**, 199, 209 (1941).
293. Diaz, C. J., Mendoza, H. C., and Rodriquez, J. S., *Klin. Wochschr.* **18**, 965 (1939).
294. Sealock, R. R., Galdston, M., and Steele, J. M., *Proc. Soc. Exptl. Biol. Med.* **44**, 580 (1940).
295. Neuberger, A., and Webster, T. A., *Biochem. J.* **41**, 449 (1947).
296. Glynn, L. E., Himsworth, H. P., and Neuberger, A., *Brit. J. Exptl. Pathol.* **26**, 326 (1945).
297. Felix, K., Leonhardi, G., and von Glasenapp, I., *Z. Physiol. Chem.* **287**, 133 (1951).
298. Felix, K., and Teske, R., *Z. Physiol. Chem.* **267**, 173 (1941).
299. Gros, H., and Kirnberger, E. J., *Klin. Wochschr.* **32**, 115 (1954).
300. Boscott, R. J., and Cooke, W. T., *Quart. J. Med.* **23**, 307 (1954).
301. Bloxam, H. R., Day, M. G., Gibbs, N. K., and Woolf, L. I., *Biochem. J.* **77**, 320 (1960).
302. Menkes, J. H., and Jervis, G. A., *Pediatrics* **28**, 399 (1961).
303. Medes, G., *Biochem. J.* **26**, 917 (1932).
304. Robinson, R., and Smith, P., *Nature* **189**, 323 (1961).
305. Fitzpatrick, T., "The Metabolic Basis of Inherited Disease," p. 428. McGraw-Hill, New York, 1960.
306. Smithwick, R. H., Greer, W. E. R., Robertson, C. W., and Wilkins, R. W., *New Engl. J. Med.* **242**, 252 (1950).
307. Engel, A., and von Euler, U. S., *Lancet* **ii**, 387 (1950).

308. Sjoerdsma, A., *Pharmacol. Rev.* **11**, 374 (1959).
309. Crout, J. R., and Sjoerdsma, A., *J. Clin. Invest.* **43**, 94 (1964).
310. Von Studnitz, W., Käser, H., and Sjoerdsma, A., *New Engl. J. Med.* **269**, 232 (1963).
311. Stanbury, J. B., " The Metabolic Basis of Inherited Disease," p. 273. McGraw-Hill, New York, 1960.
312. Stanbury, J. B., Kassenaar, A. A. H., Meijer, J. W. A., and Terpstra, J., *J. Clin. Endocrinol. Metab.* **15**, 1216 (1955).
313. Stanbury, J. B., Meijer, J. W. A., and Kassenaar, A. A. H., *J. Clin. Endocrinol. Metab.* **16**, 848 (1956).
314. Querido, A., Stanbury, J. B., Kassenaar, A. A. H., and Meijer, J. W. A., *J. Clin. Endocrinol. Metab.* **16**, 1096 (1956).
315. Hutchison, J. H., and McGirr, E. M., *Lancet* **i**, 1035 (1956).
316. Stanbury, J. B., and Hedge, A. N., *J. Clin. Endocrinol.* **10**, 1471 (1950).
317. Stanbury, J. B., Ohela, K., and Pitt-Rivers, R., *J. Clin. Endocrinol. Metab.* **15**, 54 (1955).
318. Stanbury, J. B., and McGirr, E. M., *Am. J. Med.* **22**, 712 (1957).
319. Fölling, A., *Z. Physiol. Chem.* **227**, 169 (1934).
320. Fölling, A., *Nord. Med. Tidskr.* *(Stockholm)* **8**, 1054 (1934).
321. Jervis, G. A., *Arch. Neurol. Psychiat.* **38**, 944 (1937).
322. Jervis, G. A., *J. Mental Sci.* **85**, 719 (1939).
323. Hsia, D. Y.-Y., Knox, W. E., and Paine, R. S., *A.M.A. J. Diseases Children* **94**, 33 (1957).
324. Sutherland, B. S., Berry, H. K., and Shirkey, H. C., *J. Pediat.* **57**, 521 (1960).
325. Jervis, G. A., *Res. Publ. Assoc. Res. Nervous Mental Disease* **33**, 259 (1954).
326. Meister, A., *Pediatrics* **21**, 1021 (1958).
327. Knox, W. E., " The Metabolic Basis of Inherited Disease," p. 321. McGraw-Hill, New York, 1960.
328. Smith, A. S., and Strang, L. B., *Arch. Disease Childhood* **33**, 109 (1958).
329. Jepson, J. B., Smith, A. J., and Strang, L. B., *Lancet* **ii**, 1334 (1958).
330. Cawte, J. E., *Med. J. Australia* **ii**, 15 (1954).
331. Dann, M., Marples, E., and Levine, S. Z., *J. Clin. Invest.* **22**, 87 (1943).
332. Fölling, A., Closs, K., and Gammes, T., *Z. Physiol. Chem.* **256**, 1 (1938).
333. Closs, K., and Braaten, K., *Z. Physiol. Chem.* **271**, 221 (1941).
334. Closs, K., and Fölling, A., *Z. Physiol. Chem.* **254**, 250 (1938).
335. Woolf, L. I., *Biochem. J.* **49**, 9 (1951).
336. Stein, W. H., Paladini, A. C., Hirs, C. H. W., and Moore, S., *J. Am. Chem. Soc.* **76**, 2848 (1954).
337. Jervis, G. A., Block, R. J., Bolling, D., and Kanze, E., *J. Biol. Chem.* **134**, 105 (1940).
338. Borek, E., Brecher, A., Jervis, G. A., and Waelsch, H., *Proc. Soc. Exptl. Biol. Med.* **75**, 86 (1950).
339. Perry, T. L., and Jones, R. T., *J. Clin. Invest.* **40**, 1363 (1961).
340. Jervis, G. A., *Proc. Soc. Exptl. Biol. Med.* **81**, 715 (1952).
341. Penrose, L. S., and Quastel, J. H., *Biochem. J.* **31**, 266 (1937).
342. Jervis, G. A., *J. Biol. Chem.* **126**, 305 (1938).
343. Fölling, A., Mohr, O. L., and Ruud, L., *Publ. Norwegian Acad. Sci.* **13** (1945).

344. Prescott, B. A., Borek, E., Brecher, A., and Waelsch, H., *J. Biol. Chem.* **181**, 273 (1949).
345. Jervis, G. A., *J. Biol. Chem.* **169**, 651 (1947).
346. Udenfriend, S., and Bessman, S. P., *J. Biol. Chem.* **203**, 901 (1953).
347. Jervis, G. A., *Proc. Soc. Exptl. Biol. Med.* **82**, 514 (1953).
348. Wallace, H. W., Moldave, K., and Meister, A., *Proc. Soc. Exptl. Biol. Med.* **94**, 632 (1957).
349. Mitoma, C., Auld, R. M., and Udenfriend, S., *Proc. Soc. Exptl. Biol. Med.* **94**, 634 (1957).
350. Kaufman, S., *Science* **128**, 1506 (1958).
351. Meister, A., Udenfriend, S., and Bessman, S. P., *J. Clin. Invest.* **35**, 619 (1956).
352. Moldave, K., and Meister, A., *J. Biol. Chem.* **229**, 463 (1957).
353. Armstrong, M. D., and Robinson, K. S., *Arch. Biochem. Biophys.* **52**, 287 (1954).
354. Pare, C. M. B., Sandler, M., and Stacey, R. S., *Lancet* **i**, 511 (1957).
355. Jepson, J. B., *Lancet* **ii**, 1009 (1955).
356. Schreier, K., and Flaig, H., *Klin. Wochschr.* **34**, 1213 (1956).
357. Boscott, R. J., and Bickel, H., *Scand. J. Clin. Lab. Invest.* **5**, 380 (1953).
358. Armstrong, M. D., Shaw, K. N. F., and Robinson, K. S., *J. Biol. Chem.* **213**, 797, (1955).
359. Armstrong, M. D., and Shaw, K. N. F., *J. Biol. Chem.* **213**, 805 (1955).
360. Udenfriend, S., and Mitoma, C., *Symp. Amino Acid Metab.*, p. 876. Johns Hopkins Press, 1955.
361. Tashian, R. E., *Science* **129**, 1553 (1959).
362. Taniguchi, K., and Armstrong, M. D., *J. Biol. Chem.* **238**, 4091 (1963).
363. Hsia, D. Y.-Y., Driscoll, K., Troll, W., and Knox, W. E., *Nature* **178**, 1239 (1956).
364. Hsia, D. Y.-Y., and Paine, R. S., *J. Mental Deficiency Res.* **1**, 53 (1957).
365. Knox, W. E., and Messinger, E., *Am. J. Human Genet.* **10**, 53 (1958).
366. Berry, H. K., Sutherland, B. S., and Guest, G. M., *Am. J. Human Genet.* **9**, 310 (1957).
367. Cullen, A. M., and Knox, W. E., *Proc. Soc. Exp. Biol. Med.* **99**, 219 (1958).
368. Dancis, J., and Balis, M. E., *Pediatrics* **15**, 63 (1955).
369. Miyamoto, M., and Fitzpatrick, T. B., *Nature* **179**, 199 (1957).
370. Boylen, J. B., and Quastel, J. H., *Nature* **193**, 376 (1962).
371. Bickis, I. J., Kennedy, J. P., and Quastel, J. H., *Nature* **179**, 1124 (1957).
372. Cawte, J. E., *J. Mental Deficiency Res.* **1**, 111 (1957).
373. Nadler, H. L., and Hsia, D. Y.-Y., *Proc. Soc. Exptl. Biol. Med.* **107**, 721 (1961).
374. Hartman, W. J., Akawie, R. I., and Clark, W. G., *J. Biol. Chem.* **216**, 507 (1955).
375. Fellman, J. H., *Proc. Soc. Exptl. Biol. Med.* **93**, 413 (1956).
376. Boylen, J. B., and Quastel, J. H., *Biochem. J.* **80**, 644 (1961).
377. Oates, J. A., Nirenberg, P. Z., Jepson, J. B., Sjoerdsma, A., and Udenfriend, S., *Proc. Soc. Exptl. Biol. Med.* **112**, 1078 (1963).
378. Perry, T. L., *Science* **136**, 879 (1962).
379. Pare, C. M. B., Sandler, M., and Stacey, R. S., *Lancet* **ii**, 1099 (1958).
380. Perry, T. L., Hansen, S., Tischler, B., and Hestrin, M., *Proc. Soc. Exptl. Biol. Med.* **115**, 118 (1964).
381. Bessman, S. P., and Tada, K., *Pediatrics* **23**, 1004 (1959).

382. Schrappe, O., *Nervenarzt* **23**, 175 (1952).
383. Block, R. J., Jervis, G. A., Bolling, D., and Webb, M., *J. Biol. Chem.* **134**, 567 (1940).
384. Allen, D. W., and Schroeder, W. A., *J. Clin. Invest.* **36**, 1343 (1957).
385. Grümer, H.-D., Koblet, H., and Woodard, C., *J. Clin. Invest.* **41**, 61 (1962).
386. Brown, D. M., Armstrong, M. D., and Smith, E., *Proc. Soc. Exptl. Biol. Med.* **89**, 367 (1955).
387. Bickel, H., Gerrard, J., and Hickmans, E. M., *Acta Paediat.* **43**, 64 (1954).
388. Woolf, L. I., Griffiths, R., and Moncrieff, A., *Brit. Med. J.* **I**, 57 (1955).
389. Bickel, H., Gerrard, J., and Hickmans, E. M., *Lancet* **ii**, 812 (1953).
390. Armstrong, M. D., and Tyler, F. H., *J. Clin. Invest.* **34**, 565 (1955).
391. Kretchmer, N., and Etzwiler, D. D., *Pediatrics* **21**, 445 (1958).
392. Goldstein, F. B., *J. Biol. Chem.* **236**, 2656 (1961).
393. Waisman, H. A., Wang, H. L., Harlow, H., and Sponholz, R. R., *Proc. Soc. Exptl. Biol. Med.* **101**, 864 (1959).
394. McKean, C. M., Schanberg, S. M., and Giarman, N. J., *Science* **137**, 604 (1962).
395. Boggs, D. E., McLay, D., Kappy, M., and Waisman, H. A., *Nature* **200**, 76 (1963).
396. Carver, M. J., and Paska, R., *Nature* **197**, 493 (1963).
397. Culley, W. J., Saunders, R. N., Mertz, E. T., and Jolly, D. H., *Proc. Soc. Exptl. Biol. Med.* **111**, 444 (1962).
398. Auerbach, V. H., Waisman, H. A., and Wycoff, L. B., *Nature* **182**, 871 (1958).

Author Index

Numbers in parentheses are reference numbers and indicate that an author's work is referred to although his name is not cited in the text. Numbers in italic show the page on which the complete reference is cited.

A

1

Subject Index

Volumes I and II

A

Abrine, *see* *N*-methyltryptophan
Absolute configuration, 144
Acetaldehyde, from threonine, 681
Acetate,
  activation of, 498
  from γ-aminobutyrate, 629
  from glycine, 640
  from lysine, 947
Acetoacetic acid,
  in leucine degradation, 744
  from phenylalanine, 899, 905
  from tyrosine, 899, 905
Acetoacetyl-coenzyme A, from lysine, 945
α-Aceto-α-hydroxybutyric acid, in isoleucine biosynthesis, 734, 737
Acetoin, from α-acetolactate, 733
α-Acetolactate,
  from pyruvate, 733
  in valine biosynthesis, 733, 737
α-Acetolactate, decarboxylase, 733
2-Acetoxyglutarate, 692
Acetyl adenylate, 445, 498
Acetylation,
  of amino acids, 445
  of aspartate, 445
  of glutamate, 710
  of lysine, 944
  of ornithine, 695, 710, 715
N-Acetylamino acids, activation of, 558
γ-*N*-Acetylaminobutyraldehyde, transamination of, 346
4-(β-Acetylaminoethyl)imidazole, enzymatic formation of, 835
δ-*N*-Acetylaminovaleraldehyde, transamination of, 346
N-Acetylaspartic acid, 9, 139
  from aspartate, 445, 695

Acetyl-coenzyme A, 445, 945
  from isoleucine, 752
  in leucine biosynthesis, 742
  in leucine degradation, 744
  in synthesis of α-ketoadipic acid, 936
Acetyl-coenzyme A, carboxylase, incorporation of CO_2 into biotin of, 746
γ-*N*-Acetyl-α,γ-diaminobutyric acid, 73
N-Acetyl-3,4-dihydroxyphenylethylamine, 916
N-Acetyl-L-djenkolic acid, 74
Acetylethylcarbinol, formation of, 734
N-Acetylglucosamine, 468–470
N-Acetylglutamate, 444
  in carbamyl phosphate formation, 691
N-Acetylglutamate transacetylase, 710
N-Acetylglutamic acid, in ornithine biosynthesis, 709
N-Acetylglutamic acid-γ-semialdehyde,
  conversion to ornithine, 709
  transamination of, 346, 355, 709, 710
N-Acetyl-γ-glutamyl phosphate, in ornithine biosynthesis, 710
N-Acetylglycine, dissociation constant of, 30
O-Acetylhomoserine, natural occurrence of, 94
α-*N*-Acetyl-3-hydroxykynurenine, 854
N-Acetyl-6-hydroxy-5-methoxytryptamine, 875
N-Acetyl-5-hydroxytryptamine, *see* Melatonin
6-*O*-Acetylisopropyl thiogalactoside, 282
α-*N*-Acetylkynurenine, 854
ε-*N*-Acetyllysine, 941
ε-*N*-Acetyl-L-lysine acylase, 941